Civil War Medicine

Challenges and Triumphs

Civil War Medicine

Challenges and Triumphs

Alfred Jay Bollet, M.D.

GALEN PRESS, LTD. • TUCSON, ARIZONA

Galen Press, Ltd.
P.O. Box 64400
Tucson, AZ 85728-4400
Phone: (520) 577-8363   Fax: (520) 529-6459
Orders: (800) 442-5369 (U.S./Canada)
www.galenpress.com

ISBN: 1-883620-08-2 (hardcover)
ISBN: 1-883620-03-1 (softcover)

Cover photos: Train of ambulance wagons ready for duty near the Harewood Hospital in Washington, July 1863. Courtesy of Massachusetts Commandery of the Military Order of the Loyal Legion of the United States (MOLLUS) and the U.S. Army Military History Institute. Ward of Carver General Hospital. Courtesy of National Archives and Records Administration, No. 111-B-173.

Library of Congress Cataloging-in-Publication Data
Bollet, Alfred J.
  Civil War Medicine : challenges and triumphs / Alfred Jay Bollet.
    p.   cm.
  Includes bibliographical references)p.) and index.
  ISBN 1-883620-08-2
  1. United States—History—Civil War, 1861-1865—Medical care.
  2. United States—History—Civil War, 1861-1865—Health aspects.
  I. Title.
E621.B65 2000
973.7′75—dc21   99-089509

Printed in the United States of America

10 9 8 7 6 5 4 3 2 1

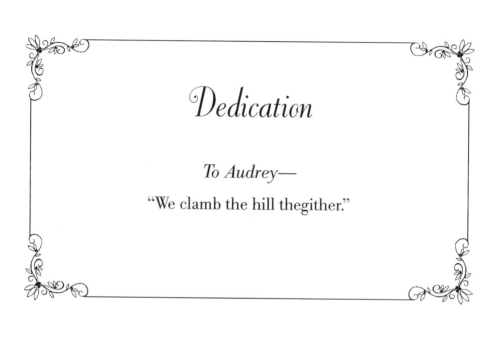

Dedication

To Audrey—

"We clamb the hill thegither."

Contents

Preface

The Union and Confederate Medical Departments performed dismally as the Civil War began; they quickly improved and delivered excellent medical care. Their disastrous start was widely reported—their improvements weren't! This resulted in the erroneous assumptions that huge numbers of limbs were lost to unnecessary amputations and that surgery was often done without anesthesia. In fact, when the subject of Civil War medicine arises, most people's first response is usually "Oh! All those amputations!" even 130 years after the war ended.

One reason for the lasting negative evaluation of Civil War medicine is the understandable tendency of sick and wounded soldiers and their families to thank God when things go well, but to blame physicians when things go badly. Thus, of the thousands of statues memorializing the generals and soldiers who fought so determinedly and suffered so much, not one memorializes a Civil War physician for his role in the war. (There are a few monuments dedicated to physicians who participated in the war, such as Dr. Hunter Holmes McGuire in Richmond, Virginia, but they are memorialized primarily for post-war achievements.)

Yet, fifty-one surgeons were killed in battle or died of wounds during the war, proportionately more than in any other staff corps. (A total of 335 surgeons died while in service, most from disease.)[1,2] "Encyclopedias" of Civil War facts usually include one surgeon general (Federal doctor William Hammond) and several women from both sides who participated in nursing care, but there is no mention of the men who ran the unprecedented huge hospitals; medical directors of large armies; surgeons-general who totally reorganized the medical corps and instituted programs of research; or the many other physicians who made important contributions to the care of Civil War soldiers.

Until I began to study the medical history of the Civil War, I had similar negative opinions. But the records I found were at odds with my prior conceptions of Civil War medicine and the more material I read, lay and medical, American and European, the more it confirmed that "history" has left the Civil War medical departments of both sides with an undeservedly negative reputation.

As a result, I have undertaken an in-depth examination and analysis of the records, in part to give belated credit to the unsung and ill-remembered Civil War physicians. This book shows that the medical services responded remarkably well to the immense demands by achieving survival rates for disease and wounds not known in previous wars and by developing innovations that later became standard components of battlefield and disaster medicine.

I have relied in part on participants' diaries and biographies, many written by or about individual doctors and nurses, and have extensively studied descriptions of military and medical events written by participants and historians. The medical literature of the Civil War era has also been a rich source of information. The six-volume *Medical and Surgical History of the War of the Rebellion* (hereafter abbreviated as *Medical and Surgical History*), published by the Surgeon General's Office after the war, provides not only raw statistical data that can be analyzed using today's methods, but also extensive discussions of the wartime diseases and wounds written by first-hand witnesses. These volumes also contain reports to the Surgeon General's Office that were saved and compiled with great effort during and after the war with the express intent of learning as much as possible from the medical experiences and passing that information on to other physicians, at home and abroad, as well as to future generations. For example, Dr. Robert Murray, the head of the medical corps (medical director) of Grant's Army of the Tennessee, recorded the exemplary efforts of one of his surgeons during the first enormous battle of the war, at Shiloh, in April 1862:

> Assistant Surgeon Irwin deserves very great credit for his admirable management on the field, as well as for his promptness and professional skill in the care of the wounded. . . . by securing tents from the neighboring camps and collecting camp furniture, he succeeded in organizing and putting into good working order a hospital for three hundred patients, partly the wounded of his own command . . . who were wounded on the field on Sunday, and partly of Confederate wounded. They were so well taken care of in every way, that [after the battle, when the wounded were being sent north to hospitals in the cities] I designated them as the last to send aboard of the boats.[3]

The War of the Rebellion: A Compilation of the Official Records of the Union and Confederate Armies (hereinafter called *Official Records*, or *O.R.*), also published in the decades after the war, contains abundant useful medical information included in the reports from the field. That information recently became much more accessible thanks to CD-ROMs. American and British medical journals published during the war years give additional insight through contemporary evaluations of the medical events. Although many of the lessons learned by Civil War physicians soon became outdated due to the development of bacteriology in the decades immediately after the war, these documents reveal a great deal about the intentions and the efforts made by Civil War physicians to improve their effectiveness.

Contemporary textbooks and manuals provide further evidence for the medical thinking and practices of the time. Official publications sponsored by the U.S. Sanitary Commission and prepared by leading medical authorities are particularly useful. Some were intended to teach newly militarized doctors; others evaluate their actions retrospectively and point to lessons learned during the war.

The documentation of the medical experiences during the earlier Crimean and later Franco-Prussian wars allows comparison between the quality of Civil

War military medicine and that of contemporaneous European wars. The opinions of European military physicians about their counterparts' actions during the Civil War are similarly revealing. Almost all are complimentary, at least in the later years of the war. Medical leaders in Europe adopted the innovations from the conflict they called the "American War" in their own battles shortly after the Civil War ended. These included the greatly improved ambulance vehicles, the use of boats and trains to transport sick and wounded comfortably, a trained ambulance corps, a field hospital system to care for the wounded near the battlefield, and the establishment of huge, highly organized, well-managed military hospitals.

The preponderance of the existing data refers to the Union army, since the bulk of the Confederate records were destroyed in the fire that consumed much of Richmond on April 2, 1865. The remaining records of individual Confederate hospitals and surgeons are incomplete, but their data are similar to the Union data as far as can be determined. The *Medical and Surgical History* gives data for the white and the black troops separately. At times, I have combined these numbers to ascertain the total number of cases of a given disease. Elsewhere, when trends in frequency or in mortality rates during the course of the war are the subject, I analyzed only data from the white troops since only the white soldiers served for the entire four years of the war. I have discussed both sets of data when I compare patterns of disease in black and white troops. In some instances, medical data for only the white soldiers is available (such as the findings in draftees examined before enlistment after the Conscription Act went into effect in 1863). Unless the source is specified ("white Union troops" or "black troops"), the data quoted is for the entire Union army, black and white.

Any review of the data of the era involves a problem in terminology. Although many diseases have the same names today, some terms familiar during the Civil War are vastly different from our current nosology. Before the birth of bacteriology, disease classification was handled similarly to the way Linnaeus classified plants and animals, using, for example, Orders and Classes. "Fever" was still considered a disease instead of a symptom, although many individual types of "fever" were diagnosed. Nevertheless, it is possible to recognize and classify many specific syndromes due to the details in recorded case histories, descriptions of autopsy findings, and physicians' discussions. I have taken the liberty, therefore, of discussing the syndromes using present-day disease terminology and understanding. My interpretations might be considered unwarranted speculation since I lack the types of evidence we rely on today, particularly laboratory tests and imaging procedures. Yet, I believe that professional and lay audiences alike are interested in a modern interpretation of the clinical and autopsy findings that are available.

It is important to analyze the Civil War medical experiences with a view to *when* in this long war they occurred. Disease patterns, the ability of the medical personnel to deal with disease, preventive measures, arrangements for evacuation and transport of wounded from the battlefield, and many aspects of the treatment of gunshot wounds all changed as the war progressed. (In fact, the statistics document considerable improvement in the survival of men with gunshot wounds treated after the terrible first year, as well as a marked decrease in the frequency of serious diseases.) Military historians routinely analyze the changes that occurred as commanders grew more experienced and the more competent ones came to the fore. Similar evolutionary improvements can be traced in the medical services of the war.

Some critics of the medical efforts during the Civil War seem unaware of many basic historical facts regarding medicine. In the decade before the war, surgeons at one of the premier hospitals of the time (and since), Massachusetts General Hospital, performed fewer than 200 surgical procedures of any kind on average *per year*. Yet, within months of the opening hostilities, surgeons, most of whom had no relevant surgical experience to draw from, were required to perform vastly greater numbers of surgical procedures in a matter of *hours*.

As one historian of World War II wrote, "A commander should be judged in the light of the information he has at the moment he makes his decision."[4] This principle applies no less to the decisions of surgeons on (and behind) the battlefield. The issues we should address in evaluating the performance of Civil War medicine include whether surgeons were up-to-date with respect to the knowledge of their time. Did they apply that knowledge effectively? Did they analyze, and thus learn from, their experiences? Did they abandon rules and procedures designed for a tiny professional frontier army and develop a new system to care for huge, volunteer armies suffering enormous numbers of casualties? Equally important, were they generally kind and caring toward the wounded and sick soldiers, or brusque and brutal as some contemporaries claimed? I have attempted to cover the bad as well as the commendable aspects of their record to enable readers to judge for themselves.

REFERENCES

1. Key JD: The U.S. Army Medical Department and Civil War medicine. *Mil Med.* 1968 Mar;133(3):185-86.
2. Mitchell SW: On the Medical Department in the Civil War. Address to Physicians' Club of Chicago, February 25, 1913. *J Am Med Assoc.* 1914;62(19):1445-50.
3. Barnes JK: *The Medical and Surgical History of the War of the Rebellion (1861–1865).* Washington, D.C.: Gov. Printing Office, 1870–1888. Medical Section, vol. 1, Appendix, p. 37. [henceforth referred to as *Medical and Surgical History*]
4. Hart BHL: *History of the Second World War.* New York: G.P. Putnam Sons, 1970, p. 359.

❧ Acknowledgements ❧

First, special thanks to my wife, Dr. Audrey Brown Bollet, for her invaluable support, patience, understanding, suggestions, and advice.

I have tried to make this book understandable for both medical and non-medical readers, for those well informed about the military events of the Civil War and for less-informed readers. If I have succeeded, I must thank Jennifer Gilbert of Galen Press, Ltd. profusely for that, as well as for her prodigious efforts to condense, clarify, and generally improve the manuscript. I also thank Kenneth V. Iserson, M.D. for advice and suggestions, and for numerous specific facts.

I also appreciate the cooperation and help provided by the staffs of the following libraries: Eleanor S. Brockenbrough Library, Museum of the Confederacy, Richmond, VA (Collections of Winder Hospital Records, Stuart Hospital Records, and Dr. J. S. Tanner's records of Hoke's Division of the Army of Northern Virginia; and records of the military general hospital in Lake City, Florida, as well as other military hospitals in Richmond); National Archives and Research Administration (especially Dr. Michael Musick); New York Academy of Medicine; National Library of Medicine; Historical Library, Yale University School of Medicine; Medical Library, State University of New York at Stony Brook; Medical Library, University of Virginia School of Medicine; Alderman Library, University of Virginia; Royal College of Physicians and Royal College of Surgeons of Dublin; New York Historical Society Library; New York State Medical Society; Danbury Hospital (Danbury, CT); Nassau County Medical Center; North Shore University Hospital (Manhasset, NY); and Winthrop University Hospital Library. Also, the Museum of the City of New York; the Military Bookman; the U. S. Army Military History Institute; the Military Order of the Loyal Legion of the United States (MOLLUS); and Lien Huong, a Library of Congress staff member and president of the Library and Education Assistance Foundation for Vietnam (LEAF-VN) all made invaluable contributions.

I also thank those who reviewed the manuscript for their excellent advice: John Staige Davis, IV, M.D.; Gordon E. Dammann, D.D.S.; Peter J. D'Onofrio, Ph.D.; John Lattimer, M.D., Sc.D.; William L. Moore, Jr., M.D.; Irving Schulman, M.D.; Thomas Adrian Wheat, M.D.; Alan Reeter, M.S.E.E.; Bert Kammerer; Donald Witzke, Ph.D.; Robert Fisher, M.L.S.; and the marvelous librarians at the University of Arizona Health Sciences Library: Nga T. Nguyen, B.A., B.S., and Senior Library Specialist Hannah Fisher, R.N., M.L.S., AHIP. I also thank Lynn Bishop for the excellent cover design, and Anne Olson of Casa Cold Type for designing the interior layout of the book.

Major-General H. A. Barnum

Henry A. Barnum, then a major in the 12th New York Volunteer Regiment, was wounded at Malvern Hill during the Peninsula Campaign on July 1, 1862. According to the records of the Army Medical Museum, a conoidal musket ball entered his abdomen midway between the umbilicus and the anterior spinous process of the left ilium (hip bone), passed through the ilium, and emerged posteriorly. The wound was considered fatal, and Barnum was left at a field hospital, where he was captured on July 2. He was taken to Libby Prison in Richmond; the 18-mile trip was made in a commissary wagon. On July 17, he was taken to Aiken's Landing on the James River and exchanged. He was then taken by boat to Albany, New York, and by rail to Syracuse. A surgeon in Albany enlarged the wound and removed fragments of the hip bone; an abscess formed anteriorly and drained spontaneously.

In January 1863, Barnum was promoted to colonel, and he returned to the field in command of a new regiment (149th New York). In March, a second abscess formed and drained itself. He led his regiment at Gettysburg. Another abscess formed posteriorly, and a surgeon passed a "seton of oakum" through the length of the wound. This was later replaced by linen threads. Barnum remained in the field and was promoted to brigadier general. He participated in Sherman's Atlanta campaign, the March to the Sea, and the march through the Carolinas, receiving additional wounds in the forearms and side. In August 1865, when this photograph was taken at the Army Medical Museum, he still wore a thread through the entire length of the wound. (Photo courtesy of Otis Historical Archives, NMHM, NCP-3787.)

The Evolution of Battlefield Surgery during the Civil War

T HE USUAL IMAGE OF CIVIL WAR MEDICINE is of men screaming with pain on operating tables in front of a house and surrounded by piles of amputated arms and legs. The true story has been submerged by myths, the actual agonies supplanted by fanciful ones, and the actual medical history simply ignored. Two of these myths involve amputations and anesthesia.

First, while it is true that amputations were the most common surgical procedure of the war, available data, as well as thoughtful analyses, show that many lives were saved by these operations. Public criticism for performing too many amputations inhibited the actions of surgeons, and a British surgeon who visited Union hospitals in the middle of the war wrote that American surgeons were overly cautious about performing amputations, losing many lives that he thought could have been saved. Overall, the data show that wounded soldiers treated by either Union or Confederate surgeons had a lower mortality in all situations, including amputations, than the British and French in the Crimean War (1854–56).

Second, many historians claim that a majority of the surgery during the war was done without anesthesia. In reality, surgery under anesthesia began in 1846, and, although it was irregularly used in the Crimean War, during the Civil War it was fully accepted and used almost universally. In fact, chloroform was used for almost all surgery done in the field, and ether (or a mixture of the two) was used in hospitals, not only for operations but also for painful wound treatments.

The erroneous idea that anesthesia was not used arose mainly because soldiers wrote letters home that often described surgeons working over howling, writhing men held down by assistants. (Such observations were common, since surgeons operated in the open during the day to take advantage of sunlight; lack of adequate lighting was a major impediment to effective wound treatment by Civil War surgeons.) Passing soldiers did not realize that anesthesia had been given, but in amounts just sufficient to make a man insensible to pain. In this stage, an anesthetized person moans, shouts, and writhes whether or not an operation is being performed, thus the Civil War surgeon needed men to hold the patient still so that he could work. These misinterpretations gave rise to one of the Civil War's enduring myths.

TREATMENT OF THE WOUNDED
EARLY IN THE WAR

To understand how much the medical departments on both sides improved after the first year, their actions early in the war must be compared to those of later years. (Although similar phenomena occurred on both sides, more illustrations will be taken from the Union side, since more data are available.)

For example, when the First Battle of Bull Run was fought on July 21, 1861, an incompetent Union surgeon general, accustomed to a small pre-war frontier army, decided to wait until there was actual fighting before preparing for casualties. None of the wounded reached Washington in an ambulance the day of the battle. At that time, Union ambulances were under the authority of the Quartermaster Department, rather than the Medical Department, and their hired civilian drivers, fearing for their own safety, abandoned the field. Union wounded were left to be captured, to die in the field, or to drag themselves the thirty miles back to Washington. Some days later, an improvised wagon train retrieved several hundred wounded and hauled them from Manassas to Washington on a tortuous, bumpy ride that made them scream in agony.[1]

When they arrived in Washington, the medical system was not prepared to receive them. The ambulances had to deposit their wounded in makeshift "hospitals" set up in dilapidated warehouses, churches, schools, and public buildings. Public reaction was summed up in a *New York Times* editorial on July 27, 1861:

> We are all inexpressibly pained to learn . . . that very inadequate provisions had been made by the regular authorities, for the proper care of the wounded

in the late battle. It seems incredible . . . that some of our gallant soldiers for sheer want of hospital garments, [are] even yet sweltering in their bloody uniforms, festering with fever and maddened with thirst.[3]

When Gen. George Brinton McClellan's Army of the Potomac invaded the York-James Peninsula in Virginia during the Spring of 1862, the administration of the Union Medical Corps had barely changed. No system for evacuating the wounded existed. Small regimental hospitals, overwhelmed with their own men, turned away those from other regiments. Many of the wounded lay untreated in the sun for days, until the air was filled with the stench of pus and decaying tissue and the injured men's moans and cries. Some wounded men lay on the floors of boxcars or open wagons, perhaps with straw to cushion the floor but with no food, medical supplies, or nursing personnel. Hospital boats provided by volunteer civilian organizations were haphazardly loaded with the wounded and sick, the treated and untreated. Most vessels lacked even food and water and had no sanitary facilities. When these boats came up the Chesapeake and the Potomac to Washington and other Northern cities, the condition of the wounded appalled onlookers. Newspapers reported a picture of neglect, even purposeful cruelty, and this image has persisted unmodified, despite later improvements.

TREATMENT OF THE WOUNDED
AFTER THE FIRST YEAR OF THE WAR

By the time of the Battle of Antietam (September 17, 1862), described as "America's bloodiest day," much had changed in the Federal Medical Department. An innovative system for care of the wounded instituted by a new surgeon general, William Alexander Hammond, and a new medical director of the Army of the Potomac, Jonathan Letterman, was largely in place and progressively improving. Stretcher bearers now removed the wounded from the firing line and took them to regimental assistant surgeons located just behind the front lines. These surgeons triaged the wounded, stopped bleeding, administered opiates, and dressed wounds. Trained ambulance attendants then moved the wounded to field hospitals set up in existing buildings or tents just beyond artillery range.

Very little surgery of any kind was done before the war, and hardly any of the newly militarized surgeons had any training or experience treating wounds. By the end of the second year of fighting, new rules controlled some surgeons' excessive zeal to perform operations: surgery could only be done by specially selected individuals chosen for their experience and skill. But they could not operate until a board of three consultants examined each patient and decided what type of surgery, such as an amputation, was necessary. Wound treatment improved as Civil War surgeons gained experience, and many novel surgical procedures were attempted, among them removing damaged intestine, sealing sucking chest wounds, rudimentary neurosurgery, and multiple-staged repairs (plastic surgery).

The system was constantly being improved, as demonstrated by the performance during the three-day Battle of Gettysburg (July 1–3, 1863). Each night, all the wounded from both sides were collected and taken to field hospitals; all necessary surgery was decided on and done within 48 hours of a man being wounded. The death rate among the wounded who survived to reach medical care was dramatically decreased from 25% to 35% of those wounded in the war's first two years to 9.5% at Gettysburg and in other battles during the third year.

Innovations in the transport of wounded soldiers resulted in tremendous improvements in their comfort and safety. After being brought to field hospitals by specially trained ambulance teams, wounded men were often moved on newly fitted hospital boats, especially along the Mississippi, its tributaries, and the Atlantic waterways. These boats had rows of beds, good sanitary facilities, elevators to move men between decks, operating rooms, special diet kitchens, and, usually, some female nurses. Hospital trains had nurses, physicians (occasionally), stretchers mounted with rubber slings to minimize jolting, kitchen and sanitary facilities, and adequate medical supplies.

The men could be moved to large general hospitals in a city or to one of the specialty hospitals established during the war to care for a specific type of injury. These Civil War hospitals were another remarkable achievement: before the war, hospitals in the United States and abroad were little more than the almshouse infirmaries from which most had evolved. There had been only *one* forty-bed unit that deserved to be called a hospital in the entire pre-war army! By the war's end, the Union and Confederate Medical Corps operated a total of about 400 hospitals of unprecedented magnitude and complexity that contained nearly 400,000 beds and required novel administrative methods. Many of these dramatic innovations in American wartime medicine were later imitated in Europe, especially the system of field hospitals, the hospital trains, and the hospitals' administration.

TREATMENT OF THE WOUNDED
AT THE END OF THE WAR

By the Siege of Petersburg (June 1864–April 1865), one of the last great battles of the war, the transport and treatment of the wounded had advanced far beyond its shaky beginnings. A railroad line ran parallel to the Union trenches, and wounded men were treated right behind the lines and then moved by rail to a large tent hospital at City Point, the army's supply base on the James River. Convalescents were moved by boat to northern cities, freeing up beds for other wounded soldiers. Now, surgeons, who had become more experienced, cared for the wounded using greatly improved techniques and equipment.

The Civil War's bloody crucible was a watershed episode in the treatment of battlefield casualties. It inaugurated a staged, well-organized emergency medical system and established a standard for medical care that would challenge physicians' skills for decades to come. The system of battlefield care to ambulance to field hospital system developed during the Civil War remained the pattern of organization for battlefield medicine, both European and American, during all the huge wars fought for nearly a full century, until it was replaced by helicopter evacuation directly from the battlefield.

REFERENCES

1. U.S. War Department: *The War of the Rebellion: A Compilation of the Official Records of the Union and Confederate Armies*. 127 vols. in 69. Gettysburg, PA: National Historical Society, 1972 (orig. pub. Washington, D.C.: U.S. Gov. Printing Office, 1880-1901), p. 77.
2. Oates SB: *A Woman of Valor: Clara Barton and the Civil War*. New York: MacMillan, 1994, p. 22.
3. *New York Times*. July 27, 1861, p. 8.

ABBREVIATIONS USED IN TEXT

HW — *Harper's Weekly.*

LC — Library of Congress, Prints and Photographs.

Medical and Surgical History — Barnes JK: *The Medical and Surgical History of the War of the Rebellion, (1861–1865)*. Washington, D.C.: GPO, 1870–88.

MOLLUS — Military Order of the Loyal Legion of the U.S.

NARA — National Archives & Records Administration.

Navy O.R. — U.S. Navy Dept., Rush R, Woods RH, eds.: *Official Records of the Union and Confederate Navies in the War of the Rebellion.* Washington, D.C.: GPO, 1897–1927.

NMHM — National Museum of Health and Medicine, Armed Forces Institute of Pathology.

O.R. — U.S. War Dept.: *The War of the Rebellion: A Compilation of the Official Records of the Union and Confederate Armies.* 127 vols. in 69. Washington, D.C.: GPO, 1880–1901. (Reprint: National Historical Society, 1972.)

PE — Dammann G: *A Pictorial Encyclopedia of Civil War Medical Instruments and Equipment.* Missoula, MT: Pictorial Histories, 1983.

PHCW — *The Photographic History of the Civil War.* New York: Review of Reviews, 1911. (Reprint: Blue & Grey Press, 1987.)

SS — Gross SD: *System of Surgery*, 4th edition, 2 vols. Philadelphia, PA: Henry C. Lea, 1866.

USAMHI — U.S. Army Military History Institute.

∾ 1 ∾

In the Beginning: Ill-Prepared and Overwhelmed

The ancient and fossilized arrangements of the Medical Department, planned only for a petty military force of less than fifteen thousand men—and few of them ever assembled in a body of a thousand strong—prove, as every dictate of common sense should have shown, utterly inadequate to the immense army suddenly assembled. Our military costume-mongers would fain stretch the coat of Tom Thumb to cover the limbs of the giant.

– The New York Times, July 27, 1861

THE FIRST YEAR OF THE CIVIL WAR WAS A MEDICAL DISASTER. The abandonment of most of the wounded after the First Battle of Bull Run; the terrible care survivors received if they dragged themselves to a "hospital"; and the rampant dysentery, measles, typhoid fever, pneumonia, and "consumption" (tuberculosis) attest to the lack of preparation and the medical bungling. Volunteers, who enlisted with patriotic fervor, were struck down by deadly diseases before reaching the battlefield, their letters home reflecting "a kind of terror and despair that is not found in any account of their [later] battles."[1]

Newspaper reports and editorials at the outset of the Civil War drew a vivid image of the often-tragic medical events. After the initial battles, reports of the enormous number of amputations horrified the public, and surgeons were accused of operating simply to gain experience. The images created in that chaotic first year persist in Civil War histories despite the enormous improvements in the care and evacuation of the wounded, the decreased frequency of most diseases, and the control over who did the surgeries and how they were performed.

Erroneous statements regarding the status of American medical science, made at the time and in the decades following the Civil War, have been repeated authoritatively.[2] American medical education and the quality of Civil War physicians have also been compared unfavorably to their European counterparts. Condemnations of both the Union and Confederate armies' medical service continue to appear even in highly regarded historical works, as if the first year's disasters represented the total medical experience. Historians rarely compare the Union Medical Department's record to the initially dismal performance of the other army bureaus. In fact, *all* military departments were completely unprepared for a war that was expected to last less than ninety days but stretched to four years.

The development of knowledge and skills in military surgery produced results far better than those in previous American and European wars. Deaths from disease and mortality following gunshot wounds were proportionately far fewer than those of the French in the next major European war, the Franco-Prussian War of 1870–71, despite France's position as the undisputed leader in medicine, particularly in military surgery, in the middle of the nineteenth century.

THE INFLUENCE OF THE CRIMEAN WAR

The American public focused on the medical disasters of the first year of the Civil War in part because of the widely publicized experiences of the British and the French in the Crimea. Disease by itself, the public learned, would have destroyed the entire initial British Expeditionary Force were it not for replacement troops. In the first six months of 1855, the hospitalization rate for disease among the British forces was recorded as 135%, although authorities admitted that a large number of patients had not been registered. At one point, more soldiers were in the hospital than were on duty. Altogether, 29% of the British Expeditionary Force died of disease during those six months—10% in one month alone.[3] More men were sent, and the death rate decreased; overall, nearly 22% of the French and British soldiers sent to Turkey and the Crimea died during the two-year conflict.[4] Both the British and the French had three times as many deaths from disease as from battle injuries (the ratio was about 11:1 among the Russians). In comparison, the same ratio among Union soldiers over the course of the Civil War was 2:1, a figure probably echoed among the Confederate forces.

In late November 1855, the first famous war correspondent, William Howard Russell, detailed the medical mismanagement and the official disregard for the welfare of the troops in the Crimea:

> The dead, laid out as they died, were lying side by side with the living, and the latter presented a spectacle beyond all imagination. The commonest accessories of a hospital were wanting; there was not the least attention paid to decency or cleanliness—the stench was appalling—the foetid air could barely struggle out to taint the atmosphere . . . and for all I could observe, these men died without the least effort to save them. There they laid just as they were let gently down upon the ground by the poor fellows, their comrades, who brought them on their backs from the camp with great tenderness, but who were not allowed to remain with them. The sick appeared to be tended by the sick and the dying by the dying.[5]

Newspapers had kept Americans well informed about events during the Crimean War, including the improvements made by Florence Nightingale and her small band of thirty-eight nurses. After the British Sanitary Commission sent Nightingale and her team to the area, the improved cleanliness and other sanitary measures resulted in a decrease in the monthly death rate to 2.5% by January 1856.[6]

Public outrage in Britain over the poor medical care and the filthy evacuation hospitals was directed against medical personnel as well as the army commanders, whose incompetence in providing necessary medical supplies was exceeded only by their military ineptitude, as immortalized by Tennyson's *The Charge of the Light Brigade*. Numerous post-war Royal Commissions investigated the misfortunes of the soldiers; the last report appeared in 1859. As the Civil War began and America's young men marched off enthusiastically in hastily organized parades, American newspapers were filled with references to the medical disasters in the Crimea and in the battles at Solferino and Magenta in Italy (see Box, p. 11). Similarly, several medical publications published detailed analyses of the Crimean War death-rate figures, including the French surgeon general's data, which appeared in translation in the *American Journal of the Medical Sciences*.

THE U.S. SANITARY COMMISSION

Despite the belief on both sides that the conflict would be brief, there was widespread fear of a repetition of those European tragedies in both medical and lay circles. This spurred action by American civilians concerned about the health of their armed forces. One day after Maj. Robert Anderson surrendered Fort Sumter, the first recorded meeting of a soldier's aid society, formed by a group of women, took place in Bridgeport, Connecticut. Similar societies were quickly formed in other communities. On April 29, Dr. Elizabeth Blackwell, the first woman known to have obtained an M.D. degree, organized a meeting of socially prominent women at the Cooper Institute in New York City (see Biographical Box, pp. 418-19). They decided to form the Women's Central Association of Relief of New York City, which soon established a program to train nurses for the army. (See Figure 1.1.)

Early in May 1861, men joined the women's organizational efforts following a chance meeting between the Rev. Dr. Henry Whitney Bellows, pastor of All Souls Unitarian Church in New York City, and Dr. Elisha Harris, a prominent New York physician. These men formed the U.S. Sanitary

Figure 1.1: Women's Central Association of Relief office inside Cooper Union, New York City, April 29, 1861. The organization made the arrangements to recruit and train nurses for Dorothea Dix. Executive Secretary Louisa Lee Schuyler is seated at the table, second from the left. (Courtesy of the Museum of the City of New York.)

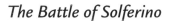

The Battle of Solferino

On January 25–27, 1859, the forces of the Austrian Empire fought a bloody battle at Solferino in northern Italy against Italian forces commanded by the King of Sardinia, Victor Emanuel I, and his ally, Napoleon III of France. In classic eighteenth-century fashion, cavalry attacked an infantry arranged in squares. Evacuation and care of the wounded were equally antiquated; houses and even some palaces in the area became makeshift hospitals.

Homeowners wandered the streets looking for help from one of about 140 doctors available to serve approximately 40,000 wounded. Many wounded soldiers waited up to four days for transport. Some died while dragging themselves to a hospital, and others were buried while still alive. It took three weeks to collect all the wounded.

Such medical horror stories after the battle spurred a movement to improve the care of wounded soldiers, particularly prisoners of war. American and Canadian volunteer doctors observed that patients were treated regardless of their nationality, and whether or not they were prisoners. The physicians' experiences helped to develop medical policies early in the Civil War.

These policies were echoed during the Convention for the Amelioration of the Condition of the Wounded Soldiers of Armies in the Field, which took place in Geneva in 1863 (the "Geneva Convention").[7] The participants, who included unofficial representatives of the U.S. Federal government and the U.S. Sanitary Commission, agreed that medical personnel, if captured, should be treated as non-combatants and released as soon as practicable, while ambulances and military hospitals were to be recognized as neutral.[8]

Commission, and the Women's Central Association of Relief of New York City became a component of the larger organization. Charles Stillé, who became a member of the executive committee of the U.S. Sanitary Commission, later wrote a history of the Commission in which he emphasized how knowledge of the Crimean experience caused apprehension among American civilians when the war began.[9,10] In his official history, Stillé explained:

> Earnest men who loved their country, and who had some humane consideration for the health and lives of those who were defending it, determined that something should be done to avoid a similar catastrophe

11

here. They knew that the British people had been able only to investigate and deplore the causes which had led to so direful a result. They felt that here a wise, thorough, and persistent effort should be made at the outset of the war, guided by the Crimean experience, to forestall the insidious march of those diseases, which, if unchecked, would inevitably overwhelm our army and with it [leave] our country in ruin.[11]

Representatives of the Sanitary Commission met in New York with the army's medical purveyor (responsible for acquiring medical supplies and drugs) and offered to provide them with medical supplies and other items. They were rebuffed. Several Commission representatives then traveled to Washington on May 16, 1861, to meet the acting surgeon general of the army, Col. Robert C. Wood, who had just assumed that position after the death of the pre-war surgeon general, Thomas Lawson. Wood was polite but non-committal during the meeting, humoring them in the hope that they would go away.[12] (A more complete description of the U.S. Sanitary Commission is given in Appendix E.)

As volunteer troops rushed to defend Washington, the army's inability to meet the needs of their rapidly expanding forces became obvious. Stillé described the scene:

> During the months of May and June, 1861, regiment after regiment arrived at the National Capital in a most unsatisfactory condition, so far as concerned their real efficiency as soldiers. These regiments had made their journey in cattle cars, as crowded and as ill-provided as if they were carrying beasts to the shambles; while most of them were utterly unprovided with any means of relief for those of their number who had become ill or exhausted from their long exposure. On arriving, no preparations had been made for their reception. Men stood for hours in the broiling sun or drenching rain, waiting in vain for rations and shelter, while their ignorant and inexperienced Commissaries and Quartermasters were slowly and painfully learning the duties of their positions. At last, utterly worn out and disgusted, they reached their camps, where they received rations as unwholesome as distasteful to them, and endeavored to recruit their wasted energies while lying upon rotten straw, wrapped in a shoddy blanket.[13]

Stillé feared military discord and loss of lives from disease. He was appalled by the disenchantment with the "national cause" and by "a dangerous spirit of mutiny" engendered by the "incapacity of their officers." He also noted the "alarming prevalence of certain diseases, well known in camps, which led officers of experience in the regular army to predict that fifty percent of the volunteers, before the end of the summer, would fall victim to diseases entirely preventable by wise measures of precaution rigidly enforced."[14]

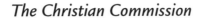

The Christian Commission

On November 14, 1861, the Christian Commission was organized by the Young Men's Christian Association (YMCA) in New York City to provide food, medical supplies, and comfort to soldiers. Women in the organization performed nursing services. The main organizer, Vincent Colyer, later became president of the YMCA. Initially, the Christian Commission worked in conjunction with the U.S. Sanitary Commission until the relationship became strained.

Staffed by unpaid volunteers, the Christian Commission felt a duty to provide moral and spiritual as well as physical aid. It distributed Bibles along with food, medical supplies, and material to write letters home. It also strenuously fought the consumption of alcohol by the troops. Some critics contended that the Commission's religious interests took too much precedence over its other activities. The Christian Commission raised and spent over 6 million dollars to support its work in the war. It went out of existence on February 11, 1866.[15]

THE UNION SURGEONS GENERAL

The medical disasters during the first year were in large part due to the incompetence of the Union Surgeon General's Office, which was completely unprepared for these new challenges. The Union's surgeon general at the start of hostilities was eighty-year-old Thomas Lawson. He had been an army surgeon for fifty-five years, and was a veteran of the War of 1812 and the Mexican War. Lawson became surgeon general when John Quincy Adams was president and, as befitted a peacetime officer, his main concern was frugality. He considered even the purchase of medical books to be an unnecessary extravagance. Ill when the war began, Lawson died of "apoplexy" on May 15, 1861.[16]

After Robert C. Wood served an interim appointment, the post was assigned to the most senior member of the Medical Department, Clement Alexander Finley, who had been the chief surgeon in the Black Hawk War of 1832 (in which Abraham Lincoln also served). Like Lawson, Finley was unable to think beyond the needs of small frontier army posts and also believed it was wasteful to spend money on medical equipment and textbooks. His lack of vision is illustrated by his decision to wait for a battle before ordering necessary medical supplies and dressings.[17] Contemporary critics described both men as "utterly ossified and useless." One critic, George Templeton Strong, called them "old codgers, paralyzed by routine habits acquired in long dealing with an army of ten or fifteen thousand and utterly unequal to their present task."[18]

After Bull Run, the Sanitary Commission damningly opined that "in no Department of the Government were its preparations less suited to meet the emergency than in that of the Military Hospitals."[19] Finley yielded to the pressure and agreed to permit the Sanitary Commission to assist the volunteer army but not the regular army troops, because he assumed that the volunteers would not make good soldiers. That suited the Sanitary Commission, since they recognized that the regular army was rapidly becoming a tiny percentage of the Union's total force, and they established their offices in the Treasury building on September 16, 1861.[20]

In December of that year, Horace Greeley, editor of the powerful *New York Tribune*, attacked Finley for his incompetence. The medical director of Gen. Thomas W. Sherman's expedition to Hilton Head and Port Royal, South Carolina, had ordered the construction of a hospital. Astonishingly, Finley countermanded the order on the grounds that "the mild climate of South Carolina deletes the necessity of a hospital."[21] In a blistering editorial, Greeley charged that the Medical Bureau, instead of fighting "its natural and official enemies typhus, malaria, and smallpox, defective ventilation of tents, imperfect drainage of camps, and lazy regimental surgeons," was fighting the Sanitary Commission. The Medical Bureau, he held, "is not accused of misfeasance or malfeasance, but of nonfeasance. It seems to have done nothing since the war began. It is simply inefficient and inert, when inaction is the gravest of official misdemeanors."[22]

The Medical Department's poor early showing was part of the Union army's general lack of readiness. The Commissary and Quartermaster Departments, for example, were unprepared for the needs of an army so much larger than the peacetime force. The resulting chaos in housing and feeding the volunteers contributed to the soldiers' illnesses. Indeed, corruption saturated the entire tenure of Secretary of War Simon Cameron. In mid-January 1862, after censure by the House of Representatives, Cameron was sent to Saint Petersburg, Russia, as ambassador. He was replaced by Edwin M. Stanton, who was both able and honorable, and who served as secretary of war for the remainder of the conflict.[23]

THE CONFEDERATE MEDICAL DEPARTMENT

The Confederate forces had similar problems with their newly organized departments. The Commissary Department, headed by Lt. Col. Lucius Bellinger Northrop, failed to arrange sufficient food supplies for the unexpectedly large force gathered at Manassas. General Pierre G. T. Beauregard wrote to his friends in Congress: "We have been without subsistence for several days, some of my regiments have not had anything to eat for more than twenty-four hours."[24] Beauregard was blamed for the failure of the Confederate forces to follow up their victory at Manassas; he blamed heavy rains and a lack of supplies. Most Southerners blamed the failure to move on Washington on "rain, mud, and Northrop."[25] Bitter recriminations between Northrop and the field commanders continued for years in post-war publications such as "Battles and Leaders of the Civil War" (a series of articles published in *Century Magazine* between 1884 and 1887).[26]

In contrast to the Union army, the Confederate Surgeon General's Office had consistent leadership that began early in the war. After two brief and unsatisfactory interim appointments, President Jefferson Davis named a former U.S. Army physician from Charleston, Samuel Preston Moore, as surgeon general on July 30, 1861, nine days after Bull Run. (See Biographical Box, p. 16.) Moore served for the duration of the war and is generally credited with having done a superb job.

During the war, Moore was criticized severely for his austere, formal manner and his insistence on paperwork and traditional army protocol. Aristides Monteiro, a noted Virginia surgeon, wrote, "To please the head of the department, surgeons must be cruel, severe; and, above all things stupid, submissive and sycophantic."[27] Even his milder critics cited Moore's failure to send senior physicians into the field where they believed the doctors' experience would be most valuable. Moore, believing that their knowledge of military procedure would expedite developments, gave them administrative roles, thus more effectively utilizing the few experienced physicians available. (When the efficient William Hammond was appointed surgeon general in Washington, he adopted a similar policy.) Moore was also criticized for insisting that the women who volunteered as hospital matrons in charge of hospital wards follow military formalities. On the other hand, he was always ready to listen to complaints, and the overall appraisal of his administration long after the war by former subordinates and historians of Civil War medicine was strongly positive.[28,29]

Samuel Preston Moore (1812–1889)

Samuel Preston Moore had a solid Southern background. He was born and educated in Charleston, South Carolina, and received his M.D. degree from the Medical College of South Carolina in 1834. The following year, after passing the U.S. Army medical board's examination, he was appointed assistant surgeon and assigned to a series of frontier posts. He served during the Mexican War and also in Texas and New York. Serving as the army's medical purveyor in New Orleans when South Carolina seceded, he resigned his commission and went into practice in Little Rock, Arkansas. On July 30, 1861, he was asked to become "acting" surgeon general, and was confirmed by the Confederate Senate late in November.

(Photo courtesy of PHCW.)

TRIPLER AND THE ARMY OF THE POTOMAC

Federal military preparedness improved rapidly after Maj. Gen. George Brinton McClellan introduced badly needed training and administrative organization to the force that he named the Army of the Potomac. Substantive reforms in medical care, however, had to wait until after the nearly year-long tenure of Dr. Charles S. Tripler. (Upon Surgeon General Finley's recommendation, McClellan had appointed Tripler, a regular-army physician, as the Army of the Potomac's medical director on August 12, 1861.) (See Figure 1.2.)

Tripler attempted to get control of the medical personnel and the chaotic medical conditions among the volunteer regiments, which were just then being combined into an army. Initially, he was unable to determine which regiments had medical officers or even which regiments were present. None of the artillery batteries and cavalry detachments had medical officers. Regimental surgeons often sent sick men to a hospital in Washington without making prior arrangements, instead leaving them "to pass the night in the ambulances, wandering about the streets from hospital to hospital seeking admission."[30] To address the many complaints about incompetent regimental surgeons, Tripler appointed an examining board, which evaluated as many surgeons as it could and recommended the discharge of several.

Tripler is described as a "strict constructionist"—everything was done according to regulations. While he worked hard and made many improvements in the Army of the Potomac's medical care, he was not up to the huge, unprecedented task he faced. By late 1861, the bulk of the army consisted of recruits and, at any given time, 20 to 50 percent of the men in most units were sick. The fall of 1861 through the following winter was the period of greatest epidemic disease for all the Civil War armies. Virtually all soldiers suffered from repeated attacks of diarrhea and dysentery, measles (a serious disease in adults), and typhoid fever (one of the biggest killers of the war).

The root cause of the problem was the crowding of men who had no immunity to the common epidemic diseases. (In subsequent wars, boot camps provided the same situation.) Many army surgeons tried to improve sanitation and thus prevent disease, but line officers often considered them "impertinent and obtrusive, and the suggestion of the medical officers to those ends were too frequently disregarded and ignored."[31] The physicians' influence was weakened, in part, because, early in the war, voluntary and politically appointed officers felt that the military adventure was temporary and so they didn't want to learn army regulations and procedures.

Tripler did what he could to control sickness. Typical of the thinking of the era, he focused on "unhealthy air," referred to as "miasmas," and particularly on the toxic air believed to be emanating from the marshes along the Potomac River. Since the marshes were a primary breeding ground for mosquitoes and malaria developed with astounding frequency, his thinking had some validity. He deplored what he called the "unhygienic conditions" allowed to prevail in many training areas, where flies abounded, because inexperienced regimental officers saw no need for latrine facilities or safe drinking water. Tripler correctly blamed much of the epidemic disease on these conditions. He also complained about inadequate medical screening before enlistment, which resulted in recruits with physical disabilities. In addition, he proposed vaccination for those who were not protected against smallpox as indicated by a history of the disease or the presence of a vaccination scar.

Unfortunately, Tripler wrongly believed that the sick did much better in regimental rather than in general hospitals, stating, "I consider general

Figure 1.2: Charles Tripler, medical director of the Army of the Potomac from the fall of 1861 to the end of the Peninsula campaign, July 1, 1862. (PHCW)

hospitals general nuisances."[32] Regimental hospitals were necessarily small infirmaries placed in the regiment's training camp, in which the surgeon and assistant surgeon of the regiment cared for the seriously ill while performing their regular duties. Sanitary conditions in the infirmary were as bad as in the rest of the camp and the quality of medical care was generally poor, since regimental surgeons were often appointed by state governors without being examined. Nursing care was provided by other soldiers, if at all. General hospitals, however, had assigned staff, served men from any military unit, were usually located in a town or city, and were much larger than their regimental counterparts.

One reason for Tripler's opposition to general hospitals was his experience that men returned to duty with their regiment much less frequently if they were sent to a division or general hospital. There, men were more likely to get sympathetic treatment, furloughs, or reassignments from the staff. After Tripler was replaced in July 1862, the Army of the Potomac abolished regimental hospitals and introduced a huge system of well-staffed division, corps, and general hospitals. Other Union armies initiated similar improvements at roughly the same time.

To his credit, early in the fall of 1861, Tripler sent General McClellan a formal proposal for reorganizing the ambulance system. While emphasizing that his suggestions were limited to be compatible with "current law," he proposed that Congress change the law to allow the establishment of a full ambulance corps. This body, he suggested, would be analogous to the Quartermaster Corps, which provided supplies for the army and, at that time, controlled all wagon (and ambulance) use. He also requested a trained corps of ambulance attendants and litter bearers under the command of regimental medical officers, and suggested a reasonable number of ambulances for each regiment. An almost identical plan was implemented a year later, despite the lack of new legislation, after William Hammond became surgeon general and Jonathan Letterman replaced Tripler as the medical director of the Army of the Potomac.

Notably, Tripler also suggested improvements in nursing care for hospitalized soldiers. In his memorandum on medical personnel, he suggested "employment of an adequate corps of male and female nurses by the medical director, to act under his supervision." Tripler added that this was "another important suggestion of the Sanitary Commission, and recommended by Major-General McClellan."[33]

Tripler tried to adapt to the enormous problems he faced but, overwhelmed by the immense number of casualties during the Peninsula campaign in 1862, he finally asked for reassignment. Critics point out that to Tripler, "the regulations were the end and aim of all, not merely the means to a greater end."[34] Apparently it never occurred to him that an unprecedented military predicament might require unprecedented actions. In a final tribute to Tripler, General McClellan wrote, "I know that everything possible has been done to insure the prompt care of the wounded on the field, and their rapid and comfortable removal to the rear."[35] Clearly, he could not imagine the unprecedented improvements that would now begin to occur.

REFORMS IN THE UNION MEDICAL BUREAU

Pressured by the Sanitary Commission and the press, U.S. Secretary of War Edwin Stanton removed the incompetent Surgeon General Finley. Ignoring the seniority system, he appointed the relatively junior physician recommended by the Sanitary Commission, William A. Hammond, on April 25, 1862. Although Hammond had personality conflicts with Stanton and was removed in 1863, he and his successor, Joseph K. Barnes, were excellent administrators. The Sanitary Commission no longer had difficulty being heard, in large part because of their relationship with Hammond, although the need for its services progressively diminished as the army's medical staff improved their performance. (See Biographical Box, pp. 20-21.)

Hammond made remarkable innovations in the Medical Bureau's organization. The most important were the reorganization of medical personnel in the field and an orderly, graded system to move the wounded, freeing beds near the battle sites when a military campaign began. Within this system, patients moved from field aid stations to field hospitals, then to division or corps hospitals near the battle or encampment, and, subsequently, to

William Alexander Hammond (1828–1900)

Born in Annapolis, Maryland, William Alexander Hammond received his M.D. degree from the University of the City of New York (later, New York University) in 1848. He spent a year at the prestigious Pennsylvania Hospital as a house physician, a position similar to that of a resident physician receiving specialty training today. After a few months in practice, he took the exam for the U.S. Army and, in 1849, was appointed assistant surgeon, the lowest rank in the Medical Corps (equivalent to first lieutenant).

While serving on various frontier posts and at West Point, Hammond did physiological research and published several papers on nutrition. In the fall of 1859, he resigned from the army and accepted the Professorship of Anatomy and Physiology at the University of Maryland in Baltimore. After the 6th Massachusetts was attacked by a mob of Confederate sympathizers while passing through Baltimore, Hammond attended some of their wounded at Baltimore Infirmary. He immediately resigned his professorship and reentered the army, but had to again assume the lowest rank in the medical corps, that of assistant surgeon.

Initially, he was appointed medical purveyor at Frederick, Maryland. He then organized an army hospital in Baltimore before being assigned to the staff of Maj. Gen. William S. Rosecrans in western Virginia as inspector of camps and hospitals. In that role, he attracted favorable attention from the Sanitary Commission, which recommended him for the position of surgeon general. General McClellan selected Hammond from a list proposed to him by the Sanitary Commission and he was appointed to that post in April 1862.

continued . . .

(Photo courtesy of Gil Barnett Collection at USAMHI.)

William Alexander Hammond, continued

Hammond had a long-running personality conflict with Secretary of War Edwin Stanton—both were haughty, proud men and they clashed immediately. When Hammond issued an order banning calomel and tarter emetic, both containing mercury, from the army's supply tables, many military physicians strenuously protested, weakening Hammond's hold on his position (see Chapter 9, *Treating Disease*).

Although Stanton had generally supported Hammond's actions, his history of support from the now out-of-favor McClellan and the personality clashes led him to remove Hammond from office in 1863 and then to have him court-martialed on the trumped up charge of misusing supplies. Hammond was convicted and dismissed from the service as of August 18, 1864.[36] *The New England Journal of Medicine* (known then as *Boston Medical and Surgical Journal* and just as influential as today) editorially supported Stanton and condemned Hammond regarding calomel in 1863. Shortly after the war, however, the *Journal* reversed its position, saying that Hammond's action was medically correct, even if undiplomatic, and concluded that he was falsely convicted in the court-martial.[37]

After he left the army, friends helped Hammond establish a medical practice in New York City, where he specialized in neurology. He became a lecturer in nervous and mental diseases at the College of Physicians and Surgeons and, in 1867, he accepted a similar position created for him at Bellevue Hospital Medical College. He continued in that position after Bellevue merged with the University of the City of New York (it later became known as New York University College of Medicine). In 1888, Hammond moved to Washington, and he practiced there until his death from heart disease in 1900.

A prolific author even while surgeon general, Hammond is considered one of the founders of the specialty of neurology in the United States. Among his publications was a *Treatise on Diseases of the Nervous System* in 1871, which was the first textbook on nervous diseases published in the U.S. [38] He also established the *Journal of Nervous and Mental Diseases.*[39]

In 1879, a decade after Stanton's death, when Hammond had become a successful and prominent figure in American medicine, he attempted to have the court-martial reversed. He obtained support from a senator, a personal review by the secretary of war, and intervention by President Rutherford B. Hayes. A congressional commission decided the entire trial had been based on Stanton's personal antipathy toward Hammond and the verdict was reversed. Hammond's name was added to the list of retired U.S. Army officers.[40]

hospital facilities in major army depots or nearby cities. When prolonged hospitalization seemed likely, soldiers were sent to large general or convalescent hospitals in major cities near their homes. Whenever possible, they traveled in specially designed hospital ships and, later, hospital trains outfitted with medicines, supplies, and appropriate staff. (This system is detailed in Chapter 4, *"Thank God for Jonathan Letterman"*.)

Hammond placed able administrators in the Medical Department and improved the quality of the personnel and facilities down the line. After the system was implemented, well-organized staffs, including surgeons, nurses, and cooks, accompanied or met patients at each stage of their journey and the requisite food, medicines, and supplies were usually available at predetermined depots.[41] Supply shortages or delays in transport were chiefly due to unpredictable military events, such as cavalry raids that destroyed railroad bridges, or to unexpected decisions to move an army swiftly, which placed restrictions on the number of ambulances allowed in the wagon trains. Huge bloody battles causing tens of thousands of wounded sometimes overloaded the system, especially in the spring campaign of 1864 in the east.

Hammond brought several capable young physicians into the Surgeon General's Office, including John H. Brinton, Joseph J. Woodward, George Otis, and John Shaw Billings. They were instructed to establish a "medical museum," in which research would be conducted on the medical and surgical problems of the war and illustrative specimens would be collected. This museum was, in fact, a research institute that evolved into an internationally respected research organization, the Armed Forces Institute of Pathology.[42]

Equally important to the improvements in the Surgeon General's Office was Hammond's appointment of Dr. Jonathan Letterman to succeed Tripler as medical director of the Army of the Potomac. Among many improvements, Letterman reorganized the ambulance system and placed it under the control of the Medical Corps instead of the Quartermaster Department. Hammond recommended that a similar system be established throughout the Union army, but Maj. Gen. Henry W. Halleck, the general-in-chief, opposed the plan and Secretary of War Stanton sided with Halleck. However, late in 1863, Congress implemented the plan throughout the army.

MEDICAL RECORDS OF THE CIVIL WAR

Hammond's staff also improved the system for reporting medical data to the Surgeon General's Office. They collected and organized data on the diseases and deaths in each Union army as well as reports from individual surgeons,

Keeping Specimens in the Army Medical Museum

Dr. John H. Brinton, who had been in charge of developing the U.S. Army Medical Museum, reminisced about the difficulties of obtaining specimens in an 1896 commencement address at the Army Medical School. He remembered an episode concerning an amputated extremity:

> On one occasion a man from the ranks demanded the return of a limb, an arm I think. He was informed that the member in question could not be given up. "But it is mine," said he, "part of myself," earnestly enforcing his claim, and his demand to the lay mind seemed reasonable. Yet to surrender a specimen was very much like yielding a principle.
>
> "Stop," said the quick-witted young assistant curator to the claimant, "For how long have you enlisted?" "For three years or the war." "Then," replied the official, "the contract is not yet terminated, come back at the end of the war or at the end of your three years' service and you can have your bone. In the meantime, one detachment of you is stationed at this Museum on government duty, the other wherever you may be ordered. Such is the opinion of the Attorney General." The reply and its reason seemed conclusive, and the bone remained in its place.[43]

intending to analyze and publish them after the war. These data and the resulting commentary became the *Medical and Surgical History of the War of the Rebellion*.[44] Published between 1870 and 1888, the six huge volumes are a major source of information about Civil War medicine; they record approximately 6.5 million diagnosed episodes of illness and the treatment of approximately 250,000 wounded men. The volumes also contain descriptions, photographs, and drawings of specimens submitted to the medical museum; some of the earliest photomicrographs; and literature reviews, several dating back to Hippocrates. Europeans regarded this publication as the Americans' first major contribution to academic medicine.

Systematic military medical record keeping dated back several decades. The British kept excellent records during the Crimean War—in fact, it was the first war in which such information was faithfully recorded—and both

Union and Confederate medical officers imitated their record-keeping policies. Before the Civil War, the U.S. Army listed diagnoses using Latin terminology, as the British had done in the Crimea. But to ensure comprehension by the large number of recently militarized physicians (many were new graduates), the Federal Surgeon General's Office began to use the English names for diseases. In general, the lists of diagnoses filled out by Union regimental surgeons employ terms still used today.

Regimental surgeons submitted weekly lists of the men relieved of duty because of illness and each army unit submitted weekly lists of diagnosed illnesses and injuries to the Surgeon General's Office, using forms provided for that purpose. Initially, the records from the small, poorly staffed regimental hospitals were of spotty quality. Later, when the hospitals served larger military units and had specially designated staffs, record keeping was vastly improved. Civil War physicians objected to the paperwork, but analyses of the data during the war kept them up-to-date on developments regarding diseases and the results of different types of surgery.

The Confederate Medical Department was organized by physicians who had been in the Federal army before the war. In general, they kept the same types of records, although they used the Latin names for diseases. The Confederate records were gathered in Richmond but were consumed in the fire that destroyed many government offices on April 2, 1865. As a result, Confederate data are incomplete; historians must rely on fragmentary hospital records and the recollections of individual Confederate physicians. After the war, Dr. Joseph Jones of Georgia collected as much data as he could from former Confederate surgeons and made estimates of the frequency of various diseases. The information he was able to collect shows patterns of disease similar to those in the Union army. Surviving hospital records indicate that similar treatments were used and that the results of care were also roughly equivalent. Much of the available Confederate data was included in *Medical and Surgical History*.

No records exist concerning the enormous number of soldiers seen by regimental surgeons each morning after the bugler blew "Surgeon's Call," or "Sick Call." Only soldiers sick enough to be hospitalized or relieved from duty became part of the statistical record. The statistics are also affected by the fact that mid-nineteenth-century physicians had no diagnostic laboratory or imaging tests to use when making diagnoses. Diagnoses were made by a process that today might be called "pattern recognition"; only fully developed syndromes were recognized. Less severe cases generally were not characteristic enough to be diagnosed, and milder forms of diseases were often labeled with essentially meaningless terms, such as "remittent fever" and "continuous fever."

Despite these limitations, the data collected were reasonably good, particularly after the incompetent surgeons had been weeded out during the war's first year and the new army physicians became accustomed to military paperwork and procedures. The number of cases and the outcomes of each disease for each major military unit are listed, month by month, for a period of more than five years. While it was intended to benefit generations of military physicians and their patients, the information was outdated immediately after publication by developments in the field of bacteriology.

For example, one of the army surgeon's responsibilities was to gather data on climatic influences on disease in a "meteorological register," an ancient approach to studying disease that yielded little, if any, new or useful

The Regimental Surgeon at Sick Call

A regimental surgeon described a typical day's work during a peaceful interval at an encampment following the Battle of Antietam:

> I was up at Surgeon's Call and before breakfast prescribed for eighty-six patients at the door of my tent. After meal I visited the hospitals and a barn where our sick are lying, and dealt in medicines and write [sic] prescriptions for one hundred more; in all visited and prescribed for one hundred and eighty-six men. I had no dinner. At four o'clock this labor was completed and a cold bite was eaten. After this, in the rain, I started for Sharpsburg, four miles distant, for medical supplies from the Medical Purveyor at that place.[45]

Another surgeon remembered his daily tasks similarly:

> The surgeon's regular daily duty began with the morning sick call. Every morning, whether in camp or on the march, the bugler sounded this call. The orderly sergeant of each company brought to the surgeon's quarters those reporting sick. He gave a list to the surgeon, who examined each man and prescribed; the hospital steward entered the prescription on the hospital record, and if possible gave the man his medicine then and there. The surgeon on the surgeon's book reported the men according to their condition; as "to hospital," "to duty," "excused from duty," "light duty," etc.[46]

information. Nevertheless, *Medical and Surgical History* remains an extremely valuable record of the medical events and epidemiology of the time, giving a detailed picture of the nature and relative frequency of the most severe illnesses. Moreover, the numerous brief case histories, autopsy findings, pictures of patients, and surgical or autopsy specimens make it possible to reevaluate some of the diagnoses using today's knowledge.

MEDICAL CARE IN THE FEDERAL AND CONFEDERATE NAVIES

Both the Union and the Confederate Navy Departments had medical bureaus. The chief of the Federal Medical Bureau (equivalent to the surgeon general in the army; the navy adopted the title of surgeon general in 1871) during the entire war was William Whelan, appointed to that post on October 1, 1853. Just after the war ended, on June 12, 1865, he was succeeded by Phineas J. Horowitz. Surgeons and assistant surgeons served on the larger vessels accompanying the blockading squadrons, and others served at navy yards and in the naval hospitals, as well as on examining and retirement boards. The title "fleet surgeon" was equivalent to the army's "medical director."[47]

The Confederate Navy Department designated Surg. William A. Spottswood as head of the Office of Medicine and Surgery on June 10, 1861, and he served until sometime in 1864 or 1865. (It is not clear who succeeded him.) The Confederate navy maintained hospitals at Richmond, Wilmington, Charleston, Savannah, Mobile, and Charlotte, and also at Norfolk and Pensacola until these sites were abandoned in 1862. In New Orleans, the *St. Phillip* was used as a receiving hospital ship for naval personnel, who were taken to Charity Hospital in the city.[48]

During the war, the few existing Union naval hospitals were enlarged and new ones were created. The naval hospital in Boston was extended by using beds in the neighboring marine hospital. In Philadelphia, a hospital was set up in the "Naval Asylum." Extra space was found for the pre-war naval hospital in New York in a temporary building, in a marine barracks, and by building an addition. In Washington, St. Elizabeth's Hospital, the government "Hospital for the Insane," provided space for a naval hospital throughout the war. The naval hospital that had been located at Norfolk was abandoned, along with the navy yard, shortly after the war began. When it was reoccupied on September 1, 1862, it was used primarily for sailors from the North

Atlantic Blockading Squadron. Temporary hospitals for sailors from other blockading squadrons were also set up in New Bern, North Carolina, and Beaufort and Port Royal in South Carolina. A temporary structure was erected at Pensacola to replace the hospital destroyed by the Confederates when they evacuated that port; it served the West Gulf Blockading Squadron.

The Federal Treasury Department, which ran the Marine Hospital Service for merchant seamen (later renamed the U.S. Public Health Service), turned over its hospital at Key West for use by the East Gulf Blockading Squadron. Sick and injured naval personnel in the Mississippi River Squadron were first cared for in an army hospital in Mound City, Illinois, and, later, in a separate navy facility. A naval hospital was opened in New Orleans in December 1863, and the Mound City Hospital was moved to Memphis during that year to be closer to the action lower on the Mississippi River. At Mare Island, California, there was a hospital for the Pacific Squadron. There were also temporary naval hospital facilities at Washington and at Plymouth, North Carolina. Arrangements were sometimes made for naval personnel to be admitted to the army hospitals, especially at Beaufort and Ocracoke in North Carolina.[49]

THE ARMY SURGEONS

Physician quality was the subject of much criticism early in the war and in Civil War histories since. Before the Civil War, there were 113 surgeons in the regular U.S. Army; when fighting broke out, 24 of those joined the Confederate army and 3 were dismissed for disloyalty. By the end of the war, only 1% of the more than 12,000 doctors who served in the Union Medical Department were veterans of the pre-war army, while less than 3% of approximately 3,200 Confederate surgeons had prior military experience.

Most army physicians served in volunteer state regiments, which were organized under the aegis of each state's governor. In all, the Union governors commissioned 2,109 surgeons and 3,882 assistant surgeons. Most of their official military ranks included the term "surgeon," thus the terms "physician" and "surgeon" were interchangeable. At the end of the war, 547 surgeons and assistant surgeons also served in both the Federal regular army and in the "U.S. Volunteers," a category created by Congress to supplement the regular army. In addition, 5,532 civilian physicians worked for the Union army for varying periods under contract and were paid per diem. They were officially designated "acting assistant surgeons." The Confederate Medical Department totaled 3,236 medical officers—1,242 surgeons and 1,994 assistant surgeons—in addition to an unknown number of civilians who served as contract surgeons.

Several regular army surgeons who served at the start of the war were outstanding; they became the medical directors of major army units, staffed the Surgeon General's Office, and made valuable contributions to the organization of patient care. However, the pre-war surgeons as a group did not engender respect. An evaluation by the Sanitary Commission early in the war resulted in the following description:

> Of the [pre-war] Surgeons many were incapacitated for all duty, and one-half were unfitted for service in the field. The average length of service of the first thirteen on the list was thirty-two years, and that of the remaining, twenty-three years . . . These officers [had been] scattered at isolated points on the frontier, without access to books, having no contact with their professional brethren in civil life, and with very little opportunity while their duties confined them to the medical care of a single company of soldiers, of improving themselves in a knowledge of that science which is perhaps of all others the most progressive . . . The conditions of things by which the surgeons of the army were surrounded before the war, was necessarily towards complete stagnation in respect of everything which could stimulate a true professional zeal.[50]

Volunteer surgeons who served as regimental and hospital physicians when war broke out did not inspire much respect either. Their ineptitude troubled both their soldier-patients and their medical supervisors. State governors often appointed regimental surgeons in the same way they appointed line officers, friendships and political considerations often overriding issues of competence. Some men called themselves doctors, but had no medical degree. In some regiments, volunteers elected the physicians in the same fashion that they elected other regimental officers. Here too, friendships often outweighed competence.

In 1834, Congress had established a Federal examination system for appointment to the regular army's medical corps. Beginning in the fall of 1861, the states gradually established similar examining boards for surgeons appointed to volunteer regiments. Some governors, unwilling to relinquish their appointment power, opposed these examinations, but the boards became virtually universal and helped to improve the quality of physicians in the volunteer regiments.

In addition, army physicians who had been appointed during that first year were reevaluated and many were discharged for incompetence. According to the records of the Sanitary Commission inspectors, only 129 of

Military Ranks in the Medical Corps

The official designations of medical officers changed during the war as a shortage of doctors and new functions, such as running huge hospitals, necessitated additional inducements. Army ranks were not rigidly followed, since legislation limited the number of positions at each level. A vacancy had to exist for a man to receive the appropriate rank, but people could be assigned the function and its responsibilities for long periods without receiving the formal promotion. When doctors were assigned to duty in general hospitals, the formal table of organization was more varied and ranks equivalent to major or below were usually assigned. Higher ranks were assigned concomitant with responsibilities, meaning that physicians' ranks were reduced when their responsibility decreased. Very few medical officers attained a permanent army rank above that of major.[51]

Medical Corps Designation	Army Rank
Entire U.S. Army	
Surgeon General	Colonel (before 1861)
	Brigadier General (1862 and after)
Assistant Surgeon General	Colonel
Medical Inspector	Colonel
Individual Field Armies & Medical Departments (of regions*)	
Medical Director of army (2 or more corps)	Colonel
Medical Director of regional military dept. with hospital (4,000 beds)	Lieutenant Colonel
Medical Director of small region	Lieutenant Colonel
Divisions	
Medical Director of division	Lieutenant Colonel
Brigades	
Surgeon	Major
Regiments	
Surgeon	Major or Captain
Assistant Surgeon	Captain or First Lieutenant
Acting Assistant Surgeon	(Civilian, on contract or awaiting formal army appointment after passing examination)

*The regions would be called "theaters of action" in later wars; they included the Atlantic Region, Gulf Region, Northwest, Mississippi, etc. The number of regions and their specific geographic area varied during the course of the war as the sites of action changed.

the 200 regimental surgeons evaluated late in 1861 were considered able to "discharge their duties with competence . . . creditable energy and earnestness." Others were at least "tolerable" in quality, but nineteen were reported as "negligent and inert."[52] The official *History of the United States Sanitary Commission* describes the problem at the beginning of the war:

> The low standard of professional ability in the army at that time was perhaps unavoidable, for the Surgeons had been selected from civil life, in many cases, with hardly greater care than had been shown in the choice of the other officers of the Regiments. Besides, they were called upon to treat diseases in the Military Hospitals, with which they had been little familiar in private practice, and under circumstances in which they were necessarily unable to consult books which might have enlightened their ignorance.[53]

As a means of obtaining the most competent men for the army medical corps, Surgeon General Hammond reorganized the boards of examination and insisted on higher standards for the candidates. Late in 1861, the Sanitary Commission sent volunteer civilian medical inspectors into virtually all the military hospitals, where they received good cooperation despite their unannounced arrivals. As the war went on, they were largely replaced by army medical inspectors (in Chapter 8, see Hospital Inspections).[54] Accordingly, the remaining three years of the war showed a marked improvement in the quality of the army's physicians and this quality was maintained. The Confederate Medical Department established a similar system of hospital inspectors. Unannounced inspections of military hospitals continued on both sides throughout the war.

A total of 5,532 civilian physicians worked for the Union army under contract for varying periods, hence the term "contract surgeons"; officially, they were "acting assistant surgeons, U.S. Army." Contract surgeons were primarily used in the general hospitals, particularly those remote from the battlefields. Many physicians were temporarily designated "acting assistant surgeons" while waiting for their appointment examinations or, if they had passed the exam, before receiving their commissions and orders.[55]

During the early, chaotic period of the war, and especially during the Peninsula campaign, many contract surgeons served in the field as regimental surgeons, and the term "contract surgeon" developed a generally bad connotation. The civilian physicians were often more of a handicap than help; some wanted only to perform surgery and refused to do what they were assigned. Bad feelings developed between the enlisted commissioned physicians and the civilians, who received not only more pay per diem than the army doctors, but also transportation expenses.

There were many occasions, however, in which contract surgeons provided valuable, praiseworthy assistance. Congress had limited the number of positions for army physicians, so many doctors who worked as contract surgeons had already passed the appointment examination, but were waiting for positions to become available. Not infrequently, state governors called on civilian surgeons for special service. The governor of Ohio, for example, issued such calls repeatedly because of heavy casualties among Ohio regiments in Tennessee, particularly after the battles at Fort Donelson, Shiloh, Stones River, and Chickamauga. The Sanitary Commission reported these physicians' work and praised their efforts.[56]

After the Battle of Gettysburg, when the Army of the Potomac left the area to pursue the Confederate forces, most of the surgeons went with them because they expected another battle. The roughly 20,000 wounded were left to be cared for by about 100 physicians, so a call went out for volunteer physicians and nurses. Large numbers responded and did exemplary work (in Chapter 4, see The Big Picture: Evolution of the Union Ambulance and Field Medical Systems). During the campaign against Gen. Robert E. Lee's army in May and June 1864, casualties were overwhelming and physician volunteers were again urgently requested. Civilian physicians responded and served admirably, maintaining excellent relationships with the army physicians. Yet, the initial reputation contract surgeons earned, like most negative facts about Civil War medicine, has persisted.

Contract surgeons also volunteered to work in the army's general hospitals in major cities. Many were leading physicians in their community who were too busy to completely give up their regular practices, too old for full-time duty, or medical school professors whose students were an important source of medical manpower throughout the war. These experienced physicians greatly contributed to patient care and to the study of some diseases.[57]

Medical students were also enlisted in the army for brief periods when there was a shortage of physicians, particularly later in the war. They were designated "medical cadets," and given a status equivalent to the cadets at West Point. Officially, they were ranked immediately below brevet second lieutenants. (Brevet ranks were temporary and did not necessarily change an officer's permanent rank.) Most of their duties resembled those of today's medical corpsman. They aided assistant surgeons near battles, helped in field hospitals, changed dressings, and performed other nursing duties.[58] Many of these students returned to school, completed their education, and then served as assistant surgeons in the army before the war ended.

THE EXAMINING BOARDS

Examining boards for physicians seeking regular army commissions met in various cities almost continuously throughout the war. Officially appointed by the secretary of war, each board consisted of "not less than three medical officers" who were designated by the surgeon general.[59] State examining boards oversaw physician appointments to the volunteer regiments. The Confederate army had the same system of examinations at the state and national levels. Typically, the examinations would last three or four and sometimes as long as six days. There was a high failure rate. Many candidates, fearing failure, cancelled their scheduled examination, and about half of those who did appear withdrew before the exam was completed, apparently too discouraged by their performance or too stressed to continue. Many of the latter blamed illness, and one candidate had an epileptic seizure while being questioned. (See Figure 1.3.)

The boards also evaluated surgeons seeking promotion. The detailed examination records from June 17, 1862, of two regimental surgeons seeking promotion to brigade surgeon illustrate the breadth of the subject matter covered. The two candidates first were questioned about anatomy, pharmacology (called *materia medica*), and therapeutics. The next day they were questioned about chemistry and medical practice and, on the third day, about physiology and obstetrics. (The inclusion of obstetrics indicates that this was a comprehensive examination not limited to militarily pertinent topics.) The fourth day concerned medical jurisprudence and toxicology; one candidate was also asked to perform surgical operations on a cadaver. On the fifth day, hygiene and pathology were discussed; one of the two candidates withdrew. The assessment of the other candidate continued with a clinical examination of patients on Douglas Hospital's wards, after which he had to perform operations on a cadaver. He passed.[60]

Essays were also an examination requirement. One topic assigned to a candidate for assistant surgeon in March 1862 was, "Give an account of Chronic Diarrhea as observed in the army, its causes, pathology, and treatment." Other topics included: "Give an account of the various fractures to which the bones of the forearm are subject, together with the causes, symptoms and modes of treatment." "Describe the subclavian arteries, their origin, course, branches and relations." "Describe the physiology of digestion and specify the peculiar function of each of the digestive organs in the process." "Discuss dislocation of the femur and discuss pyemia." These subjects indicate the boards' attempts to thoroughly assess candidates' medical knowledge.

Figure 1.3: Examining a surgeon for an appointment in the U.S. Navy. (Sketch by Charles Ellery Stillman, a surgeon and artist who served in the U.S. Navy during the war.)

Few physicians passed the pre-war examinations for the regular army. In one 1858 exam, for example, only 3 out of 25 candidates passed, while only 4 out of 21 passed another exam in 1860. However, in 1861, with war imminent, 63 out of 156 candidates were approved at one examination, and another board meeting in Washington examined 130 candidates, of whom 120 were approved. In many instances, the army boards reexamined appointees that had been passed by the states' examining boards, weeding out unqualified doctors. After reviewing examination results in 1862, Surgeon General Hammond decided that a standard scoring system was needed. The overall examination was divided into twelve branches, with a maximum of 50 points obtainable on each section and a total possible score of 600. It was necessary to score 400 total points to attain the position of surgeon and 300 to become an assistant surgeon.[61]

Surgeon General Hammond reported that, despite a lowering of standards, the army remained short of surgeons.[62] Nonetheless, efforts were made to keep qualifications reasonably high, as shown by the summary in the report for the last year of the war written by Surgeon General Joseph Barnes:

An Episode at a Confederate Medical Examining Board

An examining board session was described by the biographer of a prominent Louisville physician, David Wendell Yandell, who had been medical director of Gen. Albert Sidney Johnston's army at Shiloh. Yandell became president of a Kentucky examining board that surveyed applicants for the state's Confederate regiments.

The examinations were oral, and were harrowing experiences for eager, although nervous, doctors. On one occasion the victim of Yandell's intense grilling about gunshot wounds brightened when asked what he would do for a "shot right through there," the Medical Director [Yandell] pointing to his own knee. "Well, Sir, if it was you that was shot through there, I would not do a damned thing," announced the applicant.[64]

There is no record documenting whether the applicant passed the examination.

"152 candidates were invited before these [examining] boards, 58 of whom passed satisfactory examinations, and were appointed accordingly; the remainder were rejected or failed to appear, or withdrew before examination was completed."[63]

REFERENCES

1. Pullen JJ: *The Twentieth Maine: A Volunteer Regiment in the Civil War.* Philadelphia, PA: Lippincott, 1957, p. 39.
2. Tomes NJ: American attitudes toward the germ theory of disease: Phyllis Allen Richmond revisited. *J Hist Med Allied Sci.* 1997 Jan;52(1):7-16.
3. *U.S. Sanitary Commission Bulletin.* 1864;1:422.
4. Scrive G: A medico-surgical account of the Crimean War, from the first arrival of the troops at Gallipoli to their departure from the Crimea. Quoted in: *Am J Med Sci.* 1861 Oct;42:463-74.
5. Russell WH: *Russell's Dispatches from the Crimea, 1854–1856.* (Nicholas Bentley, ed.) New York: Hill & Wang, 1966, p. 154.
6. Maxwell WQ: *Lincoln's Fifth Wheel: The Political History of the U.S. Sanitary Commission.* New York: Longmans, Green & Co., 1956, p. 5.
7. Dunant JH: *A Memory of Solferino (Un Souvenir de Solferino).* Washington, D.C.: American National Red Cross, 1939.
8. *New York Evening Post.* September 15, 1864. Sanitary Commission papers, New York Public Library, Box 1025.

9. Livermore MAR: *My Story of the War. A Woman's Narrative of Four Year's Personal Experience as a Nurse in the Union Army, and in Relief Work at Home, in Hospitals, Camps, and at the Front during the War of the Rebellion. With Anecdotes, Pathetic Incidents, and Thrilling Reminiscences Portraying the Lights and Shadows of Hospital Life and the Sanitary Service of the War.* Hartford, CT: A.D. Worthington, 1888.

10. Wormeley KP: *The Other Side of the War, with the Army of the Potomac: Letters from the Headquarters of the United States Sanitary Commission during the Peninsular Campaign in Virginia in 1862.* Boston: Ticknor, 1888.

11. Stillé CJ: *History of the United States Sanitary Commission: Being a General Report of Its Work During the War of the Rebellion.* New York: Hurd and Houghton, 1868, p. 28.

12. Maxwell, *Lincoln's Fifth Wheel*, pp. 6,7.

13. Stillé, *United States Sanitary Commission*, p. 33.

14. Ibid., p. 34.

15. Faust PL, ed.: *Historical Times Encyclopedia of the Civil War.* New York: Harper & Row, 1986, p. 140.

16. "Apoplexy" was a loosely defined term that usually meant a stroke or a cerebrovascular accident but often was used to mean any sudden illness. Therefore, it is only a guess as to its meaning in any case report. The term was not used in any official records of the Civil War.

17. Adams GW: *Doctors in Blue: The Medical History of the Union Army in the Civil War.* Dayton, OH: Press of Morningside, 1985, p. 28.

18. Gillett MC: *The United States Army Medical Department, 1818–1865.* Washington, D.C.: Center of Military History, U.S. Army, 1987, pp. 153-54.

19. Stillé, *United States Sanitary Commission*, p. 93.

20. Maxwell, *Lincoln's Fifth Wheel*, 1956.

21. Brooks SM: *Civil War Medicine.* Springfield, IL: C.C. Thomas, 1966, p. 6.

22. Adams, *Doctors in Blue*, p. 228.

23. Munson EL: Union Surgeon Generals and their work. In: *The Photographic History of the Civil War.* New York: Review of Reviews, 1970 (orig. pub. 1911), vol. 4B, appendix D.

24. Moore JN: *Confederate Commissary General Lucius Bellinger Northrop and the Subsistence Bureau of the Southern Army.* Shippensburg, PA: White Mane Pub., 1996, p. 107.

25. Chesnut MBM: *Mary Chesnut's Civil War.* New Haven: Yale Univ. Press, 1981, p. 124.

26. Imboden JD: Incidents of the First Bull Run. *Battles and Leaders of the Civil War.* vol. 1. New York: Thomas Yoseloff, 1956, p. 229; Johnston JE: Responsibilities of the First Bull Run. *Battles and Leaders of the Civil War*, vol. 1, p. 240.

27. Cunningham HH: *Doctors in Gray: The Confederate Medical Service.* Baton Rouge: Louisiana State Univ. Press, 1958, p. 249.

28. Deering R: Field and temporary hospitals. In: *The Photographic History of the Civil War.* New York: Review of Reviews, 1970 (orig. pub. 1911), vol. 4B, p. 239.

29. Cunningham, *Doctors in Gray*, p. 249.

30. Report of Surg. Charles S. Tripler, Medical Director of the Army of the Potomac, of the operations of the medical department of that Army from August 12, 1861, to March 17, 1862. *O.R.*, Series I, vol. V, p. 77.

31. Ibid., p. 85.

32. Ibid., p. 79.

33. Ibid.

34. Duncan LC: *The Medical Department of the United States Army in the Civil War.* Gaithersburg, MD: Butternut Press, 1985 (orig. pub. 1912), p. 101.

35. Army medical intelligence. *Am Med Times.* 1862 Aug;5:69.

36. Gillett, *United States Army Medical Department, 1818–1865*, p. 226.

37. Editorial. *Boston Med Surg J.* 1865;71:125.

38. Klawans HL: *The Medicine of History from Paracelsus to Freud.* New York: Raven Press, 1982, p. 123.

39. Johnson A, Malone D, eds.: *Dictionary of American Biography*. vol. 8. New York: C. Scribner & Sons, 1930, p. 211.
40. Duncan LC: The days gone by. the strange case of Surgeon General Hammond. *Military Surg*. 1929 Jan;64:98-110 and *Military Surg*. 1929 Feb;64:252-62.
41. Gillett, *United States Army Medical Department, 1818–1865*, p. 225.
42. Henry RS: *The Armed Forces Institute of Pathology: Its First Century, 1862–1962*. Washington Office of the Surgeon General: Department of the Army, 1964.
43. Brinton J: Address at the Closing Exercises of the Army Medical School, 1895–6. *J Am Med Assoc*. 1896;26:599-605.
44. Barnes JK: *Medical and Surgical History of the War of the Rebellion*. Washington, D.C.: GPO, 1870–88.
45. Holt DM: *A Surgeon's Civil War: The Letters and Diary of Daniel M. Holt, M.D.* Kent, OH: Kent State Univ. Press, 1994, p. 34.
46. Hart AG: *The Surgeon and the Hospital in the Civil War*. Gaithersburg, MD: Olde Soldier Books, 1987 (orig. pub. 1902), p. 9.
47. Munden KW, Beers HP: *The Union: A Guide to Federal Archives Relating to the Civil War*. Washington, D.C.: National Archives & Records Administration (NARA), 1980.
48. Beers HP: *The Confederacy: A Guide to Archives of the Government of the Confederate States of America*. Washington, D.C.: NARA, 1986, pp. 348-49.
49. Report of Actg. Rear-Admiral S.P. Lee, Commanding the North Atlantic Blockading Squadron, U.S. Flagship *Minnesota*, Newport News, VA, February 12, 1863; *Official Records of the Union and Confederate Navies in the War of the Rebellion*. Series I, vol. VIII, p. 522. [henceforth referred to as the *Navy O.R.*]
50. Stillé, *United States Sanitary Commission*, pp. 116-17.
51. Gillett, *United States Army Medical Department, 1818–1865*, p. 252+.
52. Wiley BI: *The Life of Billy Yank: The Common Soldier of the Union*. Baton Rouge: Louisiana State Univ. Press, 1952, p. 130.
53. Stillé, *United States Sanitary Commission*, p. 110.
54. Munden, Beers, *A Guide to Federal Archives*, pp. 304-5.
55. Adams, *Doctors in Blue*, p. 45.
56. *U.S. Sanitary Commission Bulletin*. 1863;1:211.
57. Annual Report of Surgeon General Barnes, 1865. Summary in: *Br Med J*. 1866 (September 22);2:339.
58. U.S. Army: *Revised United States Army Regulations of 1861*. Washington, D.C.: GPO, 1863, No. 1320, p. 315.
59. Ibid.
60. NARA, RG112, Entry #308.
61. Ibid.
62. Annual Report of the Surgeon General to the Secretary of War, NARA, Microfilm M997.
63. Annual Report of Surgeon General Barnes, *Br Med J*, 1866.
64. Baird ND: *David Wendel Yandell: Physician of Old Louisville*. Lexington, KY: Univ. Press of Kentucky, 1978, p. 43.

~ 2 ~

Sects and Science:
Civil War Medicine in Context

*Think for a moment, sir, of the situation in which we physicians are placed.
We have no legislative chambers to enact laws for us. We are our own
lawyers, or at least we must discover the laws on which our profession rests.
We must discover them and not invent them; for the laws of nature are not
to be invented.*

– Letter from Dr. Pierre Louis, in Paris, to Dr. James Jackson, Sr.
in Boston, March 22, 1833

LISTER'S DISCOVERY OF ANTISEPSIS and the development of bacteriology shortly after the Civil War heralded a revolution in medical science. The importance of these developments has led many historians to belittle the state of medical science before bacteriology and to ignore the medical progress that had been made in the early nineteenth century. In one history of Civil War medicine, the author asserts that "the Civil War took place at the very end of the medical 'Middle Ages'—immediately before bacteriology."[1] The implication that no medical science or skill existed before bacteriology is false and misleading. In fact, considering the astounding progress in medical science since the middle of the twentieth century, one could say with equal veracity that World War II occurred at the end of the medical "Middle Ages."

To accurately evaluate the quality of Civil War medical care, it is necessary to review the actual state of medical science, as well as its general reputation, at that time.

It is certainly true that in the middle of the nineteenth century, the medical profession was held in relatively low esteem and beneath that of other professions such as law and the clergy. Despite a developing scientific base and improvements in medical education, medical therapy had little to offer and was often as harmful as it was helpful. Medical licensure laws had been repealed or were ignored almost everywhere in the United States; anyone could call himself or herself a doctor, and "it were only mild exaggeration to say that everyone did."[2] A proliferation of unorthodox pseudo-medical sects appeared, each offering what seemed to be attractive health care choices. Nevertheless, the medical profession was held in higher esteem in the United States than it was in Britain, where doctors were only beginning to be treated as "gentlemen."[3] And Britain was kinder than Europe: British doctors generally concealed their profession during their travels.[4]

One of the persistent false impressions is that Civil War physicians were unaware of contemporary European medical science. Critics allege they did not know how to use modern diagnostic equipment such as the stethoscope, microscope, clinical thermometer, and ophthalmoscope.[5] Actually, medical journals and army physician's reports to the Surgeon General's Office show that Civil War physicians were as aware of these instruments as were their international counterparts. Editorials in both American and British medical journals complimented the quality of Civil War physicians' knowledge, at least after the first disastrous year.

Civil War physicians recorded detailed data on individual cases and calculated disease frequency and various outcomes using Pierre Louis's method (see Biographical Box, p. 45). The average size of the population of soldiers in each group was specified, as well as detailed raw data for additional analyses. The motivation for keeping such careful records and performing so many autopsies is clear: Civil War physicians wanted to learn and to record their experiences to help educate future generations of physicians. These data, documented in *Medical and Surgical History*, demonstrate that Civil War medicine was not the product of a backwater, behind-the-times medical profession, as many authors have asserted, but was equal to the European scientific standards for clinical medicine.

Judging Civil War physicians' actions by later standards, a process that has been called "generational chauvinism," is poor history.[6] Physicians can only use the knowledge, techniques, and equipment that are available to them. One could also ask: Why didn't World War I surgeons use penicillin (there were descriptions in the literature of antibacterial agents that probably were penicillin)? Why didn't World War II surgeons use helicopter ambulances? Why didn't mid-twentieth-century physicians use dialysis and transplants to save patients with chronic renal failure? Medical research laid the foundation for the progress that occurred immediately after the Civil War and, as will be documented, physicians who served during the war helped to further that progress.

MEDICAL SCIENCE IN THE MID-1800S

Long before the Civil War, physicians began to apply the same scientific methodology that had led to major advances in the physical sciences. Anatomy, the field in which the first challenges to ancient dogma occurred, was one of the primary subjects taught in medicine during the early 1800s. It was also one of the reasons medical schools and their students were in disrepute; the surreptitious stealing of recently buried bodies for dissection, so-called "body snatching," caused numerous scandals, several urban riots, and even the burning of some medical schools. (Body snatching persisted until laws allowed people to donate their bodies for scientific purposes and embalming allowed the dissection of cadavers over a period of months rather than days.)[7]

During the seventeenth century, there were major advances in medical science, beginning with the description of disease in terms of anatomic pathology. This gradually brought medicine out of the "dark ages" of speculation about altered "humors" and vague theories concerning the nature of illness. It became relatively common for physicians to examine bodies after death, thereby learning about the structural changes caused by disease.

Initially, pathological investigations focused on organ damage, but, near the end of the eighteenth century, attention shifted to the individual organ's tissues. The field of microscopy emerged early in the nineteenth century, allowing physicians to study the cells in tissues. A detailed review of the insights gained is unnecessary here, but it is important to emphasize the contributions of Rudolph Virchow of Berlin. He is regarded as the father of modern pathology and was one of the era's medical giants.

Virchow established the cellular basis of pathology, beginning with the doctrine that cells always arise from other cells. Previously, it was believed that cells formed spontaneously; for example, pus cells were thought to form in the liquid exudate of the pus. Joseph Woodward, an American microscopist who played a prominent role in the Civil War, translated and published a summary of Virchow's major work on cell theory in the *American Journal of the Medical Sciences* in 1860, the same year that the book was

39

Joseph Janvier Woodward (1833–1884)

Born in Philadelphia, Joseph Janvier Woodward received his M.D. degree from the University of Pennsylvania in 1853 at age twenty, too young to practice medicine. He had an intense interest in microscopy, and helped teach medical students while doing photographic research on microscopic images during the early stages of this technology. Woodward entered the army early in the war. During the Peninsula campaign, Surgeon General William Hammond called him to Washington from field service with the Army of the Potomac; he spent the rest of his career in the Surgeon General's Office.

At first, Woodward was given the job of planning military hospitals. Hammond suggested that he write a text on running a military hospital and, in late 1862, Woodward published *The Hospital Steward's Manual: For the Instruction of Hospital Stewards, Ward-Masters, and Attendants in Their Several Duties.* Although he had time to write only at night, he completed another book, *Outline of the Chief Camp Diseases of the United States Army as Observed during the Present War,* in November 1863.

When plans for a formal army medical museum and library were made, Dr. John H. Brinton was appointed curator, with Woodward as his assistant. Brinton, assisted by Woodward, was also in charge of preparing the *Medical and Surgical History.* When a new surgeon general transferred Brinton out of the Surgeon General's Office (because of his relationship to the then out-of-favor Major-General George Brinton McClellan), Woodward succeeded him. He played a major role in producing the first two medical volumes published in 1870 and 1879. (The third medical volume was not published until 1888, after Woodward's death. The three surgical volumes were written by others.) Fluent in Latin, Greek, German, French, Spanish, and Italian, Woodward reviewed all the medical literature in those languages for the publications.

continued . . .

(Photo courtesy of NMHM.)

40

Joseph Janvier Woodward, continued

After the war, Woodward received international acclaim for his photo-microscopy. He was the first American to use aniline dyes to stain specimens for microscopic examination (as early as July 1864), but he never received full recognition for this work. After the war, he also pioneered the use of electric light for photomicrographs. When he was invited to deliver an endowed lecture at the Smithsonian Institution in 1873, Woodward supplemented his talk with over 200 lantern slides (including photomicrographs), a startling innovation. In 1876, he developed the award-winning exhibit for the Army Medical Department at the Centennial International Exposition in Philadelphia.

Elected to many illustrious societies, he was an original member of the National Academy of Sciences, a president of the Philosophical Society of Washington, and an honorary member of both the Royal Microscopical Society and the Quekett Microscopical Club of London. He also served as vice-president of the American Medical Association in 1875 and, in May 1881, was the first army officer to be elected president of that organization, which at that time was heavily dominated by academic physicians. Woodward turned down numerous offers of prestigious medical school faculty positions, preferring to stay in the army.

Woodward performed the autopsies on both President Lincoln (see Box, pp. 170-72) and John Wilkes Booth. Later, he was one of the physicians criticized for the care given President James A. Garfield after he was shot in 1881. After this, Woodward's health, already poor, deteriorated further, and he was hospitalized for severe depression in 1883. He died in 1884, an apparent suicide.[8]

published in Germany. Woodward was correct in his opinion that Virchow had "contributed perhaps more than any other single individual . . . to the progress which scientific medicine has achieved in recent years."[9]

Well before 1861, postmortem examinations had become standard procedures in Europe and the United States. The term "autopsy," derived from *auto* (self) and *opsy* (referring to vision), signified "to see for one's self," referring to the fact that clinicians usually performed the autopsies themselves to learn more about the disease and to check the accuracy of their physical examinations. When physicians correlated clinical manifestations with anatomic findings, many of them found they were dealing with previously unrecognized syndromes. For example, after performing their own autopsies between 1827 and 1849 at Guy's Hospital in London, Doctors Bright, Addison, and Hodgkin defined the diseases that carry their names. New diseases were also described during the same period in Paris (for example, by Laennec, whose description of cirrhosis of the liver still bears his name) and in Dublin (by Graves, Stokes, Adams, Corrigan, and others).

The new scientific approach to pathology benefited the Civil War medical staff's research efforts. Despite the enormous number of patients and the other pressures on Civil War surgeons, many postmortem examinations are recorded in the official records, documenting that surgeons intended to learn from their experiences. These autopsy records contain detailed descriptions, drawings, and even photographs, facilitating modern re-analysis of many of the diagnoses. For example, given the evidence they provided, we can confirm their diagnoses of fatal cases of typhoid fever by the changes in the lymphoid follicles in the small intestine and the classic complication of perforation of the intestine through one or more of these follicles.

THE BEGINNINGS OF CLINICAL SCIENCE

A similar scientific approach was widely applied in physiology and in clinical, or "bedside," medicine during the first half of the nineteenth century. The "systems" approach to medicine that blamed all diseases on abnormalities of the "humors" or another theoretical entity began to be replaced by scientific thinking, which challenged old theories and speculation with experimental results and observations.

The first notable clinical advances were in the techniques used for patient examinations. These included the invention of the stethoscope, refining percussion (tapping on different parts of the body to elicit specific sounds), and improved history taking. Physicians began to obtain detailed information from patients, both verbally and by physical examination, and they kept detailed records documenting their findings. These observations greatly enhanced clinicians' abilities to detect abnormalities, since they were no longer limited to a few symptoms and an examination of the skin, tongue, and pulse. Correlating their clinical examinations with their anatomical findings at autopsy resulted in rapid improvements in physicians' diagnostic abilities.

A prime figure in developing the modern physical examination was Théophile Laennec of France, who invented the stethoscope. Because of his illness and premature death from tuberculosis in 1826, Laennec taught few of the American students studying abroad, but he had a major impact on French medicine. His influence made physical diagnosis a primary interest and skill of Parisian physicians.[10] As a result, in the second quarter of the nineteenth century, Paris became the center of the new scientific approach to clinical medicine. Essentially, the city was a large, informally organized postgraduate medical school, and American medical graduates who could afford the trip flocked to Paris to learn the new techniques.[11]

THE PARIS CONNECTION

While earlier generations of American surgeons had gone to London, Leiden, Edinburgh, or Dublin, from about 1820 to 1870—the golden age of French medicine—they received their inspiration from France. The physician with the most influence on American physicians studying in Paris, and thus on Civil War medicine, during these years was Pierre Louis, who is considered the founder of scientific clinical investigation. He was revered by most of the American medical students who studied abroad.

More than 1,000 American physicians studied in Paris during the first half of the nineteenth century. On their return to the United States, most became leaders in the profession and served as medical school faculty. One of their main educational improvements was the introduction of courses in physical diagnosis, especially auscultation; some faculty even gave special courses in the use of the stethoscope separate from the formal medical school courses. Some of the most noteworthy Parisian graduates are introduced below.[12]

Oliver Wendell Holmes (1809–1894), who became prominent in American medicine, was among Pierre Louis's admiring students. Holmes recorded their fondness for their French teacher, writing, "We had addicted ourselves almost too closely to the words of another master, by whom we were ready to swear as against all teachers that ever were or ever would be. This object of our reverence, I might almost say idolatry, was . . . Pierre Charles Alexandre Louis."[13] Holmes imitated Louis's bedside teaching techniques, including demonstrating percussion and auscultation using the stethoscope, for medical students at Massachusetts General Hospital beginning in the late 1830s.[14]

Henry I. Bowditch of Boston, another of Louis's students, was associated with the U.S. Sanitary Commission during the Civil War and led the fight to establish an ambulance corps throughout the armies similar to that in the Army of the Potomac. Bowditch was well known for his translation of Louis's works into English (1836) and for his own books on the stethoscope (1846), consumption in New England (1862), and public hygiene.[15] He also introduced removal of fluid from the chest for the treatment of pleurisy and made numerous other significant contributions.

Alfred Stillé (1813–1900), a professor at the University of Pennsylvania, also trained in Paris. He took part in the clinical investigations conducted for the U.S. Sanitary Commission during the Civil War. Stillé later emphasized the influence of Pierre Louis on scientific clinical medicine, and his articles on diseases during the war utilized Louis's "numerical method" of statistical analysis.[16] A hospital inspector for the Sanitary Commission during the war, Stillé wrote many reports for the Commission.[17] His brother, Charles Stillé, was also a member of the Commission, and its chief historian.

Joseph Leidy (1823–1891), an early American investigator in microscopic anatomy and pathology, was also one of Louis's students.[18] In 1849, Leidy demonstrated the presence of bacteria in the intestine and, by the time of the Civil War, had become a professor of anatomy at the University of Pennsylvania. During the war, Leidy functioned as a contract surgeon in Philadelphia hospitals and performed at least sixty autopsies on deceased Union soldiers. He held the lowest rank, acting assistant surgeon, but he had been Dr. Joseph Woodward's mentor and so, in *Medical and Surgical History*, he is referred to deferentially as "Professor Leidy." Leidy correctly surmised that flies transmitted wound infections. After the war, he separated parasitic amebae from non-pathogenic, single-celled organisms; demonstrated the cause of hookworm disease; and made additional contributions to parasitology and other scientific fields, including paleontology, anthropology, botany, and geology.[19]

A Southern physician, **Francis Peyre Porcher (1825–1895),** also studied under Pierre Louis and became a close friend of Oliver Wendell Holmes. Like Holmes, Porcher was a microscopist, and he wrote an influential book on microscopic changes in diseased tissues. He also taught *materia medica* and was a naturalist. Porcher investigated the flora of the South, seeking plants that could serve as replacements for the drugs that became difficult for the Confederacy to obtain during the war because of the blockade (see Chapter 9, *Treating Disease*). He published a 600-page book on his findings and made many suggestions about therapeutic uses of plants, but he failed to find a substitute for quinine or any other useful drugs.[20,21]

Other Southerners who went to Paris to further their medical education and who played a role in the Civil War include **James Lawrence Cabell,** an early graduate of the University of Virginia. After getting an M.D. degree in Baltimore and practicing there and in Richmond, he traveled to Paris.

Dr. Pierre Charles Alexandre Louis (1787–1872)

After a brief try at other careers, Pierre Louis graduated from the medical school of the University of Paris in 1813 and went into practice in Russia. A few years later, feeling dissatisfied with his meager medical knowledge during an epidemic of diphtheria, he returned to Paris for more instruction. Once there, he quickly realized that he was not learning much from the leaders of Parisian medicine and struck out on his own, arranging to be a physician-in-residence at the largest charity hospital in Paris. He carefully recorded his observations of patients and conducted autopsies on those that died. After about five years, he took time off to analyze his data.[22]

Louis watched his patients closely from day to day, his observations at autopsy enabling him to perfect his physical diagnosis skills. His system of obtaining information from patients fixed the time of the disease's onset; the patient's age, occupation, residence, and illnesses in family members; the nature and severity of the symptoms; and the order of their occurrence. He also noted the *absence* of important possible symptoms: "His notes did not state opinions, but facts."[23,24] His methods became the basic technique for gathering and organizing information from patients and remain so to this day.

Based on his analyses, Louis published several important books and papers. One book on tuberculosis established that there was always a tubercle in the lung when there were tubercles elsewhere.[25] He also distinguished typhoid fever from "typhus fever," which at that time was prevalent in large European cities.

The most fundamental change Louis brought to medicine was drawing conclusions from the analysis of groups of cases, rather than trying to generalize experience based on individual cases. When they returned home, his American students introduced his methods of obtaining information from patients, physical diagnosis, and analyzing data.

Using simple arithmetic, Louis applied the newly developed science of statistics to clinical medicine. For more than a century thereafter, U.S. students were taught medical statistics as the "numerical method of Louis." In one of the first studies using his numerical method, Louis analyzed the value of bloodletting in the treatment of pneumonia, showing that recovery was not affected by how much and how often patients were bled, or when the bleeding was begun. This work, published in the 1830s, was a key turning point leading to the abandonment of bleeding as therapy and, by the time of the Civil War, it was rarely used.

Returning in 1837, he became professor of anatomy, physiology, and surgery at the University of Virginia and later headed the Confederate hospital in Charlottesville. **David Yandell** of Louisville, medical director of Gen. Albert Sidney Johnston's army at Shiloh, also was Pierre Louis's student.

William Farr (1807–1883), an Englishman who studied under Louis, was a founder of the field of epidemiology. Farr's method of keeping records and analyzing disease experiences was based on Louis's techniques. During the Crimean War, the British Army adopted his methods, and, according to Joseph Woodward, an "Army Board" recommended the adoption of the classification system "devised by Dr. William Farr of London" to make the Union army's records comparable to those of the British.[26] Thus, the extensive recording and the analyses done in the Union Surgeon General's Office during and after the Civil War used Farr's methods based on Louis's techniques. These data resulted in the comprehensive *Medical and Surgical History*. Although only Farr is mentioned in the introduction, Florence Nightingale worked closely with him to develop these statistical methods after the Crimean War, and her contribution influenced the Civil War records.

OTHER NOTABLE TEACHERS OF AMERICAN PHYSICIANS

Other Europeans also taught American physicians and influenced American medical science at the time of the war. Some of their students played significant roles in Civil War medicine. In Paris, Claude Bernard (1813–1878) led the development of experimental physiology beginning in the 1840s. S. Weir Mitchell, one of his American students, became a prominent faculty member at Philadelphia medical schools. During the Civil War, he was in charge of the medical team at the military's Turner's Lane Hospital, established to study soldiers with nerve injuries, and he helped to establish the field of neurology in the United States. (In Chapter 6, see Early Neurosurgery.)

In Germany, Justus von Liebig (1803–1873) began the studies that he called "animal chemistry" in 1826 at Giessen. Later he renamed the field "organic chemistry" and, still later, it became known as biochemistry. Much of his work was centered on nutrition. One American who studied under von Liebig, Joseph Jones, became professor of medicinal chemistry at the Medical College of Georgia. Jones, an inspector for the Confederate surgeon general, published many studies (some during the Civil War) on the chemical changes that occur in disease. His work at Andersonville delineated the nature of the illnesses that caused so many deaths in that prison.

CIVIL WAR MEDICAL RESEARCH SOCIETIES

American medical research also got a boost from Pierre Louis. He and his students founded the Society of Medical Observation in Paris in the 1830s, at which they presented their observations and criticized each other during regular meetings. (At the insistence of his students, Louis was made perpetual president of the Society and had the last word during the discussions.) American research societies were founded primarily by Louis's former students, and were modeled after the Society of Medical Observation. One of the earliest was the Boston Society for Medical Observation, founded in 1835. Many of these medical research societies have persisted into the twenty-first century and are now prestigious national organizations. Their meetings are still patterned after those of Louis's original Society.

In August 1863, the Confederates created a national organization, The Confederate Association of Army and Navy Surgeons. Not surprisingly, they elected Surgeon General Moore as their president. The association met on Saturday evenings "every fortnight" in Richmond, and all "those in active service in the field" were made corresponding members.[27] The association's constitution specified that members would present papers for open discussion and that subjects requiring special investigation would be identified for presentations at subsequent meetings.

The organizational meeting was reported in the first issue of the *Confederate States Medical and Surgical Journal* in January 1864, along with a copy of its constitution. (See Figure 2.1.) Despite a severe paper shortage, the journal was published monthly in Richmond through March 1865. The April 1865 issue was ready for the printer when Richmond fell. The editors solicited original papers and reports from military and civilian hospitals so that the "statistics [of their experiences] may be slowly and patiently elaborated and placed on record."[28] The journal's emblem contained a depiction of Hippocrates and the motto *experientia docet*, or "experience teaches."

Military surgeons knew they were taking part in a great historical event and considered keeping detailed records and performing research part of their responsibility, as illustrated by their apologies in official reports when surgeons could *not* do research. (See Box, p. 49.) During the campaign to capture Atlanta, for example, the surgeon-in-chief of the 23rd Army Corps in Sherman's army at Decatur, Georgia, wrote, "The opportunities for making medical researches have not been good with us, for of necessity ours has been to some extent a receiving and forwarding hospital, though on a few occasions we were able to retain the cases for some time, so that considerable

Figure 2.1: *Confederate States Medical and Surgical Journal.*

numbers were returned to duty." He went on to analyze what diseases they had observed and their probable causes.[29] Similarly, a prominent Confederate surgeon, Paul Eve, explained the lack of research when he was in charge of Gate City Hospital in Atlanta:

> after Chickamauga ... [there were] a total of 715 [wounded men] to be prescribed for, operated upon and their wounds dressed by six medical officers, besides treating 678 medical cases. It will be evident to all, that under these painful circumstances, the claims of humanity suppressed for the time those of science. We could not even regularly register the cases, much less study statistics, &c, in reference to them.[30]

The Association of American Physicians, founded in the 1880s and still one of the most prestigious U.S. medical organizations, is a prime example of Louis's enduring influence. It was founded to foster medical, particularly

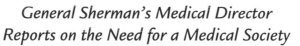

General Sherman's Medical Director
Reports on the Need for a Medical Society

During the Civil War, both the Union and Confederate armies established similar research societies. The Union had a national organization, as well as division- and corps-level societies at which research papers were presented and discussed. In one of his reports, General Sherman's medical director, Surg. Henry S. Hewit, explained the need for a medical society:

> I found the surgeons of the department divided into two classes (on coming among them), one with extravagant ideas of the power of conservative surgery and greatly exaggerated opinions of its value, and the other despising conservatism and disposed to deny its utility altogether. It is not difficult to understand how such differences should exist, when the results of conservatism in civil life are contrasted with the failures constantly met with in military practice. The men who had read much and seen little were highly conservative, while those who had read little and seen much were the reverse. I made an effort, by the organization of a medical society, before the army left the vicinity of Knoxville, and using every means to secure full attendance and fair discussion, to apply the remedy, by an interchange of knowledge and experience, to false and extreme ideas, and to obtain a safe mean of opinion and practice.[31]

clinical, research. The founders promptly elected their mentors, five senior physicians who had all been Louis's students, as honorary members. This and other medical research organizations with similar goals, as well as the societies that sprang from them, can be considered direct intellectual descendants of the Society of Medical Observation in Paris.

CONCEPTS OF EPIDEMIC DISEASE IN THE MID-1800S

Are some diseases contagious, that is, spread from person to person? We now know that many diseases can be spread that way, but, in the middle of the nineteenth century, the concept of contagion was confused and controversial. The debate was as much political as it was scientific, since accepting a disease as contagious implied the need for quarantine. Enforced isolation interfered with personal liberty and civil libertarians argued against it, using arguments similar to those used today to oppose mandatory testing for HIV infection or the forced isolation of patients with tuberculosis. Quarantine also interfered with commerce, and business groups vigorously opposed the classification of diseases as contagious. These "anti-contagionists" almost always prevailed in debates until bacteriology gained favor in the decades after the Civil War.

CONTAGION

Despite their apparent acceptance of the anticontagious theory, physicians usually based their actions on experience. They knew that several diseases spread from person to person and that affected patients needed to be isolated. Smallpox, for example, was unequivocally accepted as contagious and isolation was enforced. Indeed, so-called "pest hospitals" had been established for smallpox patients, among others. Another disease physicians believed to be contagious was the infection called "hospital gangrene," one of the most devastating wound complications of the Civil War, and so named because it spread primarily among hospitalized patients. Surgeons incorrectly believed that malevolent "miasmatic" influences emanated from affected patients and that these could cause the same disease in other patients' wounds. Because of this, they isolated hospital gangrene cases in separate hospital wards. Although they did not know that the causative agents were actually living organisms, their empirical observations led to actions that did limit the spread of this disease.

The terms "contagion" and "infection" were generally considered synonymous, but contagion was used for diseases believed to be produced by indirect contact (such as measles and scarlet fever), while infection was used for those that required physical contact (such as "itch" and syphilis). Contagious diseases were thought to be produced either by "a virus, capable of causing them by inoculation, as in small-pox, cow-pox, hydrophobia, syphilis, &c." or by a poisonous miasma emanating from a sick individual, as in plague, typhus, measles, and scarlatina. "Virus," derived from the Latin word for poison, was "understood [to be] a principle, unknown in its nature and inappreciable by the sense, which is the agent for the transmission of infectious diseases. Thus we speak of the variolic vaccine and syphilitic viruses."[32] Physicians were by no means unanimous in deciding what diseases were contagious.

Physicians had considered the possibility that bacteria caused diseases since at least 1546, when Giralamo Fracastoro (also known as Fracastorius)

suggested it. He called bacteria "seminaria." While physicians on both sides in the Civil War continually observed bacteria upon microscopic examination of diseased ("putrefied") tissue, particularly in hospital gangrene, attempts to show their causative role in disease were unconvincing. Bacteria were considered to be either secondary invaders or the result of spontaneous generation. In *Medical and Surgical History*, Woodward wrote:

> An allusion may be made to the idea that the peculiar characteristics . . . [of hospital gangrene] are due to the local presence of microscopical fungi. This idea is not borne out by facts. Accurate examination with a high magnification power of cases of every stage, . . . utterly failed to demonstrate any cryptogamic organisms [hidden organisms capable of multiplying] except the ordinary bacteria which are to be observed in every decomposing animal substance.[33]

Dr. Joseph Jones, investigating the high mortality at the prison camp near Andersonville for the Confederate surgeon general, made similar observations on tissues from patients with hospital gangrene (see Chapter 15, *Prison Camps*). Theodore Billroth, the most famous surgeon of the late-nineteenth century and the chief surgeon of the Prussian army in 1863, also failed to appreciate the role of microscopic organisms in wound infections, including the spread of traumatic erysipelas.[34]

MIASMAS, FOMITES, AND CIVIL WAR SANITATION

With no knowledge of microbiology, epidemic diseases were thought to be caused by "miasmas," or "viruses," invisible poisons that floated through the air. These poisons were thought to act like an enzyme, and thus were also called "ferments," since their typical action was fermentation or spoilage of wine, milk, and other substances. Part of the term "enzyme" was included in the name for the category of diseases that these agents were believed to cause: "zymotic diseases." The zymotic diseases (considered infectious diseases today) included typhoid and other fevers, smallpox, acute and chronic diarrhea, yellow fever, measles, mumps, diphtheria, scarlet fever, erysipelas, and the intermittent fevers.

Miasmas were often thought to be due to vegetable "decompositions" or "saturations."[35] Marshes and swamps were considered to be a major source of these poisons, giving off toxic air that was described using the Italian term, "malaria," or bad air. In the late 1800s, the term "malaria" was restricted to a specific group of diseases associated with swamp emanations. But during the Civil War, those diseases associated with swamp miasmas usually were called "intermittent fevers." The concept of transmission of disease by insects was rarely considered and, in fact, widely ridiculed, even for a few years after Walter Reed demonstrated the mosquito's role in yellow fever at the end of the century.

Given the circumstances, it was reasonable to believe that diseases emanated from the unbelievably foul stench in which people were immersed. It is hard for modern readers to imagine the odors that confronted people at the time of the Civil War. Sewage dumped unceremoniously into city streets, infrequent bathing, and bad sanitary practices made "sickening odors" commonplace. Delicate society women carried perfume-laden handkerchiefs in front of their faces when they went out in public for protection from the offensive and "poisonous" odors, and nurses often gave similar cloths to patients to protect them from the foul emanations in the hospital.[36]

An excellent example of contemporary thinking about miasmatic odors can be found in a letter from Capt. Charles Francis Adams, Jr. to his father. Adams wrote, "An army, any army, does poison the air. It is a city without sewage . . . Animals die, as they do not in cities, and . . . what with fragments of food and decaying substances, all festering under a midsummer sun, an army soon breeds a malaria which engenders the most fatal of fevers."[37]

Because the foul odors from decaying corpses, both human and animal, were also thought to contain poisonous miasmas, burial was considered urgent. In a letter to his wife, a physician recorded his concern a week after the Battle of Antietam: "The dead were almost wholly unburied, and the stench from it was such as to breed a pestilence in the regiment."[38] Similar anticontagious thinking resurfaces today when a disaster, such as an earthquake, leaves hundreds or thousands of unburied human or animal remains.

Soldiers themselves also contributed to the pervasive foul stench. They were supposed to bathe once a week, but enlisted men and officers alike ignored the order. Bathing might take place during the summer when a stream or pond was conveniently located near a campsite. However, during the rest of the year, bathing was rare since it was difficult to obtain warm water. It was said that a Civil War army on the march could be smelled before it could be seen. John Billings, an artilleryman from Massachusetts, wrote that upon entering one of the large conical Sibley tents on a rainy morning, one would "encounter the night's accumulation of nauseating exhalations from the bodies of twelve men . . . [this] was an experience which no old soldier has ever been known to recall with great enthusiasm."[39]

Physicians understood that personal clothing and bedclothes (termed "fomites") transmitted disease-producing agents. It was also recognized that some form of filth aboard ships carrying passengers with yellow fever contaminated the surrounding docksides, affected residents of the city, and set off devastating epidemics. Such concepts, although erroneous, led to the beneficial practice of imposing quarantines on affected ships and their crews until evidence of yellow fever disappeared. The cleanup of all dirt and sources of odors around the harbor was part of the preventive quarantine procedures. If fully enforced, these measures worked, erasing the fear of yellow fever with its attendant case-fatality rates (the proportion of individuals with a disease who died), which were often as high as 50%. Such quarantine measures also helped to silence the "anti-contagionists," libertarians, and business interests who opposed quarantines. During the Civil War, rigorously enforced quarantine measures in occupied Southern port cities, particularly New Orleans, which had been repeatedly devastated by yellow fever before the war, effectively prevented the dreaded epidemics (in Chapter 11, see Yellow Fever).

Medicine's leaders also took up the banner of sanitation. On July 3, 1861, over two weeks before the First Battle of Bull Run, a "Committee on Military Surgery" reported to the Surgical Section of the New York Academy of Medicine about "matters of practical interest which are not discussed in the ordinary books on surgery." Their report first detailed the death statistics from the Napoleonic through the Crimean Wars and noted that there was a far greater mortality from disease than from battle injuries, with a particular emphasis on scurvy. The report concluded:

> From the facts which have been presented, it is very evident that the lives of military men are much more endangered by disease than by wounds received in battle. It is then one of the highest duties of an army surgeon to make himself well acquainted with the correct principles of military hygiene, and to exert his influence to the greatest possible extent on promoting the health . . .[40]

The committee also described the hygienic principles regarding the selection of encampment sites; the protection of troops from the weather, including the appropriate clothing; the "disposition of excrement and offal"; the preparation of food and drinks; the prevention of exhaustion; ambulance services; surgical principles, such as removal of foreign bodies; and the "proper" examination of recruits before enlistment.[41]

Early in the war, when diarrheal disease was most common in the armies, sanitation was at its worst. Men from rural areas were accustomed to using outhouses or to relieving themselves in any convenient patch of vegetation; they would not tolerate officers trying to change their behavior. The pre-Civil War curriculum at West Point contained no subjects related to maintaining

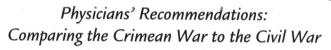

Physicians' Recommendations: Comparing the Crimean War to the Civil War

One reason for the terrible unsanitary conditions that prevailed during the Crimean War was physicians' lack of control over the hospitals, primarily the main hospital in Scutari, Turkey. British military authorities rejected the advice of the director general of the Medical Department (roughly the equivalent of the U.S. surgeon general) to give physicians administrative control, instead imposing administrative responsibilities on hospital stewards.

As a result, medical recommendations were generally ignored, and filth, overcrowding, and miserable sanitation prevailed, including assigning two patients to the same bed, often one of them dead. British officers, true gentlemen who had bought their commissions, paid even less attention to the hygienic recommendations of army physicians, their social unequals, than did American line officers. During the Crimean War, British army physicians were not even welcome in officers' clubs.[42]

Reports of the conditions and the astronomical death rate, in particular those by William Howard Russell of *The Times*, generated a public outcry that ultimately caused the fall of the British government. Subsequently, it was pointed out that "It was the American army which blazed the trail in this matter when, during the Civil War of 1861, military commandants were replaced by medical officers endowed with executive and disciplinary powers."[43]

the health of the troops, and many older regular army officers could not be bothered—military camps were "supposed to smell that way." Moreover, the authority of medical officers early in the war was weakened because everyone believed theirs was a temporary job. Even those officers who believed that sanitation was important had little influence over their undisciplined troops. The resulting atmosphere around encampments was sometimes described as a "patriotic odor."[44] At least Civil War soldiers respected their opponents' need for relief, which was fortunate since diarrhea was such a constant feature of military life. A tradition arose, honored by both sides throughout the war, to refrain from shooting a man "while he is attending to the urgent call of nature."

Contaminated water was a constant problem. During marches, men often contaminated the water used by other soldiers further downstream. Some soldiers wrote that when cavalry horses were watered upstream, the coffee tasted different. Wells were used for drinking water whenever possible but usually they were quickly exhausted. At long-term winter campsites, men often drank, cooked, bathed, washed their clothes and utensils, and flushed excrement with the same water supply for months at a time.

After pressure from medical officers and the U.S. Sanitary Commission, the army's rules for cleanliness and sanitation were gradually clarified and officers were taught their importance. Latrines, called "sinks," were supposed to be established at each campsite, dug deep, and covered with a layer of dirt each day. The rules for the depth of the pits and the amount of dirt were rarely obeyed early in the war and the odor of the area discouraged many soldiers from using them. Compliance improved as senior army officers began to understand the importance of hygienic measures, although many soldiers stubbornly resisted officers' orders to use the normally inadequate latrine facilities.[45]

The adoption of sanitation principles was one of the successes that resulted from the Sanitary Commission's lobbying efforts. Civil War soldiers learned to put their camps upwind of stagnant water and build fires to affect airflow in the hopes of protecting themselves from "toxic miasmas."[46] These measures minimized the number of mosquitoes in their camps and may have actually diminished the frequency of malaria. When sources of foul odors were cleaned up, epidemic diseases declined in frequency, particularly intestinal infections such as typhoid fever and dysentery. In fact, the sanitary movement in American cities was stimulated by the successes from improved sanitary practices during the Civil War. The first city board of health was established in New York City in 1861 and the first state board of health in Massachusetts in 1869.[47] Proper sewage disposal began in American cities around this time; the discovery of the bacterial etiology of disease accelerated this development.

DID AMERICAN PHYSICIANS HAVE UP-TO-DATE INFORMATION?

The efforts of American physicians to stay abreast of European medical developments before and during the Civil War were notable and, it seems, successful. American medical journals of the era regularly contained articles summarizing or translating new information published in western Europe.

For example, one of the most prominent medical journals of the time, the *American Journal of the Medical Sciences*, had a regular section entitled "Foreign Intelligence." The *Confederate States Medical and Surgical Journal* contained a similar section each month, entitled "A Chronicle of Medical Science," which contained material "collated from recent foreign works and periodicals." This section concentrated on developments in Paris and contained information obtained from blockade-runners, but it also included relevant material drawn from Union sources.

Both the Union and Confederate Surgeon Generals' Offices tried to keep their medical staffs aware of developments in Europe and new information learned over the course of the war. Since training in military medicine was not part of any medical school curriculum, several books on surgery emphasizing the treatment of gunshot wounds were rushed into print as early as 1861. Among them were books by prominent American and foreign academic surgeons, including Frank Hastings Hamilton (see Biographical Box, p. 58) of Bellevue Hospital in New York, Samuel D. Gross of Philadelphia, and John Julian Chisolm (see Biographical Box, p. 59) of Charleston.[49] Sir

Educational Notices from the Surgeon General's Office

Whenever important new information became available, both Surgeon Generals' Offices sent notices to their medical officers. Circular No. 6, for example, sent from the Federal Surgeon General's Office on March 10, 1864, was an early publication from Turner's Lane Hospital. It included this introduction:

> The following paper on reflex paralysis, the result of gunshot wounds, founded chiefly upon cases observed at the U.S. General Hospital, Christian Street, Philadelphia, by S. Weir Mitchell, M.D., George R. Morehouse, M.D., and William W. Keen Jr., M.D., is published for the information of Medical Officers, in the belief that immediate and practical benefit may be derived from it. Joseph K. Barnes, Acting Surgeon General.

Later that year, the three surgeons wrote a book that summarized their observations and included descriptions of several previously unknown syndromes. The U.S. Army Medical Department distributed the book to their military surgeons.[48]

Thomas Longmore, a surgeon in the Crimean War who later became the British surgeon general, published an article on gunshot wounds in the 1861 British textbook *Holmes' System of Surgery*. His article "was reprinted in the United States and was officially distributed by the United States Government to the hospitals and medical officers during the Civil War."[50] During the second half of the war, both armies established training programs in the treatment of war wounds for newly inducted physicians.

U.S. MEDICAL EDUCATION IN THE MID-1800S

American institutions of higher education in the early and mid-nineteenth century have been called "intellectual backwaters." Medical education has been similarly criticized and its glaring weaknesses as compared to modern medical education cited as a reason for the ostensibly poor performance of the Civil War medical departments. Admittedly, medical education was weak, but it was essentially the same as in Britain and, except for the absence of military medical schools, was not vastly different from that in France or Germany. Yet somehow, American medical education produced army physicians who saved the lives of a higher proportion of wounded and sick soldiers than their European contemporaries.

In the early years following American independence, most physicians who entered practice did not have a formal education—they were apprenticed to practicing physicians who usually did not have any formal education either. The few medical schools that existed were in major cities, notably Philadelphia and Boston, and trained only a small number of practitioners. This inadequate medical education greatly contributed to the profession's lack of status and poor self-image.

A variety of unorthodox medical "systems" competed with standard medicine in the mid-1800s. Homeopathy, which is still practiced, had its own medical schools, as did other pseudo-medical disciplines such as eclectic medicine, botanic medicine, Thomsonianism, and the Grahamites. Each emphasized a specific approach to therapy based on unscientific theories, but avoided most of the toxicity from drugs and bloodletting caused by the orthodox profession's "heroic therapy."

What was the fundamental difference between these so-called sects and the profession that Samuel Hanneman, the founder of homeopathy, called "allopathic" medicine? At the time of the Civil War and for a long time thereafter, the difference was not the effectiveness of therapy. George Bernard Shaw said it succinctly, and accurately, in the preface to *The Doctor's*

A Union Surgeon
Frank Hastings Hamilton (1813–1886)

After graduating from Union College in New York in 1830, Hamilton apprenticed to a physician, then attended a series of medical lectures at the College of Physicians & Surgeons of the Western District of New York at Fairfield. He was licensed to practice medicine in 1833 and, in 1835, he received a formal M.D. degree from the University of Pennsylvania. He was then made professor of surgery at the medical school in Fairfield and the next year took the same chair at Geneva Medical College in New York, where he remained until 1844.

After studying abroad, he helped found the medical department at the University of Buffalo in 1846, becoming their first professor of surgery. Twelve years later, he became professor of surgery at Long Island College Hospital in Brooklyn and, in 1861, was named professor of clinical and military surgery at the recently formed Bellevue Hospital Medical College.

At the onset of Civil War, Hamilton volunteered for army duty and was placed in charge of a field hospital at First Bull Run. He was rapidly promoted from brigade surgeon to medical inspector. In September 1863, he resigned from the army and returned to Bellevue, where he became professor of surgery and surgical pathology.

An author, he had written a *Practical Treatise on Fractures and Dislocations* in 1860 and published the first edition of his *Treatise on Military Surgery and Hygiene* in 1862. After the war, Hamilton helped to publish the *Medical and Surgical History* and in 1872 wrote the *Principles and Practice of Surgery*. When President Garfield was wounded, Hamilton consulted on the case and helped to treat the president. Shortly thereafter, he retired, having become too ill with tuberculosis to continue working.[51]

Dilemma in 1911: "The distinction between a quack doctor and a qualified one is mainly that only the qualified one is authorized to sign death certificates, for which both sorts seem to have about equal occasion."[52]

Competition from these sects was a major concern of nineteenth-century medical societies, and physicians struggled to make a clear distinction between themselves and these unorthodox practitioners. After the War of 1812, colleges and medical schools opened throughout the country. By 1850, there were forty-two medical schools in the United States; by the time of the Civil War, there were at least eighty-seven.[53] By 1860, the majority of

A Confederate Surgeon
John Julian Chisolm (1830-1903)

Born in Charleston, South Carolina, Chisolm received his M.D. degree at the Medical College of South Carolina and then studied in London and Paris. Returning to Charleston, he organized an innovative series of nightly medical lectures, giving the surgery lectures himself. He also ran a free hospital for slaves. In 1858, Chisolm was appointed professor of surgery at the Medical College in Charleston, becoming the youngest professor of surgery in the United States. He traveled through Italy in 1859 during the war between Austria and the alliance of Italy (Sardinia and the Piedmont) and France. While in Milan, Chisolm observed the treatment of the wounded from the Battles of Solferino and Magenta.

Returning to Charleston when the Civil War began, he treated the Union soldiers injured at Fort Sumter. Based on his experiences, he then quickly wrote a book, *A Manual of Military Surgery for Use of the Surgeons in the Confederate Army*, which was available by the First Battle of Bull Run. During the war, he worked at the huge military hospitals in Richmond and set up a plant to manufacture drugs in Charleston. He prepared two more editions of his manual during the war; it was the Confederate surgeons' main source of information on military surgery.[54]

After the war, Chisolm returned to his professorship in Charleston, where he was made dean of the medical school. He returned to Europe in 1866 and studied ophthalmology. He then went to Baltimore in 1869 and became chief of eye and ear surgery at the University of Maryland, a post created specifically for him. Declining professorships at several other institutions, Chisolm organized an eye and ear hospital in Baltimore, where he made several innovations in eye surgery, including the introduction of local anesthetics and aseptic technique. About 1887, he examined Helen Keller and advised her father to take her to Alexander Graham Bell, who arranged for her education. Chisolm is buried in Baltimore.[55]

orthodox medical practitioners had received a formal medical education. Many of the medical schools were in rural areas where costs could be kept low, although there were no hospitals or other clinical facilities nearby for use in these educational programs. Since hospitals were rudimentary institutions and most medical care was given at home, this was not as serious a defect as it became later in the century—students simply arranged clinical experience on their own, mostly through apprenticeships.

The initiative for new medical schools usually came from the professors, typically a local group of physicians who approached a nearby college with a proposal. From the doctors' perspective, a college lent their enterprise legitimacy and the legal authority to grant degrees; from the college's perspective, a medical school meant added prestige without any investment, since medical schools were self-financed using the students' tuition. Sometimes, the physical facilities consisted of only two rooms, one for lectures and one for dissections, and a limited library. In Augusta, Georgia, however, the medical school was established in an imposing, neoclassical building with huge columns that dominated the downtown area, giving the medical school added prestige.

Faculty usually consisted of from five to seven unsalaried professors who sold tickets to their lectures and profited from the advantages that professorial appointments gave them in private practice. The school charged a matriculation fee and a graduation fee. In the United States, clinical instruction in hospitals was rare, even in urban schools.[56] Since the professors collected fees, medical schools of the era were usually referred to as "proprietary schools," a term which acquired a derogatory connotation when it was used to describe the poorest quality schools during the era of medical education reform in the early twentieth century. However, even prestigious medical schools, such as Harvard, Pennsylvania, and Jefferson, were proprietary by this definition before and for quite a while after the Civil War.

Courses generally consisted of a series of lectures offered by the medical school from October to March. The same lectures were repeated the second year, with the expectation that students would learn more the second time around. The only entrance requirement was the ability to pay the tuition; graduation required payment for the diploma and little else.[57] The "graded curriculum," in which different courses were offered in the second year, was unusual in America and Britain during much of the nineteenth century; it was considered a great reform when it was introduced after 1850.[58] Younger physicians at the time of the Civil War (the vast majority of those who served after the first chaotic months were in this category) had received at least the rudimentary formal medical education typical of the era.

Neither private nor proprietary medical schools were exclusive to North America.[59] In Britain, many medical schools were proprietary but were also linked to hospitals. The first hospital-based medical school in the United States was Bellevue Hospital Medical College, established in New York in 1860. Bellevue had provided postgraduate clinical instruction for many years and, because of its excellent faculty, quickly became one of the leading institutions in the country.

Since few American medical schools had links to a teaching hospital, formal clinical training was negligible or absent. Lecture attendance was usually supplemented by the old system of apprenticeship with a practicing physician. The medical school granted the degree but usually did not supervise clinical training by the preceptor. Premedical educational requirements were weak or nonexistent—applicants needed only to be male and pay the tuition and fees. In addition, medical licensure laws, where they existed, were either repealed by the 1830s and 1840s or not enforced.[60]

Unlike Germany and France, Britain and the United States did not develop military medical schools.[61] Union Surgeon General William Hammond wrote to the heads of American medical schools in December 1862 requesting that students be taught hygiene and military surgery so that new graduates, who often enlisted directly into the army or became contract surgeons, would have some preparation for their duties.[62]

Aside from the orthodox, or allopathic, U.S. and Canadian medical schools, there were eleven U.S. schools for the unorthodox sects, including botanic, eclectic, and homeopathic medicine.[63] These schools generally admitted women freely, with women composing a large proportion of their practitioners. Licensing was loose or non-existent, allowing their graduates to practice.

Before 1850, no allopathic medical school in the world admitted women, although an unknown number of women went to medical school disguised as men and, subsequently, practiced medicine in male attire. In Michigan, Margaret Cannon Osborne learned medicine from a preceptor and practiced medicine openly as a woman. Elizabeth Blackwell entered a medical school in Geneva, New York, in 1847, although that school never admitted another woman student. The world's first medical school for women, The Female Medical College of Pennsylvania, was begun in 1850. Blackwell estimated that by 1859, 300 women had managed to "graduate somewhere" in medicine. By 1870, there were four medical colleges for women in the United States. Dr. Blackwell participated in a campaign that led to the establishment of the London School of Medicine for Women in 1875.[64]

While medical reforms occurred more slowly in the United States than in France and Germany, the increased emphasis on science made change inevitable. The American Medical Association (AMA) was formed in 1847 by a group of medical school professors who wanted to reform medical education. In 1849, an AMA committee pointed out that "no one acquainted with the progress of medicine can hesitate to recognize its rapid expansion into a science."[65]

MEDICAL EDUCATION IN EUROPE

Governments in Europe spent exorbitant sums for military hospitals and to train army surgeons. Military medical schools in Paris, Berlin, Vienna, and St. Petersburg achieved such excellent reputations that civilian students pressed for admission.[66] The first elite military medical schools were established in 1795 in Berlin and Paris. The noted German pathologist, Rudolph Virchow, graduated in 1843 from Friedrich-Wilhelm Institute, a military medical school at the University of Berlin. Since the school trained medical officers for the Prussian army, tuition was free. The faculty contained many notable physicians, including Johannes Müller, who is considered to be the founder of German scientific medicine.[67]

Medical education in Germany took four years, compared to two years in the United States, and included experience similar to the clinical apprenticeship. In the 1830s, the German states had a total of twenty-four university medical schools, and an additional thirty called "schools of practical medicine" located in smaller communities. Germany began to reform medical education in the 1850s and the practical schools disappeared. Universities began to build research institutes and to add laboratory experience to their curriculums. Major scientific developments, sometimes referred to as a medical "revolution," were supported by the German government, with a view to rebuilding the prestige and honor of the German states after the military embarrassments of the Napoleonic era.

In the 1830s, France had three university medical faculties and twenty-two *écoles secondaires* (provincial medical schools). By mid-century, there were nine military and naval medical schools. Paris was considered the first postgraduate medical school in the world, albeit an informal one. The great reputation of Parisian medicine was based on the bedside teaching of such notable physician-teachers as Pierre Louis, who were paid directly by the young physicians who accompanied them, making their highly regarded medical education essentially a "proprietary" system.[68]

As German and Austrian medical science developed, Berlin and Vienna replaced Paris as the leading cities in medicine. France remained largely indifferent to the scientific advances in German medicine, and university medical education did not find a foothold.[69] Medical education in France also lasted four years, and students spent their mornings in the hospital from the first year gaining clinical experience. However, there was little emphasis on science and no state support for scientific research until much later. Furthermore, French medical schools were constantly being shut down by student disorders.

As in the United States, most British physicians were general practition-ers. In the 1830s, the British government moved to increase the level of train-ing of general practitioners. A new university medical school was opened and, by 1834, there were thirteen provincial medical schools with requirements similar to those of the "secondary medical schools" on the continent and to the "country medical schools" then spreading throughout the United States.[70]

During the same time period, American medical schools proliferated at an even faster rate and the requirements for graduation were even more var-ied than in Britain. Medical education in both countries consisted largely of grafting newly organized courses in practical science onto a program of apprenticeship or hospital training taken at the student's initiative. The British and American schools differed from those on the continent in the lim-ited role played by government. The competition for students and the absence of public authority over the granting of degrees and licensure worked to keep down demand for reform.

The British and American systems were very similar in having weak premedical requirements, brief periods of study, a lack of scientific training, and a preference for practical as opposed to theoretical education.[71] The British did not establish a military medical school until 1857, in the after-math of the medical disasters of the Crimean War.

Like the American medical schools, the British institutions offered a standard lecture series and had small faculties. When a new school was founded at Leeds, England, in 1831, the seven faculty members stated that their curriculum would follow the example of "every great town on the Continent of Europe, and in the United States of America." Similar to the schools in the United States, the Leeds institution had four months of lec-tures, compared to the nine or ten months on the continent.

A distinctive mark of British (and American) medical education during these years was the continued heavy reliance on apprenticeships for clinical experience. According to one historian of medical education, "One reason for the shorter academic terms in Britain and America indeed was the expec-tation that the student would get his bedside or hospital training during the rest of the year."[72] A mid-Victorian book on medicine pointed out that the training of a practitioner in Britain in 1830 varied from classical university study at Oxford or Cambridge to a series of courses in a provincial hospital or a "broom-and-apron apprenticeship in an apothecary's shop."[73] Many authorities in Britain could grant licenses to practice medicine, and some people practiced without any degree or license at all. Eventually, there were demands for reform. Between 1824 and 1833, the faculty at Edinburgh voted to set the course of study for a medical degree at four years and to require six months of hospital attendance. It was possible, however, to obtain an entire medical education by apprenticeship until a reform law in 1858 failed to include this as an acceptable form of study.[74]

USE OF STETHOSCOPES AND THERMOMETERS

Among the erroneous criticisms of Civil War physicians is author George Worthington Adams's assertion that "auscultation and percussion . . . was a great scientific attainment of 1800–1820 in Europe, but only the better educated American surgeons practiced it during the war, and its adjunct, the stethoscope, was a novelty even to them."[75] To back up this statement, he observed that the Harvard medical school catalogue makes no mention of the possession of a stethoscope "until 1868, thirty years after its invention." Adams and others also contend that Civil War physicians did not know how to use microscopes or ophthalmoscopes and did not bother to use thermometers.[76,77]

However, there is ample evidence that American physicians were well acquainted with the stethoscope and percussion (tapping on the chest to elicit various diagnostic sounds) techniques, even at Harvard, before 1868. Oliver Wendell Holmes imitated the bedside teaching techniques of Louis and demonstrated percussion and auscultation using the stethoscope to medical students at Harvard's Massachusetts General Hospital in the late 1830s. Similar to today's practice, medical students bought their own stethoscope to use, rather than using one that belonged to the medical school. Stethoscopes were also used at Harvard's sister institution in Boston, Tremont Medical School, which shared faculty with Harvard.[78] Several medical school catalogues of the time also list the use of the stethoscope and other skills of physical diagnosis in their course descriptions. In fact, American physicians' familiarity with the stethoscope inspired one of Oliver Wendell Holmes's humorous and pointed poems (see Box, p. 66).

The skill of Civil War physicians in the use of percussion and of auscultation with the stethoscope is clearly recorded in the *Medical and Surgical History*'s case records that detail physical examinations of hearts and lungs. Among them are those of Dr. Jacob DaCosta of Philadelphia, who described 300 cases of functional heart abnormalities that he studied in depth during the war.[79] (See Figure 2.2.) His meticulous observations document the characteristic findings of progressive ventricular hypertrophy (thickening) and enlargement, and demonstrate the skills in physical diagnosis using percussion and auscultation with a stethoscope that modern medical students strive to attain. (In Chapter 12, see "Soldier's Heart," where DaCosta's observations are discussed.)

In reality, Civil War physicians' skill in detecting which lobe of the lung contained the pathology exceeded that of most modern physicians, who rely on x-rays for that purpose. And while there are no detailed records of the 4,169 soldiers diagnosed with "valvular heart disease," a stethoscope would have been necessary to hear the diagnostic murmurs. Case records of Civil War soldiers include additional diagnoses and physical findings, such as inflammation of the pericardium (the sack around the heart) and the pleura (the lining of the lungs), fluid in the chest, friction rubs (arising from inflammation of the pleura), and murmurs of endocarditis, that required the skillful use of stethoscopes and percussion techniques.

Civil War physicians are also criticized for their failure to use even the few thermometers they had.[80] Yet they were by no means behind their contemporaries in Europe in this regard. Thermometers were cumbersome to use, as they were usually placed in the armpit for a long period of time, and so were just "not used very much."[81] Body temperature was ascertained only during the investigation of unusual diseases, such as in Confederate physician Joseph Jones's study of "traumatic tetanus" published during the war.[82] Not until 1867 did German professor of medicine Carl Wünderlich introduce thermometry to bedside medicine. The profound impact of his work is summarized by the expression: "He found fever a disease and left it a symptom."[83] After Wünderlich's report, thermometer use became widespread among American physicians.

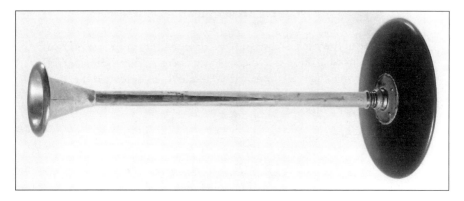

Figure 2.2: Stethoscope similar to those used by Dr. Jacob DaCosta at Turner's Lane Hospital in Philadelphia during the Civil War. (Courtesy of Gretchen Worden, Mütter Museum, College of Physicians, Philadelphia, PA.)

"The Stethoscope Song"
by
Oliver Wendell Holmes

Around 1853, Dr. Oliver Wendell Holmes poked fun at teaching the use of the stethoscope. His poem describes a young student who has returned from training in Paris with Pierre Louis, similar to Holmes himself:

> *There was a young man in Boston town*
> *He bought him a Stethoscope nice and new,*
> *All mounted and finished and polished down,*
> *With an ivory cap and a stopper too.*

> *It happened a spider within did crawl,*
> *And spun him a web of ample size,*
> *Wherein there chanced one day to fall*
> *A couple of very imprudent flies.*

The presence of the flies allowed Holmes to make fun of the French terms that were used to describe the sounds heard with the French instrument. When his mistakes in interpreting the buzzing of the flies as heart murmurs and lung sounds were discovered,

> *This poor young man was all aghast;*
> *The price of stethoscopes came down;*
> *And so he was reduced at last*
> *To practise in a country town.*

The humor of the clinical confusion he described was not lost on contemporary medical and lay audiences, who were all quite familiar with the stethoscope and how it was used. Holmes even described the measures taken to prevent a recurrence of the problem of the spider and the trapped, buzzing flies:

> *The doctors being very sore,*
> *A stethoscope they did devise,*
> *That had a rammer to clear the bore,*
> *With a knob at the end to kill the flies.*[84]

USE OF THE MICROSCOPE

Civil War physicians routinely used microscopes to make diagnoses and to study the pathologic changes due to disease. Nevertheless, some historians have asserted that the "backward" Civil War physicians did not know how to use the microscope. Although it had been invented two centuries earlier, "the headquarters of the Army Medical Department did not have [a microscope] until 1863," and the Harvard Medical School catalogue didn't acknowledge possession of a microscope until 1869.[85]

The truth is considerably different. The microscopic study of minute anatomic and pathologic tissue changes developed rapidly in the United States and elsewhere during the two decades before the Civil War. Oliver Wendell Holmes taught microscopy to medical students at both Harvard and Tremont medical schools from the 1840s on, using his own instruments and a set of slides he prepared himself.[86] Medical schools usually did not own any microscopes, but the professors did. Advertisements by microscope manufacturers appeared in the medical journals of the time. Several American scientific societies had sections devoted to microscopy, and at least one national society entirely devoted to microscopy was founded before the Civil War.[87]

Civil War case records clearly refute the erroneous assertion that Civil War physicians lagged behind their European contemporaries in microscopy. From these and other reports, it is possible to document that microscopic examinations of urine were done frequently, even in field hospitals, and with considerable skill, as shown by their recognition of blood cells, uric acid crystals, and casts. For example, *Medical and Surgical History* lists 9,454 cases of "inflammation of the kidneys." In some of these cases, analyses of the urine are described as revealing albumin and, upon microscopic examination, red cells, fat globules, and uric acid crystals.[88] An 1864 article in *American Medical Times*, authored by a Civil War physician, documents the use of the microscope in a clinical study of 100 patients with measles done at a Chattanooga field hospital. In evaluating the

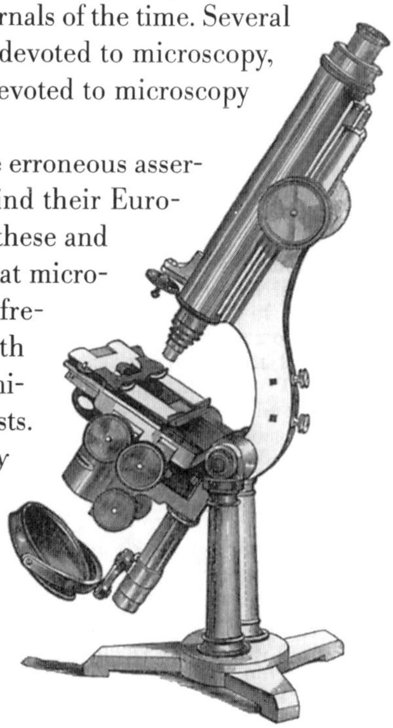

Figure 2.3: Smith & Beck's large compound microscope, typical of the Civil War era. (1866) (*SS*, p. 434.)

Physical Examination of the Lungs in Cases of Pneumonia

The following case reports, excerpted from *Medical and Surgical History*, describe physical findings which could only have been detected through the use of a stethoscope and chest percussion, and thus document that Civil War physicians used these techniques. One asterisk (*) indicates specific lung sounds only heard with a stethoscope; two asterisks (**) indicate the physical findings using chest percussion.

Case 4, Regimental Register, 28th Mass., April 11, 1863: . . . dulness over left nipple; crepitant râles* distinct. . . . 14th: rubbing sound* heard over upper part of left thorax, râles* below and dulness overall. . . . 17th: . . . no rubbing sound*, dulness** less marked.

Case 9, Third Division Hospital, Alexandria, VA: Diminished resonance** over right side anteriorly with subcrepitant ronchus* [sic] below.

Case 10, Ladies' Home Hospital, New York City: . . . dulness** posteriorly over the upper portion of the lower lobe of the left lung with feeble respiratory murmur* and moist bronchial râles*.[89]

"urinary organs," the author mentions that "daily examinations were made to detect albumen and casts."[90] Casts are formed by the deposition of proteinaceous material in the tubules of the kidneys and are the size of the internal diameter of these microscopic tubules, necessitating the use of a microscope for detection.

At least one army physician was an international leader in the field of microscopy. From early in the war, the Federal Surgeon General's Office and many of their hospitals in the field had serviceable microscopes, and a number of interesting observations are recorded in their case histories. In 1863, the Federal Surgeon General's Office purchased a compound achromatic microscope, the latest innovation in microscope technology, for the research being conducted by the Army Medical Museum and, specifically, for the use of Dr. Joseph Woodward. Much of Civil War medicine's leadership in the field of microscopy was due to Woodward's work with that 1863 compound microscope.

Woodward, an international leader in the field of microscopy, made many contributions to histologic techniques (microscopic examination of body tissues). He stained tissue sections with carmine, the standard of the time and the stain used by Rudolph Virchow, and also experimented with aniline dyes while working in the Surgeon General's Office.[91] These dyes had been developed from coal tar by an Englishman, William Perkin, and were used primarily by the textile industry. While the Germans had used them for tissue stains as early as 1862, Woodward discovered their utility independently. He wrote Virchow, asking his opinion of the staining technique, but, as far as can be determined, never received a reply. The technique was a major advance that was quickly adopted internationally after Virchow reported his observations.

Woodward is also credited with making some of the first photomicrographs using true photographic techniques (some daguerreotype photomicrographs had been made earlier) while working in the Surgeon General's Office, an important contribution to technique in microscopy.[92] Many of his photomicrographs were published in *Medical and Surgical History*.

USE OF THE OPHTHALMOSCOPE

According to *Medical and Surgical History*, army physicians did not use ophthalmoscopes (used to see inside the eye) during the war, and this fact has been used to criticize the quality of Civil War medicine.[93] While there were some American physicians who were skilled in the use of the ophthalmoscope, they would also have been aware of the problems associated with its use in this era before electric light.[94]

Hermann von Helmholz, a German physician originally educated as a military surgeon in Berlin, became a specialist in optics and first described the ophthalmoscope in 1851. His instrument used a series of lenses with an oil lamp or sunshine as a light source. Its usefulness was limited until it had been modified several times. The most practical modification—adding a built-in light source—occurred in 1885, when a New Yorker named Dennett added small electric bulbs.[95]

Although the army did not possess any of these crude ophthalmoscopes, the field of ophthalmology was developing rapidly in the United States at the time of the Civil War. Records show that Civil War surgeons matched the standards of their contemporaries in Europe in their treatment of eye injuries (in Chapter 6, see Treating Eye Injuries). Clinics and, later, hospitals devoted to eye diseases appeared as early as 1818. The first medical specialty society in the United States, the American Ophthalmological Society, was founded during the Civil War. In 1863, the Federal army established Desmarres Hospital, in Washington City (D.C.), to treat eye injuries and the Confederate army organized a similar facility in Athens, Georgia, in the summer of 1864.[96,97]

In sum, American medicine and medical education were, by and large, on a par with that of Europe at the time of the Civil War. Only a handful of medical schools in Britain and on the Continent were better than the best American medical schools. The biggest difference lay in the formal clinical experience offered in many Continental schools compared to the more informal system of clinical apprenticeships in the United States. American physicians studying abroad had returned with the latest advances, particularly in physical diagnosis and pathology. But the true test of the quality of American medicine and medical education lay in the quality of the medical and surgical care provided to the soldiers on both sides during the Civil War.

REFERENCES

1. Adams GW: *Doctors in Blue: The Medical History of the Union Army in the Civil War.* Baton Rouge: Louisiana State Univ. Press, 1996, p. 228.
2. Cunningham HH: *Doctors in Gray: The Confederate Medical Service.* Baton Rouge: Louisiana State Univ. Press, 1993, p. 16.
3. Brieger GH: *Medical America in the Nineteenth Century.* Baltimore, MD: Johns Hopkins Univ. Press, 1972, pp. 62-74.
4. Johnson P: *The Birth of the Modern World Society 1815–1830.* New York: Harper Collins, 1991.
5. Adams, *Doctors in Blue;* Cunningham, *Doctors in Gray;* Stevens R: *American Medicine and the Public Interest.* New Haven, CT: Yale Univ. Press, 1971, pp. 9-10.
6. McPherson JM: *Drawn With the Sword: Reflections on the American Civil War.* London: Oxford Univ. Press, 1996.
7. Iserson KV: *Death to Dust: What Happens to Dead Bodies?* Tucson, AZ: Galen Press, Ltd., 1994.
8. Rutkow IM: Biographical introduction. In: Woodward JJ: *Outlines of the Chief Camp Diseases of the United States Armies as Observed during the Present War.* Philadelphia, PA: Lippincott, 1863. Repub.: San Francisco: Norman, 1992.
9. Woodward JJ: Review of Virchow R: Cellular pathology, as based upon physiological and pathological histology. *Am J Med Sci.* 1861 Apr;41:465-79.
10. Nuland S: *Doctors: The Biography of Medicine.* New York: Vintage Books, 1989, p. 200.
11. Bonner TN: *Becoming a Physician: Medical Education in Great Britain, France, Germany, and the United States, 1750–1945.* New York: Oxford Univ. Press, 1995, p. 164.
12. Warner JH: *Against the Spirit of the System: The French Impulse in Nineteenth-Century American Medicine.* Princeton, NJ: Princeton Univ. Press, 1998, p. 217.
13. Holmes OW: *Medical Essays.* Boston: Houghton Mifflin, 1909, p. 43.
14. Hoyt EP: *The Improper Bostonian: Dr. Oliver Wendell Holmes.* New York: Morrow, 1979, p. 90.

15. Means JH: *The Association of American Physicians: Its First 75 Years.* New York: McGraw-Hill, 1961; Garrison FH: *An Introduction to the History of Medicine with Medical Chronology, Suggestions for Study and Bibliographic Data.* 4th ed. Philadelphia, PA: W.B. Saunders, 1929, p. 632.
16. Warner, *Spirit of the System,* pp. 46-71, 168, 169.
17. Stillé CJ: *History of the United States Sanitary Commission: Being a General Report of Its Work during the War of the Rebellion.* New York: Hurd & Houghton, 1868.
18. Garrison, *History of Medicine,* p. 521.
19. Warren L: *Joseph Leidy: The Last Man Who Knew Everything.* New Haven, CT: Yale Univ. Press, 1998.
20. Porcher FP: *Resources of the southern fields and forests, medical, economical, and agricultural. being also a medical botany of the Confederate States; with practical information on the useful properties of the trees, plants and shrubs.* Charleston, SC: Steampower Press of Evans and Cogwell, 1863.
21. Indigenous remedies of the South. (editorial) *Conf States Med Surg J.* 1864;1:106.
22. Bollet AJ: Pierre Louis. The numerical method and the foundation of quantitative medicine. *Am J Med Sci.* 1973 Aug;266(2):92-101.
23. Harvey AM: *The Association of American Physicians, 1886–1986: A Century of Progress in Medical Science.* Baltimore, MD: The Association, 1986, p. 27.
24. Yankauer A: Pierre Charles-Alexandre Louis: the impact of a clinical trial. *Pharos.* 1996 Spring;59(2):15-19.
25. Louis PCA: *Researches on Phthisis. Anatomical, Pathological, and Therapeutical* [sic]. 2nd ed. London: The Syndenham Society, 1844.
26. *Medical and Surgical History,* Medical Section, vol. 1, p. xvi.
27. Association of Army and Navy Surgeons: Constitution. *Conf States Med Surg J.* 1864;1:13-16.
28. Ibid.
29. Report of Surg. Charles S. Frink, U.S. Army, Surgeon-in-Chief, 23rd Army Corps. *O.R.,* Series I, vol. 38/2, p. 693.
30. Eve PF: Answers to certain questions propounded by Prof. Charles A. Lee, M.D., Agent of the U.S. Sanitary Commission relative to the health, etc., of the late Southern army. *Nashville J Med Surg.* NS, 1866;1:16.
31. Report of Surg. Henry S. Hewit, U.S. Army Medical Director. *O.R.,* Series I, vol. 38/2, p. 521.
32. Dunglison R: *Medical Lexicon: A Dictionary of Medical Science.* 9th ed. London: Sampson Low, 1853.
33. Woodward JJ. In: *Medical and Surgical History,* Surgical Section, vol. 3, p. 832.
34. *Medical and Surgical History,* Surgical Section, vol. 3, p. 484.
35. Chipman NP: *The Andersonville Prison Trial: The Trial of Capt. Henry Wirz.* (reprint) Birmingham, AL: Notable Trials Library, 1990, p. 129.
36. Patterson GA: *Debris of Battle: The Wounded of Gettysburg.* Mechanicsburg, PA: Stackpole, 1997.
37. Denney RE: *Civil War Medicine.* New York: Sterling, 1994, p. 228.
38. Holt DM: *A Surgeon's Civil War: The Letters and Diary of Daniel M. Holt, M.D.* Kent, OH: Kent State Univ. Press, 1994, p. 28.
39. Robertson JI: *Soldiers Blue and Grey.* Columbia: Univ. South Carolina Press, 1988, p. 70.
40. New York Academy of Medicine: *Military Hygiene and Therapeutics. Report of Committee on Military Surgery to the Surgical Section, July 3, 1861.* New York: S.S.&W. Wood, 1861.
41. Ibid.
42. Lawson G: *Surgeon in the Crimea: The Experiences of George Lawson Recorded in Letters to His Family 1854–1855.* London: Military Book Society, 1968.
43. Cantlie N: *A History of the Army Medical Department.* vol. 2. Edinburgh: Churchill Livingston, 1973, p. 205.

44. Steiner PE: *Disease in the Civil War: Natural Biological Warfare in 1861-65.* Springfield, IL: C.C. Thomas, 1968, p. 17.
45. Adams GW: Confederate medicine. *J South Hist.* 1940;6:151-88
46. *Medical and Surgical History,* Medical Section, vol. 3, p. 649.
47. Kiple K: *Cambridge World History of Disease.* Cambridge: Cambridge Univ. Press, 1993, p. 202.
48. Mitchell SW, Morehouse GR, Keen WW: *Gunshot Wounds and Other Injuries of Nerves.* Philadelphia, PA: Lippincott, 1864. Repub.: San Francisco: Norman, 1989.
49. See Bibliography for information about their books.
50. Cantlie, *History of the Army Medical Department,* vol. 2, p. 408.
51. Johnson A, Malone D, eds.: *Dictionary of American Biography.* vol. 8. New York: Chas. Scribner & Sons, 1930, p. 185.
52. Shaw GB: *Complete Plays with Prefaces.* New York: Dodd Mead, 1962, pp. 18-19.
53. Dammann G: *A Pictorial Encyclopedia of Civil War Medical Instruments and Equipment.* vol. 3. Missoula, MT: Pictorial Histories Pub., 1983, pp. 29-31.
54. Riley HD, Jr.: Medicine in the Confederacy. Part 2. *Mil Med.* 1956 Feb;118(2):150.
55. Dotson RS: "Ophthalmology during the War between the States." Presented at the Society of Civil War Surgeons. Knoxville, TN: March 2, 1998. (lecture)
56. Starr P: *The Social Transformation of American Medicine.* New York: Basic Books, 1982, pp. 123-25.
57. Stevens R: *American Medicine and the Public Interest.* New Haven, CT: Yale Univ. Press, 1971.
58. Bonner, *Becoming a Physician,* p. 9.
59. Ibid.
60. Starr, *Social Transformation of American Medicine,* pp. 124-25.
61. Ibid.
62. Gillett MC: *The United States Army Medical Department, 1818–1865.* Washington, DC: Center of Military History, U.S. Army, 1987, p. 181.
63. Bonner, *Becoming a Physician,* p. 206.
64. Smith D: A persistent rebel. *Am Hist Ill.* 1981;15:28.
65. Bonner, *Becoming a Physician,* p. 187.
66. Ibid., p. 123.
67. Nuland, *Doctors,* p. 308; Garrison, *History of Medicine,* p. 451.
68. Bonner, *Becoming a Physician,* p. 165.
69. Ibid., pp. 188, 231, 191.
70. Ibid., p. 169.
71. Ibid., p. 198.
72. Ibid., pp. 169-70, 174.
73. Peterson MJ: *The Medical Profession in Mid-Victorian London.* Berkeley: Univ. of California Press, 1978, p. 5.
74. Bonner, *Becoming a Physician,* pp. 167, 195.
75. Adams, *Doctors in Blue,* p. 51.
76. Ibid., pp. 50-51.
77. Cunningham, *Doctors in Gray,* p. 17.
78. Hoyt EP: *The Improper Bostonian: Dr. Oliver Wendell Holmes.* New York: Morrow, 1979, p. 90.
79. DaCosta JM: On irritable heart. *Am J Med Sci.* 1871;61:17; *Medical and Surgical History,* Medical Section, vol. 3, p. 862.
80. Adams, *Doctors in Blue,* p. 51.
81. Billings JS: Medical reminiscences of the Civil War. Transactions of the College of Physicians of Philadelphia. 3rd Series. 1905;27:115-121.
82. Jones J: Traumatic tetanus. *Conf States Med Surg J.* 1864;1(5):1.
83. Garrison, *History of Medicine,* pp. 430-31.

84. Holmes OW: *Poems by Oliver Wendell Holmes*. Boston: Ticknor, Reed & Fields, 1853, pp. 271-77.
85. Adams, *Doctors in Blue*, p. 51.
86. Hoyt, *Improper Bostonian*, pp. 101, 201-2.
87. Warner DJ: The campaign for medical microscopy in Antebellum America. *Bull Hist Med*. 1995 Fall;69(3):367.
88. *Medical and Surgical History*, Medical Section, vol. 3, pp. 881-83.
89. Ibid., p. 733.
90. Bartholow R: A report on camp measles. *Am Med Times*. 1864 May 14;8:231, 242.
91. Woodward JJ: On the use of aniline in histological researches; with a method of investigating the histology of the human intestine and remarks on some points to be observed in the study of the diseased intestine in camp fevers and diarrheas. *Am J Med Sci*. 1865;49:106-13
92. Burns SB: Early medical photography in America (1839–1883), VI. Civil War Medical Photography. *NY State J Med*. 1980 Aug;80(9):1444.
93. Adams, *Doctors in Blue*, p. 51.
94. Gross SD: *A System of Surgery, Pathological, Diagnostic, Therapeutic, and Operative*. Philadelphia: Blanchard & Lea, 1862.
95. Duke-Elder S, ed.: *System of Ophthalmology*. vol. VII. *The Foundations of Ophthalmology: Heredity, Pathology, Diagnosis, and Therapeutics*. London: Kimpton, 1962.
96. Index to Hospital Register, NARA, RG94, stack area 9W3, row 3, compartment 2.
97. Cunningham, *Doctors in Gray*, p. 215.

~ 3 ~

Civil War Surgery: Desperate Measures for Desperate Wounds

I had rather longed for the wounded to arrive, for rheumatism wasn't heroic, neither was liver complaint, or measles; even fever had lost its charms.

— Louisa Mae Alcott, *Hospital Sketches*

BEFORE THE TWENTIETH CENTURY, disease had been the predominant cause of death in armies. Nevertheless, histories of military medicine usually focus on the fate of the wounded. In fact, one man removing an arrow from another is the basis of both the ancient Chinese and Egyptian glyphs for "healer." During the Civil War, critics of the medical services followed this pattern, focusing their attention on the surgical care of the wounded (as do modern critics). However, the Civil War literature actually reveals that these surgeons saved the lives of a higher proportion of wounded soldiers than surgeons in any of the armies that participated in the Crimean War.

The medical departments of both armies constantly worked to improve their surgical performance, conducting research in the field and at the medical museum in the Surgeon General's Office, discussing their observations at frequent meetings of specially formed army medical societies, and publishing papers in the medical journals. Civilian medical societies and journals held similar discussions and published similar papers analyzing, evaluating, criticizing, and often praising the performance of the army surgeons. Case reports detail many successful surgical innovations, such as reconstruction of facial deformations, treatment of depressed skull fractures, and treatment of chest and abdominal wounds. Trials of a method to seal and prevent the leakage of air into the chest following penetrating wounds used the same principles as later approaches. The use of antiseptics to treat severe wound infections, especially the devastating disease known as hospital gangrene, was eminently successful, and preceded the widespread use of such agents that Joseph Lister introduced later in the decade. Development of an efficient and effective ambulance system, new methods of transporting wounded, and establishment of huge, efficiently run hospitals (subjects covered in later chapters) also contributed to the vast improvements in surgical care and survival rates.

Despite these and other surgical advances, Civil War physicians were unable to influence the public's perception of their efforts. After the Battle of Antietam in September 1862, Medical Director Jonathan Letterman was so disturbed by the public criticism of the army's surgeons that he wrote:

> The surgery of these battle-fields has been pronounced butchery. Gross misrepresentations of the conduct of medical officers have been made and scattered broadcast over the country, causing deep and heart-rending anxiety to those who had friends or relatives in the army, who might at any moment require the services of a surgeon. It is not to be supposed that there were no incompetent surgeons in the army. It is certainly true that there were; but these sweeping denunciations against a class of men who will favorably compare with the military surgeons of any country, because of the incompetency and short-comings of a few, are wrong, and do injustice to a body of men who have labored faithfully and well.[1]

This report could be said to summarize the general reputation, both then and now, of Civil War surgery.

ANESTHESIA DURING THE CIVIL WAR

The most prevalent misconception about Civil War medicine is that major surgery was usually performed without using anesthesia. Nothing could be farther from the truth. Immediately after the successful demonstration of the use of ether at Massachusetts General Hospital in October 1846, physicians in the United States and Europe began to use anesthesia for surgical operations. However, it was not used universally for over a decade. Many senior surgeons opposed the routine use of anesthesia, believing that its effects were harmful and that pain was a "healthy stimulus" needed to rouse a moribund person from torpor. Some surgeons continued to oppose anesthesia on medical grounds through the 1850s.

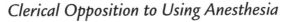

Clerical Opposition to Using Anesthesia

Some clergy fought the use of anesthesia, saying that it opposed God's plan for mankind's suffering. When the head of obstetrics at Edinburgh, James Simpson, introduced the use of chloroform during deliveries in 1847, the Scottish clergy blasted him from the pulpit and in print, saying that misery in childbirth was God's punishment for Eve's transgression with the apple.

Simpson answered with a biblical quote of his own, a reference to the first obstetrical event in the Bible, the birth of Eve. The passage begins, "First, God put Adam to sleep." Opposition to obstetrical anesthesia ceased when Queen Victoria used it for the birth of her eighth child, Prince Leopold, on April 7, 1853.[2]

Anesthesia was new at the time of the U.S. war with Mexico (1846–47) and American army surgeons rarely used it. By the time of the Crimean War, its use was firmly established for major operations. However, in the British Army Medical Department, "a large minority of surgeons objected to its use in cases of severe injury, especially where much blood had been lost, on the grounds that patients in these cases frequently did not recover because of the depressing nature of the drug." Inspector General Sir George Hall, the British Army's principle medical officer in the Crimea (roughly equivalent to a Civil War medical director), opposed the use of chloroform during that conflict. In his words, "however barbarous it may appear, the smart of the knife is a powerful stimulant, and it is much better to hear a man bawl lustily, than to see him sink silently into his grave."[3] After the Crimean War, British Army surgeons still did not use anesthesia when operating on Britons wounded in the siege of Delhi (1857) during the Sepoy Rebellion in India. Few of the wounded recovered and almost none of the amputees survived, perhaps because no anesthesia was used, although the amount of disease and other conditions that affected care of the wounded were also factors.[4,5]

By the 1860s, opposition to the use of anesthesia in the United States was rare. A prominent surgeon, lecturing on military surgery in 1862 at the College of Physicians and Surgeons in New York, asserted that "the day is past where the administration of anesthetics in surgical operations is a subject for discussion."[6] Professor J. J. Chisolm summarized the attitude of Confederate surgeons in his *Manual of Military Surgery*:

> The universal use of chloroform to allay the pain of surgical operations is a complete vindication for the utility of this remedy, and proof of its necessity . . . *We do not hesitate to say that it should be given to every patient requiring a serious or painful operation.* We may hear, now and then, of an accident from its administration; but who can tell us of the immense number who would have sunk from operations, had it not been administered?[7] [Original italics]

Anesthesia was used almost universally from the beginning of the Civil War. For example, after the Battle of Rich Mountain, Virginia (later West Virginia), on July 11, 1861, ten days before First Bull Run, the medical director of General McClellan's army reported that several amputations were performed and that "chloroform was administered in all operations involving much pain. There were no fatal results from the use of this anesthetic."[8] In *Medical and Surgical History*, the authors emphasized that

> the importance of an early and complete examination of the wounded seems to have been fully realized by the surgical staff. This examination was generally conducted under the influence of anesthetics for the purpose of accurate diagnosis; in its course, balls and foreign bodies were extracted, bleeding vessels secured, and splinters of bone removed; upon its conclusion such operations were performed as in the judgment of the surgeon were necessary.[9]

During the course of the war, Union records show that at least 80,000 operations were done using anesthetics and only 254 were done without anesthesia. Anesthesia was also given whenever wound treatments were going to be painful. The most notable example was the use of bromine to treat hospital gangrene, which became widespread during the last two years of the war. The wound was irrigated by introducing a bromine solution into the margins of the gangrenous area, a very painful procedure. This treatment, performed in hospitals, was always done under general anesthesia, usually ether.[10] Anesthesia was also used to treat tetanus in an attempt to relieve the painful, persistent muscle spasms (in Chapter 7, see Tetanus).

There is only one instance on record during the war in which anesthesia was available but not used. The medical director of the Army of the Mississippi, reporting on the Battle of Iuka on September 19, 1862, stated,

> the battle was fought so close to the [improvised field] hospital that the men detailed as bearers could go to the field and return at short intervals. The moment a man fell, he was taken up, and in three minutes his wounds

Typical Erroneous Report about the Use of Anesthesia

Too often, the experiences of Civil War soldiers have been distorted or misinterpreted, such as in one book that quotes letters of soldiers who witnessed patients being physically restrained during surgery and assumed that the procedure was done without anesthetic. Today's physicians know that the men were actually in the excitement phase of anesthesia, but these reminiscences are the basis of untrue statements that surgery was often done without anesthesia.

One modern author, for example, inaccurately described a typical Civil War field hospital scene:

> Instances were many when the only "anesthesia" used was a bullet or a piece of wood thrust between a soldier's teeth to keep him from biting his tongue while the surgeon cut, sawed and sutured. A New Jersey soldier who watched two amputations wrote of the patients, "Neither of them seemed to be under the influence of chloroform, but were held down by some four men, while nothing but a groan escaped them as the operation proceeded." . . . Screams of agony and pain, however, usually accompanied every case put upon the operating table. Such sounds were clearly audible to the masses of prostrate men lying nearby on the ground and awaiting their turn.[12]

Today, the impression persists that Civil War surgery was performed with patients given only a shot of whiskey and a bullet between the teeth. One might believe as many bullets were bitten as fired.

The need for assistants to hold down patients in the early phases of anesthesia persisted well into the twentieth century, until better agents for inducing the anesthetic state became available. However, other patients no longer witnessed the agitation and vocalizations that Civil War soldiers recorded since the procedures were done inside hospital operating rooms.

were being dressed. All necessary operations were performed at once, and the records show but a trifling mortality. No anesthetics were used, and not a groan or sign of pain was heard. . . . Our loss was one hundred and forty-five killed, five hundred ninety-eight wounded. [11]

The wounded men's lack of pain may have been due to the temporary analgesia caused by endorphins released into the body (endogenous substances with morphine-like effects) coupled with nearly immediate surgery after their injuries. The exact number of operations performed after the Battle of Iuka is unknown.

Occasionally, anesthetics were unavailable after major battles when there were mass casualties. Lack of anesthetics occurred more often among the Confederates, largely as a result of the blockade, although ether and chloroform were produced in several Southern "laboratories." Whenever Confederate cavalry raided a Union supply train, food and chloroform were among the most treasured prizes. For example, on May 24, 1862, when Stonewall Jackson's cavalry captured a Union supply train near Winchester, Virginia, it was the "medical stores," including 1,500 cases of chloroform, that they quickly "liberated."[13]

Chloroform was the anesthetic preferred in the field because, in contrast to ether, it was not explosive. Surgeons could, therefore, use chloroform near a battle and at night, close to candles and gas lanterns. Transporting chloroform was also easier since it occupied less space than did an equivalent supply of ether. However, there was valid concern about patient safety with chloroform. Surgeons were aware that no fatalities had been reported from the use of chloroform in the Crimean conflict, but, by the time of the Civil War, several deaths had been attributed to it in civilian practice. Any wartime fatalities of this nature had to be reported to the Surgeon General's Office.

Hospital-based procedures were performed with ether or a mixture of the two anesthetics. In his account of wound treatment in the Army of the Potomac in 1864, Dr. John Shaw Billings stated: "The anesthetic commonly used has been a mixture of ether and chloroform, in the proportion of one part of the latter to two of the former. Pure chloroform has been much used however, and several deaths have occurred from its effects."[14] Although chloroform had some advantages over ether, its smaller margin of safety curtailed its use in surgery, but it continued to be used to some extent until the middle of the twentieth century.[15]

According to the noted Confederate surgeon Dr. Hunter Holmes McGuire, chloroform was administered in the Confederate armies over 28,000 times and "no death was ever ascribed to its use."[16] In preparing *Medical and Surgical History*, analyses were made of the use of anesthesia in 8,900 major cases. Chloroform was used in 6,784 cases with thirty-seven deaths, a rate of 0.5%; ether was used in 1,305 cases with four deaths, a rate of 0.3%. A mixture of the two agents was employed in 811 cases with five deaths, a rate of 0.6%.[17]

The low death rate from anesthesia itself is remarkable, given that the anesthetic agents were normally administered by an assistant, often any handy soldier. The assistant dripped the liquid onto a towel or a napkin folded into a cone, and held it over the patient's mouth and nose. The relative safety of chloroform during the war may have been partly due to its use in the open air or in well-ventilated rooms, in contrast to the closed operating rooms of civilian practice. The most important factors, however, were probably the patients' youth, the limited depth of the anesthesia, and the brief period of its use. Speed was still considered the main attribute of a good surgeon, and many were able to perform amputations near the hip, a complicated and difficult procedure, in two minutes.[18]

During the Civil War, patients were given an anesthetic only until they were insensitive to pain. At these superficial levels of anesthesia, patients remain in a state of excitement or delirium. In such a state, they might moan or shout and, usually, thrash about, but they were not conscious and had no memory of the operative procedure or their behavior. Several men had to assist surgeons by holding patients on the operating table during surgery to control these spontaneous agitated movements. Because surgical procedures were often done outdoors, passersby could observe the tumult, and their letters and comments led to the widespread and incorrect belief that Civil War surgery frequently was done without anesthesia (see Figure 3.1).

Judging from descriptions of the procedures, patients given anesthesia were never put below what later became known as the "second stage" of anesthesia. Only when the principles of anesthesiology began to be understood in the late 1800s and early 1900s were operations performed with patients in a much deeper level of anesthesia that included muscle relaxation. Much later, endotracheal tubes and ventilators enabled the patient to continue to breathe if the depth of anesthesia resulted in a cessation of spontaneous breathing.

SURGERY BEFORE THE CIVIL WAR

Few surgeons who served in the war had prior surgical experience. Before the introduction of anesthesia in October 1846, little major surgery had been done, and then only under the most desperate circumstances. In these instances, speed counted most. Anesthesia allowed surgeons to perform more deliberate extensive procedures, but infection undid most of their efforts. As

Figure 3.1: Portion of a field hospital scene by Thomas Nast from *Harper's Weekly*. Note the battle still occurring in the background and wounded being carried in for treatment. The soldiers marching past are about to observe an amputation being done outside. Previously treated men are lined up against the building and their amputated limbs surround the operating table. Descriptions of this picture have emphasized the bottle near the patient's head, suggesting that it contained whiskey used as the only anesthetic. It is much more likely that it contained chloroform. The scene, although invented, probably represented events during the Seven Days' Battles at the end of June 1862.

a result, very little innovation in surgical technique had occurred by the time of the Civil War and surgery was still rarely attempted in civilian settings.

There also were no surgical training programs. A student physician might witness a few procedures and, at some point, be called on to do one alone. As a result, few physicians had experience with anything more than minor surgical procedures before the war. In their reminiscences, Civil War surgeons lamented their lack of preparation. "Many of our surgeons had never seen the inside of the abdomen in a living subject," one physician recorded. "Many of the surgeons of the Civil War had never witnessed a major amputation when they joined their regiments; very few of them had treated gunshot wounds."[19]

Statistics from Massachusetts General Hospital, one of the premier hospitals then (and now), illustrate the state of nineteenth-century surgery. Between 1836 and 1846, only 39 surgical procedures were performed *annually*. In the first ten years after the introduction of anesthesia (1847–57), the annual average jumped to 189 surgical procedures. During this period, about 60% of the surgical procedures were amputations, 10% were palliative procedures for breast cancer, and 30% were treatments for superficial lesions, such as removing small cysts or draining abscesses.[20] Hernias were occasionally repaired, but neurosurgery and opening the abdomen or chest were not even attempted. After the Civil War, the volume of surgery in civilian hospitals increased enormously with the introduction of antiseptic and, later, of aseptic techniques. Between 1894 and 1904, for example, an average of 2,427 surgical procedures were done annually at Massachusetts General Hospital and, by 1914, over 4,000 operations were performed each year.

These figures pale in comparison to the work done by the Civil War's military surgeons. Despite their lack of preparation, physicians treated over 400,000 trauma patients among Union forces alone—about 245,000 of them with gunshot wounds—and performed at least 40,000 operations.[21] During the course of the war, formal and informal surgical training programs were established and newly inducted Union surgeons attended a special course on the treatment of gunshot wounds.[22] Surgeons on both sides rapidly developed skills and knowledge that improved the general treatment of wounds, and they devised many new surgical procedures. As one Confederate surgeon commented, "I have lost much, but I have gained much, especially as a medical man. I return home a better surgeon, a better doctor."[23]

THE WEAPONS: MINIÉ BALLS, SABERS, AND ARTILLERY SHELLS

Weapons became more effective and more deadly during the course of the war. In the beginning of the conflict, many soldiers, particularly Confederates, used antiquated firearms. One Union surgeon attributed the low mortality from wounds at the Battle of Ball's Bluff (October 21, 1861) to the use of round balls and some buckshot, rather than the conical minié balls used almost uniformly later in the war.[24] (See Figure 3.2.)

The nature of the causative weapon or missile was specified in 141,961 (57.7%) of the wounds documented in *Medical and Surgical History*. As can be seen in Table 3.1, the vast majority of the wounds treated were caused by the minié ball. It is likely that artillery projectiles (grape, canister, shell fragments, etc.) caused a much higher proportion of those fatal injuries, although there are no data specifying the cause of the battlefield deaths.

Several surgeons commented on the increasing proportion of artillery wounds as the war went on, but the available figures do not distinguish between data collected early and late in the war. For example, artillery apparently caused a higher proportion of the wounds treated at Gettysburg than had occurred in previous battles, attributed to the increased accuracy of the artillerists. Their skill undoubtedly continued to improve for the rest of the war, thus leading to more wounds from artillery projectiles.[25]

Despite the classic image of saber-wielding cavalry and field officers, saber and bayonet wounds were surprisingly rare; there were only 922 (0.4% of the total) with a mortality rate of 7.7%. The 26 fatal saber wounds

TABLE 3.1
Types of Weapons and Number of Wounds Treated

Type of Weapon	Number	% of Recorded Cases
Conoidal (minié) ball	108,049	76.0%
Round or musket ball	16,742	12.0
Fragment of shell	12,520	9.0
Pistol or buckshot	3,008	2.0
Grape, canister, etc	1,153	1.0
Solid shot	359	0.3
Explosive musket ball	139	0.1
Unknown missile	103,829	—

Compiled from data in *Medical and Surgical History*, Surgical Section, vol. 3, p. 696.

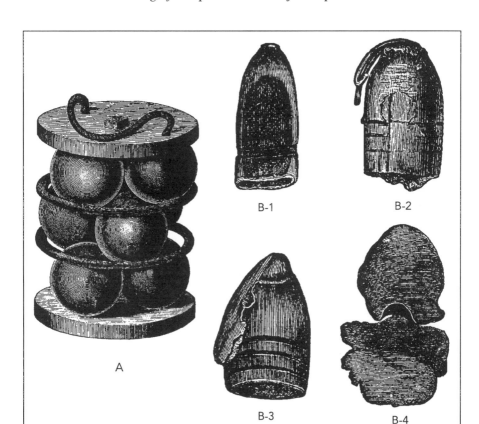

Figure 3.2: Projectiles used in the Civil War
(Figures are not to scale.)

A—Grape-shot consisted of nine cast-iron balls of varying sizes, arranged in rows of three, and kept in position by a series of plates held together by a vertical rod with nuts on each end. When fired from a cannon, "the parts become separated and each part acts as a distinct projectile," very effective when fired into ranks of advancing infantry. (*Medical and Surgical History*, Surgical Section, vol. 3, p. 697.)

B—Examples of bullets that became distorted after passing through the chest and impacting on bones and tissues. Case histories were included with each specimen. For example, the conoidal ball (B-1) penetrated a soldier's chest on December 13, 1862, at Fredericksburg, became considerably flattened and distorted, and was extracted by a surgeon on January 19, 1863. The soldier recovered and was pensioned. (*Medical and Surgical History*, Surgical Section, vol. 3, p. 697.)

A Fatal Extremity Wound:
The Death of General Albert Sidney Johnston

Confederate Gen. Albert Sidney Johnston surprised Grant at Shiloh in the first huge battle of the Civil War. His medical director, Dr. David Wendell Yandell, was at his side on the first morning of the battle. As the Union army fell back early in the fighting, Johnston's forces came upon the second line of Federal tents which sheltered a large number of unattended wounded men. Since no other surgeon was in sight, Johnston insisted that Yandell "look after these wounded people, the Yankees among the rest."

Yandell sent a courier to the rear to summon other medical officers while Johnston rode on. A short time later, a spent minié ball struck the general just behind the knee, tearing the popliteal artery. Within fifteen minutes, Johnston bled to death. Ironically, in an unprecedented move, Yandell had taken the precaution of issuing tourniquets to all Johnston's staff officers. The lifesaving device was in Johnston's pocket, but no one with him knew how to use it.[26]

described in *Medical and Surgical History* primarily affected the head, while the 30 fatal bayonet wounds were mostly to the head and chest. By comparison, in European armies, bayonets and sabers caused about 2% of the wounds, the main exception being the French forces in Mexico, whose weapons caused 22% of the wounds.[27] According to one Civil War surgeon, "I never saw a bayonet wound. In the Bloody Angle struggle at Spotsylvania there were 14 bayonet wounds; probably as many men were severely kicked by mules."[28] Despite the prominence of cavalry in Civil War operations, the low frequency of saber wounds was because the cavalry generally fought at long range with carbines and pistols, and often dismounted to fight as infantry.[29] (See Figures 3.3 and 3.4.)

WOUNDS IN DIFFERENT SITES

The authors of *Medical and Surgical History* made an estimate of the comparative frequency of wounds in different sites. They used the relatively little data they had for those "killed in battle" (only 1,173 cases) and the figures for those admitted to hospitals to make an estimate of the distribution of *all*

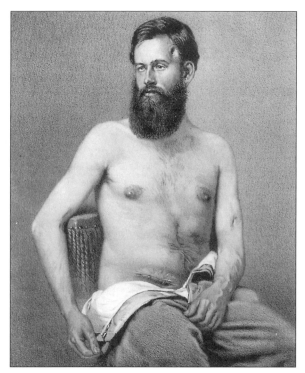

Figure 3.3: Edson D. Bemis

A private in the 12th Massachusetts Volunteers, Edson Bemis suffered a gunshot fracture of the shaft of the left humerus at the Battle of Antietam on September 17, 1862. He returned to duty and later was promoted to corporal. He was wounded by a musket ball in the right lower abdomen, just above the inguinal ligament, at the Battle of the Wilderness on May 6, 1864. This wound healed slowly and he again returned to duty.

On February 5, 1865, during the Siege of Petersburg, a ball struck the left frontal area of his head and traveled back and up, taking bone with it. On examination, a portion of the brain and its covering membranes could be seen in the wound. There was considerable hemorrhage, and he was paralyzed on the right side. The ball was removed from his brain and his condition immediately improved. He remained in bed "uninterested in conversation" (suggesting a frontal lobe injury) until two weeks later, when he suddenly improved markedly, conversed freely, and was able to walk about the ward.

This image was made at his discharge from the hospital on July 13, 1865. At that time, brain tissue could be felt through the healing wound, which still discharged small amounts of pus. In 1870, he informed the surgeons at the Army Medical Museum that "I am still in the land of the living. My health is very good," but that he had headaches and some difficulty with his memory and in hearing. He was married and had just had his first child. (*Medical and Surgical History*, Surgical Section, vol. 1, Plate V opp. p. 162.)

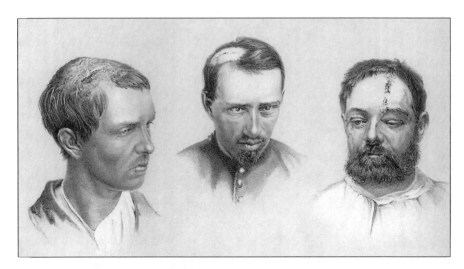

Figure 3.4: Drawings from photographs of patients who sustained saber wounds of the head, typically inflicted by cavalry. The patient on the left received two saber cuts near Burke's Station, Virginia, on April 6, 1865. After shaving the area, the wound edges were approximated with adhesive and seemed to heal rapidly, but pus appeared under the skin two months later and the wound required drainage. The patient was discharged two weeks later. (*Medical and Surgical History*, Surgical Section, vol. 1, p. 4, Plate I.)

battlefield injuries. On this basis, they calculated that 31% of all battlefield injuries (among those killed and wounded) were in the upper extremities; 30% were in the lower extremities; 15% were in the head, face, and neck; and 23% were in the trunk (Table 3.2).[30] The authors noted that their findings for wound distribution were strikingly similar to the distribution of injuries in the Crimean War and the Franco-Prussian War.

TABLE 3.2

Distribution of Wounds Among Those Listed as Killed in Battle or Admitted to Hospitals

Site	Killed in Battle	Wounded
Trunk	51%	18%
Head and neck	42	11
Lower extremities	5	35
Upper extremities	3	36

Compiled from data in *Medical and Surgical History*, Surgical Section, vol. 3, p. 692.

Trunk and head wounds were much more likely to be fatal than extremity wounds, and soldiers with these types of wounds were less likely to be evacuated to field hospitals and registered as wounded (Table 3.3). Relatively few extremity wounds were fatal on the battlefield unless a major artery was hit and massive hemorrhage occurred. There was a higher proportion of head and upper extremity wounds. This can be explained by the protection of the trunk and legs against enemy fire provided by parapets in siege operations and in "trenches, ditches, trees, etc." The "excessively large percentage of wounds of the hands and fingers, frequently noted by writers on military surgery [in other countries]" was due to the excessive exposure of the hands during combat.[31]

The authors of *Medical and Surgical History* noted the effect of triage practices and the greater immediate fatality of some wounds upon the reported wound distribution statistics. More recent authors, however, have ignored these factors, assuming that the figures for distribution of treated wounds are, in fact, the figures for all wounds. Some authors have even assumed that artillery fire was generally ineffective, based on the small proportion of artillery wounds treated at depot hospitals. In fact, artillery

TABLE 3.3

Total Cases and Fatality Rates by Location of Wounds
(figures are for cases with known outcomes)

	Total Number of Cases	Fatality Rate
Spine	642	55.5%
Abdomen#	8,438	48.7
Pelvis	3,159	29.7
Chest*	20,264	27.8
Head	12,089	15.0
Flesh wound of neck	4,895	15.0
Lower extremities	86,413	13.8
Flesh wound of back	12,681	6.9
Upper extremities	87,793	6.5
Face	9,416	5.9

*In 8,269 cases, the chest cavity was penetrated; the fatality rate was 65.1% in these cases.
#For abdominal wounds, death resulted from wounds of the intestine, stomach, liver, or spleen, as well as from injury to the "blood-vessels, omentum and mesentery."
Medical and Surgical History, Surgical Section, vol. 3, p. 691.

wounds were more likely to be immediately fatal and thus were not included in the statistics for nature of injury or wound distribution.

There was a relatively low mortality from wounds of the face, neck, and back. The likelihood of fatality was low if a bullet failed to penetrate the skull or enter the chest cavity, and these men were the most likely to be evacuated and treated. Only progressive overwhelming infection or severe hemorrhage would cause fatalities from such relatively superficial ("flesh") wounds. If the missile penetrated the skull or entered the chest cavity, the soldier probably did not live to be evacuated and thus enter the statistics for treated wounds.

UNDERSTANDING CASUALTY STATISTICS

The documented amount of medical care both armies delivered was obviously understated. Most Civil War sources state that about 95% of the wounds were inflicted by bullets predominantly hitting the extremities rather than the trunk or the head. Artillery caused the remaining 5% of the damage; less than 1% of the wounds were caused by sabers and bayonets. These figures, however, are based on the wounded who were registered and received medical treatment at a field hospital. They do not reflect the injuries to soldiers who were killed on the battlefield, who died before reaching the aid station, or who were considered mortally wounded and, because of triage considerations, were not evacuated. At least early in the war, these men were left to die after they were given opium and water and made as comfortable as possible; although technically these men were treated by medical personnel in the field, all of them were listed only as "killed in battle."

The medical statistics also do not include the "walking wounded" who were treated at aid stations in the field and sent back to their units, and thus were never registered as wounded. These unregistered men help explain the discrepancy between the number of wounded listed in the official report of the Union adjutant general and the hospital figures recorded during the same period. Generally, the medical figures were about 10% lower than those of the adjutant general, a discrepancy occasionally noted officially.[32] These superficially injured men returned to their units directly after treatment by the assistant surgeon or to an aid station close to the battlefield, and were neither relieved of duty nor hospitalized. Company commanders, however, included them in the total numbers of wounded reported to the adjutant general after the battle.

Pressed to treat huge numbers of wounded, surgeons in the field and their assistants did not try to keep accurate records. Even so, in at least one

Dirty Hands and Dirty Equipment

The lack of attention to cleanliness is one of historians' most frequently quoted criticisms of Civil War physicians. Those physician-veterans who lived to see the era of bacteriology were particularly forceful on that point as well. W. W. Keen, a Union medical cadet at Antietam and one of the leading American surgeons by the end of the century, wrote:

> We operated in old blood-stained and often pus-stained coats, the veterans of a hundred fights . . . We used undisinfected instruments from undisinfected plush-lined cases, and still worse, used marine sponges which had been used in prior pus cases and had been only washed in tap water. If a sponge or an instrument fell on the floor it was washed and squeezed in a basin of tap water and used as if it were clean. Our silk to tie blood vessels was undisinfected. . . . The silk with which we sewed up all wounds was undisinfected. If there was any difficulty in threading a needle we moistened it with . . . bacteria-laden saliva, and rolled it between bacteria-infected fingers. We dressed the wounds with clean but undisinfected sheets, shirts, tablecloths, or other old soft linen rescued from the family ragbag. We had no sterilized gauze dressing, no gauze sponges . . .[33]

Confederate surgeons did not have marine (natural) sponges, and generally used fresh material to clean or wash wounds, therefore avoiding the cross-contamination Keen describes. The other procedures, however, were the same.

instance, the numbers were quite close: after Chancellorsville, Medical Director Letterman reported 9,518 wounded, while the adjutant general recorded 9,759.[34]

In general, military histories list the figures for battle casualties as a combined total of the killed, the wounded, and the missing. Although such casualty figures are pertinent to a description of the total loss of military strength, the number of "total casualties" does not tell us the number of wounded needing treatment. The number missing after a battle, of course, is highly variable. But, when detailed figures are available for the numbers of killed and wounded, they almost always reveal a ratio of wounded to killed of 4:1 or 5:1, and sometimes even higher. Thus, about 80% of the total "killed and wounded" is actually the number of men who received medical care after a battle and were evacuated to a field hospital.

Surgeons were aware of the relative numbers of killed and wounded during battles. For example, immediately after the war, Dr. Joseph Jones, tried to reconstruct the records that were destroyed in the Richmond fire, and estimated the losses that occurred in the Peninsula campaign by "allowing one-fifth for the killed and three-fifths for the wounded," with the remainder being the number missing (i.e., presumably captured).[35]

SURGERY DURING THE CIVIL WAR

Civil War surgeons used the best information available at the time to help their patients. Drawing on the experiences of European military surgeons and learning from their own experiences, they saved as many lives as possible. These military physicians, with little or no surgical experience, were suddenly faced with caring for a huge number of wounded men under wartime conditions. Although hampered by lack of knowledge about bacteria, they continually demonstrated a willingness to rise to the tremendous challenges by adapting to changing circumstances and, when necessary, inventing techniques to solve new surgical problems.

Wounds of any kind received careful treatment since infections were nearly impossible to treat. The area around the wound was shaved, if necessary, and the wound was debrided, that is, cleansed of dead and badly injured tissue, grossly visible dirt, pieces of clothing, and other foreign material. When possible, wounds were irrigated to enhance the cleansing. Surgeons attempted to be as thorough as possible when debriding wounds, but a lack of time sometimes limited its effectiveness since only minimal amounts of anesthesia were used and speed was essential. Surgical debridement is still a fundamental technique in wound treatment, although the removal of damaged tissue is more thorough due to improved anesthesia, lighting, and equipment.

Because bullets were thought to have a deleterious effect on wound healing, Civil War surgeons made a determined effort to find and remove them. Most of the time, surgeons inserted a finger (usually dirty) into the wound and felt for the bullet. In his 1861 textbook, Chisholm described the standard procedure:

> [the finger is] the best probe for finding a bullet [since it is] an intelligent instrument, and, appreciating what it feels, it will not only discover the character of foreign bodies . . . but it will avoid making new lesions in the depth of the wound.[36]

Surgery textbooks on both sides of the Atlantic endorsed this principle until very late in the nineteenth century. (It was subsequently modified only in regard to covering the finger with a sterile glove.)

If the bullet was not found by palpation, a long, thin ceramic-tipped metal wand was inserted into the wound. This device was widely used in Europe and was named after its inventor, a French military surgeon named Nélaton. (See Box, p. 94.) Surgeons expected that when the probe made contact with the bullet, there would be a sound or the sensation of hitting something, or that the tip would at least have a scratch on the surface when it was removed. The Nélaton probe was, of course, never sterilized and it punctured and damaged tissue as it was inserted or moved. Thus, it did some harm, but also some good if it led to extraction of the bullet.

Since finding and extracting bullets during surgery was considered vital (and x-rays would not be discovered for three decades), the staff of the Army Medical Museum did extensive research on battlefield casualties. During autopsies they tried to distinguish between entrance and exit wounds and to reconstruct the soldier's position when he was hit, hoping to eventually predict a bullet's path. Foreign visitors were favorably impressed by their work during the war.

In the Northern armies, bleeding vessels were tied with silk or cotton thread. Confederate surgeons often used horsehair as suture material. The horsehair was boiled to make it more pliable, a procedure that, incidentally, also made it sterile (at least temporarily), although hands and equipment were never sterilized. Surgeons applied dressings with whatever cloth was available, sometimes reusing bandages from other cases. Patriotic women on both sides prepared bandages by scraping the lint off sheets and tablecloths to make material that could be used to pack and dress wounds. Usually, the wounds or the dressings to be applied to them were coated with cerate, a soothing ointment made of beeswax.

Hemorrhages, which often occurred a week or more after a wound was treated, were a serious problem. They were unpredictable and the bleeding was often arterial, requiring quick action to save the patient's life. Such secondary bleeding was usually blamed on a surgeon's imperfect ligation of the arteries or on the application of overly tight ligatures, causing tissue death. Recurrent, moderately severe bleeding was treated with local compresses saturated with a styptic or "astringent" preparation, such as persulfate of iron. Usually, a compress was secured over the bleeding tissues and the limb was rewrapped with a compression dressing applied from the distal end of the extremity and proceeding up toward the trunk. Hamilton's textbook of

The Nélaton Probe

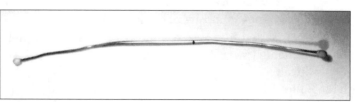

The Nélaton probe (this one about 8¼ inches long) was a flexible wand used to find and extract bullets. Physicians concluded that they had found the bullet if the porcelain tip struck a hard object after being inserted in the supposed track of the bullet or had pieces of lead on it when removed. Although the use of this probe was widely criticized the late 1800s, it was a standard procedure in both Europe and the United States at the time of the Civil War.

The probe was designed by a French military surgeon and its use was strongly recommended by leading authorities on military surgery. Among these was Dr. Frank Hastings Hamilton, a professor of surgery at Bellevue Medical College in New York and a volunteer medical inspector for the surgeon general. In 1863, Hamilton wrote, "In my opinion, this probe ought to be added to the instruments which the government supplies and as an outfit to army surgeons."[37]

Apparently it was, and "silver bullet-probes" remained in field kits as standard army issue at least until the beginning of the United States' participation in World War II. Brendan Phibbs recalled being shocked upon finding a Nélaton probe among the equipment he had been issued while training to become a WWII combat surgeon.[38]

(Photo courtesy of Gordon Dammann. From: Dammann G: *A Pictorial Encyclopedia of Civil War Medical Instruments and Equipment.* Missoula, MT: Pictorial Histories, 1983, p. 23.)

military surgery suggested that if secondary hemorrhage could not be arrested "by posture, by moderate pressure, by cold applications, or by the persulfate of iron, no time ought to be lost in securing [ligating] the bleeding vessel above the wound."[39]

If manpower permitted, dressings were changed daily in the initial period after the injury. In his textbook, Hamilton suggested that "for wound treatment, water dressings at a temperature agreeable to the patient are very

William Williams Keen (1837–1932)

Having begun his career as a medical cadet at Antietam, by the 1890s, W. W. Keen was probably the most celebrated neurosurgeon in the United States. When the Civil War began, he was a medical student in Philadelphia, and, after serving as a medical cadet, he returned to complete his medical education.

For the remainder of the war, Keen worked at Turner's Lane Hospital in Philadelphia, serving under Dr. S. Weir Mitchell. He collaborated with Dr. Mitchell and Dr. George R. Morehouse in clinical studies on soldiers with nerve injuries, and as co-author of their classic book, *Gunshot Wounds and Other Injuries of Nerves.*

After the war, Keen helped develop the field of neurosurgery. He was the first surgeon in the Americas to successfully remove a benign brain tumor in 1887. He perfected many neurosurgical techniques and introduced several new European techniques to the United States. He also published over fifty papers on neurosurgical topics, in addition to writing articles on other subjects and a classic textbook of surgery. In 1893, he assisted in a secret operation for oral cancer on President Grover Cleveland aboard a yacht. In 1921, he traveled to Campobello Island to consult on the illness, which turned out to be poliomyelitis, of former vice-presidential candidate (and future president) Franklin D. Roosevelt.[41]

generally conceded to be the best."[40] Commonly, cold water was used for irrigation with the reasonable expectation that the cold would decrease inflammation. However, since the inflammation was mainly due to infection, warm water, although difficult to obtain in the quantity needed, would have been more beneficial.

REFERENCES

1. *O.R.*, Series I, vol. XIX/1, p. 113.
2. Woodham Smith CBF: *Queen Victoria: From Her Birth to the Death of the Prince Consort.* New York: Knopf, 1972.
3. Cantlie N: *A History of the Army Medical Department.* vol. 2. Edinburgh: Churchill Livingston, 1973, p. 192.
4. Keen WW: Surgical reminiscences of the Civil War. *Transactions of the College of Physicians of Philadelphia.* 3rd Series. 1905;27:95-114.
5. Cantlie, *History of the Army Medical Department*, vol. 2, p. 238.
6. Detmold W. Quoted in: *Am Med Times.* 1862;5:334.
7. Chisolm JJ: *A Manual of Military Surgery for Use of the Surgeons in the Confederate Army.* 3rd ed. Columbia, SC: Evans & Cogswell, 1864, p. 427.

8. Report of Surg. J.J.B. Wright. *Medical and Surgical History*, Medical Section, vol. 1, Appendix XIV, p. 14.

9. *Medical and Surgical History*, Surgical Section, vol. 3, p. 866.

10. Mitchell SW: "On the medical department in the Civil War." Address to Physicians' Club of Chicago, February 25, 1913. *J Am Med Assoc*. 1914 May 19;62(19):1445-50

11. Report of Surg. A.B. Campbell. *Medical and Surgical History*, Medical Section, vol. 1, Appendix CXCVIII, p. 249.

12. Robertson JI: *Soldiers Blue and Gray*. Columbia: Univ. South Carolina Press, 1988, p. 162.

13. Tanner RG: *Stonewall in the Valley: Thomas J. "Stonewall" Jackson's Shenandoah Valley Campaign, Spring 1862*. Garden City, NY: Doubleday, 1976, p. 233.

14. Billings JS: Report on the treatment of diseases and injuries in the Army of the Potomac during 1864. *Medical and Surgical History*, Medical Section, vol. 1, Appendix CLIV, pp. 199-202.

15. Goodman L, Gilman A: *The Pharmacological Basis of Therapeutics*. 2nd ed. New York: Macmillan, 1956, p. 65.

16. Cunningham HH: *Doctors in Gray: The Confederate Medical Service*. Baton Rouge: Louisiana State Univ. Press, 1958, p. 227.

17. *Medical and Surgical History*, Surgical Section, vol. 3, p. 887.

18. Gillett MC: *The United States Army Medical Department, 1818–1865*. Washington, D.C.: Center of Military History, U.S. Army, 1987, p. 285.

19. Kemper GWH, Former Ass't. Surg. 17th Reg. Indiana vol. Quoted in personal communication with Nancy Eckerman, Librarian, Univ. of Indiana.

20. Rutkow IM: *Surgery: An Illustrated History*. St. Louis: Mosby-Yearbook, 1993, p. 433.

21. *Medical and Surgical History*, Surgical Section, vol. 1, pp. xxiv, xxv.

22. King JE: Shoulder straps for Aesculapius: the Atlanta campaign. *Mil Med*. 1954 April;114(4):296-306.

23. Cunningham, *Doctors in Gray*, p. 269.

24. Report of Surg. A. B. Crosby. *Medical and Surgical History*, Medical Section, vol. 1, p. 11.

25. Report of Asst. Surg. A. T. Calhoun. In: Brinton JH: *The Brinton Manuscripts*. NARA, RG94, Entry #628.

26. Baird ND: *David Wendell Yandell: Physician of Old Louisville*. Lexington, KY: Univ. Press of Kentucky, 1978, p. 48.

27. *Medical and Surgical History*, Surgical Section, vol. 3, p. 696.

28. Mitchell, "On the medical department in the Civil War," 1913.

29. *Medical and Surgical History*, Surgical Section, vol. 3, p. 696.

30. Ibid., p. 692.

31. Ibid., pp. 692, 694.

32. *Medical and Surgical History*, Medical Section, vol. 1, p. 148.

33. Keen WW: Military surgery in 1861 and 1918. *Ann Am Acad Pol Soc Sci*. 1918;80:14-15.

34. *Medical and Surgical History*, Surgical Section, vol. 1, p. xxxiv.

35. Jones J: Observations upon the losses of the Confederate armies from battle, wounds and diseases, during the American Civil War of 1861–65, with investigations upon the number and character of the diseases supervening from gun-shot wounds. *Richmond Louisville Med J*. 1870;9:644.

36. Chisolm, *Manual of Military Surgery*, 1st ed., 1861.

37. Hamilton FH: Nélaton's probe with a case. *Am Med Times*. 1863;7:288-89.

38. Phibbs B: *The Other Side of Time: A Combat Surgeon in World War II*. Boston: Little Brown, 1987, p. 55.

39. Hamilton FH: *A Treatise on Military Surgery and Hygiene*. New York: Balliere Bros, 1865. Reviewed in: *Am J Med Sci*. 1865 Jul;60:113-21. Art. XVII (by W.F.A).

40. *Am J Med Sci*. 1865 Jul;60:113-21. Art. XVII (by W.F.A).

41. Bingham WF: W. W. Keen and the dawn of American neurosurgery. *J Neurosurg*. 1986 May;64(5):705-12.

4

"Thank God for Jonathan Letterman": Field Surgeons, Field Hospitals, and Ambulances

I was the Chief Surgeon of the European Theater of Operations during World War II, a position similar to that of Letterman in the Army of the Potomac. At that time I often wondered whether, had I been confronted with the primitive system which Letterman fell heir to at the beginning of the Civil War, I could have developed as good an organization as he did. I doubt it. There was not a day during World War II that I did not thank God for Jonathan Letterman.

— Maj. Gen. Paul Hawley, in a letter to Rev. Dr. Henry Riddle
(date unknown)

S INCE THE DAWN OF TIME, armies have struggled to successfully treat their wounded. In the mid-nineteenth century, as weapons became deadlier and medical care for the wounds they inflicted improved, it was soon clear that an entirely new military medical system was necessary. Speed was of the essence and organization on an unprecedented scale was required. But a reorganization of military medicine and the efficient management of such an enormous system were gargantuan tasks. Only an extraordinary individual could accomplish it. Such a man emerged—Dr. Jonathan Letterman. He is one of the heroes of this book and the father of both the modern military and the emergency medical systems.

Dr. Jonathan Letterman

Medical Director of the Army of the Potomac, July 1862–January 1864.
(Courtesy of Library of Congress, Prints and Photographs Division, LC-00162.)

THE NEW AMBULANCE AND FIELD HOSPITAL SYSTEM

While the public ignored most of the innovations in the military medical system made during the Civil War, two improvements have received consistent praise. One was the organization and administration of a vast system of military hospitals, huge in number, size, and complexity (see Chapter 8, *Civil War Hospitals*). The other was the implementation of an ambulance service and a field hospital system that allowed the rapid evacuation of wounded soldiers.

Such a military medical transport system was unprecedented—no previous army had organized as efficient an ambulance service or delivered better medical care. For example, it took ten days to gather and treat the wounded after the Battle of Waterloo in 1815. In contrast, the day after the Battle of Gettysburg ended, "not one wounded man of the great number who had fallen was left on the ground."[1]

After the Civil War, European armies quickly copied the "American system." The "American ambulance," a field hospital with its own "flying ambulances" to retrieve wounded French soldiers, was set up in Paris during the Franco-Prussian War. This hospital, an imitation of a Civil War field hospital run by an American veteran, had the best reputation and survival statistics of any hospital in the Franco-Prussian War. It also received the most honors of any medical unit in that war.[2-4]

INITIAL WOUND TREATMENT

While soldiers often died quickly if struck by artillery fire, those struck by bullets usually lived a while, often in great pain. This reality was at odds with most media depictions of battlefields during the Civil War. Many of the injured suffered from severe thirst, caused by blood loss and summer heat, and were well aware that they were mortally wounded. If they were not quickly evacuated from the battlefield, they would be exposed to the elements, including rain and cold nights; on at least one occasion, men were exposed to a fire spreading from the surrounding countryside.

Under the system of triage instituted during the Civil War, men thought to have mortal wounds were made as comfortable as possible and either left to die (and listed officially as "killed in battle") or evacuated last. Because of the massive number of wounded men, surgeons and the ambulance personnel concentrated on those they thought could be saved. Most penetrating abdominal, chest, and head wounds were beyond the skills of that era's surgeons; they were, therefore, considered "mortal wounds," a self-fulfilling prophesy. Soldiers thought to have the best chance of survival were treated at field dressing stations and then were the first ones evacuated by ambulance to a field hospital further in the rear. (See Figure 4.1.) The "mortally" wounded, if still alive, were evacuated when conditions permitted. This triage system is essentially the same method still employed in war and disaster situations when there are limited medical resources.

Injured soldiers were moved from the battle area to the regimental dressing station as soon as the fighting lessened. C. B. Johnson, a hospital steward (the Civil War equivalent of today's medical corpsman), noted:

> [The] emergency case or hospital knapsack was always taken with the regiment when the firing line was about to be approached, and where the First Assistant Surgeon was in charge and was ready to render first aid to any who might be wounded.[5]

A field dressing station usually was set up just behind the lines in an area reasonably sheltered from the enemy's direct small-arms fire, although

Figure 4.1: Scene of a field hospital in late 1862 at the Battle of Antietam, after Letterman's ambulance service was instituted. Note the line of wagon ambulances in the background, the man with an amputated leg being put into an ambulance for evacuation, and others waiting for treatment while the surgeons (at left) work outdoors. *(HW)*

it almost always was still within artillery range. Regimental assistant surgeons, often aided by a hospital steward manned these stations. According to Johnson: "Among the surgical supplies were chloroform, ether, brandy, aromatic spirits of ammonia, bandages, adhesive plaster, needles, silk thread for ligatures, etc. . . . Instruments were washed in water and wiped dry to keep them from rusting."[6]

Each regiment generally had a surgeon and an assistant surgeon. The regimental surgeon often worked alone at the field hospital. His assistant usually worked in an aid station closer to the battlefield, administering emergency care. Such care included stopping bleeding, applying splints and some type of wound dressing, giving opiates, and making triage decisions about who would be the first to be carried back to a field hospital. At the field hospital, which was set up in an available building or in tents, supervising surgeons made treatment decisions and operating surgeons performed any operations deemed necessary. (See Chapter 3, *Civil War Surgery*.)

A surgeon's first goal was to stop the bleeding by applying direct pressure or a tourniquet. (See Figure 4.2.) He then covered the wound with a bandage, administered an opiate (usually morphine) to decrease the pain, and provided drinking water. Powdered morphine was administered freely, "doled out with a pocket knife [sprinkled directly into the wound] without worrying about superfluous exactitude in doling out the blessed relief that morphine brings to men in pain."[7] A swallow of whiskey was often provided as well. In a letter to his mother, a regimental assistant surgeon described his function at a field aid station: "We merely applied temporary dressings, arresting hemorrhages, etc., saw them put into ambulances and sent to the rear." He added that most of the

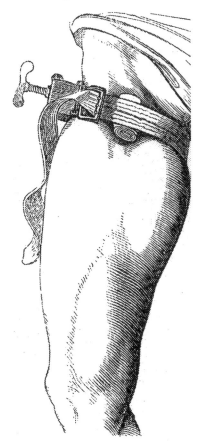

Figure 4.2: Tourniquet applied to the femoral artery. (*SS*, p. 647.)

soldiers "don't make as much fuss at having a leg or arm amputated as I have seen in civil life at the drawing of a tooth."[8]

Besides bandaging wounds at the field dressing station, surgeons used splints to immobilize fractures whenever possible. A variety of new types of splints were developed during the war, and splinting became increasingly more effective. Adhesive and plaster casts were used to some extent, but they generally took too long to apply. The other drawback was that, in some instances, they became too tight after the injured part swelled, cutting off circulation to the extremity. In 1863, Surgeon John T. Hodgen devised a splint that immobilized a fractured extremity yet permitted access for dressing changes; it was considered a major advance and was used often. Others fashioned similar splints (see Figure 4.3).

After being treated at the field dressing stations, sick or wounded men needing more extensive or prolonged care were transferred to larger better-equipped hospitals in the rear. That is where Letterman's new ambulance service demonstrated its value.

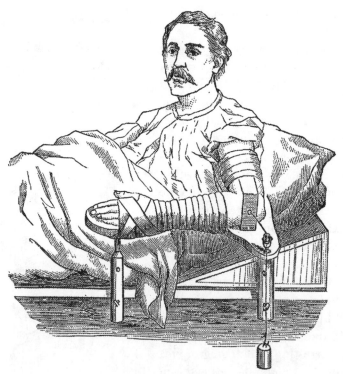

Figure 4.3: Drawing showing the use of a complex splint including weights, known as Lossen's splint, to immobilize the bone following fracture of the upper arm (humerus). (*Medical and Surgical History*, Surgical Section, vol. 2, p. 825.)

AMBULANCES

Until 1859, the U.S. Army had no vehicles specifically designed as ambulances. (See Figures 4.4 and 4.5.) When the war began, some two-wheeled ambulances, pulled by one or two horses or mules, were being used. They could hold three men at most, and so were too small. They were also poorly constructed and broke down quickly on the muddy rutted roads of the era. Called "gutbusters" by the soldiers, these ambulances gave harsh jarring rides and frequently overturned, dumping occupants onto the ground and aggravating their injuries.[9,10]

The excruciating ambulance rides were due in large part to the dismal U.S. road system, particularly in the South. Some main "turnpikes" had a macadam surface made up of compacted layers of broken stone, which was considered good for wagons but was bad for shoes. Most other roads were rough dirt thoroughfares that were rutted and almost impassable in wet weather. In an attempt to make the roads passable, logs of varying diameters were cut and spread cross-wise to create a wooden road surface. This process, called "corduroying," decreased the likelihood that wagons would become mired in mud, but the resulting ride was jolting, especially for the ill and injured. One veteran described his ambulance ride over a corduroyed road after being wounded at Chancellorsville:

> The ambulance rocked and rolled and it was with difficulty we could keep our seats, the men who had to lie down were thrown against each other and the sides of the wagon. As the wheels advanced they would strike a large log, go over it, and then fall to the next log perhaps a foot or more below. It was hard to control the horses, they would go over the large ones with a jump and that meant torture. One can hardly imagine the suffering of those who had broken bones, or who had their arms or legs amputated, with the stumps not yet healed.[11]

Ambulances were often in short supply. Most ambulances were controlled by the Quartermaster Department of each army corps. The commissary officers had their own priorities, so ambulances could be commandeered for a variety of purposes, including the transport of officers' baggage, and thus were frequently unavailable to transport the wounded or sick.

When Jonathan Letterman took over as medical director from Charles S. Tripler, the major battles on the peninsula had just ended. Fully one-quarter of the Army of the Potomac—20,000 sick and wounded—were in hospitals near Harrison's Landing, the army's base on the James River, where the fleet's guns helped to protect them. Letterman immediately convinced

Figure 4.4: An army supply wagon fitted out as an ambulance. It could be loaded from the front or rear, and carried six patients sitting and six more lying ("two of which, if necessary, suspended on fracture beds") plus a water keg and all the equipment, provisions, and bandages necessary. (*Medical and Surgical History*, Surgical Section, vol. 3, p. 956.]

Figure 4.5: A Confederate field ambulance wagon. (Drawing by Prof. J. J. Chisholm. *Medical and Surgical History*, Surgical Section, vol. 3, p. 956.)

General McClellan to form an ambulance corps. McClellan, an able administrator even if a poor field commander, ordered the implementation of Letterman's suggestions in the Army of the Potomac on August 2, 1862. His order directed that the new ambulance corps be placed under the Medical Department; that it have its own animals, vehicles, and personnel; and that the Corps be used for sick and wounded men and "nothing else."[12,13] (McClellan's order can be found in Appendix D.)

The order also required that trained personnel be designated as stretcher-bearers and teamsters. Before this, wounded soldiers had been a major liability during battle. One surgeon recorded that, at first, regimental band members transported the most severely wounded men, until soon there were no band members left.[14] Normally, a wounded man's comrades would abandon their positions in the battle line to help carry him to the field aid station, thus depleting the firing line by two to four additional soldiers per casualty. Moreover, because of the time spent finding the field station, these men rarely returned to the action. They used litters improvised from available materials, including poles through the sleeves of coats, gates removed from fences, window shutters, doors, ladders, blankets lashed to poles, and four-armed "chair seats." Occasionally, in rough country, men used mule litters called "cacolets," chair-like contrivances strapped to the side of a mule's back. The army's fighting power was significantly strengthened when specific men were designated as stretcher-bearers and there were ambulances and dependable drivers stationed nearby, thus enabling the regular troops to continue fighting.

Thanks to McClellan's decision to implement Letterman's system, the Army of the Potomac developed an effective ambulance service well before the Western Federal armies. Surgeon General Hammond proposed adopting this new ambulance system for the entire Federal army, and, in a letter to Secretary of War Stanton on September 7, 1862, he lamented "the scarcity of ambulances, the want of organization, the drunkenness and incompetency of the drivers, [and] the total absence of ambulance attendants."[15] Although both General-in-Chief Halleck and Secretary of War Stanton rejected Hammond's request, General Grant was wise enough to implement a similar system on March 30, 1863, ignoring the War Department's opposition.[16]

On March 11, 1864, Congress finally made the Medical Corps' Ambulance Service official army policy. By then, however, most of the Union army had already adopted it. The new law based the number of ambulances on a regiment's size: a regiment with 500 or more men would have three ambulances, while one with fewer than 200 men would have only one. Extra ambulances and wagons were to accompany each Corp's headquarters. Despite this lofty proposal, shortages of ambulances persisted.

The Confederate ambulance system was greatly improved during the war largely due to the suggestions of Dr. Hunter Holmes McGuire, who had been the medical director of Thomas J. (Stonewall) Jackson's corps.[17] The Confederates adopted a system resembling that of the Union armies. Although ambulances technically remained under the Quartermaster's control, they were actually controlled by the medical directors and chief surgeons.[18] The Confederacy, constantly in need of all medical equipment, used captured Union ambulances, simply altering the lettering: the "U" was converted to a "C", leaving the "S" and "A" "still on duty."[19]

Union army boards met repeatedly to improve ambulance design during the course of the war and, eventually, four-wheeled vehicles with springs became the norm.[20] Although the ride was never pleasant and medical care was negligible during transport, the new evacuation system helped minimize the amount of time wounded soldiers spent in the ambulance wagons. A key component of this new system was the establishment of field hospitals to which men could be quickly taken by trained personnel and given immediate care—enabling the ambulances to quickly return to the field for new patients.

FIELD HOSPITALS

At the beginning of the war, regimental hospitals were established in campsites and near battlefields, with poor communication and coordination between them and the larger general hospitals. For example, during this period, patients sent from camps around Washington often were unable to find a hospital in the city that would take them.[21] In early engagements, stretcher-bearers had to search for the appropriate field hospital, leading to confusion and delayed treatment. Wounded men were sometimes turned away from regimental field hospitals if they were from the wrong regiment and the staff was overwhelmed with their own casualties.

The development of a system of evacuation and care based on improved, enlarged field hospitals was one of Jonathan Letterman's major contributions. When he became the Army of the Potomac's medical director, he reorganized the field medical service, primarily on a divisional basis. By late 1862, regimental hospitals were abolished and the practice of turning away men from another unit ceased.

Under Letterman's direction, the better-staffed division hospital became the primary field unit. Each typically had a surgeon-in-chief, three operating surgeons, nine assistant surgeons, a medical officer who was responsible for food and shelter, and numerous assigned enlisted soldiers who functioned as nurses. The surgeon-in-chief was one of the most experienced surgeons and was usually a member of the operating team.[22] There were also some brigade-level hospitals, but most of the surgery on wounded soldiers was performed in division hospitals. Hospital tents and medical supplies for field hospitals were issued on a brigade and divisional basis. This availability of facilities and the organization of surgical care for the wounded remained a standard for both European and American armies through World War II. (For information on Civil War army organization, see Appendix B.)

A Regimental Surgeon Describes a Civil War Field Hospital

In 1902, Maj. Albert G. Hart included this description in his monograph on Civil War surgeons and hospitals:

> When a battle was expected, the general location of the hospital was made by the military department or by the corps surgeons. It was intended to be in the rear of the ground on which the division was expected to fight, and beyond the enemy's artillery fire, one and a half or two miles in the rear of our line of battle; if possible a good supply of water must be at hand. All the tents were set up, dressings, instruments, and tables for dressing and operating prepared, and everything made ready for our work.

> Three assistant surgeons and one surgeon were detailed to follow each brigade. They established a temporary depôt just out of reach of the enemy's musketry fire. Here the ambulances stopped. The detailed nurses with stretchers followed immediately behind the line of battle. The wounded men, if able to walk, with the permission of their company officers hurried back to the temporary depôt. Those unable to walk were carried by the nurses on the stretchers. No soldier was permitted to leave the ranks to assist the wounded, unless to carry the dead and wounded back a few yards. Temporary dressings were applied. Serious operations only were performed in extreme cases at the temporary depôt. Those unable to walk were taken in ambulances to the division hospital. There the serious work began, and was continued until the best thing possible in our surroundings was carried out for every man.[23]

Mobile field hospitals, which could go "wherever the needs of battle demanded and wheeled vehicles could penetrate," were promptly adopted by all Civil War armies, and by other countries. They evolved into the mobile hospitals employed during fast-moving military campaigns, such as the dash across France by Gen. George Patton's Third Army and the Mobile Army Surgical Hospitals (M.A.S.H.) units of the Korean War.

Wounded men who survived long enough to arrive at the field hospital received treatment from experienced surgeons who could perform more extensive procedures, such as amputations. Yet the hospitals' design would now be considered rustic. Whenever possible, these hospitals were located near streams to provide running water. Operating tables were often the "requisitioned" front door from a nearby house that had been laid over barrels. These operating theaters were usually outdoors, since, over the course of the war, physicians became convinced that surgery done in the open air led to fewer wound infections.

Adequate lighting was always a problem, and outdoor operating rooms also provided the best light—day or night. The better lighting allowed surgeons to clean wounds more thoroughly, as it was easier to find and remove bullets and other foreign material. Since fighting usually continued until dark, the wounded were often brought in at night; many operations were performed with only candles and smoky coal-gas lanterns to illuminate the operative field. One surgeon remembered his experiences operating "in total darkness, with two or three dim lanterns, in a drizzling rain and six inches of Virginia mud." Another, while at Gettysburg, recalled that "my only light was a square block of wood with five auger holes, in each of which was placed a candle."[24] Clara Barton described one surgeon's despair after the Battle of Antietam that he still had "at least one thousand wounded . . . and that two inches of candle is all the light I have or can get."[25] Using such light sources outside, however, decreased the haze that the lanterns created and provided a measure of safety when using anesthetics.

MEDICAL TRANSPORTATION SYSTEMS

Once ill and injured soldiers had arrived at field hospitals near the battlefield, a way had to be found to get them safely and efficiently to the appropriate larger, more distant hospitals that could care for their ills. For this, Letterman devised a complex and innovative medical transportation system that employed both trains and ships.

HOSPITAL TRAINS

Before the war, no thought had been given to using trains as ambulances. However, during the war, both sides relied on the recently developed railroad system to move men and material, including their sick and wounded soldiers, whenever possible.

Evacuation by trains caused extreme suffering early in the conflict because ordinary boxcars, some with straw thrown on the floor, served as the railcar ambulances. (See Figure 4.6.) According to a contemporary source, the sick and wounded from the Peninsula campaign were placed in

> common burden cars, where, like so many sheep, jarred and jolted by every movement, without any of the comforts and conveniences which their condition demanded, and without proper food, clothing, or attention, they often passed hours and even days in indescribable agony. There was scarcely a practical abuse in the whole administration of the Medical service which called more loudly for remedy.[26]

Later in the war, hospital cars were specifically designed for use in ambulance trains.[27] The Sanitary Commission's official history describes these improvements:

> A very slight description of these hospital cars will give some idea of the increased comfort provided for the patients conveyed in them. The ordinary field and hospital litter or stretcher was used in loading, unloading, and carrying the patients. These simple litter-beds, with pillows, mattresses, and comforts attached, were then ingeniously and securely swung, in tiers three high, and end to end upon light stanchions, and there suspended by stout tugs of India rubber, which gave sufficient elasticity to obviate all jar to the bed and its patient. Thirty of these beds were thus swung along the side of each Hospital car. A number of invalid chairs and a broad couch filled the remainder of the available space. A pantry furnished with medicines, utensils, beverages, and substantial food, ready for serving to the patients hot or cold, made up the sum of creature comforts, while nurses, abundantly provided with towels, socks, blankets, sponges, etc., kept every man clean and warm, however long the trip or stormy the weather. All the usual appliances and skill of a well-regulated Hospital were at hand.[28]

They also described the railroad evacuation system's increased efficiency:

> The Hospital train from Atlanta to Louisville made the journey of more than five hundred miles according to an established timetable, and reached its destination with the exactness and speed of trains on well-maintained rail roads in time of peace.[29]

Figure 4.6: Interior of an improvised hospital car with upright stanchions from the floor to the roof, to which up to three litters could be securely lashed. One of several designs for railroad cars used as ambulances. The stanchions in this car prevented the feeling of insecurity that patients had in some other designs. (*HW*)

In addition to the hospital cars, these trains included cars for cooking and dining and for use as sleeping quarters for medical staff assigned to accompany the wounded. The trains were clearly identified by a bright red smokestack, engine, and tender and by the markings "U.S. HOSPITAL TRAIN" in enormous red letters,[30] and they carried three red lanterns at night. There is no record that enemy forces ever molested any hospital train.[31]

Before the end of the war, the evacuation of wounded was as well organized and efficient as the military situation permitted. With medical staff assigned to ambulance trains, a minimum number of regimental medical officers had to be withdrawn from the battlefield to provide continued care. Also, the ability to move wounded and sick men quickly from the field of action to nearby general hospitals decreased the need to transport tents and equipment for field hospitals. Although many wounded still had to endure the traumatic ride in an army wagon for short distances, increasing numbers made the bulk of their journey in the relative comfort of well-staffed and well-equipped hospital trains or boats. If a hospital stay was necessary en route toward their home region, it was likely to be in an efficiently organized, well-staffed, and well-supplied facility.

The Confederate Medical Department also used trains whenever possible, although the Southern railroad lines were much less developed than those in the North. They did not build special ambulance cars for their trains; the dearth of rolling stock and manufacturing facilities precluded it. Boxcars on trains brought supplies to the troops and returned carrying wounded and sick soldiers, usually with some straw thrown on the floor, water, food, and, when possible, some nursing and medical personnel to accompany them.[32]

The railroads were most useful to the Confederates in Virginia, where good service existed from Manassas Junction south to Gordonsville, and then on to Richmond. There was good east-west service from Richmond across the mountains to the Shenandoah Valley. From Staunton, in the Valley, there was service to Tennessee at Knoxville and then on to Chattanooga, but that segment was often cut and service was irregular. After the battles fought in

An "American-Style" Ambulance Train

The use of American ambulance trains as models for European armies in later years was described at a meeting of the Aid Society in Berlin in 1870. German pathologist Rudolph Virchow gave a graphic account of his journey as commander of the first "sanitary train" organized for the removal of sick and wounded from Franco-Prussian War battlefields. Supplied with surgeons, attendants, beds, and "food, medicines, etc.," Virchow said that "the carriages were fitted up on the plan adopted in the American War," but had only twelve beds per car.

Virchow had many problems while commanding the German train. Originally fitted for 120 men, the train actually carried 136, plus 14 officers' servants and 2 officers' wives. And, although it was a military train, civilian travelers jumped aboard at every stop because no other trains were running. Worst of all, the latrines were left behind. He noted, however, that this train, despite the problems, was much better than prior transportation methods when even severely wounded soldiers were brought to Berlin in ordinary passenger carriages without surgeons or, usually, nurses.[33]

northern Virginia, such as First and Second Manassas, the wounded were transported quickly by rail to Gordonsville and then to hospitals in Richmond or Charlottesville. After Antietam and Gettysburg, wounded were taken by ambulance to Winchester and then down the Valley Turnpike (which had a macadam surface) to Staunton; once there, they could be sent south to Lynchburg or east to Charlottesville, Gordonsville, and Richmond. Depot hospitals, known as "receiving and forwarding hospitals," were set up at key points, such as Gordonsville and Staunton, to provide care en route and to serve as distribution centers.

HOSPITAL SHIPS

In addition to a more extensive railway system, Union forces had the advantage of naval superiority and many waterways on which to move supplies and troops. In the east, the Potomac and the other rivers which fed into the Chesapeake were particularly serviceable, as were the Atlantic coastline and the Gulf of Mexico. In the west, the Mississippi and its tributaries, specifically the Ohio and Tennessee Rivers, were equally valuable. The Commissary Department used these waterways to transport supplies to the battle areas, and the Medical Department made similar use of them to transport sick and wounded soldiers back to depot hospitals.

No specially designed or fitted hospital ships were available when the fighting began, so soldiers were transported on ordinary cargo and passenger ships, particularly during Grant's campaign in Tennessee early in 1862 and during the Peninsula campaign in Virginia in the spring of 1862.

During the Peninsula campaign, the Sanitary Commission obtained ships and staffed them for use as floating hospitals. (See Figure 4.7.) Many wealthy "society women" volunteered to serve aboard the Sanitary Commission's ships, nursing, feeding, cleaning, and tending to the sick and wounded in wholly unprecedented ways, since up to that time few women gave nursing care outside their homes. The letters these women wrote to newspapers during the Peninsula campaign, as well as their diaries and autobiographies, provided graphic descriptions of these soldiers' suffering and the breakdowns in the army's arrangements to care for them. They contributed to the public's lasting image of Civil War medical care.

Although the lack of proper facilities on board and the absence of military discipline and organization led to considerable chaos on these boats, the value of hospital ships was obvious. The Sanitary Commission later donated their hospital boats to the army, which staffed and ran them for the rest of the war. However, these ships were not generally placed under the control of the Medical Department until early in 1865.[34] The army also

Figure 4.7: Drawing of the chaotic scene during the Peninsula campaign of April–July 1862, showing an evacuation point at Fort Monroe on the Chesapeake. Note the hospital boats provided by the Sanitary Commission and the female nurses in the foreground. Sick and wounded men lie on railroad flatcars covered with canvas awnings. A "contraband" is moving supplies with a hand-truck. (*HW*)

The Hospital Boat Red Rover

A ward on the hospital boat *Red Rover*. (*HW*)

The *Red Rover* was a captured Confederate steamer refitted for service as a hospital boat at St. Louis and put into service at Cairo, Illinois, on June 12, 1862. Nursing was arranged by Sister Angela, the Mother Superior of the Sisters of the Holy Cross.

The captain, George D. Wise, described the steamer in a letter to his superior, Commodore A. H. Foote:

> I wish that you could see our hospital boat, the *Red Rover*, with all her comforts for the sick and disabled seamen. She is decided to be the most complete thing of the kind that ever floated, and is every way a decided success. The Western Sanitary Association gave us, in cost of articles, $3,500. The ice box of the steamer holds 800 tons. She has bathrooms, laundry, elevator for the sick from the lower to the upper deck, amputating room, nine different water-closets, gauze blinds to the windows to keep the cinders and smoke from annoying the sick, two separate kitchens for sick and well, a regular corps of nurses, and two water-closets on every deck.[35,36]

purchased other boats and refitted them as true hospital ships. Many of these became famous during the war for the improvements they brought in the evacuation and care of the wounded.

Many of the smaller ships used to transport wounded soldiers did not have any doctors on board. Larger boats usually had several doctors and many nurses. Assistant Surgeon W. D. Turner served aboard the U.S. hospital steamer *Memphis* during the sieges of Forts Henry and Donelson and the Battle of Shiloh. According to his report, the *Memphis* made fourteen trips and carried a total of 7,221 sick and wounded men to general hospitals; only 125 of these men died.[37] During those voyages, Turner performed 78 operations, mostly amputations. The steamers *Hiawatha, J.J. Roe, War Eagle,* and *Crescent City* were also fitted out for the transport of wounded and provided similar service. Other hospital ships, including the *D.A. January,* the *Imperial,* and the *Empress,* took the ailing soldiers to Louisville, Cincinnati, Evansville, and St. Louis, as well as to Mound City and Cairo in Illinois. The *Empress* made six trips, transporting 3,012 sick and wounded, during which 10 men died of wounds and 45 of disease.[38]

Ships like the *D.A. January* were specially equipped as floating hospitals, with surgeons, nurses, and abundant supplies. Major surgical procedures could be performed on board. After the war, the Medical Department was so proud of the *January* that it made an elaborate model, detailing the wards, operating areas, and other facilities. The model was exhibited at the Centennial Exposition in Philadelphia in 1876 and today is in the National Museum of Health and Medicine in Washington, D.C.

Some western governors outfitted hospital ships and tried to limit their use to soldiers from their state, causing a great deal of confusion when wounded were carried aboard. An order was given prohibiting such distinctions and, thereafter, any wounded man, even Confederates, could be cared for on any ship.[39]

The Confederates also had hospital ships similar to the Union's vessels. Not much is known about the Confederate boats, however, because most of their records were destroyed. The *CSS Nashville,* shown in Figure 4.8, was used to transport men after the fall of Vicksburg.

THE BIG PICTURE: EVOLUTION OF THE UNION AMBULANCE AND FIELD MEDICAL SYSTEMS

During the course of the war, both sides developed ambulance and field hospital systems of unprecedented effectiveness. The following synopsis

Figure 4.8: The Confederate hospital ship *CSS Nashville* evacuating wounded after the fall of Vicksburg in July 1863. Note the men carrying a patient on a stretcher up the improvised gangplank. (Courtesy of USAMHI.)

illustrates the progressive improvements in the evacuation and care of the wounded during the war, and the return of chaos in mid-1864 when the system was overwhelmed by casualties and unplanned army movements during the major battles in Virginia. (A similar chronology of the Western campaigns would also illustrate these points.)

FIRST BULL RUN (JULY 21, 1861)

Believing that the war would last less than ninety days, the army did not upgrade its Medical Corps before the first battles. At First Bull Run (Manassas), the provisions for the care and evacuation of the wounded were identical to those in the pre-war army. Civilian wagoners provided the only ambulance service, but as soon as danger appeared, they hastened home, leaving the wounded to make the thirty-mile journey back to Washington on their own. Days later, an improvised train of civilian two-wheeled ambulances, hacks, and omnibuses retrieved several hundred wounded soldiers who were still on the battlefield or en route to Washington.

The wagons deposited their cargo in a variety of structures near the bridges over the Potomac. Among these quickly designated "hospitals" were warehouses, churches, dilapidated schools, and several government buildings. At the U.S. Patent Office, where Clara Barton worked as a clerk, patients were taken to the second floor and placed on tables "knocked together from pieces of scaffolding," surrounded by cabinets containing models of inventions.[40,41]

PENINSULA CAMPAIGN (MARCH–JULY 1862)

After First Bull Run, the army realized that the war would last more than a few months and began to prepare for more casualties. Yet, when the largest Union army, the Army of the Potomac, invaded the York-James Peninsula in the spring of 1862, the sick and wounded overwhelmed their medical facilities. Actually, disease, especially typhoid fever and dysentery, killed more men than at any other time during the war. The first huge battles were fought in the east, in particular during the Seven Days' fighting (June 25 to July 1, 1862).

Although Medical Director Charles Tripler had suggested reorganizing the Army of the Potomac's ambulance service in the fall of 1861, the plan had not been implemented. As a result, the ambulance and field hospital systems proved to be woefully inadequate during this campaign. Tripler had proposed training a corps of ambulance attendants and litter bearers and reserving a reasonable number of ambulances for each regiment that could not be commandeered for other purposes. That plan was similar in most details to the one Dr. Jonathan Letterman implemented after he succeeded Tripler.

Trying to make do with what was available, Tripler planned to send the wounded back to Washington if the army fought within a 72-hours' ride of the city. However, the general hospitals available for the Army of the Potomac were "a few old hotels or other similar buildings . . . in the cities of Alexandria, Washington, Georgetown, and a small portion of the Naval Academy building at Annapolis."[42] Sensing that this would be inadequate, Tripler recommended that the surgeon general arrange for hospital beds for casualties in Baltimore, Philadelphia, and New York as well, and he personally inspected the potential sites. Eventually, such hospitals were established and were used extensively during the entire war.

After several smaller battles lower on the peninsula, including those at Yorktown and Williamsburg, the large Battle of Fair Oaks (Battle of Seven Pines) took place near Richmond on May 31 and June 1, 1862. (See Figure 4.9.) It took until June 7 to evacuate, primarily by rail, the more than 3,000 wounded Union soldiers to port facilities and the waiting hospital ships. Some died during transport. Sanitary Commission observers described wounded men as being "packed like freight into boxcars. . . . When the sufferers reached the army's base on the James River, at a locale called White House, the stench of rotting flesh was rising on the summer air."[43] Newspaper reports of the confusion and poor medical care generated a public outcry. The Surgeon General's Office, which had been cool to the Sanitary Commission, now quickly accepted their offers of assistance.

The Sanitary Commission obtained and hastily staffed four boats to transport the wounded, but they lacked provisions, equipment, and organization. Nevertheless, the wounded were immediately brought aboard and deposited haphazardly, "even on gangways and stairs. Shattered and shrieking wounded were carried aboard by 'contrabands' banging the stretchers against pillars and posts and walking on men on the decks, dumping the wounded anywhere."[44,45]

The official report of the Sanitary Commission documented the disciplinary problems that hampered efforts to care for the sick and wounded during the Peninsula Campaign:

> In practice, [the Sanitary Commission] was responsible for the care of all those who were hurried, without the slightest attention to their first wants, from "the front" to the base on the river. By an agreement between the Commission and the Medical Director, certain boats were to be reserved

Figure 4.9: A field hospital shown as the wounded gathered the day after the Battle of Savage Station on June 29, 1862. A surgeon is examining the leg of a wounded man in the foreground. (James F. Gibson, photographer. Courtesy of Library of Congress, Prints and Photographs Division, LC-B811-0491.)

for a certain description of cases only, and their points of destination were to be regulated by the nature of the disability of the patients thus selected. All these wise provisions were wholly neglected in practice. Owing to the absence of some proper representative of the Medical authorities, no such selection of patients was made, and day after day, a vast crowd of sufferers, differing in every respect, except in a desire to escape from the horrors they had endured, were forced upon the boats in charge of the Commission.

By virtue of the same agreement, these boats were to have been placed under military discipline. But this provision also was neglected, and in addition to their proper duties in the care of the sick, the Agents were obliged to manage and pacify disorderly and insubordinate crews.[46]

Dr. Charles Tripler resigned as the medical director of the Army of the Potomac near the close of this campaign. Despite his many good observations and actions, the job he was asked to do seemed to have totally overwhelmed him. The new surgeon general, William Hammond, obtained General McClellan's approval to appoint Dr. Jonathan Letterman as the Army of the Potomac's new medical director.

Observations by U.S. Sanitary Commission Members during the Peninsula Campaign

Stillé included these comments from Sanitary Commission observers in his book:

Some [wounded] were just as they had been left by the fortune of war (four days before); their wounds, as yet, undressed, smeared with filth and blood, and all their wants unsupplied. Others had had their wounds dressed one, two, or three days before. Others, still, were under the surgeon's hands, receiving such care as could be given them by men overburdened by the number of their patients, worn out by excessive and long-continued labor, without an article of clothing to give to any for a change, or an extra blanket, without bands or dressings, . . . with few medicines and no stimulants, and nothing but corn meal gruel, hard bread, and bacon, to dispense as food. . . .

Accordingly the Daniel Webster, a vessel capable of transporting with proper arrangements two hundred and fifty patients was assigned . . . and a volunteer force, composed of . . . a large number of male nurses, and a few ladies accompanied it to York River. . . . The steamer arrived in the river during the siege of Yorktown. The Commission had already dispatched thither in anticipation of events, a large amount of supplies . . .

A glance at the condition of things on their arrival revealed . . . the same deplorable deficiency in adequate preparation for the reception of the sick and wounded, which had so often before been observed. The first sick men whom they saw, were found crowded in a number of log huts, which had been previously used by the rebels as barracks. The place was a most pestilential one, surrounded by swamps, and there, the unfortunate soldiers who had been attacked by sickness, were dying by scores of fever, still clothed in their uniforms and wearing their caps.[47]

When Letterman arrived in early July, 20,000 sick and wounded men (one-quarter of the Army of the Potomac) were in hospitals at the Army's James River base. Letterman convinced General McClellan to institute an Ambulance Corps, improving the situation and forever changing military medicine.

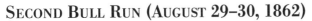

SECOND BULL RUN (AUGUST 29–30, 1862)

While McClellan's Army of the Potomac was evacuating the peninsula, the Battle of Second Bull Run occurred between Gen. John Pope's newly formed Army of Virginia and Gen. Robert E. Lee's Army of Northern Virginia. (Pope became famous for his dispatches to Washington labeled "From Headquarters in the Saddle," which finally led to a comment, attributed to President Lincoln, that "his headquarters were where his hindquarters should be.")

Only a portion of the Army of the Potomac arrived in time to join the battle, and most of McClellan's medical supplies and equipment were still en route. Pope's army had not yet adopted Letterman's newly designed ambulance service, and had only a fraction of the necessary ambulances. As a result, when Robert E. Lee and Stonewall Jackson outmaneuvered and outfought Pope, leaving at least 4,400 Union soldiers in need of hospital care, the new medical evacuation system was available only to those wounded from McClellan's army.

The chaotic attempts to treat and evacuate the wounded after Second Bull Run rivaled those of First Bull Run for ineptitude, disorder, and the resultant suffering. Upon hearing distressing reports, Surgeon General Hammond sent a medical inspector, Dr. Richard H. Coolidge, to the Manassas area. When Coolidge arrived at the main army base at Centreville, he immediately arranged for ambulances to transport the wounded to the railroad depot at Fairfax Station, Virginia. From there, they could be moved by train to Washington, but the trip to the railroad itself was arduous and painful. One wagon train contained nearly fifty double-horse ambulances heavily loaded with helpless suffering men. A similar train, operating independently of Coolidge, kept going all night to reach Washington, generating reports of "many wounded men on the road moving toward Washington."[48]

Because Pope's medical staff was overwhelmed, the War Department called for civilian volunteers. On August 30, a train with physicians and nurses left Washington. After thirteen hours, they arrived at Fairfax Station, where, typical of the total fiasco that plagued the situation, they were told they would have to walk the remaining fifteen miles to the area where wounded had been amassed. Those who started walking were stopped by guards; after telegraphing Washington, they were ordered back to the capital. Another group of volunteers headed out in a long wagon train with civilian teamsters and wagon masters, many of whom had been drinking freely beforehand. The group lost its way and ended up in Alexandria; they also returned to the capital without treating any wounded.[49]

Clara Barton, one volunteer who did reach the battlefield, provided invaluable aid in caring for the wounded, and her diaries are among the best sources of information about these events. Barton saw about 3,000 wounded men lying beside the railroad track at Culpeper, Virginia, the surgeons working desperately, with "ghastly heaps of cut off arms and legs" and screams of pain that swept across the area "in gusts."[50] On September 9, ten days after the battle, about 600 Union wounded still had not been retrieved. An improvised train of ambulances and civilian vehicles brought them to Washington by moonlight, and that same day the last wounded arrived at Seminary Hospital, a Union facility in Fairfax.[51]

Threatened by Gen. Stonewall Jackson's flanking moves, Pope withdrew the Union army from his base at Centreville toward Washington, causing most of the medical and hospital supplies and a large number of wounded to fall into Confederate hands. The wounded suffered severely from hunger, thirst, and exposure first to heavy rain and then to hot sun.[52] Confederate medical personnel joined the Union surgeons who had stayed behind to care for the wounded men as best they could, in one of many such cooperative efforts. The medical director of Pope's army, Thomas McParlin, wrote in his official report that, on September 1,

> [I] took charge of a flag of truce and numerous surgeons, attendants and volunteer assistants, with what ambulances could be found, . . . and went to the battlefield. . . . [There] Medical Director L. Guild, of General Lee's army, joined me . . . Surgeons were left in parties to care for wounded found, with what supplies they had, working with Confederate medical officers and assistants.[53]

Similar efforts continued over the next few days, and McParlin added, "I am happy to say that the Confederate officers and soldiers shared with our wounded their scanty store."[54]

Because part of the Army of the Potomac reached the field, Medical Director Letterman could compare the operation of his ambulance service to that of Pope's unorganized corps. In his official report, Letterman pointed out that the performance of

> ambulances belonging to the Army of the Potomac, a few of which were able to reach the battlefields, and those of corps in which the system ordered by General McClellan did not exist, I have been informed, was very striking in favor of the former.[55]

BATTLE OF ANTIETAM (SEPTEMBER 17, 1862)

McClellan's Army of the Potomac combined with the troops from Pope's disbanded Army of Virginia, and they moved north into Maryland. There they grappled with Lee's forces at South Mountain and then at Antietam, on what is usually referred to as "America's bloodiest day." Letterman's ambulance system was not completely in place, since McClellan's order was issued about the time the army began moving north from the peninsula,[56] but it is still credited with saving many lives. During the evacuation of the Peninsula, most of the medical supplies had been left behind at Fort Monroe, Virginia, and thus Letterman was forced to improvise. Nevertheless, the ambulance and hospital units, while far from their potential efficiency, greatly improved the Medical Department's performance.

The carnage at Antietam included 9,416 wounded Union soldiers in addition to the 2,010 killed. The Confederates evacuated 16,399 wounded and left behind about 2,500 more who were cared for primarily by Federal surgeons; they lost 3,500 men "killed in battle."[57] Three days earlier at South Mountain, 1,806 Union soldiers had been wounded and 443 were killed. Thus, during a four-day period, a total of nearly 14,000 men needed surgical care from the Union medical personnel.

The new ambulance service functioned well, although staff training was incomplete. All the wounded who could be moved were taken to hospitals in nearby cities, chiefly Frederick, Maryland, as soon as practicable. Several field hospitals were established for the more seriously wounded, and Letterman commented that wounded cared for in the open air or in tents did better than those cared for in improvised hospitals in barns or houses.

Clara Barton, who received donations from friends and well-wishers (mainly from her home state of Massachusetts), obtained her own wagons with medical supplies to carry her to Antietam immediately after the battle. There, Barton provided invaluable nursing aid, as she had at Second Bull Run.

After the battle, many civilian surgeons again volunteered to help with the wounded. As had happened a few months before on the peninsula, ill-feelings and recriminations developed between army personnel and the "contract surgeons," some of whom were given expenses on a daily basis, thus receiving far more pay than did the army surgeons. There were allegations that contract surgeons performed needless operations merely for the experience and that they were unavailable when the work was laborious or did not interest them. Civilian surgeons claimed that they were badly treated by the army surgeons. Newspapers criticized both groups, and this dismal

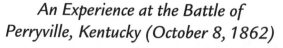

An Experience at the Battle of Perryville, Kentucky (October 8, 1862)

After operating and dressing wounds all night, Surg. Charles Quintard, who was also a chaplain in the Confederate Army of Tennessee, wrote to his wife:

> About half past five in the morning of the 9th, I dropped—I could do no more. I went out by myself and leaning against a fence, I wept like a child. And all that day I was so unnerved that if anyone asked me about the regiment, I could make no reply without tears. Having taken off my shirt to make bandages, I took a severe cold.[58]

image of Civil War medicine has persisted despite the subsequent improvements in both the civilian volunteers and the army surgeons. Because of the public criticism of the army surgeons after the Battle of Antietam, many soldiers' family members traveled to the area as rapidly as they could to care for them; some even managed to take their wounded relatives home. Letterman felt that removing the men caused a number of lives to be lost unnecessarily.

BATTLE OF FREDERICKSBURG (DECEMBER 13, 1862)

Fredericksburg was another unmitigated military disaster for the Army of the Potomac, but it marked the end of the chaos that had plagued the Medical Department in the first eighteen months of the war.

Under the command of Gen. Ambrose Burnside, 9,028 men were wounded in one day, with another 1,180 killed and 2,145 missing. During this carnage, Letterman's medical service received its first full trial and "wonders were performed."[59] Within twenty-four hours after the fighting ended, the ambulance teams had removed virtually all the wounded from the field, primarily to field hospitals made up of tents.

Many local homes were taken over for use as hospitals; Clara Barton was again of great service at the Lacy House, which was the Second Corps' Hospital.[60] Walt Whitman visited the hospital while looking for his wounded brother. He described surgeons working in every room, as well as the hideous sight that greeted him:

at the foot of a tree, immediately in front, a heap of feet, legs, arms, and human fragments, cut, bloody, black and blue, swelled and sickening—in the garden, near a row of graves.[61]

Nevertheless, Letterman's system proved itself in the lives that it saved and the suffering that it lessened. Colleagues in the Medical Department subsequently praised Letterman for his achievements at Fredericksburg.

BATTLE OF GETTYSBURG (JULY 1–3, 1863)

The Army of the Potomac's ambulance and field hospital system performed satisfactorily after the Battle of Chancellorsville (May 1–3, 1863), but its most severe test came at Gettysburg two months later. When they arrived at the battlefield, the medical staff was already working under a considerable handicap. During the rush to follow Lee into Maryland and Pennsylvania, Gen. Joseph Hooker resigned as commander of the Army of the Potomac and was succeeded by Gen. George Gordon Meade. Meade directed that wagon trains include a minimal number of ambulances and concentrate instead on transporting ammunition and other military supplies. The army endured forced marches to the battle sites; many units traveled thirty miles a day. Weary surgeons generally marched along with the men, since all the wagons and ambulances carried supplies or exhausted and sick soldiers. Most of the medical personnel, as well as a large part of the army, arrived after the fighting had already started, thus they had no time to make preparations.

The flood of wounded started while the meager supplies were still being unpacked. No tents were available for field hospitals, so both sides commandeered homes, churches, barns, the railroad station, and even covered bridges for this purpose. Each evening after the fighting subsided, stretcher bearers and ambulances collected the wounded; each morning, before the fighting began at dawn, all the wounded (both Union and Confederate) within Union lines were receiving care.[62] (See Figure 4.10.) This was an unprecedented achievement, and it was accomplished during the largest battle that has ever been fought on American soil.

Letterman calculated that 14,193 wounded were collected and cared for during the battle. In addition, he reported that 6,802 Confederates "fell into our hands" after the battle. These men were among the most seriously wounded, and had been left behind, too ill to be transported, when the Confederate army retreated across the Potomac. Many Confederate surgeons stayed behind to help care for them.[63]

With nearly 21,000 wounded soldiers to treat, the surgeons working in Union medical facilities at Gettysburg labored day and night, completely

Figure 4.10: Train of ambulance wagons ready for duty near the Harewood Hospital in Washington in July 1863. The ambulances probably were waiting to pick up wounded from the trains bringing them from Gettysburg. This photograph documents the improved organization of the Ambulance Corps after the Letterman system was adopted by the Army of the Potomac. (Courtesy of Massachusetts Commandery of the MOLLUS; USAMHI.)

overwhelmed. "I worked until three o'clock in the morning," wrote Surgeon Peltier of the 126th New York (3rd Division), "then slept about an hour on the ground among the wounded."[64] Their job became even more onerous on July 6, when the Army of the Potomac began to pursue Lee's forces. Letterman took most of the army's 650 surgeons and many of the ambulances with him, leaving relatively few men to care for the immense number of wounded. Eventually, Surgeon General Hammond sent fifty replacement ambulances, but the shortage of physicians remained. As Letterman wrote in his official report,

> The greater portion of the surgical labor was performed before the army left. The time for primary operations had passed, and what remained to be done was to attend to making the men comfortable, dress their wounds, and perform such secondary operations as from time to time might be necessary. One hundred and six medical officers were left behind when the army left; no more could be left, as it was expected that another battle would within three or four days take place, and in all probability as many wounded thrown upon our hands as at the battle of the 2d and 3d, which had just occurred.[65]

Letterman left Dr. Henry Janes in charge of the 106 surgeons who remained behind. When the medical tents finally arrived on July 15, Janes set up a general hospital that he named "Camp Letterman." It opened on July 22 and had six rows with about 400 tents in each row; each tent had twelve beds. The wounded were collected from the improvised hospitals, and observers noted a line of stretchers a mile and a half long conveying the men to their new quarters.[66]

The railroad service into Gettysburg had been interrupted before the battle and it was not reopened until July 10, when Hermann Haupt succeeded in replacing the burnt railroad bridge. Both the Sanitary Commission and the Christian Commission provided badly needed supplies and food for several days until the army's supplies began to arrive in the quantity needed.

Volunteer physicians and nurses began responding to appeals immediately after the battle to help care for the wounded. A large number of women provided food, nursing care, and other services; some became relatively famous for their contributions. One of the first women to appear, Cornelia Hancock, noted the preponderance of unofficial volunteers and wrote: "Miss [Dorothea] Dix was in camp today and stuck her head in the tents, but she does not work at all, and her nurses are being superseded very fast."[67] Initially, some local civilians tried to profit from the plight of the wounded but, once communication was fully restored, thousands of civilians poured into the area to help and self-sacrifice and devoted care for both Union and

Efficiency of the Union Medical Department at Gettysburg

Surgeon John McNulty, a Union corps medical director, sent this report to Dr. Jonathan Letterman after Gettysburg:

It is with extreme satisfaction that I can assure you that it [the ambulance and field hospital system] enabled me to remove the wounded from the field, shelter, feed them, and dress their wounds within six hours after the battle ended, and to have every capital operation performed within twenty-four hours after the injury was received.[68]

Letterman made the same point in his official report and in his memoirs.[69]

Confederate wounded was the rule. On September 23, the Christian Commission and the ladies of Gettysburg arranged a banquet for all the wounded, blue and gray.[70]

The soldiers and volunteers who recorded their experiences all commented on the foul stench permeating the air around Gettysburg, which began even before the fighting ended. Unburied bodies and suppurating wounds produced the terrible odor and "poison lurked in every breath of air," according to one newspaper report. Other witnesses noted that the "female nurses tried to get between the wounded and the wind."[71] Ultimately, the hastily buried dead from both sides were exhumed and placed in the first National Soldiers' Cemetery. The cemetery was dedicated in a special ceremony on November 19, during which President Lincoln gave a short speech containing a "few appropriate remarks," now known as the "Gettysburg Address." The day after the President's speech, Camp Letterman closed when the last of the wounded departed, four and a half months after the great battle ended.[72]

There is some variation in the accounts of the value of the "contract" physicians at Gettysburg. In his official report, Letterman stated, "No reliance can be placed on surgeons from civil life during or after a battle. They cannot or will not submit to the privations and discomforts which are necessary, and the great majority think more of their own personal comfort than they do of the wounded."[73] He also made a derogatory comment about the army surgeons who were used to working in hospitals and had not been with the army in the field during a major battle, saying, "Little more can be said of those [medical] officers who have for a long period been in hospitals."

Letterman did not actually observe the volunteers at work. Medical Inspector John M. Cuyler arrived on July 10 and stayed through most of the period that the wounded were being treated at Gettysburg. He reported: "As far as my observation extends, the medical officers of the army, and the citizen surgeons who were employed during the emergency discharged their arduous duties with fidelity and ability. I never saw men work harder and complain less of the difficulties that surrounded them."[74]

When the wounded recovered sufficiently, they were carried to the railroad station in the town of Gettysburg and sent by hospital trains, which ran on a regular schedule to major cities in the region. The railroad line to Gettysburg, however, was unable to handle enough trains to carry all the wounded men; many had to be conveyed by road to Frederick. In evaluating the rail transport system, *Medical and Surgical History* recorded that "after the Battle of Gettysburg, 20,342 wounded came under the care of the medical officers of the Army of the Potomac, and in two weeks 15,425 had been forwarded to Baltimore, York, Harrisburg, and New York City."[75]

When they were able to travel, more than 2,500 of the Confederate wounded were sent by train to a terminal on the New Jersey shore of the Hudson River. To bypass New York City, where there had been recent draft riots, they were put aboard boats and taken to a hospital on Davids' Island on the north shore of Long Island Sound. There, recovering Union men were moved to make beds available for the Confederate wounded.

THE GREAT BATTLES IN VIRGINIA (1864)

As the Army of the Potomac, now under Generals Grant and Meade, fought its way south against General Lee's forces, the Medical Corps experienced considerable chaos. Despite the improved ambulance and field- and depot-hospital systems and well-formulated plans for the care and evacuation of wounded, the rapid unplanned movement of Grant's army away from its base and the enormous number of casualties from the resulting battles soon overwhelmed the Medical Corps. According to official reports, 21,463 Union soldiers were wounded during the battle in the tangled maze called the Wilderness on May 5 and 6. Because Congress had finally passed the reorganization bill on March 1, 1864, the ambulance service was now fully operational and "every wounded man who could be reached by stretcher-bearers was brought off the field" and taken to field hospitals by 9 PM on May 6.[76]

Dr. Thomas McParlin (see Figure 4.11) replaced Letterman as the Army of the Potomac's medical director. (Letterman had been transferred by the new surgeon general, Joseph K. Barnes, who, apparently because of his connections to General McClellan, had replaced Hammond. Disgusted with his new, unimportant assignments, Letterman resigned from the army in January 1864.) McParlin's official report described a particularly grim event during the Battle of the Wilderness:

> It was a series of fierce attacks and repulses on either side, and the hostile lines swayed back and forth over a strip of ground from 200 yards to a mile in width on which the severely wounded of both sides were scattered. This strip of woods was on fire in many places, and some wounded, unable to escape, were thus either suffocated or burned to death. The number who thus perished is unknown, but it is supposed to have been about 200. The stretcher bearers of the Ambulance Corps followed the line of battle closely, and displayed great gallantry in their efforts to bring off the wounded lying between the lines, but with very small success, it being almost impossible to find wounded men lying scattered through the dense thickets, and the enemy firing at every moving light, or even at the slightest noise.[77]

Figure 4.11: Dr. Thomas A. McParlin. He succeeded Letterman as medical director of the Army of the Potomac and served in that capacity during the bloody campaigns of 1864 and 1865. (Courtesy of Roger D. Hunt Collection, USAMHI.)

The chaos resulted in large measure from Grant's unexpected move south after the bloody standoff in the Battle of the Wilderness. Instead of pulling back over the Rapidan River, as Burnside and Hooker had done under similar circumstances, Grant surprised his troops, including Medical Director McParlin, by moving south in an attempt to outflank Lee. Seeking speed and mobility, Grant took only essential supplies, but still his wagon train was about seventy miles long, and choked the narrow roads that the ambulances also needed.[78]

When the campaign began, McParlin had 619 ambulances and supply wagons parked in neat rows at the Brandy Station depot, across the Rapidan River and a short distance north of the Battles of the Wilderness and Chancellorsville. After the battles, he moved as many of the sick and wounded as possible to Washington and broke down the division hospitals so that their personnel and medical facilities could move with the army.[79]

McParlin, though, was ordered to send the wounded from the Wilderness to distant Fredericksburg, rather than the nearby Brandy Station. From there, they would be sent to hospitals in Washington. This change of plans kept ambulance wagon trains from interrupting the flow of supplies to the army over the few crowded roads. But the result was that many of the wounded were transported over the terrible road system much farther and for a much longer time than was anticipated.

The switch of the medical depot to Fredericksburg was as unexpected as Grant's sudden move south, and the town had made no preparations for the care of the wounded soldiers, who began arriving by the thousands. Everything the Medical Corps needed was in short supply. McParlin telegraphed the surgeon general requesting extra surgeons and supplies since there were only thirty or forty surgeons to treat the thousands of wounded. McParlin's plan was to send most of the wounded by rail to the port facility at Aquia Landing on the Potomac and then north by boat. Another port facility, at Belle Plain, was also about seven miles from Fredericksburg, but it had only one dock and could only be reached by road, requiring another jolting ambulance ride for the seriously wounded men.[80]

However, Confederate guerrillas cut the rail line to Aquia, so many of the wounded had to remain in Fredericksburg's hospitals. As a result, the Army of the Potomac's surgeons were still caring for casualties from the Wilderness when the Battle of Spotsylvania began on May 8. In some of the most vicious fighting of the war, which lasted until May 19, another 19,678 Union soldiers were wounded. There were too many for the assigned stretcher bearers to handle, so healthy soldiers had to assist, once again removing fighting men from the field. The wounded were collected into groups on the field, in "hollows by the roadside, which afforded protection against musketry," with a medical officer and full canteens of water. When the fighting ceased, they were collected into four large groups but, unfortunately, "all the ambulances were absent being [still] engaged in conveying the wounded of the battle of the Wilderness to Fredericksburg and much confusion and delay in the collection of the wounded occurred in consequence."[81]

The wounded began to be evacuated from the field hospitals to Fredericksburg before all the wounded from the Battle of the Wilderness had been transported there. Even with the enhanced and dedicated Ambulance Corps, there were too many wounded for them to handle. Even when there were ambulances, they occasionally had to remain idle, since the horses that

"More Work than There Were Hands to Do"

This item about Fredericksburg appeared in the *Boston Daily Advertiser* on June 3, 1864:

> . . . 15,000 wounded men pouring at the shortest notice into a town which its best estimate perhaps contained a population of one-third of this much. No preparation by human power is adequate to meet such a case fully, under the multiple uncertainties of military movements. The government supplied transportation for the wounded, and yet there was suffering by delay, of which it is harrowing to read. The medical staff provided the necessary supplies and attendance, we will believe, with as much promptness and completeness as was possible—and yet men lay for days untended, wounded men were for days without food or proper shelter . . . The evidence all goes to show that with the best that official diligence and private zeal could do, there was for the few days of actual crisis more work than there were hands to do.[82]

pulled them became exhausted from their arduous continuous labor. Every type of vehicle available was pressed into service. Many were springless wagons, and the shrieks and groans of the wounded during the jolting ride over rutted roads added to the pandemonium. Again, vivid reports of these events appeared in newspapers and, later, in published diaries, adding to Civil War medicine's negative image.

In Fredericksburg, a city of 5,000 in peacetime, 14,000 wounded were treated, many in commandeered private homes.[83] Thousands more, also in need of food and medical attention, passed through the town. Adding to the confusion, "malingerers" swelled the number of soldiers seeking aid. Medical Director McParlin estimated that "about 5,000 of these men were at Fredericksburg at different times; the tales invented by them for the purpose of exciting compassion of citizens and strangers gave rise to many of the false reports of suffering and destitution among the wounded which were for a time prevalent in the North." About 600 malingerers were turned over to army authorities for punishment.[84] (In Chapter 12, see Malingering.)

The army again issued appeals for volunteer surgeons, nurses, and supplies. The Sanitary Commission and the Christian Commission responded, and many civilian surgeons came forward to provide assistance. William Morton, a dentist and one of the inventors of surgical anesthesia, came to Fredericksburg during this period as a volunteer. He personally administered anesthesia to hundreds of soldiers who were undergoing surgery. Assisting the other physicians were "reserve surgeons," a corps organized at the state level and paid as contract surgeons, with the governor vouching for their competence.

The *American Medical Times* described the contributions made by the volunteer physicians and the "reserve surgeons," noting that nearly all the necessary operations were performed in the field, not at the hospitals in Fredericksburg, which were staffed largely by the volunteer surgeons. While these surgeons changed dressings, prescribed medicine, and helped to run the hastily organized hospitals, they did not perform any operations, as they had two years earlier during the Peninsula campaign.[85] Despite these volunteers' help, newspapers reported "a great lack of physicians" in Fredericksburg, although no stories criticized the civilian surgeons' performance.

To diminish the suffering that occurred when the wounded were moved by ambulance, McParlin kept the most seriously injured at Fredericksburg

British View of the "American War"

Appalled by the number of casualties in Grant's campaign, the British medical literature compared the staggering losses to those in European wars. On June 18, 1864, a note in the journal *Lancet* stated that the reported casualties "of more than of 45,000" in the first fourteen days of the campaign made the "losses in European battles, even in campaigns extending over months or years, fall into insignificance before the losses of this solitary, as yet unfinished campaign."[86]

The article also noted that

[the] killed and wounded in the Crimea from 19 Sept 1854 to 8 Sept 1855, amounted to 13,139 . . . [During the Napoleonic War] the losses in the [campaign on the Iberian] Peninsula in the 41 months ending the 25th of May 1814, were 40,937. In fourteen successive sieges, the losses of the French and English armies in killed and wounded were under 25,000, the aggregate force employed numbering 287,900. Few European wars offer a parallel in killed and wounded to the present Federal campaign.[87]

until gunboats cleared the Rappahannock River of mines and obstructions (May 20th) and the railroad line to Aquia Landing was reopened (May 22nd). To free Army of the Potomac facilities and personnel, McParlin arranged for soldiers whose wounds prevented their return to battle for a month or more to be transferred to Washington. Later, when the army moved further south, the plans for evacuating the wounded by boat had to be quickly changed. The supply and evacuation port at Aquia was now too far from the battlefields, and the wounded endured longer, more painful rides to Fredericksburg and then to Aquia. More critical, these long journeys were detrimental to the prompt evacuation of the wounded, since they kept the relatively scarce ambulances away from the battlefield, where they were desperately needed. So McParlin moved the depot hospitals to the army's new base at White House Landing, on the James River east of Richmond.

From White House, the men who had received emergency care could be loaded directly onto equipped and staffed hospital boats and taken north via the Chesapeake Bay. During an engagement along North Anna River between May 23rd and 27th, an additional 1,460 men were wounded, followed by 10,570 more after the fighting around Cold Harbor (May 31–June 3, 1864). McParlin constantly modified the treatment and evacuation plans to maintain a continuous organized flow of men heading to the depot hospitals and then north by boat. The basic organization, adaptation to changing circumstances, and ultimate smooth functioning were very different from the chaotic care provided during the Peninsula campaign. But, when the hospital ships arrived in Washington, packed to their upper decks with groaning wounded men, the effect on the public still evoked condemnation of the Medical Department.

SIEGE OF PETERSBURG AND THE APPOMATTOX CAMPAIGN (JUNE 1864 TO APRIL 1865)

An old problem reappeared when the army spent about ten months during 1864–65 relatively immobile in trenches outside Petersburg, Virginia: sanitation. Diarrhea was again a major issue, as was bronchitis during the cold winter months. Since by now the troops were nearly all veterans who were immune to it, typhoid fever was rarely observed, but recrudescent malaria was common, even in January. A steady supply of wounded also kept the Medical Corps busy. The disastrous Battle of the Crater, so called because a Union miner placed a large amount of explosives under Confederate lines, which blasted a huge crater, occurred during this period. Several other major battles were fought as the siege line was extended to the west.

Flexible Hospital Arrangements during the Appomattox Campaign

The medical inspector in the Army of the Potomac's Ninth Corps noted the progressive improvement of the army's field hospital system. A flexible organization allowed seriously wounded soldiers and those in need of operations to remain in the Corps' field hospital when the army left in pursuit of the Confederates. Medical Inspector Samuel Adams reported:

> many lives were saved, many of the cases of penetrating and perforating wounds of the chest and abdomen and compound fractures of the thigh, and amputations, which would have died under transportation, were progressing most favorably.[88]

Evacuation and care of the wounded, however, was at its best. Large depot hospitals were established at City Point near the James River wharves so that patients could be loaded onto hospital boats without enduring an injurious and painful ambulance ride. A railroad line from the port ran west along the trench line, near enough that the wounded could be quickly evacuated by rail from the field stations to the hospitals at City Point. A continuous flow of wounded northward in hospital boats kept beds available at the depot facilities.

The description of one depot hospital provides a picture of the magnitude of the medical operation in the early stages of this campaign. Expecting carnage similar to that of the horrendous previous year, the hospital's "capacity was increased to 8,800 beds in 90 wooden pavilions plus 452 tents, serving five of the corps of the Army of the Potomac and the Cavalry Corps in anticipation of the Spring campaign. Initially, it was stocked with supplies for 2,500 patients for 10 days. By June 1865, 21,561 patients were treated," of whom only 316 died.[89]

When the campaign that led to General Lee's surrender at Appomattox was about to begin in the spring of 1865, as many men as could be moved were sent to City Point to open beds near the fighting. To ensure that they would be able to transport the wounded, Medical Director McParlin obtained a reserve of ambulances, staffed hospital trains, and supply wagons. A wagon train of thirty-six vehicles loaded with hospital supplies accompanied the army as it moved. To provide continued care of wounded while en route, McParlin ignored standing orders and "caused the boxes of several of the ambulances to be filled [only] with battlefield supplies; chloroform, morphine, lint, plaster, roller, and whiskey, instead of the beef stock and hard bread [hardtack] directed by the supply table."[90] Those were the supplies that military surgeons had found to be essential when treating acutely injured patients.

When Lee evacuated Petersburg and Richmond in an attempt to move his army to North Carolina, Grant pursued him, determined to prevent the escape. The armies' quick movement again threw the careful plans for the collection and evacuation of the wounded into disarray. Both armies moved west so rapidly that they had to abandon their wounded, leaving them almost strewn along the roadside. They moved away from the railroad lines and the waiting hospital trains, but the campaign ended in time for the medical facilities to quickly catch up.

Between May and October 1864, after the move from Brandy Station, the Army of the Potomac utilized its depot hospitals at Fredericksburg, White House, and City Point. Although hundreds of the wounded men who passed through these depots en route to the hospital boats were not registered, "between those dates there were received into and retained for treatment for at least 48 hours, 65,540 sick and wounded officers and men. Of these, 51,313 were transferred to the various U.S. General Hospitals at the north, 11,706 have been returned from the hospital direct to duty with their commands, and 15,161 died."[91]

IMITATION: THE SINCEREST COMPLIMENT

European armies sent military observers to both sides during the American Civil War and later adopted Letterman's system of a Medical Department-controlled ambulance corps and field hospitals with evacuation to general hospitals. Two German physicians, members of the Prussian army's large trained reserve who became internationally famous leaders in medicine, both served in the Franco-Prussian War and commented on the American experience during the Civil War. Theodore Billroth, who was a major innovator in abdominal surgery, was impressed with the ambulance evacuation system. Rudolph Virchow was particularly complementary about the establishment and administration of the field and general hospital system.

American armies continued using the ambulance and field hospital system adopted during the Civil War, especially during the two World Wars. During the Spanish-American War, there were relatively few battle casualties but more serious epidemic diseases, especially typhoid fever and yellow fever. Unfortunately, an ambulance system comparable to the standards developed during the Civil War was not used. As one army historian put it, "We did not have anything like it in 1898."[92]

In 1867, the French held a world's fair in Paris with pavilions containing exhibits showcasing the latest developments from many countries. The United States exhibited Civil War ambulances, including the newly designed "Autenrieth Medicine Wagon" that transported supplies and medications, and a "field service" unit that included a moveable field hospital "representing the peak of military medicine." The public, however, showed more interest in another American invention—the rocking chair.[93]

"The American Ambulance" in Paris

Dr. Thomas W. Evans, an American dentist and a close friend of Emperor Napoleon III and Empress Josephine, exhibited "The American Ambulance" at the Paris World's Fair. (The French term "ambulance" denoted a field hospital; the vehicle itself was called an "ambulance volante.") He wrote of his experience:

In the year 1867, during the Exposition Universelle in Paris, I exhibited a number of ambulance wagons, and models of field and post hospitals, together with a collection of the excellent hospital and sanitary appliances which, after careful trial, had been adopted in the United States Army. . . . To this exhibit was awarded one of the eight grand prizes given at that exhibition. It was the only "Grand Prix" obtained by an American. Indeed, I found that my endeavors to make this apparatus known to European surgeons and army officials, as well as to introduce in camps the new methods used for the hospitalization and treatment of the sick and wounded, were greatly appreciated in military circles.[94]

continued . . .

"The American Ambulance" in Paris, continued

He then described his establishment of an American Civil War-type field hospital during the Franco-Prussian War:

> [At the start of the Franco-Prussian war] I proposed, therefore, to establish an ambulance in Paris, where the wounded could be treated, so far as possible, under conditions similar to those which had been attended with the best results in the United States—in short, to give a practical demonstration of the great advantages to be secured by making extensive use of field hospitals "under canvas," instead of crowding the wounded into churches and public and private buildings, as has been the custom in all armies and in all times. . . . such an ambulance was subsequently established in Paris, and that a large number of wounded were there taken care of during the siege, in the winter of 1870–71, in a way that realized in every respect my intentions and my hopes. It attracted the attention not only of the surgeons connected with the Service de Santé and the military hospitals, but of the principal officers of the army and the members of the Government. The surgical results reported by those in charge of this ambulance were surprising. The Press was filled with commendatory notices concerning its organization and management. Other ambulances were opened in Paris by the French Société de Secours aux Blessés, in which the same system and the same appliances were closely copied. And the Government of the Defense Nationale, at the end of the siege, as an expression of its appreciation of the services rendered by this model American field-hospital, conferred the decoration of the Legion of Honor on no less than seventeen Americans.[95]

Not mentioned in Evans's description were the facts that he had written a history of the U.S. Sanitary Commission and, at the start of the Franco-Prussian War, had organized the "American International Sanitary Commission." This commission was supposed to apply the knowledge of military medicine gained in the American Civil War. He obtained the services of an American surgeon, John Swinburne, who had served as a contract surgeon during the Peninsula campaign, to run his field hospital in Paris.

REFERENCES

1. Mitchell SW: "On the medical department in the Civil War." Address to Physicians' Club of Chicago, February 25, 1913. *J Am Med Assoc.* 1914 May 19;62(19):1445-50.
2. Horne A: *The Fall of Paris. The Siege and the Commune, 1870–71.* New York: Penguin, 1990.
3. Carson G: The dentist and the empress. *Amer Heritage.* 1980;31(4):65-80.
4. Evans TW: *History of the American Ambulance Established in Paris during the Siege of 1870–71 together with the Details of Its Methods and Its Work.* London: Low, Marston, Low & Searle, 1873.
5. Johnson CB. Quoted in: Commager HS: *The Blue and the Gray.* Vol. II. Indianapolis: Bobbs-Merrill, 1950, pp. 195-96.
6. Ibid., pp. 194-98.
7. Keen WW: Surgical reminiscences of the Civil War. *Transactions of the College of Physicians of Philadelphia.* 3rd Series. 1905;27:95-114.
8. Kimball MB. Quoted in: Freemon FR: *Microbes and Minie Balls.* Rutherford, NJ: Fairleigh Dickinson Univ. Press, 1993, p. 194.
9. O.R., Series I, vol. V, p. 77.
10. Maxwell WQ: *Lincoln's Fifth Wheel: The Political History of the U.S. Sanitary Commission.* New York: Longmans Green, 1956, 75.
11. Bauer KJ, ed.: *Soldiering: The Civil War Diary of Rice C. Bull.* New York: Berkley Books, 1977, pp. 84-85.
12. O.R., Series I, vol. XI/1, p. 210.
13. *The Photographic History of the Civil War.* New York: Review of Reviews, 1970, vol. 4B, Appendix.
14. Billings JS: Medical reminiscences of the Civil War. *Transactions of the College of Physicians of Philadelphia.* 3rd Series. 1905;27:115-21.
15. Duncan LC: *The Medical Department of the United States Army in the Civil War.* Gaithersburg, MD: Butternut Press, 1985, p. 109.
16. Gillett MC: *The United States Army Medical Department, 1818–1865.* Washington, D.C.: Center of Military History, U.S. Army, 1987, p. 216.
17. Riley HD, Jr.: Medicine in the Confederacy. Part 2. *Mil Med.* 1956 Feb;118(2):144-53.
18. Gillett, *United States Army Medical Department*, p. 295.
19. Roberts DJ. In: *Photographic History of the Civil War*, vol. 4B, p. 260.
20. *Medical and Surgical History*, Surgical Section, vol. 3, p. 956.
21. Gillett, *United States Army Medical Department*, p. 157.
22. Ibid., p. 235.
23. Hart AG: *The Surgeon and the Hospital in the Civil War.* Gaithersburg, MD: Olde Soldier Books, 1987, (orig. pub. 1902), p. 41.
24. Keen, "Surgical reminiscences."
25. Oates SB: *A Woman of Valor: Clara Barton and the Civil War.* New York: Macmillan, 1994, p. 88.
26. Stillé CJ: *History of the United States Sanitary Commission: Being a General Report of Its Work during the War of the Rebellion.* New York: Hurd & Houghton, 1868, p. 161.
27. *Medical and Surgical History*, Surgical Section, vol. 3, pp. 957-71.
28. Stillé, *United States Sanitary Commission*, pp. 163-64.
29. Ibid.
30. Rutkow IM: *Surgery: An Illustrated History.* St. Louis: Mosby-Yearbook, 1993, p. 442.
31. Gillett, *United States Army Medical Department*, p. 294.
32. Wheat TA: "Receiving and forwarding hospitals of the Army of Northern Virginia." Presented at the 5th Annual Conference of the Society of Civil War Surgeons, Knoxville, March 21, 1998.
33. Notes on the War. *Br Med J.* 1871;1:174, 206.
34. Gillett, *United States Army Medical Department*, p. 295.

35. *Navy O.R.*, Series 1, vol. 23, pp. 92, 154.
36. Munden KW, Beers HP: *The Union: A Guide to Federal Archives Relating to the Civil War.* Washington, D.C.: NARA, 1980, p. 459.
37. Report of Ass't. Surg. WD Turner of U.S. Hospital Steamer *City of Memphis.* NARA, RG94, Entry #621, File A477.
38. Turner TF: *History of the U.S. Hospital Steamer* Empress. NARA, RG94, Entry #621, File A478.
39. Brinton JH: "The Brinton Manuscripts." NARA, RG94, Entry #621, File A478.
40. Report of Dr. Charles R. Greenleaf, Aug. 5, 1863. NARA, RG94, Entry #621, File A131.
41. Oates, *Woman of Valor*, p. 77.
42. *O.R.*, Series I, vol. V, p. 79.
43. Maxwell, *Lincoln's Fifth Wheel*, p. 155.
44. Ibid.
45. The term "contrabands" arose during the Peninsula campaign when fugitive slaves sought refuge behind Union lines. Major General Benjamin Butler, a politician from Massachusetts, decided not to return them to their former owners despite the existence of the Fugitive Slave Law. He cited a provision of an Act of Congress making it legal to deprive the seceded states of means to pursue the war; such means were considered "contrabands of war." Butler classified the former slaves as "contrabands" and the name stuck, becoming a general term for former slaves. Faust PL, ed.: *Historical Times Encyclopedia of the Civil War.* New York: Harper & Row, 1986, p. 161.
46. Stillé, *United States Sanitary Commission*, p. 157.
47. Ibid., pp. 146-47, 154.
48. Greenbie MLB: *Lincoln's Daughters of Mercy.* New York: G.P. Putnam's Sons, 1944, p. 64.
49. Cunningham HH: *Field Medical Services at the Battles of Manassas.* Athens, GA: Univ. of Georgia Press, 1968, pp. 62-63.
50. Oates, *Woman of Valor*, p. 77.
51. "The Brinton manuscripts." NARA, RG94.
52. Cunningham, *Field Medical Services*, p. 65.
53. *Medical and Surgical History*, Medical Section, vol. 1, Appendix, p. 116.
54. Ibid.
55. *O.R.*, Series I, vol. XI/1, p. 210.
56. Ibid., p. 220.
57. *O.R.*, Series I, vol. XIX/1, p. 106.
58. Breeden JO: The "forgotten man" of the Civil War: the Southern experience. *Bull NY Acad Med.* 1979;55(7):652.
59. Wiley BI: *The Life of Billy Yank: The Common Soldier of the Union.* Baton Rouge, LA: Louisiana State Univ. Press, 1952, p. 145.
60. Oates, *Woman of Valor*, p. 116.
61. Glicksberg CI, ed.: *Walt Whitman and the Civil War.* New York: A.S. Barnes, 1933, pp. 69-70.
62. Duncan, *Medical Department of the U.S. Army*, pp. 215-71.
63. *O.R.*, Series I, vol. XXVII/1, p. 196.
64. Duncan, *Medical Department of the U.S. Army*, p. 241.
65. *O.R.*, Series I, vol. XXVII/1, p. 198.
66. Patterson GA: *Debris of Battle: The Wounded of Gettysburg.* Mechanicsburg, PA: Stackpole, 1997, p. 154.
67. Hancock C: *South after Gettysburg. Letters of Cornelia Hancock from the Army of the Potomac, 1863–1865.* Philadelphia: Univ. of Pennsylvania Press, 1937, p. 210.
68. *O.R.*, Series I, vol. XXVII/1, p. 196.
69. Letterman J: *Medical Recollections of the Army of the Potomac / Memoir of Jonathan Letterman, M.D.* Knoxville, TN: Bohemian Brigade Pub., 1994. (Orig. pub. New York: D. Appleton, 1866 / New York: Putnam's Sons, 1883.)
70. Patterson, *Debris of Battle*, p. 171.

71. Ibid., p. 58.

72. Ibid., p. 185.

73. O.R., Series I, vol. XXVII/1, p. 198.

74. Ibid., p. 25.

75. *Medical and Surgical History*, Surgical Section, vol. 3, p. 957.

76. *Medical and Surgical History*, Medical Section, vol. 1, Appendix, p. 151.

77. *Medical and Surgical History*, Medical Section, vol. 1, p. 15.

78. Esposito VJ: *The West Point Atlas of American Wars*. vol. I. New York: Frederick A. Praeger, 1959, pp. 120-21.

79. Ibid., p. 148.

80. Map of Fredericksburg and Vicinity. *Medical and Surgical History*, Medical Section, vol. 1, p. 102.

81. Report of Surg. Thomas McParlin, *Medical and Surgical History*, Medical Section, vol. 1, Appendix, p. 153.

82. Papers of the U.S. Sanitary Commission, New York Public Library, Box 75.

83. Oates, *Woman of Valor*, p. 232.

84. Report of Surg. Thomas McParlin, *Medical and Surgical History*, p. 157.

85. Notes on the observations and movements of the Army of the Potomac during the month of May 1864. *Am Med Times*. 1864 July 16;9.

86. Federal casualties. *Lancet*. 1864 June 18;1:707-708.

87. Ibid.

88. Report of Samuel Adams, Ass't Surg. Medical Inspector, 9th Army Corps of the Army of the Potomac for March 1865. NARA, RG94, Entry #621, File A454.

89. Report of G.B. Parker, Surg. U.S. Volunteers, July 25, 1865. NARA, RG94, Entry #621, File A386.

90. *Medical and Surgical History*, Medical Section, vol. 1, p. 216.

91. Dalton EB: Report of the origin and development of the depot field hospitals of the Army of the Potomac, December 1866. NARA, RG94, Entry #621, File A251.

92. Duncan, *Medical Department of the U.S. Army*, p. 14.

93. Horne, *Fall of Paris*, p. 4.

94. Evans TW: *Memoirs of Dr. Thomas W. Evans, 1823–1897. The Second French Empire.* New York: D. Appleton & Co., 1905, p. 178.

95. Ibid.

<big>∽</big> 5 <big>∽</big>

Amputations and Excisions: "Experience Teaches"

. . . experience teaches us that although the wound appears trifling today, in attempting to save it [the limb] we will sacrifice a life a few days hence.

– Dr. J. J. Chisolm, *A Manual of Military Surgery for Use of the Surgeons in the Confederate Army*, 1861

T HE PILES OF AMPUTATED EXTREMITIES lying near improvised operating tables so horrified witnesses to Civil War surgeries that they took to calling the surgeons "sawbones." Almost all biographies of participants in the Civil War include descriptions of blood-drenched surgeons shouting "Next!" as they complete one case and turn to the next groaning soldier.[1]

In a typical portrayal, the hero in the opening scenes of the widely acclaimed movie *Dances with Wolves* is about to have his foot amputated by a callous, blood-spattered surgeon against his objections, when his colonel arrives and orders away the barbarous doctor. In the movie, the hero escapes the knife and the foot quickly heals. But what would have happened if the outcome had been determined by staphylococci and not scriptwriters? In reality, most Civil War bullet wounds became badly infected if they were not debrided or if the extremity was not amputated and such an infection usually meant death.

Experientia docet, "experience teaches," was the motto of the *Confederate States Medical and Surgical Journal*. Surgeons on both sides learned from their cases, and applied the lessons to subsequent cases. The lack of success following surgical invasion of the abdomen, chest, and head kept the number of such procedures low—amputations were the chief form of major surgery performed before and during the war. Almost 30,000 amputations were recorded by Union surgeons. (See Table 5.1.)

There unquestionably were more, since this number does not include surgeries that were performed in hospitals as revisions of previous treatments, those performed after men were discharged, or those which simply were not recorded, particularly during the chaos early in the war. Although their records are incomplete, Confederate surgeons probably did a similar number of amputations. The enormous number of amputations led to considerable criticism at the time, and the criticism continues.

Amputations were usually performed because of the massive tissue destruction by minié balls, the principle ammunition used during the war. These 0.58-caliber conical bullets traveled at a relatively low velocity, and often tumbled as they flew. When they hit, they ripped up the tissues and, usually, shattered the bones.[2] (See Figure 5.1.) As one regimental surgeon noted,

> The introduction of the rifled musket and the elongated or minié ball gave a longer range, more precision in firing and greater force to the ball, and more dangerous wounds. A wound from a smooth-bore and a round shot striking the thigh bone was often deflected with no serious injury to the bone. At the same time, a minié ball fired from a grooved musket under similar conditions might not only fracture, but crush two or three inches of the bone.[3]

TABLE 5.1
Treatment Comparison of 60,266 Cases of Shot Wounds

Treatment	Cases	Fatality Rate	Fatality Rate Upper Extremity	Lower Extremity
Treated conservatively*	26,467	17.9%	9.9%	26.2%
Excision	4,656	27.5	23.8	44.7
Amputation	29,143	25.8	12.6	40.2

*Here, the term "conservatively" means without either excision or amputation. Wounds were simply dressed or cleaned and debrided and then dressed; fractures were splinted or put in a cast, but no bone was removed.

Medical and Surgical History, Surgical Section, vol. 3, p. 879. In the original tables, there are small differences in the number of cases in various categories because of incomplete data. The authors tried to correct these discrepancies as best as they could with the information available. The variations, however, are too small to affect the overall impressions given by the calculations.

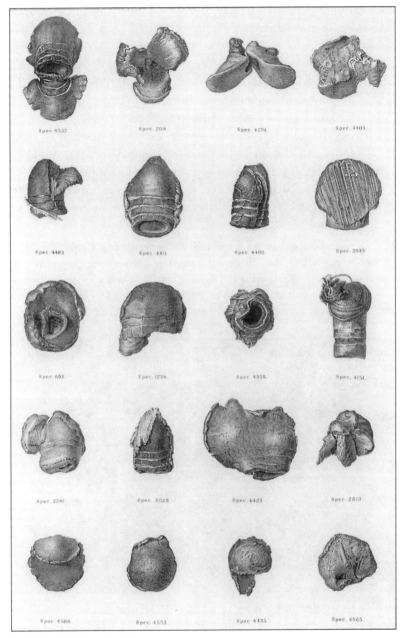

Figure 5.1: A collection of distorted bullets recovered from wounded soldiers in the Army Medical Museum. The picture, which indicates the powerful impact of tissues on the bullets, was published to illustrate the effects a bullet must have had on tissues. (*Medical and Surgical History*, Surgical Section, vol. 3, Plate LXXVIII, p. 710.)

145

The badly torn tissues virtually always became infected. These infections became the main threat to the life of injured Civil War soldiers. Since the missiles broke through the skin and carried dirty material from the skin and clothing, the fractures were defined as "compound," while the bones, broken into many fragments, were called "comminuted," terms still used today. (See Figure 5.2.) Compound comminuted fractures provide an excellent milieu for growth of bacteria, and bone infections (called osteomyelitis) were extremely difficult to treat successfully. Even today, only the prolonged use of antibiotics can eliminate the need for major deforming surgery, such as an amputation, or prevent a lingering, debilitating illness.

In his surgical textbook, Professor J. J. Chisolm described the expected result in a compound comminuted fracture caused by a minié ball when an amputation was *not* performed:

> This projectile seldom impinges upon a bone without leaving frightful traces of devastation . . . acting on the principle of a wedge, [it] splits and comminutes the bone, driving the loose spicules in every direction before it . . . [By six days] abscesses are forming in . . . [the tissues] through which the ball has passed; from the wound pus is escaping in large quantities. . . .

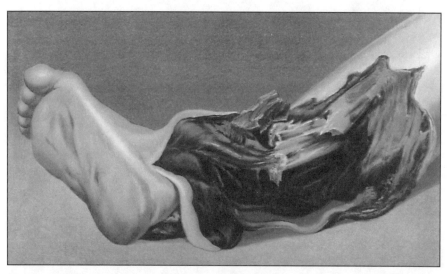

Figure 5.2: Laceration of right leg by a solid artillery projectile. The soldier was wounded early in the siege of Petersburg on July 11, 1863. The shot fractured the tibia and tore the muscles of the lower leg. An amputation was performed and he was discharged on August 7, 1865, and given an artificial leg. After he died on May 9, 1880, his private physicians notified the Army Medical Museum that an infection of the stump of his leg had resulted in his death. (*Medical and Surgical History*, Surgical Section, vol. 2, Plate LXXVI, p. 478.)

In three months, if the patient has labored through this lengthened agony, the bones are carious; the abscesses are interminable sinuses, from which are kept up a constant discharge; the patient is pale and emaciated, with flushes and diarrhea. . . . [One also must consider] the remote dangers of erysipelas and gangrene, pyemia, . . . and the questionable utility of the limb, when . . . the wound has been healed, but the limb remains weak, shrunken, stiff, painful and nearly useless.[4]

Samuel D. Gross wrote in his 1861 *Manual of Military Surgery or Hints on the Emergencies of Field, Camp and Hospital Practice*, intended for the education of newly militarized Northern surgeons, that "gunshot wounds attended with severe contamination of the bone, the fragments being sent widely around the soft parts, lacerating and bruising them severely, generally require amputations, especially in naval and military practice. Gunshot fracture of the thigh bone is generally considered by military surgeons as a sufficient cause for primary amputations."[5]

The main alternative to amputation, a procedure called excision or resection, involved removing the portion of the limb containing the shattered bone in the hopes that healing would bridge the defect (see Figure 5.3). However, the procedure left a gap in the extremity's bony support. An arm might still have some function after this procedure, but soldiers could usually stand or walk on an artificial leg better than on one that had had part of a bone removed. The procedure took much longer than amputation, which generally lasted two minutes, and, because it was a more extensive procedure, it

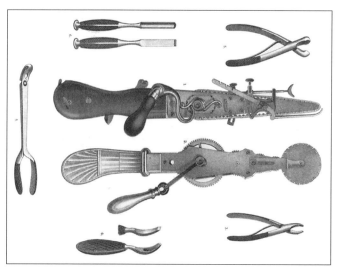

Figure 5.3: Instruments for resection. (*Medical and Surgical History*, Surgical Section, vol. 2, Plate Plate XLI, p. 256.)

carried a higher risk of hemorrhage and disastrous infection (pyemia). The mortality rate after excision was also slightly higher than that following amputation at a similar site, so the procedure became less and less popular among surgeons.[6]

In 1908, Confederate Surgeon Deering Roberts remarked on the destructive capabilities of Civil War ammunition, and compared the use of resections to amputations:

> The old round ball, of low velocity, caused many fractures in bones of the extremities. . . . The shattering, splintering, and splitting of a long bone by the impact of the minié or Enfield ball were, in many instances, both remarkable and frightful, and early experience taught surgeons that amputation was the only means of saving life. In the vicinity of a joint, the ends of the bone being more spongy, softer, and less brittle, the damage to the shaft of the bone was not so great, and the expedient of resection, largely resorted to and greatly developed by the surgeons, in many instances afforded a comparatively, if not perfectly, restored limb. Resections of the upper extremity afforded better results than those of the lower . . . Conservative surgery was, I might say, almost, if not entirely, a universal principle with the Confederate surgeon; conservatism, first, as to the life of the wounded soldier; secondly, as to his future comfort and usefulness.[7]

The term "conservative" had two possible meanings during the Civil War. In this instance, Roberts (and the medical literature in general) considered amputation the "conservative" approach, since it conserved lives due to a lower mortality rate. At other times, "conservative" carried the more modern usage, meaning less-invasive or less-deforming procedures, such as excision rather than amputation, thus conserving the limb. (Table 5.2)

TABLE 5.2
Treatment of Shot Wounds of the Extremities
in the Union Army for the Entire War

Total shot wounds of the extremities	**174,206**
Treated without any operation	140,124 (80%)
Initially treated with excision	4,656 (3% of cases treated by operation)
Cases requiring amputation after excision	305 (7% of excisions)
Initially treated by amputation	29,426 (21% of cases treated by operation)
Cases requiring re-amputation	249 (0.8% of amputations)

Medical and Surgical History, Surgical Section, vol. 3, p. 879. In the original tables, there are small differences in the number of cases in various categories because of incomplete data. The authors tried to correct these discrepancies as best they could with the information available. The variations, however, are too small to affect the overall impressions given by the calculations.

AMPUTATION TECHNIQUES

Some instruments used for amputation can appear barbaric, especially the long-bladed knives and chain saws that were used to cut through bones in inaccessible places, such as high on the femur near the hip. But others are remarkably similar to those used today. (See Figures 5.4 and 5.5.) These instruments enabled surgeons to perform difficult operations quickly, in an attempt to finish the procedure before the lightly administered anesthetic wore off.

Civil War surgeons argued long and hard about the best technique to use when performing an amputation. There were two basic procedures. The circular method left a raw, open stump that healed gradually. (See Figure 5.6.) The flap method was a more elegant procedure; it created a flap of skin to close the raw stump, which allowed quicker healing but took longer to perform.

There were other considerations as well. Time was a major one because of the numerous casualties after a major

Figure 5.4: A chain saw. (*SS*, p. 531.)

battle. Since the flap method took longer, it forced the neglect of other men and required prolonged use of anesthesia, increasing the danger of death from the chloroform. Also, it was more difficult to do at night when the lighting was poor.

An even more important consideration was the trauma of transportation after the surgery. Rides in the rickety "gutbuster" ambulances over rutted or muddy roads subjected the men to severe continuous jostling, and occasionally dumped them onto the roadside. Under these conditions, flap amputations often broke open, increasing the likelihood of infection.

The circular method was simpler, faster, and, although not as aesthetic, it withstood travel better, healed satisfactorily, and accommodated a prosthetic artificial limb. It was preferred for these reasons, although the two techniques were frequently the subject of debate at medical society meetings in both armies. A lengthy discussion of the pros and cons of the two basic techniques in *Medical and Surgical History* concluded:

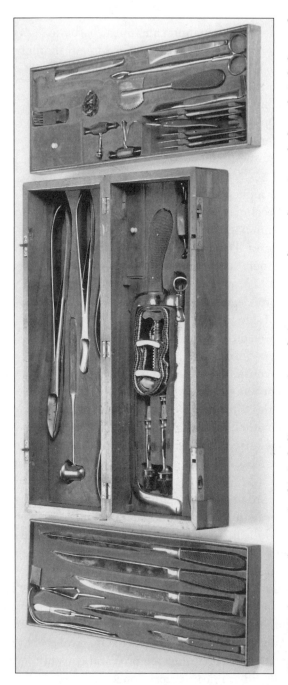

Figure 5.5: A surgeon's operating kit, including a tourniquet, knives, saws, probes, and a variety of other relatively fine and relatively crude instruments. There are single and double-edged knives and a huge hacksaw with a blade. The tourniquet consists of a long strap, stored by winding it around a screw-like device for tightening it. (Courtesy of Gretchen Worden, Mütter Museum, College of Physicians, Philadelphia.)

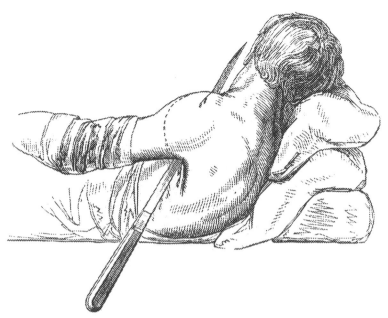

Figure 5.6: Sketch of the circular technique used to amputate the left arm at the shoulder joint. The patient also had amputation of the fingers and metacarpals of the right hand, except for the thumb. He was wounded during a raid into Alabama on April 30, 1863; the amputations were performed shortly after the injury by regimental surgeons but the soldier was captured. He was released, however, and discharged from the army and pensioned on October 19, 1863. (*Medical and Surgical History*, Surgical Section, vol. 2, p. 616.)

> [the] circular operation required less time and care in dressing, was easily handled, seldom sloughed, that its discharges were less and that it was less frequently followed by hemorrhage than the flap operation, while the latter mode would not stand transportation unless carefully supported, and was considered altogether too nice an operation for the flurry of the battlefield. As far as stumps are concerned, handsome rounded stumps were achieved by either method.[8]

PRIMARY VERSUS SECONDARY AMPUTATIONS

Surgeons had an alternative to immediate amputation: they could delay their decision. (See Figure 5.7.) When they performed amputations 48 or more hours after the injury, they used the term "secondary amputation." Civil War surgeons knew that delayed amputations during the Crimean War had a higher mortality rate than those performed immediately, but they didn't

151

know it was because infection had more time to gain a foothold and spread. (See Table 5.3.) In 1861, Dr. G. Scrive, a senior surgeon in the French army, wrote a book on the subject that was translated and published in the *American Journal of the Medical Sciences*. He concluded that

> the experience of both the English and the French armies is that the sum of human misery will be most materially lessened by permitting no ambiguous cases to be subject to the trial of preserving the limb; and, moreover, as respects the time of operating, operate with as little delay as possible.[9]

It is now known that cutting through infected tissues enhances the spread of infection by allowing it to gain access to and disseminate through the bloodstream. This results in "blood poisoning," or septicemia, which was almost always fatal at that time. In deciding whether to amputate, most Civil War surgeons were guided by the aphorism, "every hour the humane operation [of amputation] is delayed diminishes the chance of a favorable issue."[10] (In many ways this parallels the modern concept of the "golden hour" for treating trauma patients.) As Dr. Henry S. Hewit, the medical director of Sherman's Army during the 1864 Atlanta campaign, reported:

> Secondary and tertiary amputations, after osteomyelitis is kindled or fully established, are very dangerous to life, and every moment of delay in the amputations necessitates a greater sacrifice of length [more of the extremity is amputated]. With a full and careful examination and estimate of contingencies, every case must be decided upon its merits, and it is impossible as yet to promulgate a general law. It must, however, be said that the chances for life, preservation of constitution, and prevention of suffering, preponderate in favor of primary amputation.[11]

TABLE 5.3

Fatality from Amputation, Based on Timing of the Procedure

	Cases	Fatality Rate
Total of cases analyzed	23,762	27.3%
Surgery in first 48 hours	16,238	23.9
Surgery between 48 hours and a month after injury	5,501	34.8
Surgery over a month after injury	2,023	28.8

Medical and Surgical History, Surgical Section, vol. 3, p. 879. In the original tables, there are small differences in the number of cases in various categories because of incomplete data. The authors tried to correct these discrepancies as best as they could with the information available. The variations, however, are too small to affect the overall impressions given by the calculations.

Figure 5.7: Preparation for an amputation on Morris Island during the siege of Fort Wagner, early in July 1863. Dr. Samuel A. Green, chief medical officer of the island (and the person who preserved the picture), stands at the right of the table wearing a straw hat. Opposite him, also in his shirt sleeves, the medical director of the island, Dr. John J. Craven, examines the patient. Standing at the end of the table in a cap, Dr. William D. Murray, assistant surgeon of the 100th New York Volunteers, holds a wad of cloth probably used to administer anesthesia. (Courtesy of Massachusetts Commandery of the MOLLUS; USAMHI.)

In contrast to an approximately 50% mortality rate for civilian amputations in the United States and in Britain at the time of the Civil War, the mortality rate for the 29,980 total recorded amputations on Union soldiers was 26.3%. The available Confederate army data on survival are almost identical to the Union figures.[12] This lower mortality rate was due in large part to decisions to amputate early; most civilian amputations were delayed at least 48 hours. In addition, data from the French experiences in the Franco-Prussian War, five years after the end of the Civil War, reveal that a total of 13,173 amputations of all types were performed in the world-renowned French military hospitals, with 10,006 (76%) ending in death.[13]

Upon analyzing survival rates after amputation at various sites, Civil War surgeons found that the further away from the trunk the cut was made, the fewer deaths occurred. In comparing their data to those of the British in the Crimea, both Union and Confederate surgeons had generally lower fatality rates following primary amputations at various sites, as shown in Tables 5.4 and 5.5. (The British had the best results of the armies involved in that war.)

Data published in the *Confederate States Medical and Surgical Journal* confirmed that postponing amputations for 48 hours or more resulted in a considerably higher mortality rate for each site. The article also pointed out that excisions carried a higher mortality rate than amputations. The author attributed this outcome to the facts that excisions took much longer to perform and that the recovery period was longer, "exposing the patient to a much greater time to the evil influences of the hospital atmosphere . . . in all cases leaving limbs of very doubtful utility."[14] (For the problems of wound infections in hospitals, see Chapter 12, *Disease Among the Troops*.)

TABLE 5.4

Deaths from Amputation for the Union Army, 1861–1865

Site	Number of Amputations Performed	Fatality Rate
Hip Joint	66	83.3%
Knee joint	195	57.5
Thigh	6,369	54.2
Lower leg	5,523	33.2
Shoulder joint	866	29.1
Ankle joint	161	25.1
Upper arm	5,510	23.8
Forearm	1,761	14.0
Wrist joint	69	10.4
Elbow joint	40	7.6
Foot or toe	1,519	5.7
Hands or fingers	7,902	2.9
Total	**29,981**	**26.3%**

Medical and Surgical History, Surgical Section, vol. 3, p. 877. In the original tables, there are small differences in the number of cases in various categories because of incomplete data. The authors tried to correct these discrepancies as best as they could with the information available. The variations, however, are too small to affect the overall impressions given by the calculations.

Phoebe Y. Pember, a matron at Chimborazo Hospital in Richmond, thought the high mortality from secondary amputations was mostly due to the soldiers' nutritional state. She wrote,

> Poor food and great exposure had thinned the blood and broken down the system so entirely that secondary amputations performed in the hospital almost invariably resulted in death, after the second year of the war. [The] only cases under my observation that survived were two Irishmen, and it was really so difficult to kill an Irishman that there really was little cause for boasting on the part of the officiating surgeon.[15]

The case records from Chimborazo Hospital and another huge military hospital in Richmond (named after Brig. Gen. John H. Winder) document the problems of infection and support Mrs. Pember's conclusion.

For example, a soldier named O'Brien, a native of Ireland in Cropper's Virginia Artillery, fractured his ankle and foot escaping from prison. The hospital records mention that he had "indulged freely in use of ardent spirits before injury" and, after admission, had delirium tremens. Next he developed a skin infection, "erysipelas in most aggravated form," which extended from the foot to the thigh and up the right side of his body. Extensive suppuration and sloughing resulted and multiple draining sinuses formed. The leg became "carious" (weakened and atrophic), and the union of the fracture remained incomplete.

Eventually, an amputation was done at the middle third of the lower leg using the flap technique. O'Brien then developed the other serious streptococcal infection, hospital gangrene; he was treated with brandy and tincture of iron orally, with a full diet. The stump was injected with an antiseptic, "oil of terebinth," and dressed with bandages saturated in the same antiseptic. He was discharged eleven days after amputation with pus freely discharging. The date of his admission is not recorded; the amputation was performed on November 18, and he was discharged on November 29, 1864.[16]

Amputations at a joint, in particular the knee, also resulted in a very high mortality rate, probably because major joints, once opened, are extremely susceptible to infection. The British in the Crimea and the French in the Franco-Prussian War both recorded a 100% mortality rate for amputations done at "the hip." In contrast, Civil War surgeons on both sides did have patients who survived after hip amputations, but, as can be seen in Table 5.4, the mortality rate was still about 80%. It should be noted that "hip" meant an amputation high on the femur, very near the hip joint. A chain saw was introduced around the femur and the bone was cut near the joint. There is no record of actual disarticulations of the hip joint itself, which would have taken longer, been much more difficult, and surely resulted in death.

TABLE 5.5
Fatality Rate from Amputation at Various Sites

Deaths from Amputation for the British Army in the Crimean War and the Confederate Army of Northern Virginia, 1863

Amputation Site	British Army in the Crimea—% Deaths	Confederate Army of Northern Virginia Timing of Amputation	
		% under 48 hours	% after 48 hours
Hip*	100%	66%	—
Thigh*	56	38	73%
Shoulder joint	33	31	71
Lower leg	30	30	49
Arm	26	14	37
Foot	23	3	12
Forearm	5	12	22

*"Hip" meant an amputation high on the femur, near the hip joint. "Thigh" usually meant an amputation near the middle of the femur, although sometimes the location was specifically described as "upper third" or "lower third."

Crimean War data: Cantlie N: *A History of the Army Medical Department.* Vol. 2. Edinburgh: Churchill Livingston, 1973.

Confederate Army of Northern Virginia data: Sorrel P: Gun-shot wounds—Army of Northern Virginia. *Conf States Med Surg J.* 1864;1(10):153; and Chisolm JJ: *A Manual of Military Surgery for Use of the Surgeons in the Confederate Army.* 3rd ed. 1864. Repub: Dayton, OH: Morningside Press, 1992, p. 361.

Despite the charges of excessive amputations, some contemporary observers criticized the Civil War surgeons' reluctance to operate. William M. Caniff, professor of surgery at the University of Victoria College in Toronto, then the capital of British North America, visited the Union army after the Battle of Fredericksburg. He commented that American surgeons were, in his opinion, too hesitant about doing amputations. In a long essay published in the British medical journal *Lancet* on February 28, 1863, Caniff observed,

> Although a strong advocate of conservative surgery . . . I became convinced that upon the field, amputation was less frequently resorted to than it should be; that while in a few cases the operation was unnecessarily performed, in many cases it was omitted when it afforded the only chance of recovery.[17]

ATTITUDES TOWARD DISFIGUREMENT

The debate about excisions and amputations persisted throughout the war in medical societies and in medical journal articles. Many surgeons preferred the cosmetic result of a relatively functionless extremity after excision to the disfigurement of amputation, at least for the arm.

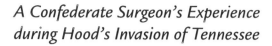

A Confederate Surgeon's Experience during Hood's Invasion of Tennessee

Dr. Deering Roberts described his experiences in December 1864, after Confederate Gen. John Bell Hood's disastrous attack on Union Gen. George Henry Thomas in the Battle of Franklin:

> In my hospital, while at Franklin, only seven men died, two of abdominal wounds, three from gunshot wounds in the head, one from amputation of thigh, and one who refused to submit to amputation—I never amputated a limb without the consent of the wounded man—after the nature of his case had been fully explained to him. Despite all arguments and reasoning, this man refused amputation, was greatly depressed and despondent from the first, and died on December 23rd, as I had expected, from gunshot injury to the forearm, complicated by nostalgia and despondency in an old man.[18]

It is important to remember that at the time there was much less acceptance of people with obvious impairments in "polite society." Until well into the twentieth century, even pregnant women were supposed to stay hidden from public view. Although gratitude toward Civil War veterans lessened the stigma, disfigured soldiers knew they faced discrimination at home and in the workplace. Many received letters from fiancées who had learned of an amputation or other physical deformity and who ended their engagements. Thomas A. Perrine of Michigan found that losing his arm meant losing his sweetheart:

> *I offered her my other hand*
> *Uninjured by the fight;*
> *'Twas all that I had left.*
> *'Without two hands,' she made reply,*
> *'You cannot handsome be.'*

The girl left him, he said, with "an empty sleeve, an empty heart."[19] This attitude toward disfigurement also affected the soldiers' appraisal of Civil War physicians, many blaming their condition on the surgeon rather than on the bullet.

Generals with Artificial Legs

Because of a shortage of experienced senior officers, several prominent Confederate generals returned to the field after having a leg amputated. Among the most notable were Generals John Bell Hood and Richard Stoddert Ewell, both of whom survived thigh amputations. Hood's leg was reportedly amputated at the hip, making him a rare survivor of that operation.

Ewell was wounded in the knee in August 1862 at Grovetown, shattering his patella and top of the tibia and part of its shaft. Dr. Hunter Holmes McGuire amputated just above the knee. Although he returned to field duty, Ewell had prolonged problems with infection in the area, which interfered with his using an artificial leg until at least a year after the war.[20]

Both generals used crutches and obtained several prosthetic legs for spares. Hood, who became known to his troops as "Old Pegleg," always carried an extra leg on campaigns. After the war, he liked to chuckle about the surprise of the Union troops who captured all his reserve horses and found that one had a leg suspended from the saddle. After the war, Hood reported his experience with at least five artificial legs of English, German, French, Yankee, and Confederate manufacture. He reluctantly confessed that the Yankee leg was the best of all.[21]

Before deciding whether to perform an excision or an amputation, surgeons had to balance appearance and function against an increased likelihood of fatal infection. (See Figure 5.8.) The evolution of their thinking is summarized in *Medical and Surgical History*:

> Toward the latter part of the war most thoughtful surgeons found it necessary to exercise a careful discrimination in the selection of cases for excision, and to refuse to [do an excision and not to amputate] in many instances in which, early in the contest, this operation would have been favored.[22]

The large number of amputees spurred advancements in the field now known as rehabilitation medicine, particularly in the development of prosthetic devices. While several types of artificial legs and arms were available

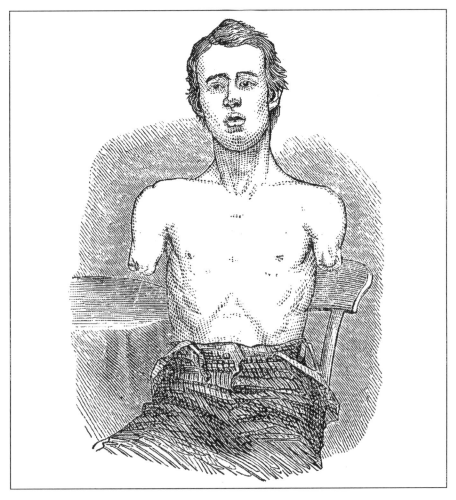

Figure 5.8: Drawing based on the photograph of a 17-year-old soldier from New York who sustained compound fractures of both elbows from an artillery shell on June 18, 1864, during the Siege of Petersburg. Amputations of both arms were deemed necessary and performed two hours after the injury, the right at the middle third by the circular method and the left in the upper third using flaps. Healing was slow and required the removal of pieces of dead bone on both sides. (Presumably, prostheses were provided, since he was transferred to Central Park Hospital in New York City, which specialized in prostheses and was called "Stump Hospital." However, there is no mention of that fact in the case report.) After the war, he worked for the Treasury Department. He died of tuberculosis on June 13, 1874. (*Medical and Surgical History*, Surgical Section, vol. II, p. 735.)

before the war, many new sophisticated devices were developed in the United States and in Europe, allowing even double-arm amputees to write and to dress and feed themselves. One such double amputee, a Private Decker, became the doorkeeper for the U.S. House of Representatives.

Two years after the war, the Federal Medical Department authorized the purchase of 4,095 prosthetic legs, 2,391 arms, 61 hands, and 14 feet.[23] For many former Confederate states, prostheses constituted the largest single expenditure in their post-war budget, since the Federal government provided no pensions or medical care for veterans. In Mississippi in the first post-war year, one-fifth of the total state budget was spent on artificial arms and legs.[24]

REFERENCES

1. Oates SB: *A Woman of Valor: Clara Barton and the Civil War.* New York: Macmillan, 1994, p. 231.
2. Howard EL: The effects of Minié balls on bone. *Conf States Med Surg J.* 1864;1:88; Sorrel P: Gun-shot wounds: Army of Northern Virginia. *Conf States Med Surg J.* 1864;1(10):153.
3. Hart AG: *The Surgeon and the Hospital in the Civil War.* Gaithersburg, MD: Olde Soldier Books, 1987, (orig. pub. 1902), p. 34.
4. Chisolm JJ: *A Manual of Military Surgery for Use of the Surgeons in the Confederate Army.* 3rd ed. Columbia, SC: Evans and Cogswell, 1861. Reprinted by Morningside Press, 1992, pp. 358-60.
5. Gross SD: *A Manual of Military Surgery or Hints on the Emergencies of Field, Camp, and Hospital Practice.* Philadelphia: Lippincott, 1861.
6. Gillett MC: *The United States Army Medical Department, 1818–1865.* Washington, D.C.: Center of Military History, U.S. Army, 1987, p. 285.
7. Roberts DJ: Field and temporary hospitals. In: *The Photographic History of the Civil War.* New York: Review of Reviews, 1970 (orig. pub. 1911), vol. 4B, p. 262.
8. *Medical and Surgical History,* Surgical Section, vol. 3, p. 880.
9. Scrive G: A medico-chirurgical account of the Crimean War, from the first arrival of the troops at Gallipoli to the their departure from the Crimea. Quoted in: *Am J Med Sci.* 1861 Oct;42:463-74.
10. Riley HD, Jr.: Medicine in the Confederacy. Part 1. *Mil Med.* 1956 Jan;118(1):63.
11. *O.R.*, Series I, Vol. XXXVIII/2, p. 524.
12. Sorrel, *Conf States Med Surg J,* 1864.
13. Debré P: *Louis Pasteur.* Baltimore, MD: Johns Hopkins Univ. Press, 1998.
14. Sorrel, *Conf States Med Surg J,* 1864.
15. Pember P: *A Southern Woman's Story: Life in Confederate Richmond.* New York: G.W. Carleton, 1879, p. 77.
16. "Records of the Winder Hospital." Eleanor S. Brockenbrough Library, Museum of the Confederacy, Richmond, VA.
17. Caniff W: Surgery of the Federal army. (Letter to the editor.) *Lancet.* 1863 Feb 28;1:251-52.
18. Roberts, Field and temporary hospitals, *Photographic History,* p. 260.
19. Llewellyn F: Limbs made and unmade by war. *America's Civil War.* 1995 Sept;8:40.
20. Welsh JD: *Medical Histories of Confederate Generals.* Kent, OH: Kent State Univ. Press, 1995, pp. 63-65.
21. Llewellyn, *America's Civil War,* 1995.
22. *Medical and Surgical History,* Surgical Section, vol. 3, p. 876.
23. Llewellyn, *America's Civil War,* 1995.
24. Foote S: *The Civil War: A Narrative.* vol. 3. New York: Random House, 1958, p. 1041.

6

Learning to Treat Wounds: The Surgeons, the Operations, and the Results

. . . Bearing the bandages, water and sponge,
Straight and swift to my wounded I go
Where they lie on the ground after the battle brought in,
Where their priceless blood reddens the grass the ground,
Or to the rows of the hospital tent, or under the roof'd hospital,
To the long rows of cots up and down each side I return,
To each and all one after another I draw near, not one do I miss,
An attendant follows holding a tray, he carries a refuse pail,
Soon to be fill'd with clotted rags and blood, emptied, and fill'd again.

— Walt Whitman, "The Wound Dresser,"
Leaves of Grass

CIVIL WAR SURGERY HAS GENERATED MANY MYTHS. Among these is a belief that regimental surgeons were free to perform any operation they wished to do. Younger surgeons were accused of performing amputations simply for the experience, without regard for their patients' welfare. While some outrages did occur on both sides at the beginning of the war, both armies brought this problem under control relatively quickly.

To increase the quality of decision making, on October 30, 1862, Army of the Potomac Medical Director Jonathan Letterman issued an order making the most experienced surgeons responsible for deciding whether operations should be performed and allowing only the most skilled surgeons perform them. His order, which remained in effect throughout the war, specified:

> In all doubtful cases [surgeons appointed to hospital posts] will consult together, and a majority of them shall decide upon the expediency and character of the operation. These officers will be selected from the division without regard to rank, but solely on account of their known prudence, judgment, and skill. The surgeon-in-chief of the division is enjoined to be especially careful in the selection of these officers, choosing only those who have distinguished themselves for surgical skill, sound judgment, and conscientious regard for the highest interests of the wounded.[1]

After the war, Dr. George T. Stevens, who served with the Army of the Potomac's Sixth Corps during most of the war, confirmed that Letterman's order was followed in the field:

> One or more surgeons of well known skill and experience were detailed from the medical force of the division, who were known as "operating surgeons"; to each of whom was assigned three assistants, also known to be skillful men ... To the operating surgeons all cases requiring surgical operations were brought, and thus the wounded men had the benefit of the very best talent and experience in the division, in the decision of the question whether he should be submitted to the use of the knife, and in the performance of the operation in case one was required. It was a mistaken impression among those at home, that each medical officer was the operating surgeon for his own men. Only about one in fifteen of the medical officers was entrusted with operations.[2]

Another Army of the Potomac surgeon, Dr. Albert Gaillard Hart, described how the system worked in the field hospitals:

> serious operations only were performed in extreme cases at the temporary depot ... If there were cases likely to need an operation, they were carried to an operating tent. Here the surgeons met, consulted, and performed the operations decided upon. Nearly all our 200 capital operations were cases sent back to us from the front with the hope of saving the limb.[3]

John Shaw Billings (see Biographical Box, pp. 163-64) noted that the front-line physicians at the Battle of Spotsylvania were willing to let more experienced surgeons make the decision to amputate: "A very few men performed operations which were unnecessary, amputating a few limbs which could have been saved, but the great majority were timid and anxious to shift the responsibility and to get the simplest dressings on as soon as possible."[4]

Letterman confirms the opinion that most physicians erred on the side of caution:

> If any objection could be urged against the surgery of those fields, it would be the efforts on the part of surgeons to practice "conservative surgery" to too great an extent . . . I had better opportunities, perhaps, than any one else to form an opinion, and from my observations I am convinced that if any fault was committed it was that the knife was not used enough. So much has been said on this matter that, familiar as I am with the conduct of the medical officers on those battle-fields, I cannot, as the medical director of this army, see them misrepresented and be silent.[5]

Dr. John Shaw Billings (1838-1913)

Born on a farm in Indiana, John Shaw Billings began his education by devouring books on every subject. He graduated from Miami University in Oxford, Ohio, in 1857 and then took the standard two-year course at the Medical College of Ohio in Cincinnati. As a requirement for graduation, Billings prepared a dissertation on the surgical treatment of epilepsy, learning more about the difficulties of accessing the medical literature than he did about the disease.

Billings was approved by the U.S. Army Medical Corps Examining Board in September 1861. Initially, he was stationed at Union Hospital in Georgetown, where two famous Civil War nurses, Hannah Ropes and Louisa Mae Alcott, later worked. He then established, and for a long period ran, a hospital at Georgetown's Cliffburn Barracks. While there, Billings performed a variety of surgical procedures, including one of the first recorded successful ankle excisions. In a letter to his future wife, he described caring for wounded soldiers brought to Washington from the Peninsula in Virginia:

> July 7, 1862 . . . I've received 200 wounded, and have been operating for 24 hours steadily, shoulder joints and elbow joints, arms, legs, etc., etc., . . . Just as I had written this, I was interrupted by the arrival of 125 more wounded, and just as I was hard at work on them, lo and behold, here comes the Medical Director, Surgeon General, Chief Inspector of Hospitals and 6 surgeons—to see me operate.

He successfully showed them his surgical skills.

In March 1863, Billings was assigned to the Army of the Potomac, caring for wounded first at Chancellorsville and then at Gettysburg. Later, he served as a medical inspector for the Army of the Potomac's medical director, then Dr. Thomas McParlin. He collated statistics, collected specimens for the medical museum in Washington (his concise messages accompanying them were admirable), and consulted on a variety of surgical procedures in the field.

continued . . .

Dr. John Shaw Billings, *continued*

On December 27, 1864, he was transferred to the Surgeon General's Office, where he assisted in running the medical museum, including performing photomicroscopy under Dr. Woodward's direction. Billings also became curator of the Library of the Surgeon General's Office. At the end of the war, Surgeon General Joseph Barnes used the $80,000 surplus in the hospital fund to further develop this library. It became the National Library of Medicine, which today is the world's leading medical library. Billings produced a periodic update of the medical literature, called the *Index Catalogue*, which evolved first into *Index Medicus*, and then the computerized database, *MEDLINE*.

During his career, Dr. Billings also helped reorganize and improve the Marine Hospital Service, now the U.S. Public Health Service. Later, he not only proposed plans for the construction of the new Johns Hopkins Hospital, but also spent fifteen years (1875–1890) supervising its construction. During part of that time, he served as president of the American Public Health Association (1880), and he was the only member of the National Academy of Science elected for "contributions other than scientific" (1883). He also garnered numerous international honors.

After thirty-five years in the army, Dr. Billings retired in 1895 and became professor of hygiene at the University of Pennsylvania. Due to his unique abilities and experiences, he was recruited to organize the newly established New York Public Library and helped it to become one of the foremost general libraries in the world. He also designed its main building on Fifth Avenue, which is still considered an architectural masterpiece. In 1905, he helped design a new teaching hospital for Harvard Medical School's new teaching hospital, Peter Bent Brigham, in Boston. Upon his death in 1913, the librarian of the Royal Society of Medicine in London wrote of Dr. Billings, "we are not likely to look upon his like again."[6]

The Confederate Army's Medical Department had similar problems at the beginning of the war with the excessive zeal of surgeons and instituted a similar solution. In the third edition of his *Manual of Military Surgery*, Professor J. J. Chisolm bluntly addressed the issue:

> Among a certain class of surgeons . . . amputations have often been performed when limbs could have been saved, and the amputating knife has often been brandished, by inexperienced surgeons, over simple flesh wounds. In the beginning of the war the desire for operating was so great among the large number of medical officers recently from the schools, who

were for the first time in a position to indulge this extravagant propensity, that the limbs of soldiers were in as much danger from the ardor of young surgeons as from the missiles of the enemy.

It was for this reason that, in the distribution of labor in the field infirmaries, it was recommended that the surgeon who had the greatest experience, and upon whose judgment the greatest reliance could be placed, should officiate as examiner, and his decision be carried out by those who may possess a greater facility or desire for the operative manual.[7]

SURGICAL INNOVATIONS

Civil War surgeons operated in an era when, by twentieth-century standards, surgery was still primitive. Civilian surgeons did not attempt new procedures, such as intestinal surgery, because their patients nearly always died. Military surgeons, despite their lack of experience in dealing with internal wounds, were faced with situations in which, if they didn't attempt such operations, their patients would die of peritonitis from bowel injuries or collapsed lungs after chest wounds. Whenever conditions permitted, they improvised and attempted desperate operations, trying to save their comrades.

In their desperation, they developed novel approaches to abdominal, chest, eye, plastic, and orthopedic surgery, as well as surgery for head wounds, later termed neurosurgery. These surgical pioneers invented techniques and used improvised equipment under field conditions and with untrained assistants, one of whom often had to hold a lamp just to illuminate the operative field. The number of patients treated in each category was too small to permit an accurate evaluation of outcomes, but, surprisingly, successful individual cases were reported.

Use of a Fork to Lift a Depressed Skull Fracture

On at least one occasion, Dr. Hunter Holmes McGuire, Stonewall Jackson's medical director and personal physician, attempted neurosurgery in the field. A friend recorded:

> I have seen him break off one prong of a common table fork, bend the point of the other prong, and with it elevate the bone in a depressed fracture of the skull and save life.[8]

(This describes an instrument not unlike some modern bone "elevators" that surgeons still use.)

As a new approach in treating neck injuries that affected breathing, surgeons performed tracheostomies, also called bronchostomies; they even left the tube in place for long periods if necessary.[9,10] Twenty tracheostomy/bronchostomy cases are recorded; thirteen of these patients died. Six of these operations were needed because of gunshot wounds, while the other fourteen were performed because of diseases, such as diphtheria or abscesses of the tonsil, which threatened to asphyxiate the patients.[11] The description of this procedure in *Medical and Surgical History* suggests considerable surgical expertise:

> A straight incision, commencing over the cricoid cartilage was made and carried downward in the direction of the median line for about one and a half inches . . . The thyroid gland was exposed [and avoided] . . . A grooved tenaculum was hooked through the trachea just below the cricoid cartilage . . . A narrow, sharp pointed knife, guided by the groove of the tenaculum, was then inserted to perforate the trachea [with some difficulty, requiring two attempts] . . . The fresh opening was then thoroughly cleansed, and through the opening a blunt-pointed narrow knife was passed and carried downward and forward until at least three rings of the trachea had been divided. . . . The operation was completed by introducing a large sized Desault's tube, which was properly retained.[12]

In at least one instance, a hollow silver tube was used initially as a tracheostomy tube, but it was replaced with "a double fenestrated cannula," which the soldier still wore six months after being shot in the neck.[13]

ARTERIAL LIGATION

Arterial ligations were one of the few surgical innovations for which Civil War surgeons are generally given credit. Early in the war, tying major arteries (ligation) was rarely attempted, although Crimean surgeons had performed the procedure and it was described in books available to American surgeons. By the second half of the war, surgeons not only were performing this life-saving procedure, but also had improved the techniques and were successfully ligating many vessels that had previously been considered inaccessible.

Since anatomy received so much emphasis in American medical schools, "all surgeons were familiar with the anastomosis or collateral circulation in blood-vessels."[14] They knew which arteries had partners or branches that could take over when they were ligated and how likely it was that collateral branches would have time to develop sufficiently to nourish an area deprived of its primary blood supply following an obstruction. Even when surgeons were not sure if an area would receive adequate blood flow after ligation, they believed it was best to stop the bleeding immediately to save a life and then hope for the best. In some cases, amputation would become necessary if gangrene developed, but ligation of a bleeding vessel could sometimes avoid that outcome.

The procedure of finding and tying a bleeding vessel, however, was one of the most difficult that Civil War surgeons had to do. Given the dreadful operating conditions, such operations were usually attempted only in life-threatening situations. (Some ligations, however, were performed because an injury to a major artery had weakened its wall and caused it to dilate, thus forming an aneurysm that threatened to rupture.)[15]

In *Medical and Surgical History*, cases of ligation of major arteries are tabulated and thoroughly analyzed. Table 6.1 summarizes physicians' experiences with these difficult emergency procedures. Remarkably, they had success ligating some vessels, such as the subclavian artery, that today's surgeons sometimes have difficulty exposing and ligating after trauma.

TABLE 6.1

Success Rate of Artery Ligation for Hemorrhage or Aneurysm

Artery	Number of Cases	Success Rate
Head and Neck		
External carotid	7	57%
Common carotid	82	24
Internal carotid	0	—
Upper Extremity		
Radial and ulnar	81	80%
Subclavian	10	70
Brachial	170	70
Axillary	49	14
Lower Extremity		
Anterior and posterior tibial	95	58%
Gluteal	6	33
Femoral	374	25
Branches of femoral	46	24
Popliteal	36	22
External iliac	26	12
Common iliac	5	0
Internal iliac	3	0

Medical and Surgical History, Medical Section, vol. 1, and *Medical and Surgical History*, Surgical Section, vol. 3, p. 762 et seq.

Confederate surgeons' experiences with arterial ligations in cases with massive hemorrhage were partially described in existing reports to their surgeon general. They ligated 9 carotid arteries (main artery to the head) with only one death and one patient lost to follow-up, 14 subclavian or axillary arteries (artery to the arm ligated high up under the shoulder) with 9 deaths, and 59 arteries in the arm or forearm with 6 deaths and 9 lost to follow-up. The rest were presumed to be survivors. The femoral artery, the main artery to the leg, was ligated in the thigh area and follow-up results were available in 48 cases, with 24 deaths.[16] These results are commendable for the time.

EARLY NEUROSURGERY

Before the Civil War, few surgeons had ever had the opportunity to perform neurosurgery or even to see it done. Military surgeons had to learn or invent methods to treat massive head injuries. Scalp wounds were rarely a problem. According to Union data, over 7,700 gunshot wounds of the scalp in Federal and captured Confederate soldiers were treated with a fatality rate of only 2%; the deaths were almost entirely from infections such as erysipelas. Fractures of the cranial bones caused by gunshots, shell fragments, or sabers were more serious and many required surgical procedures because of persistent coma or convulsions.

Surgeons were aware that trephining (making a large hole in the skull to reach inside and remove foreign bodies such as bullets or bone fragments) had been uniformly fatal during the Crimean War. Nevertheless, faced with desperately ill patients, Civil War surgeons attempted the operation in 200 cases. In dramatic contrast to the Crimean War, military surgeons had a 43% survival rate during the Civil War. Of the 160 trephined cases reported in detail, 66 survived. Most survivors were discharged and pensioned, although 6 prisoners were exchanged or paroled. Fifteen patients returned to duty and 4 went on to serve limited duty in the Veterans Reserve Corps (in Chapter 16, see The Invalid Corps). *Medical and Surgical History* reports 175 cases in which missiles were extracted from inside the cranium (skull), with a 48% mortality rate. Bone splinters were removed or depressed fractures were elevated without trephining in 454 cases; 39% of these men died.[17]

In the 1864 edition of his *Manual of Military Surgery*, Dr. Chisolm advised against trephining, even in cases of intracranial bleeding. Trephining "is always very serious *per se*," he wrote, "and is, in many instances, sufficient of itself to cause cerebral or meningeal inflammation, which will nearly always terminate fatally. The operation is as serious as the condition for which it is used, and, although the patient might recover from either, he succumbs under the combination."[18] Chisolm advocated conservative ("expectant") treatment, describing patients who recovered from intracranial hemorrhage without surgery (they all died later of an unrelated condition, but their autopsies revealed the earlier bleeding).

Civil War surgeons understood the nature and significance of concussions produced by head injuries and knew that recovery of consciousness could occur after "a few minutes, hours or days." They advocated doing as little as possible to unconscious patients, and avoided using stimulants indiscriminately, as well as bloodletting. Through analyses of autopsies on fatal cases, they learned about the phenomenon of contra-coup injury. Surgeons were warned, "Blood vessels may have given way at any other portion of the brain than at the portion corresponding to the point where the skull has been injured. The recoil of the contents of the skull from the blow may have ruptured vessels diametrically opposite to the injured point."[19]

Chisolm advised surgeons to use a finger to probe head wounds to determine if there was a skull fracture or if a bullet was lodged in or under the scalp. If the surgeon found no depressed fracture of the skull, conservative treatment was advised. Depressed fractures were known to be serious, especially if they were accompanied by evidence of pressure on the brain. Surgeons understood that the "inner table of the [two layers of bone that form the] skull is usually much more extensively broken and displaced than the outer."[20] Nevertheless, it was considered prudent not to operate. If many loose pieces of bone were found, they usually tried to remove them. But if a patient recovered consciousness and did not exhibit evidence of compression of the brain (such as paralysis), patience was advocated. As Chisolm put it, "avoid all instrumental interference, even to dilating the wound, for the purpose of facilitating a more accurate diagnosis . . . Let nature abide her time."[21] When a depressed fracture was accompanied by symptoms of compression, such as paralysis, "instrumental interference [is] justifiable."[22]

Surgeons on both sides documented that patients might survive and be functional even if a bullet was allowed to remain inside the head. Dr. Frank Hastings Hamilton thought that bullets should always be removed. In at least one case, however, he felt he had no choice but to leave the bullet in a patient's cranium. Although he expected the man to die of infection, he survived. Hamilton reported the case in the general medical literature, and this helped to advance the treatment of gunshot wounds of the head.[23]

A report from Confederate General Hospital in Charlottesville describes the treatment of eighteen men having gunshot wounds of the head with skull fractures. Bone fragments had to be removed from the surface of the brain

in several cases, two patients required trephination, and temporary neuro-
logic defects appeared in a few patients. Only three of these men died, and
one had permanent one-sided paralysis, remarkably good results for the
time.[24]

Nerve suturing was advocated for torn nerves in the extremities. At the
beginning of the war, it was widely believed that manipulation of a large
nerve could cause the heart to stop, but this myth was dispelled and surgical
approaches to treating nerve injuries were a major advance during the war.[25]

President Lincoln's Head Wound

On April 14, 1865, John Wilkes Booth shot President Abraham Lincoln
in the back of the head with a .41-caliber bullet fired from his single-shot
Derringer pistol. Lincoln and his wife were attending a play at Ford's
Theater in Washington, D.C., that night. Booth chose a moment with
loud laughter from the audience, which obscured the sound of the pistol.
The assassin immediately dropped the empty Derringer and used a hunting knife to severely slash the upper arm of Maj. Henry R. Rathbone (who
was also in Lincoln's box). Booth then jumped down to the stage.

Assistant Surgeon Charles A. Leale, one of two army surgeons in the
audience, was the first to reach the president. Leale, who was in charge
of the officer's ward at Armory Square Hospital, had obtained special
training in head wound treatment at New York's Bellevue Hospital under
Dr. Frank Hastings Hamilton. Leale noted that Lincoln was not breathing
and, because he had seen Booth brandishing a bloody knife as well as
Major Rathbone's bleeding arm, he thought at first that Lincoln must
have been stabbed. He loosened Lincoln's collar and shirt but, finding no
stab wound and seeing blood on his shoulder and an enlarged right pupil
(an indicator of increased intracranial pressure, known as a "blown
pupil"), he then suspected a head wound. When Leale palpated the back
of Lincoln's head, he felt the ball's entry wound. When he tried to probe
the wound with his fingertip, feeling for the bullet, he dislodged a blood
clot and Lincoln began to breathe again.

Leale did not find the ball under the scalp or when he probed the skull
wound as far as his fifth finger reached. He noted in his reports to the surgeon general and to a Congressional investigating committee that the
skull wound had smooth edges. This indicates that his finger did not penetrate deeply, since the fracture of the inner table of the skull would have
had sharp beveled edges and would have injured his finger.[26] (Indeed,

continued . . .

President Lincoln's Head Wound, continued

the autopsy revealed such changes in the inside layer of the bone of the skull.)

Dr. Charles S. Taft, the second army surgeon to reach the President's box, also noted that one pupil was large and the other very small, but he recorded that the left was widely dilated and the right was contracted. Both surgeons realized that the bullet had entered the brain from behind and thought that it had probably blasted pieces of the skull into the right orbit, since the right eye was protruding and discolored. Both agreed that the wound would be fatal.

Lincoln was tenderly carried across the street to a rooming house and laid diagonally across the small bed, semi-sitting with a wedge of pillows under his head and shoulders. At about 1:00 A.M., three hours after being shot, Lincoln experienced an episode of general twitching, with arm spasms which tended to turn his palms down (pronate them). Afterwards, his pupils became fixed, dilated, and non-reactive to light. These findings can be interpreted as meaning that Lincoln was now decerebrate and progressing rapidly toward death.

At about 2:00 A.M., Surgeon General Joseph Barnes used a silver probe to investigate the wound and to keep a clot from forming; later he introduced a porcelain-tipped Nélaton probe deep into the bullet track. The probe hit something solid, but there was no mark of lead on it and Barnes concluded that it had struck a piece of bone. No further attempts were made to find the bullet. The wound continued to ooze blood and brain tissue. Lincoln's breathing became intermittent and finally ceased altogether at 7:22 A.M. on April 15.

Lincoln's body was removed to the White House and placed on his bed in the "Lincoln bedroom," where Dr. Joseph J. Woodward of the Surgeon General's Office performed an autopsy beginning at noon; it was limited to the head. (Two weeks after performing the autopsy on President Lincoln, Dr. Woodward autopsied the body of John Wilkes Booth aboard *The Montauk*, a Federal monitor.) Woodward thought that the ball, which had fallen out when the skull was opened, had lodged above the left eye, but Surgeon General Barnes recorded that he thought the ball had probably lodged above the right eye.[27]

President Lincoln's family physician, Dr. Robert King Stone, was also present at the autopsy. His handwritten notes and a diagram of some of his observations were found and published almost exactly 100 years after the event. His description is very similar to Woodward's: he states that the bullet was lodged in brain substance on the left side. These contra-

continued . . .

President Lincoln's Head Wound, continued

dictions have never been resolved. As Dr. John K. Lattimer, the most detailed and informed reviewer of these observations, pointed out, all those involved in the care of President Lincoln and in the autopsy were extremely upset, under severe emotional stress, and had marked sleep deprivation by the time of the autopsy.

Woodward recorded that the bullet had entered the back of the head (the occipital bone) and passed through the entire length of the brain and through the right lateral ventricle (a brain cavity normally filled with spinal fluid); both ventricles and the track of the ball through the brain tissue were filled with clotted blood and contained several small bone fragments. There was a thick subdural clot on the surface of the brain. The roofs of both eye sockets (the orbital plates) were fractured and fragments of bone pushed up into the brain.

Debris found inside the head included the flattened ball, a sharp-edged disk of metal sheared from the ball, a burnt cloth patch that had been wrapped around the ball in the Derringer, large sharp-edged disks of bone from the inner table of the skull, and numerous small sharp fragments of thin (cancellous) bone from the plates of the skull. These fragments were photographed and preserved. According to experienced coroners, orbital plate fractures are frequent after bullet wounds to the head. They probably occur because of the pressure changes resulting from distortion of the skull as a result of the impact of the bullet and displacement of intracerebral tissues.[28]

The treatment of President Lincoln's head wound was the typical approach during the Civil War and for a long time afterward. Since the bullet had penetrated the entire length of the brain from back to front and there was extensive hemorrhage into the tissue and ventricles within the brain, there was no hope of recovery. Such wounds were virtually always fatal during the Civil War, and most still are today. The attempts to find the bullet were routine at the time, although the Surgical Section of *Medical and Surgical History* contains descriptions of twenty cases in which the bullet was allowed to remain in the cranium. However, in most of the cases, there was considerable or total disability, usually accompanied by convulsions or paralysis, and most patients died within a few years of the injury.[29]

By the end of the 1800s, with x-rays to help locate the missile, surgeons knew that trying to remove a bullet deeply embedded in the brain caused too much harm and they would leave it there, sometimes with good results. While the attempts to find the bullet in President Lincoln's head were harmful, no one really believes they affected the outcome.[30]

TREATING ABDOMINAL WOUNDS

During the war, surgeons attempted to repair torn intestines or to anastomose torn ends of the gut by removing destroyed sections and rejoining the severed ends. Some methods for suturing intestine were drawn from American and European surgical textbooks and others were invented (see Figure 6.1).

Most approaches to repairing serious intra-abdominal wounds involved enlarging the incision. But by 1876, when the Surgical Section of *Medical and Surgical History* was written, a laparotomy (making a new abdominal incision) was becoming the standard approach for such cases. The authors predicted that this procedure would be increasingly used, and it was.[31]

In most bowel-injury cases, intraperitoneal infection became apparent within days and the prognosis was poor, but there were some successes. Apparently, surgeons had more success in treating abdominal injuries when the intestine itself was not injured. In such cases, surgeons merely rinsed the intestine to clean it, replaced it into the abdominal cavity, and then repaired the torn abdominal wall. Some men also recovered after the appearance of a fecal fistula, that is, a tear in the colon that communicated with the outside through the skin. One patient who survived a fecal fistula was a Confederate prisoner captured at Gettysburg. He recovered, but, unfortunately, he was transferred from DeCamp General Hospital on Davids' Island in Long Island Sound to the prison at Elmira. His ultimate fate is not known.[32,33]

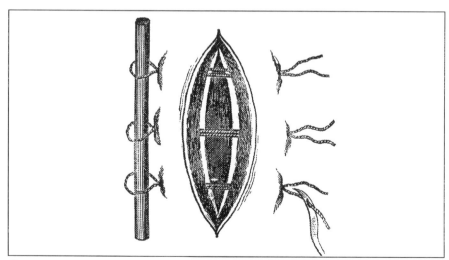

Figure 6.1: Illustration of the use of "quilled sutures" to repair an incised wound of the abdominal wall. The method includes an approximation of the edges of the torn muscles, not just the skin, to help physicians avoid causing a ventral hernia. (*Medical and Surgical History*, Surgical Section, vol. 2, p. 5.)

CHEST WOUNDS: A "CLINICAL TRIAL"

Compared to over 8,000 chest wounds treated in the Union armies, the records for nineteenth-century European wars listed very few chest wounds that were treated. The small number of cases in European wars probably resulted from their chaotic ambulance services—relatively few seriously wounded men were removed from the field in time for treatment. The chance of survival after a penetrating chest wound was dismal: in the Crimean War, the British recorded treating a total of 164 lung wounds with 133 deaths, for an 80% mortality rate; the French recorded 491 cases with a 92% mortality rate. In the Union army, the mortality rate was 65% of a much larger total number of cases, suggesting that their surgeons were more successful treating these serious injuries.

There was a "clinical trial" during the Civil War to test an innovative treatment for chest wounds. Surgeons realized that a perforation in the chest wall allowed the negative pressure inside the thorax to suck in air and collapse the lung. Severe shortness of breath resulted and, if the other lung was also compromised, death occurred quickly. At least one Union physician, Asst. Surg. Benjamin Howard, devised a way to seal the opening in the chest wall to prevent air from being sucked in: this is still an important element in the treatment of such wounds today).

Despite improvement in the immediate condition of many patients, Howard was not sure about the ultimate success of his treatment. He held the lowest rank in the Medical Department and worked in aid stations near the battlefield, where his procedure was most needed. However, his patients were quickly evacuated to field and general hospitals and Howard rarely learned how they fared. So, on June 25, 1863, he wrote to the surgeon general asking permission to attempt his procedure under circumstances in which he could follow his patients and determine its true efficacy:

> Sir: I have the honor to submit for your consideration the following mode of treatment of gunshot and penetrating Wounds of the chest and abdomen in which suppuration has not commenced. All foreign bodies within reach having been removed, and bleeding of the wound having ceased, if it be from gunshot, pare the edges of the wound all round ... bring the opposite edges together, and retain them in accurate opposition by metallic sutures; carefully dry the wound and parts immediately surrounding; place thereon a few shreds of charpie [a bandage material made from lint or old linen] arranged crosswise after the manner of warp and woof, pour on the charpie a few drops of collodion [a chemical that dried into a seal] so as to saturate it and form a sort of collodion cloth; let it dry; then apply one or two additional coats of collodion cloth; let it dry and apply

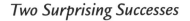

Two Surprising Successes

Many times, wounded men who were considered hopeless cases actually recovered.

After the Battle of Cedar Mountain (August 9, 1862), two assistant surgeons from a Georgia unit found a Confederate officer lying unconscious in a field. His abdominal wall had been torn open and his intestines had spilled out onto the grass and were covered with dirt. After dismissing his situation as hopeless, they were leaving when the officer awoke and demanded treatment. He was carried to a nearby farmhouse and laid on the dining room table, where they found that the intestines had not been damaged by the bullet. After washing the abdominal cavity, they removed a handful of sand and grass, cut out the broken end of a pelvic bone, and sutured the gaping abdominal wound using a sewing needle and household thread. The officer recovered and, after the war, had a successful career in the Egyptian army, along with other former Confederate officers.[34]

Another survivor's story was reported in the *Saturday Evening Post* early in the war:

> [A] regular army veteran named White was struck in head with piece of a shell, taking off the right ear, injuring his jaw and distorting his face. He lay unconscious for many hours, and whilst in this state was carried to his grave [with other casualties, mostly recently enlisted volunteers]. They arranged his blanket and prepared for lowering him into the grave, when he raised his head and called out, "Boys, what are you going to do?"
>
> "We came to bury you," was the response. "I don't see it, boys; give me a drink and carry me back. I can't be put to the ground with that raw recruit." So they carried him back, and today he is walking about very nearly well.[35]

one or two additional coats of collodion with a camel hair pencil; repeat the process until satisfied that the wound is hermetically sealed.[36]

He requested that "necessary arrangements be made to enable me to test [the] merits [of the procedure] at the earliest opportunity."[37] Surgeon General Hammond, who knew Howard well, immediately gave permission for the trial in a letter to Medical Director Letterman: "The Surgeon General desires that, at the next battle of the Army of the Potomac, Assistant Surgeon Howard be placed in charge of a field hospital for the treatment of wounds of the chest and abdomen. If necessary to send those cases from the Army, he may be sent with them."[38]

The next battle began only a week after Howard sent his letter. The army, following General Lee, had moved quickly into Maryland and Pennsylvania from the encampments around the Rappahannock. Medical Department personnel (and supplies), strung out over a long distance aboard wagons or on foot, arrived at Gettysburg after the battle had begun. Even though they were exhausted and facilities to care for wounded had to be established immediately, arrangements were made for Howard to have his own tent within the hospital facility.

After the battle, Howard was able to follow many of his patients. He recorded that a few had immediate relief of symptoms, especially for shortness of breath, and many survived. There were many failures as well. As would be expected during that era, patients who survived the initial period of treatment often died of infection, usually with pus in the pleural cavity (empyema). Howard advocated inserting a tube into the chest to drain the pus, which helped, but, even then, death frequently occurred. With no effective means to treat infection, Howard's overall results (a death rate of 61%–70%, depending on which cases were included) were not much better than those for patients who did not receive his treatment.

Mortality in such chest injuries also varied greatly depending on whether there was more than minimal laceration of the lung. Therefore, it was difficult for Howard to decide which cases to use for comparison and what mortality rate to expect in cases treated without his methods. Further, the ultimate outcome in many of Howard's cases was still in doubt when his report was prepared. Some soldiers were transferred to hospitals nearer their homes and not completely followed. Others improved to the point that they were able to desert and still others were Confederate prisoners who felt well enough to escape. Because many patients were "lost to follow-up" and thus could not be included in the final results of the trial and because comparison ("control") cases were uncertain, the value of his method remained questionable after the results were analyzed. Many physicians were not convinced that Howard's treatment saved lives and his method was not recommended for widespread use during the war.

Some surgeons did try Howard's method. Medical Inspector C. Smart of the Second Corps reported a trial by a large number of surgeons under his jurisdiction. He concluded, "Without reference to the issue in death or recovery, this operation is practiced in order to yield the relief from dyspnea [difficulty breathing] which is invariably, in the experience of these surgeons, its immediate result."[39]

Dr. Billings offered an excellent summary of the problems and conclusions concerning Howard's treatment in a report analyzing the treatment of disease and wounds in the Army of the Potomac during 1864:

> Penetrating wounds of the thorax have been, in most cases, treated like simple flesh wounds, with the exception that the lint is often applied dry to close the wound. A small number of cases have been hermetically sealed with colloidon, by the process of Assistant Surgeon Howard, U.S.A. This mode of treatment is regarded with disfavor by the majority of the medical officers of this army. Those belonging to the 3d division, Second Corps, however, have adopted the method, and have practiced it in a number of cases. I have seen two cases thus treated, and I consider it valuable when there is profuse hemorrhage and great dyspnea, as a primary and temporary mode of treatment. In such cases the immediate relief it affords is marked; quiet, tranquil respiration follows, and the grave symptoms are rapidly ameliorated. The benefit gained, however, ceases entirely when the process of suppuration has set in, a process which this mode of treatment does not at all prevent.[40]

As can be seen from this report, army surgeons maintained open minds. They had a desire to learn from experience, but needed facts, not theory, to be convinced. Unfortunately, infection defeated even appropriate forms of treatment, and the key result they were seeking, improved survival, was not observed.

The ultimate outcome of this trial was typical of many attempts at innovation during the Civil War—unavoidable and untreatable infection undid the work of the surgeons. Nevertheless, Howard's method had become the standard treatment for "sucking" wounds of the chest by World War I, and its benefit became more apparent when a tube to drain empyema was routinely inserted. A 1918 British text of military surgery drew the conclusion that "If an open sucking wound is present it should be made air-tight by sutures which include both skin and muscle, or by a gauze plug fixed by long strips of broad, adhesive strapping."[41] Assistant Surgeon Howard would have agreed.

ORIGIN OF PLASTIC SURGERY

A total of thirty-two "plastic operations" are listed in the Union records, including six reconstructions of eyelids; five of the nose; three of the cheek; fourteen of the lip, palate, or other parts of the mouth; and four of the chin. Major facial reconstruction was done in multiple steps by creating flaps of skin to replace facial structures. Because infection is often less of a problem in such facial injuries, successes were more frequent than in other innovative procedures. Confederate surgeons performed similar operations, including wiring parts of the jaw for mandibular fractures.[42] After soldiers returned home, civilian surgeons performed similar plastic surgical procedures, but these are not documented in the wartime records. Although the techniques developed by military surgeons during the Civil War became standard procedures in civilian medicine after the war, a subspecialty organization devoted to plastic surgery was not formed until 1921.

At least twenty-two civilian surgeons practiced reconstructive surgery, also called "plastic surgery" at the time, on soldiers during and immediately after the war. One, Gurdon Buck, is considered to be the "father of modern plastic surgery" and among America's greatest surgeons.[43] A graduate of the College of Physicians and Surgeons of New York, Buck operated on soldiers at St. Joseph's Hospital in Central Park and at New York Hospital. He was one of the first surgeons to photograph his cases, and, after the war, wrote an influential monograph on his experiences, *Contributions to Reparative Surgery* (1876), which included Civil War cases. Dr. Buck also developed an apparatus for treating lower extremity fractures; the modern version of this device is referred to as "Buck's traction splint" (see Figure 6.2).

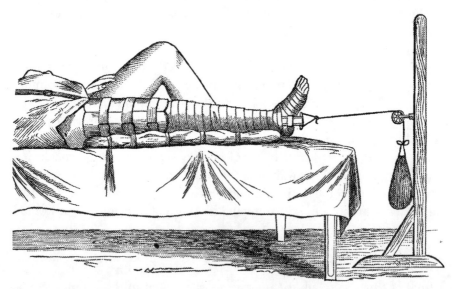

Figure 6.2: Apparatus designed by Dr. Gurdon Buck to provide traction and splinting of a fracture of the leg. It provided continuous extension of the leg by using a weight and pulley. (*Medical and Surgical History*, Surgical Section, vol. 3, p. 348.)

One of Dr. Gurdon Buck's First Cases

The case of Carlton Burgan, a 20-year-old soldier from Maryland, figured prominently in the descriptions of plastic surgery in *Medical and Surgical History* and in Dr. Buck's *Contributions to Reparative Surgery*, where it was the first case presented. Both included published photographs of the soldier's face before (a), during (b,c), and after (d) the procedures.

Burgan was admitted to an army hospital in Frederick, Maryland, on July 4, 1862, with what was believed to be typhoid fever. While he was in the hospital, a small black slough appeared at the base of his tooth (the first right upper bicuspid). It was accompanied by a "fetid odor" that became increasingly offensive. The area of necrotic tissue spread out toward the cheek and in to the

roof of the mouth. Both bicuspids and the canine tooth dropped out and the slough spread to include the right half of the upper lip, adjacent parts of the cheek, and the side of the nose. The entire right maxillary bone (which forms the right half of the palate and holds the upper teeth on that

side) also sloughed, leaving him with the equivalent of a large cleft palate. Over the next few months, healing reduced the size of the defect by about half and, on December 31, 1862, he was admitted to New York Hospital for surgery.

A dentist fashioned a false palate and teeth from vulcanite, and Burgan was able to eat and speak relatively normally. Dr. Buck then performed a series of five operations, fashioning flaps of skin from the forehead to rebuild the side of the nose and fill in the cheek. Buck noted that when the reconstructed side of the nose was touched, the patient felt the sensation in the forehead, but that after several weeks, he felt it as touching the nose. The patient was very pleased with the final result.[44,45]

Photos courtesy of Archives & Special Collections, A. C. Long Health Sciences Library, Columbia University. Also published in *Medical and Surgical History*, Surgical Section, vol. 3, pp. 348-49.

Dr. Buck's reconstructive surgery was amazingly successful. He cut away scar tissue and reconstructed chins, lips, noses, cheeks, and eyelids by creating pedicle flaps of skin from the forehead and other undamaged regions and bringing them to the area where needed, meticulously keeping the blood supply intact. Buck did these procedures in stages and operated on the patient multiple times over six or more months. This left time for the body to adjust and supply blood to the new location of the tissue. He would stop several times during a procedure (which could take as long as three hours) for the anesthesia to be renewed. To minimize scarring, he used many tiny sutures and carefully placed postoperative dressings.

DENTISTRY DURING THE CIVIL WAR

Dentistry was rudimentary when the Civil War began. The first American dental school, Baltimore College of Dentistry, had opened in 1840 with 5 students. By 1860, there were about 400 graduates from three dental schools but, given the liberal licensure laws in the United States, there were about 5,500 dental practitioners, most trained by apprenticeships. The Southern states had about 1,000 dentists at the start of the war but no dental schools.[46]

Dr. Edward Maynard, a prominent Washington dentist, tried to persuade the U.S. Army to begin a dental corps in the 1850s. Jefferson Davis, secretary of war under President Franklin Pierce, supported Maynard's plan and Surgeon General Thomas Lawson agreed. Lawson proposed a dental corps of six army dental surgeons, "to be entirely distinct from the corps of surgeons in their duties, examinations, promotions and rank." But political considerations defeated the plan: For some time, there had been a bill affecting the army's surgical corps pending before Congress, and it was thought best not to propose anything that might defeat the legislation.[47,48]

When a similar plan was proposed after the Civil War began, the War Department was still opposed to the idea. Therefore, regimental surgeons provided what dental services were available to the troops. Unfortunately, most could do little dentistry except pull teeth and lance boils of the gum. Tooth extractions were usually incomplete, leaving the roots to cause later problems. Union soldiers often consulted civilian dentists, and paid for the services from their own pockets. For example, when Gen. William T. Sherman's troops reached Savannah, they besieged local dental offices. One dentist estimated that "the emergency need alone would have required 100 dentists to work six months on these troops."[49] (One wonders if the luxurious feasting by Sherman's men during the "March to the Sea" precipitated dental problems.)

As the physical examinations for Union recruits improved, extensive cavities, numerous missing teeth, and bad periodontal disease were listed as causes for rejection. However, records show that very few men were rejected for bad teeth. The regulations required examining physicians to consider only the absence of the four front incisors a handicap, since soldiers had to tear open paper cartridges with their teeth in order to load their guns. Of the men examined, 2.4% were excused from Union military service for lack of teeth. The lack of the four front teeth was abbreviated in the physical examination records as "4F"—this designation came to mean exemption from military service for any physical disability.

CONFEDERATE DENTISTRY

The Confederates were always short of men, so they could not afford to reject men with dental problems. At the start of the war, Surgeon General Moore arranged for dentists to be commissioned as captains or majors. He calculated that by drafting dentists into the regular army, many men who might have been rejected or dismissed from military service could instead be treated and retained. When the Confederate Congress passed a law making dentists subject to military draft, Moore got the Bureau of Conscription to change the procedure so that dentists could practice dentistry when in the army.[50]

Dentists were assigned to the larger military hospitals, and every soldier admitted was required to have a dental exam. Since most dentists lived some distance from the hospital, they were provided with an ambulance wagon for transportation; they had to provide their own instruments. As the war progressed, dental instruments became increasingly difficult to obtain in the South, because the Federal government had declared all medical and surgical equipment and supplies contraband of war.

The workload for each hospital dentist was prodigious. Each day, they did about 25 fillings and 20 extractions and removed immense amounts of tartar.[51] However, as in the Union army, soldiers who needed artificial teeth had to go to a civilian dentist at their own expense. Gold had been a favorite material for denture bases, but, by the time of the Civil War, the civilian dentists were using vulcanite (India rubber heated with sulfur to harden it, a process discovered by Charles Goodyear in 1839).

To fill teeth, dentists first used a hand-rotated drill and then hand excavators to remove carious material and to undercut the tooth margins, which allowed the fillings to be retained. Next, they inserted the filling material and filed or burnished the filling smooth. If the pulp was excavated, creosotum was often inserted into the pulp chamber, followed by gold foil for small fillings or tin foil for larger ones (tin was cheaper). An amalgam of silver, tin, and mercury also was common, especially when it was difficult to insert gold. Excavations of Confederate soldiers' graves have revealed that most tooth fillings were made with gold foil, but one tooth was found filled with the radioactive material thorium. Thorium was discovered in 1828 but was not known to be radioactive until 1898. Commercially available by the mid-1800s, it is a relatively abundant mineral that can easily be shaped. The dentist probably thought it was tin. One tooth even had a filling consisting of lead and shotgun pellets![52]

DENTAL SPLINTS FOR JAW FRACTURES

James Baxter Bean, who had graduated from Baltimore School of Dental Surgery, was practicing dentistry in Florida when the war began. He volunteered his services to the Confederate army because he had developed an intraoral splint that was valuable in treating fractures of the jaw caused by gunshot wounds. Although Bean suffered "from chronic rheumatism, some of the joints of his lower extremities [being] much distorted," he helped care for soldiers in Atlanta hospitals.[53]

While on an inspection tour of the hospitals in Atlanta, Confederate surgeon Edward N. Covey observed Bean's method of treating jaw fractures. Covey was struck by the usefulness of his method and advised Surgeon General Moore, who ordered Bean to appear in Richmond for an examination of his techniques. Bean so impressed Moore and his staff that he was put in charge of a special ward at Medical College Hospital in Atlanta devoted exclusively to the treatment of jaw fractures.

When it became necessary to evacuate the Atlanta hospitals because of Gen. W. T. Sherman's approach, Bean moved to Blind Asylum Hospital in Macon. He successfully treated over forty cases at the two hospitals. It is likely that these were the first medical facilities to specialize in the treatment of maxillofacial injuries.[54] Before Bean's method, external splints of pasteboard softened with vinegar and water were applied over the face, similar to a plaster cast, to immobilize jaw fractures. They were uncomfortable and interfered with eating and talking. In addition, they were easily displaced and thus ineffective.

Bean devised an intraoral splint made of gutta percha and, later, of vulcanized rubber.[55] He used a plaster cast of the mouth to fashion a splint that had indentations in which to insert the teeth. After placing it in the patient's mouth, he adjusted the teeth and bone fragments to give proper alignment. The jaw was then closed and held in position by external bandages wrapped over the jaw and around the head. This preserved the alignment of the teeth and minimized the deformity. His technique was a major advance in the treatment of such injuries.

Interestingly, Dr. Thomas Brian Gunning, a Northern dentist, invented virtually the same intraoral splint as Dr. Bean. Gunning assisted in the care of Secretary of State William Henry Seward after the assassination attempt on April 14, 1865. (See Box below.)

The Attempted Assassination of Secretary of State Seward

On April 5, 1865, Secretary of State William Henry Seward was injured in a carriage accident. Besides a broken right arm, contusions of the head and face, and a concussion, Seward fractured both sides of his jaw (bilateral mandibular fractures between the bicuspids). Surgeons tried to hold his jaw in place with external bandages and ligatures between the teeth, but he could barely talk and was in constant pain.

Nine days later, at 10:00 P.M. on April 14, 1865 (simultaneous with President Lincoln's assassination), Lewis Payne, a conspirator in the Lincoln assassination plot, forced his way into Seward's house intending to murder him. Payne's gun jammed when he tried to get past Seward's son, Assistant Secretary of State Frederick Seward. He struck Frederick with the barrel of the gun, fracturing his skull. Payne then drew a huge Bowie-type knife (blockade runners brought these from Britain), entered the secretary's bedroom, and slashed at him repeatedly. He missed Seward several times, in part because Seward was lying on the extreme right side of the bed so that his broken right arm would not touch the mattress. A metal frame over the bed, which Seward used to assist himself in movements, also interfered with Payne's actions.

Seward's neck and right cheek were slashed. The cheek hung in a flap over the lower jaw, exposing the inside of his mouth. He was bleeding profusely. At first, aides thought that the injuries were fatal, but a pulse was detected and they heard Seward say, "I'm not dead. Send for a surgeon! Send for the police; close the house!"

The family's physician, Dr. Verdi, stopped the bleeding with pressure and ice and then stitched the wounds closed. Dr. Gunning was summoned from his New York dental practice, and he provided definitive treatment for Seward's injuries. The right side of his fractured mandible never healed, and Seward developed a false joint at the fracture site.[56,57]

TREATING EYE INJURIES

Civil War surgeons were cognizant of the latest innovations in ophthalmology, and treated patients using the standards of the time (and perhaps even a little ahead of the medical literature). The level of development of American ophthalmology is revealed in the surgeons' treatment of eye trauma during the war.

For example, until about a century after the Civil War, there was no effective treatment for the condition that the Germans termed "sympathetic ophthalmia" in 1866. This process often develops after trauma, and causes inflammation in one eye when the other eye is inflamed due to an immune response. The only way to prevent a serious loss of vision in both eyes (and even blindness in the uninjured eye) was to remove the damaged eye, called "enucleation," before inflammation developed in the other one, a treatment first suggested by an English physician named Pritchard in 1851. The fact that enucleation was ineffective once the good eye was inflamed was discussed in 1863, during the first International Conference on Ophthalmology in Heidelberg. Prophylactic enucleation became the standard treatment for this disease in the 1860s and remained so for decades.[58]

Civil War surgeons apparently knew about this phenomenon and took measures to prevent it. The first surgical volume of *Medical and Surgical History* discusses sympathetic ophthalmia at length, and records that 1,190 cases of wounds to one or both eyes were treated during the war. Of the 254 gunshot wounds of one eye, for example, "in forty-one of these cases [the] vision in the uninjured eye became affected sympathetically, and in four instances was ultimately lost."[59] *Medical and Surgical History* mentions two cases during the war in which "extirpation of the globe" was done, apparently in an attempt to prevent the loss of vision. The analysis concludes:

> A general survey of the accounts of gunshot injuries of the eye, reported during the war, instructs us that whenever foreign bodies are lodged in the globe, they should be extracted at all hazards. If it is impracticable to find them, the globe should be extirpated to preserve the other eye.[60]

Although Civil War physicians did not make use of the primitive ophthalmoscope, civilian physicians did and they knew that atropine could be used to dilate the pupils to make such examinations more useful. However, patients complained of prolonged blurred vision after atropine. Confederate physicians discovered that an extract of the calabar bean could reverse this troubling side effect and, in 1864, they reported their findings in the *Confederate States Medical and Surgical Journal*.[61] Long after the war, scientists found that physostigmine, which is still used for this and other purposes, was the active ingredient in these extracts.

American physicians also used state-of-the-art techniques to treat glaucoma. Papers published in the *Confederate States Medical and Surgical Journal* described the use of iridectomy to treat glaucoma. This is a surgical procedure in which a portion of the iris of the eye is removed, and is essentially the same as the operation performed today.[62,63]

BLOOD TRANSFUSIONS

Dr. Charles-Édouard Brown-Séquard, a famous Parisian physician and a founder of the field of neurology, toured the United States during the Civil War. On June 14, 1864, the U.S. Sanitary Commission sponsored his lecture on nerve injuries at the Smithsonian Institution. During the lecture, Dr. Brown-Séquard reviewed his experience using blood transfusions to treat life-threatening hemorrhage, mostly for obstetrical patients with massive postpartum bleeding. He suggested

> employing defibrinated blood injected very slowly into a vein far from the heart, and a small quantity of blood only. A single ounce has provided enough to save a life, and in no cases [was] more than 5 ounces necessary. The defibrinated blood may be injected without warming. There is no danger if it is quite cold.[64]

(To defibrinate blood, you stir the blood while it is clotting, and the fibrin adheres to the stirring apparatus. This prevents most of the blood cells from being bound up and lost in the clot. The development of blood typing and chemical anticoagulants, both of which would make blood transfusions truly practical, were fifty years in the future.)

Based on information from his lecture, Union surgeons tried to transfuse two wounded soldiers. One had developed hospital gangrene following a flesh wound in the leg, and when he bled a second time from the posterior tibial artery "it was deemed advisable to amputate to prevent further loss of blood." After amputation just below the knee, at the level of the tibial tubercle,

> [with loss of no more than] two table-spoonfuls of blood . . . the patient not seeming to rally, it was determined to test the method of transfusion of blood as recommended by Brown-Séquard. Blood having been obtained from the temporal artery of a strong, healthy German, an [unsuccessful] attempt was made to penetrate the internal saphenous vein [in the thigh] . . . after which an opening was made in the median basilic [the large

vein in front of the elbow], and about two ounces were transfused by means of a Tiemann's syringe. Immediately afterward a marked difference was noted in the patient's pulse, which became stronger and firmer.[65]

The patient survived.

The other soldier, also with a leg wound, had endured several copious hemorrhages from the anterior tibial artery. The limb had finally been amputated, but as "the patient [was] reacting very slowly," the physicians decided to transfuse blood. According to the record, "the right cephalic vein was chosen and an opening into it made and a syringe was filled with blood [which was warmed before introduction] from a healthy man . . . about sixteen ounces were thus transfused." Although he developed a temporary tachycardia, the immediate reaction was favorable and no later developments were described that suggested a transfusion reaction. While "the man's condition greatly improved," he developed another hemorrhage from the stump. He also had chronic diarrhea, and the report listed this as the main reason for his death.[66]

The fact that these patients were not harmed by these unsterile, untyped transfusions was probably due to the small amount of blood given and, perhaps, luck in choosing a compatible donor. These cases document that Civil War surgeons were willing to apply the latest medical advances to try to save the lives of wounded men. Sometimes, they went beyond the parameters of existing medical knowledge, trying to save lives with innovative methods. Occasionally, they met with success and, thus, contributed to the development of medical knowledge.

SURVIVAL RATES DURING THE WAR

Given the Union Medical Bureau's initial lack of preparedness and its dismal performance in the first major battles, it is important to ask if the survival rate of the wounded men improved over the course of this lengthy bloody war. The statistics suggest that they did—despite a variety of factors that might be expected to have lowered their effectiveness. (Note: The data and calculations presented were compiled by the author based on the data in the monthly tables of disease and injuries for the Union army published in *Medical and Surgical History*, Medical Section, vol. 1.)

Although the overall death rate in the Union army among soldiers treated for wounds was 14.3%, the death rate for those entered in the medical statistics varied considerably during the war. In the first full year (July 1, 1861–June 30, 1862), 17,498 men in Union armies were admitted to hospitals for wounds, mostly from the Battle of Shiloh in April and from the Peninsula campaign of April-June. Of this total, 4,479 died, for a mortality rate of 25.6%.

During the second year (July 1, 1862–June 30, 1863), the Army of the Potomac participated in the Battle of Antietam in September; General Ambrose Burnside made his suicidal attack on Marye's Heights at Fredericksburg in December; the bloody fight at Chancellorsville took place the following May; Grant was fighting around Vicksburg; and there were numerous less-spectacular engagements resulting in many wounded. A stunning 57,395 men were treated for gunshot wounds in that year, and 8,773 died. Thus, the case-fatality rate had fallen to 15.3%.

Despite the enormous number of wounded men, even more were wounded in the third year (July 1, 1863–June 30, 1864). In the East, the areas of conflict included the decisive Battle of Gettysburg in July and the Battles of the Wilderness, Spotsylvania, and Cold Harbor in Virginia the next spring. In the area called the West, the Battle of Chickamauga, the Sieges of Chattanooga and Knoxville, the breakout from Chattanooga in the "Battle above the Clouds," and the start of W. T. Sherman's campaign against Atlanta occurred. During this year, a horrendous total of 96,970 men were treated for gunshot wounds, and 9,238 of them died. The mortality rate, however, was down to an astonishingly low 9.5%. More surprising, this improvement occurred despite a marked increase in the frequency of the most serious wound infections: hospital gangrene and traumatic erysipelas (in Chapter 7, see Hospital Gangrene and Erysipelas).

The surprising mortality pattern of treated gunshot wounds for the entire Union army is mirrored by the case-fatality rates after individual campaigns. Table 6.2 lists the cases registered in the hospitals of the Atlantic Region and those treated in the Army of the Potomac, as well as the percentage of those who died of their wounds during the month of the battle and the following month (since some of the wounded died weeks after the fighting had ceased).

As can be seen, by the time of Gettysburg, the fatality rate of men who had been wounded decreased to almost one-third of the rate in earlier battles, despite a great increase in the number of casualties and little or no concomitant increase in the size of the medical staff. In fact, after Gettysburg, the majority of the medical staff accompanied the army in its pursuit of General Lee, leaving most of the wounded to be cared for by a skeleton crew.

Moreover, the marked improvement in the evacuation procedures by Gettysburg resulted in many more seriously wounded men being brought to

TABLE 6.2
Fatality Rate from Wounds in the Atlantic Region
(includes the Army of the Potomac)

	Number of Wounded	Fatality Rate
May–July 1862 (Peninsula)	7,862	26.4%
Sept.–Oct. 1862 (Antietam)	8,112	22.4
July–Aug. 1863 (Gettysburg)	10,569*	9.1
May–July 1864 (multiple battles)	37,812	12.9
July 1864–June 1865 (Siege of Petersburg)	35,700	17.9

Medical and Surgical History, Surgical Section, vol. 1, p. 80; *Medical and Surgical History*, Medical Section, vol. 1, p. 328. This is the figure given for the numbers of "gunshot wounds" treated by physicians of the Army of the Potomac in July 1863. It is considerably lower than the official figures from the adjutant general for wounded in the Battle of Gettysburg (13,709). The higher number is probably due to lightly wounded soldiers who were listed in the report by company commanders. This report was sent up the chain of command to Washington, and thus includes men who were not hospitalized. The lower figure, which includes only those men hospitalized and treated, has been used for the calculations mentioned, resulting in a higher percentage mortality than would otherwise be the case.

Medical and Surgical History, Medical Section, vol. 1.

the field hospitals for treatment. These men, who in earlier battles would have been listed as "killed in battle," were counted as wounded—a change that might be expected to *increase* the proportion of the wounded who died. These statistics suggest that Civil War surgeons had learned their lessons well and were saving the lives of men who would have died in earlier campaigns.

The mortality rates for the last year of fighting are not as favorable; the case-fatality rate had risen to 17.9%—nearly double that of the prior year. The year of July 1, 1864–June 30, 1865 included the Sieges of Atlanta and Petersburg, and armies clashed in many other locations. Hood's ill-fated attempt, late in 1864, to lure Sherman out of Georgia by attacking Thomas in Tennessee, led to the Confederate disasters at Franklin and Nashville. General Jubal Early's attempt to raid Washington was followed by Gen. Phillip Henry Sheridan's victorious campaign in the Shenandoah Valley. As a result, an additional 57,122 men were treated for gunshot wounds and 10,201 died. Despite the horrendous conditions in the fourth year, however, the number of deaths from wounds was still less than in the first two years of the war.

Scurvy and the Mortality Rate from Gunshot Wounds

Why the deterioration in outcome of wound treatment in the last year of the war? One reason was the huge number of wounded, which was larger than the number of men in entire armies earlier in the war. Another factor was the tremendous difficulty evacuating the wounded. But the most compelling explanation, which could account for the increased mortality of gunshot wounds as well as the increased fatality rate of all the major diseases, lies buried in the tables of data in *Medical and Surgical History*. The long period of service on the army diet led to an increase in the recorded incidence of scurvy and night blindness, particularly in the later years of the war. This points to more malnutrition among the troops, which could have contributed to the increases in the fatality rates from diseases and wounds.

This hypothesis is supported by the observations of many Civil War surgeons. Several specifically noted that scurvy, or the "scorbutic taint," increased the frequency of wound complications and fatalities. In reviewing Confederate medical experiences, Dr. Joseph Jones pointed out: "A scorbutic state of the system favors the origin and spread of erysipelas, and of foul gangrenous ulcers." Regarding hospital gangrene, he observed that "Scorbutic patients seem to be more liable to it than any other, or at least it is more difficult to manage in scorbutic constitutions."[67]

An article published by the Sanitary Commission (among others) stressed the importance of an antiscorbutic diet to diminish the frequency of the overwhelming form of wound infection called pyemia. And a Union surgeon specifically blamed "the scorbutic diathesis" for surgical "accidents," i.e., complications following surgery, such as massive hemorrhage or spreading infection.[68]

The relationship between scurvy and gunshot-wound deaths can be illustrated by data from Sherman's campaign to take Atlanta and, subsequently, Savannah. In May 1864, Sherman's army marched south toward Atlanta. From May 1 until September 2 when Federal troops occupied Atlanta, his men frequently clashed with Gen. Joseph E. Johnston's (and, later, John Bell Hood's) forces defending Atlanta, as the two armies maneuvered and fought along the railroad line from Chattanooga. The single-track railroad, on which service was frequently disrupted by cavalry raids, was inadequate to supply the needs of an army. The transportation of bulky vegetables was considered a low priority by the generals; they usually were satisfied if the men had hardtack, coffee, and bullets.

The incidence of *diagnosed* scurvy and night blindness increased each month until the fall of Atlanta. (It has been observed that when fully developed scurvy is diagnosed in a few soldiers, less severe forms are wide-spread in the rest of the unit. See Chapter 13, *Scurvy and Other "Dietic Diseases."*) After the fighting diminished and the railroad could be used to transport food, the incidence of scurvy and night blindness fell dramatically. (See Figure 6.3.) They became rare by late November and into December when Sherman's forces were able to forage for fresh vegetables, and other food supplies, as they marched to the sea.

During that same period, the percentage of the wounded who died each month varied in a fashion that mimicked the incidence of diagnosed scurvy. In May, at the beginning of the campaign, 4.6% of the wounded died and 1.9 cases of scurvy per 1,000 men were reported. The fatality rate of the wounded rose to 25% in the months when the troops were besieging Atlanta, and scurvy had more than doubled in incidence. After Atlanta fell on September 1 and food could again be transported, scurvy was less frequent and wound mortality fell.

FIGURE 6.3

Incidence of Scurvy and Fatality Rate from Wounds during the Siege of Atlanta*

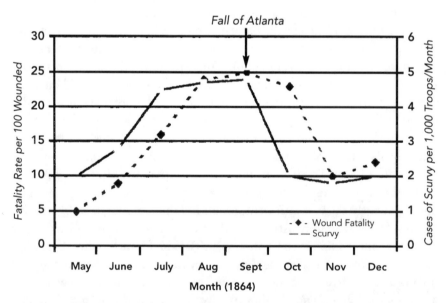

*Data extracted from and calculations made by the author are based on the information in the monthly tables of disease and injuries for the Union army published in *Medical and Surgical History*, Medical Section, vol. 1.

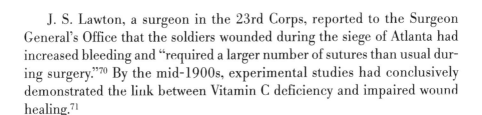

Dr. Joseph Jones on Wound Complications in the Confederate Army

In 1870, Dr. Joseph Jones reflected on possible explanations for the increase in wound complications over the course of the war:

> Secondary hemorrhage, massive bleeding occurring several days or weeks after the surgery, as well as pyemia and hospital gangrene progressively increased with the progress of the war, and after the great battles of the expiring Confederacy . . . [in 1864–65] it was of daily, and at times, almost hourly occurrence in the hospitals. . . .
>
> The great increase in secondary hemorrhage appeared to be referable to the prolonged use of salt meat, and to the consequent scorbutic condition of the blood, although active symptoms of scurvy were not manifested, the increase of pyemia and hospital gangrene, may in like manner, have been connected, in a measure at least, with the physical and chemical changes of the blood and organs, dependent upon imperfect nutrition and sameness of diet.[69]

The theory of the excessive use of salted meat as an origin of scurvy dated back centuries, and it would continue to be widely accepted for another fifty years. Physicians considered the value of fresh vegetables in preventing and treating scurvy to be a pharmacological effect, that is, a curative, and not a treatment intended to remedy a specific nutritional deficit.

J. S. Lawton, a surgeon in the 23rd Corps, reported to the Surgeon General's Office that the soldiers wounded during the siege of Atlanta had increased bleeding and "required a larger number of sutures than usual during surgery."[70] By the mid-1900s, experimental studies had conclusively demonstrated the link between Vitamin C deficiency and impaired wound healing.[71]

DID CIVIL WAR SURGEONS DO AS WELL AS THEIR EUROPEAN COUNTERPARTS?

How does the mortality rate achieved by Civil War surgeons compare to that of contemporary European military surgeons for wound treatment? Table

6.3 shows the mortality rate per 100 wounded men for various mid-1800 wars. Civil War surgeons did better than French and British surgeons in the Crimean War and a great deal better than their opponents, the Russians. No information is available for the Turks.

During the Franco-Prussian War (1870–1871), the French had a slightly higher mortality rate from wounds than did Federal wounded during the Civil War. (According to the available data, Confederate outcomes were essentially the same as the Union's results.) German surgeons had a lower mortality rate than the American physicians, perhaps in part because some major German military hospitals used Joseph Lister's antiseptic methods. At the time of the Franco-Prussian War, Germany was the only country in which antiseptic methods had been adopted, although it is unclear whether this technique was widely used.

Any comparison of the American and European medical experiences, however, must take into account not only total mortality from wounds, but the number of wounded needing care. At Antietam, over 8,000 Union soldiers were wounded in a single day. After the three days at Gettysburg, Union surgeons cared for about 20,000 wounded, one quarter of whom were Confederates too severely wounded to be transported during Lee's retreat to Virginia.[72] In contrast, the total number of British soldiers wounded during the entire Crimean War (October 1853–February 1856) was 12,094.

TABLE 6.3

Mortality Rate per 100 Wounded Men in Various Wars

Crimean War (1854–56)	
Russia	25%
Britain	16
France	9

U.S. Civil War (1861–65)*	
Federal	14%

Franco-Prussian War (1870–71)	
France	15%
Germany	11

*Confederate data is incomplete, but suggests comparable rates as Federal armies.

Cantlie N: *A History of the Army Medical Department*, vol. 2. Edinburgh: Churchill Livingston, 1973; *Medical and Surgical History*, Surgical Section, vol. 3, p. 693.

There are other important differences affecting the medical events of the U.S. Civil War and the European conflicts. First, the European wars involved standing armies or trained reserves with trained and experienced medical personnel, many of whom were graduates of military medical schools. Second, the European armies fought frequent wars, providing surgeons with much on-the-job experience. (For example, before the war with the French in 1870, the Prussians fought Denmark in 1864 and then defeated Austria in 1866.)

In contrast, only about one in 200 of the surgeons who served in the Federal army during the Civil War had any prior military medical experience. The Confederate Army's Medical Department was organized around roughly forty experienced former-U.S. Army surgeons. On both sides, the few veteran physicians were needed for administrative posts, since they were familiar with the army procedures necessary to ensure that supplies and personnel reached their intended destinations. Recently inducted civilian physicians or recent medical school graduates, for the most part, treated the casualties. Neither group had any surgical training or experience, or any background in military medicine.

Further, the Civil War was unusually long in duration, resulting in special medical problems. Because a large number of soldiers was kept in the field for several years, many Civil War physicians thought that the soldiers' exhaustion affected mortality statistics; malnutrition may have been an even more important factor. In contrast, European wars were brief—only the Crimean War lasted more than a year. The war between Austria and the Piedmont area of Italy, which was aided by France, was from March to July of 1859, the Austro-Prussian War of 1866 is known as the "Seven Weeks' War," and the Franco-Prussian War of 1870–71 lasted six months. Earlier in the century, the Napoleonic Wars were a series of intermittent, relatively short campaigns and conflicts. All the European wars mentioned that are not listed in Table 6.3 had a higher mortality rate of wounded than in the U.S. Civil War.

REFERENCES

1. *O.R.*, Series I, vol. XIX/1, p. 106.
2. Stevens GT: *Three Years in the Sixth Corps. A Concise Narrative of Events in the Army of the Potomac from 1861 to the Close of the Rebellion, April 1865.* Albany, NY: S. R. Gray, 1866, p. 181.
3. Hart AG: *The Surgeon and the Hospital in the Civil War.* Gaithersburg, MD: Olde Soldier Books, 1987 (orig. pub. 1902).
4. Billings JS: Medical reminiscences of the Civil War. *Transactions of the College of Physicians of Philadelphia.* 3rd Series. 1905;27:115-21.

5. *O.R.*, Series I, vol. XIX/1, p. 106.

6. Harvey AM: John Shaw Billings: forgotten hero of American medicine. *Persp Biol Med.* 1977 Autumn;21(1):35-57.

7. Chisolm JJ: *A Manual of Military Surgery for Use of the Surgeons in the Confederate Army.* 3rd ed. Columbia, SC: Evans & Cogswell, 1864. Repub.: Dayton, OH: Morningside, 1992, p. 409.

8. Schildt JW: *Hunter Holmes McGuire: Doctor in Gray.* Chewsville, MD: J. D. Schildt, 1986, p. 27.

9. Brockway AN: Report of surgical cases at Bellevue Hospital and DeCamp General Hospital. NARA, RG94, Entry #621, File A490.

10. *Medical and Surgical History*, Surgical Section, vol. 3, pp. 417-19.

11. *Medical and Surgical History*, Surgical Section, vol. 1, p. 415 et seq.

12. Ibid., pp. 415-16, case of Capt. John S.

13. Ibid., case of Private Young.

14. Chisolm JJ: *A Manual of Military Surgery for Use of the Surgeons in the Confederate Army.* 1st ed. Columbia, SC: Evans & Cogswell, 1861, p. 156.

15. *U.S. Sanitary Commission Bulletin.* 1863;1:76.

16. Thomas HL: Cases of gunshot injury requiring ligation of the artery. *Conf States Med Surg J.* 1864;1(11):184.

17. *Medical and Surgical History*, Surgical Section, vol. 1, p. 193 et seq.

18. Chisolm, *Manual of Military Surgery*, 3rd ed., p. 237 et seq.

19. Ibid., p. 288.

20. Ibid., p. 290.

21. Ibid., p. 291.

22. Ibid., p. 293.

23. Hamilton FH: Lectures on gunshot wounds. *Am Med Times.* 1864;8:98.

24. Cabell JL: Confederate States Hospital Reports. Eighteen cases of gun-shot wounds of the head observed at the General Hospital, Charlottesville, VA. *Conf States Med Surg J.* 1864;1(3):41-43.

25. Le Vay D: *The History of Orthopaedics: An Account of the Study and Practice of Orthopaedics from the Earliest Times to the Modern Era.* Park Ridge, NJ: Parthenon, 1990.

26. Lattimer JK, Laidlaw A: Good Samaritan surgeon wrongly accused of contributing to President Lincoln's death. An experimental study of the President's fatal wound. *J Am Coll Surg.* 1996 May;182(5):431-38.

27. Barnes JK: Testimony in the trial of John H. Suratt. *House Report No. 7 of the 40th Congress.* 1867;1:121.

28. Halpern M: Quoted in: Lattimer, Laidlaw, *J Am Coll Surgeons*, 1996, p. 431.

29. *Medical and Surgical History*, Surgical Section, vol. 1, p. 193 et seq.

30. Lattimer JK: *Kennedy and Lincoln: Medical and Ballistic Comparisons of Their Assassinations.* New York: Harcourt Brace & Janovitch, 1980.

31. *Medical and Surgical History*, Surgical Section, vol. 2, p. 206.

32. Brockway, NARA, RG94, File A490.

33. *Medical and Surgical History*, Surgical Section, vol. 3, pp. 417-19.

34. Steiner PE: *Disease in the Civil War: Natural Biological Warfare in 1861-65.* Springfield, IL: C. C. Thomas, 1968.

35. *Saturday Evening Post.* September 12, 1861. Quoted in: *U.S. Sanitary Commission Papers*, New York Public Library, Box 75.

36. *Medical and Surgical History*, Surgical Section, vol. 2, pp. 497-98.

37. Ibid., p. 498.

38. *O.R.*, Series I, vol. XIX/1, p.106.

39. *Medical and Surgical History*, Surgical Section, vol. 2, p. 509.

40. *Medical and Surgical History*, Medical Section, vol. 1, Appendix, p. 200.

41. Gray HMW: *The Early Treatment of War Wounds.* London: Oxford Univ. Press, 1919, p. 215.

42. Stark RB: The history of plastic surgery in wartime. *Clin Plast Surg.* 1975 Oct;2(4):509.
43. Bengston BP: Gurdon Buck. A plastic surgeon of the Civil War. Paper presented at the 6th Annual Conference of the Society of Civil War Surgeons. Philadelphia, PA; March 19, 1999.
44. Buck G: *Contributions to Reparative Surgery.* New York: Appleton & Co., 1876.
45. *Medical and Surgical History,* Surgical Section, vol. 3, pp. 348-49.
46. Tebo HG: Oral surgery in the Confederate army. *Bull Hist Dentistry.* 1976 Apr;24(1):28.
47. Ibid.
48. Hodgkin WL: Edward Maynard, a progenitor of the United States Army and Navy Dental Corps. *J Am Dental Assoc.* 1941 Dec;28(12):1968-78.
49. Dammann G: Dental care during the Civil War. *Ill Dental J.* 1984 Jan-Feb;53(1):12.
50. Tebo, *Bull Hist Dentistry,* 1976.
51. Burton WL: Dental surgery as applied in the armies of the late Confederate states. *Am J Dental Sci.* 1867;1:185.
52. Glenner RA, Willey P: Dental filling materials in the Confederacy. *J Hist Dentistry.* 1998 Jul;46(2):71.
53. Hyson JM, Foley GPH: James Baxter Bean. The first military maxillofacial hospital. *Maryland State Dental Assoc J.* 1997;40:77.
54. Ibid.
55. Gutta percha is an early form of plastic made from the dried sap of a tree that grew in Borneo (then Dutch East Indies), *Dichopsis gutta,* which could be heated and molded. Wilbur CK: *Antique Medical Instruments: Price Guide Included.* West Chester, PA: Schiffer, 1987, p. 25.
56. Lattimer JK: The stabbing of Lincoln's Secretary of State on the night the President was shot. *JAMA.* 1965 Apr 12;192(2):99-106.
57. Bishop J: *The Day Lincoln Was Shot.* New York: Harper & Bros., 1955, p. 255.
58. Duke-Elder S, ed.: *System of Ophthalmology.* vol. VII: *The Foundations of Ophthalmology: Heredity, Pathology, Diagnosis, and Therapeutics.* London: Kimpton, 1962.
59. *Medical and Surgical History,* Surgical Section, vol. 1, p. 345.
60. Ibid.
61. *Conf States Med Surg J.* 1864;1:197.
62. Hancock H: Observation on the operation for division of the ciliary muscle. *Conf States Med Surg J.* 1864;1:220.
63. Bowman W: On glaucomatous affections and their treatment by iridectomy. *Conf States Med Surg J.* 1865;2:46.
64. Notes of lecture by Dr. Brown-Séquard. NARA, RG94, Entry #621, File A344.
65. *Medical and Surgical History,* Surgical Section, vol. 3, pp. 58, 811.
66. Ibid.
67. Jones J: Observations upon the losses of the Confederate armies from battle, wounds and diseases, during the American Civil War of 1861-65, with investigations upon the number and character of the diseases supervening from gun-shot wounds. *Richmond Louisville Med J.* 1870;9:635-57.
68. Hunt SB: Influence of the scorbutic diathesis on surgical accidents. *U.S. Sanitary Commission Bulletin.* July 15, 1864;2:18:1549.
69. Jones, *Richmond Louisville Med J,* 1870.
70. *O.R.,* Series I, vol. XXXVIII/2, p. 580.
71. Carpenter KJ: *The History of Scurvy and Vitamin C.* Cambridge, MA: Cambridge Univ. Press, 1986.
72. *O.R.,* Series I, vol. VI, p. 98. Although the figure usually given for the number of Confederate wounded who were left behind is about 5,000, the *Official Records* mentions an estimate of between 8,000 and 10,000.

$\backsim\ 7\ \backsim$

Wound Infections: Laudable and Not-So-Laudable Pus

Pyemia, a disease very common in Europe, and a scourge of their military hospitals, was but seldom met with in the Confederate states until it became necessary to mass large numbers of wounded in crowded and badly ventilated wards, as after the many bloody battles of the past three years. When it shows itself in European hospitals, like its kindred disease, erysipelas, it is not satisfied until it has swept off its hundreds.

– Dr. J. J. Chisolm, *A Manual of Military Surgery for Use of the Surgeons in the Confederate Army,* 1864

ONCE HEMORRHAGE WAS CONTROLLED, infection was the most frequent cause of death from gunshot wounds. Civil War physicians called infections that spread through the bloodstream "pyemia," or "blood poisoning." Of those soldiers with this condition during the Civil War, 92% died.

Even minor injuries could lead to deadly infections: Early in the war, Maj. Gen. Charles Ferguson Smith skinned his leg on a sharp-edged rowboat seat while disembarking at Pittsburg Landing near Shiloh. (Smith's vigorous attack on Fort Donelson, in February 1862, led the Fort's commander to request surrender terms. Smith, described as "crusty" and "the hardest fighter of them all," advised General Grant to offer no terms. Grant phrased this as "unconditional surrender," bringing him instant fame.)

Smith's leg became infected and his condition worsened, so that he could only listen to the guns at Shiloh from his sickbed in Savannah, Tennessee. He died later that month of "blood poisoning."[1]

With today's antiseptic techniques and antibiotics, it is hard to appreciate the fear that Civil War physicians and their patients felt when blood poisoning appeared. Wound infections occurred almost universally, and spread rapidly and predictably with devastating results. Once a patient acquired such an infection, physicians could accurately predict how long he would survive. Today we know that bacteria, primarily streptococci or staphylococci, cause most serious infections, including hospital gangrene and erysipelas. Yet even with antibiotics, some streptococcal infections (such as the so-called "killer strep") continue to instill fear, confound medical expertise, and cause rapid death. The efforts of Civil War physicians to grapple with these deadly infections—without knowing anything about microbiology or the bacterial cause of infections—led to some treatments similar to those still used.

Civil War physicians used the term "inflammation" to describe the red, hot, swollen, and painful-to-the-touch skin that resulted from infection. When the infection had killed tissue, they called it "putrefaction"; we call it "necrosis." Although surgeons saw bacteria when they examined infected tissues under the microscope, they did not believe it caused the infection. Rather, they thought that these objects simply arose spontaneously in such wounds. They had reason to believe this, since numerous studies had failed to provide evidence that bacteria caused disease. Knowledge of the role bacteria plays in causing wound infections and other diseases only began in 1865, when Joseph Lister realized the importance of Louis Pasteur's work (see Box, p. 199).

Civil War surgeons knew that foreign material in wounds increased the likelihood and severity of complications, so they attempted to remove bullets, wadding, shrapnel, clothing fragments, grass, and dirt from soldiers' wounds. They also removed, by debridement, as much damaged and devitalized (without adequate blood supply) tissue as they could. Today we know that they were correct—bacteria readily obtain access to, and flourish in, such tissue. While they didn't understand the science behind it, the surgeons' actions saved lives and limbs. Their inability to remove all the foreign material and devitalized tissues without damaging more tissue was the main problem. The most effective form of debridement was amputation.

Early amputation reduced mortality by completely removing severely damaged and devitalized tissues. Usually, surgeons cut close to the wound, but sufficiently above it so that they could make the incision through non-

Lister & Pasteur: The Dawn of Antisepsis

French chemist Louis Pasteur wanted to know why wine spoiled. He discovered that bacteria-produced enzymes contaminated the wine, the bacteria entered from the air, and if air could not enter the bottles, the wine did not spoil. This observation demolished the long-held concept that microorganisms "spontaneous generated." Pasteur published his findings in a scientific journal, *Comte Redu de l'Académie des Sciences*, in 1857 and 1859. This important information was ignored, however, until Thomas Anderson, a chemistry professor in Glasgow, read the articles and forwarded them to his colleague, Dr. Joseph Lister, who was struggling with the problem of wound infections.

Lister repeated Pasteur's experiments and became convinced that the results were valid. He tried to prevent organisms from entering open wounds through the air by spraying a known antiseptic, carbolic acid, into the air over the wounds while he operated. He also used dressings soaked with carbolic acid to cover wounds after surgery. On August 12, 1865, after further developing his technique, he treated 11-year-old James Greenlees, who had been run over by the wheel of a horse-drawn cart, for a compound tibial (lower leg) fracture. Lister observed that the fracture healed without the expected infection—the first in his series of similar cases. These cases were described in his first article (1867). He reported that his method decreased the deaths following amputation in his hospital by two-thirds, from 46% to 15%.[2] He then modified his techniques, achieving even better results.[3,4]

Lister wrote to Pasteur and, later, visited him and convinced the French chemist that his observations about wine might also apply to human disease. Pasteur turned his attention to the medical aspects of bacteriology, and the rest, as they say, is history.[5]

damaged skin. This removed more damaged tissue than did the more conservative procedures of debridement and excision, but resulted in fewer deaths. While pus regularly appeared in amputation stumps, it usually remained localized.

The non-sterile equipment they used caused problems, but even more damaging were the relatively blunt knives and saws, which increased tissue injury. Although both sides used similar equipment (most either had been made in the North before the war or was imported from Europe), individual surgeons' skill at sharpening the instruments varied greatly. Those who lacked this skill wielded dull knives.

"Laudable Pus" and Pyemia

Historians often deride Civil War physicians for using the term "laudable pus." They seem to think that by saying that pus was laudable, the physicians thought that pus formation was a necessary step in the healing process, rather than an infection-caused combination of bacteria, white cells, and dead tissue.

Actually, physicians had used the term "laudable pus" for millennia— and the meaning was essentially unchanged since its use in ancient Egypt. Dr. Robley Dunglisen of Philadelphia, in his Civil War-era medical dictionary, described laudable pus as "Pus of good quality, . . . of yellow color, opake [sic], inodorous, and of a creamy appearance . . . [as opposed to] 'pus malignum'."[6] Malignant pus, also called "ichorous pus," was thinner, blood-tinged, usually had a more offensive odor, and predicted a worse outcome, often pyemia and death.

"Laudable" referred to the quality of the pus, not its presence. Dunglisen's descriptions suggest that malignant pus probably resulted from streptococcal infections, while the thicker, creamier, less-foul-smelling "laudable" pus most likely resulted from staphylococcal infections. In that pre-antibiotic era with the high mortality from pyemia, it was indeed "laudable" when the nature of the pus signified a milder type of infection that was more likely to remain localized.

Pus developed quickly in almost all patients, since surgeons usually could not help leaving contaminated dead tissue in wounds. If the patient did not die, the body cured the infection, the dead tissue fell away, and the wound healed. While pus formation was common in the wound healing process, Civil War doctors were pleased and surprised when pus did not appear in a wound; they called this favorable outcome "healing by first intention." They never considered pus formation necessary for healing. Rather, they were mainly concerned with preventing its spread, whatever the type. Illustrating this is the warning given to Confederate surgeons: "Burrowing of either ichorous or laudable pus must be assiduously guarded against."[7]

Physicians tried to learn from the bodies of those who died. Often the same physicians who had cared for a patient would perform the autopsy. Although the surgeons were not pathologists, the autopsies were relatively well done, even by modern standards. Many autopsy reports describe the

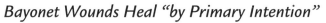

Bayonet Wounds Heal "by Primary Intention"

A report by Confederate surgeon Simon Baruch (father of Bernard Baruch, advisor to every president from Woodrow Wilson to John F. Kennedy) illustrates the role of injured, devitalized tissue in causing infection. He described two men with bayonet wounds to the chest, sustained during the Battle of Spotsylvania. Both men's chest wounds, along with "a number of others of less serious nature," healed quickly "by primary intention," meaning without infection.

Baruch pointed out that bayonet wounds form a "smooth track" (meaning that they do relatively little damage to tissues other than making a clean incision) and are almost harmless (unless they hit a vital structure). Therefore, they heal without suppuration. In contrast, minié balls, by "crushing, tearing and maiming" tissues, require "weeks for a complete recovery and . . . [lead to a] contracted and useless limb."[8]

complications of sepsis, including metastatic abscesses and infectious changes in the heart valves (bacterial endocarditis). Endocarditis remained a devastating disease until antibiotics became available, so it is no surprise that Civil War soldiers succumbed to its ravages. As Boyd's 1943 *Textbook of Pathology* described, the heart murmurs of bacterial endocarditis beat "muffled marches to the grave."[9]

HOSPITAL GANGRENE AND ERYSIPELAS

Hospital gangrene and erysipelas (streptococcal infections) were two of the most feared wound infections because they led so quickly to death. The streptococci that were prevalent during the Civil War were much more virulent than the strains commonly seen today, and were capable of causing serious infection even without much tissue injury.

The severe skin infection erysipelas, officially called "traumatic erysipelas,"[10] began superficially, although it usually required a break in the skin for the organisms to gain a foothold. Erysipelas is characterized by redness, tenderness, and other signs of inflammation. It can remain in one area or spread swiftly beneath the skin, destroying tissues deeply and widely. If the infection spreads to lymph nodes, it can pass into the bloodstream; Civil War surgeons called this "pyemia," or "blood poisoning." In such cases, new infection sites arise throughout the body, particularly on heart valves, in the lungs, and often in the nervous system, causing meningitis. These complications, observed in many Civil War cases, accounted for the high death rate among soldiers with pyemia.

Hospital gangrene, another killer, was rare in the first year of the war, but increased markedly during the second and third years. Thereafter, it decreased to the point where it became extremely rare after the war (see Table 7.1). A comparable infection seen today, necrotizing fasciitis, is often caused by simultaneous infection with several organisms, one of which is usually a virulent strain of *Streptococcus*. If such a combination of organisms was the cause of hospital gangrene during the Civil War, this would account for the disease's presence primarily in large hospitals having a variety of cases with many types of infection.

Hospital gangrene rarely appeared in field hospitals or in the larger temporary general hospitals set up in tents near the battlefields. The disease appeared mainly in the relatively permanent hospitals in cities. Once it appeared, the infection quickly spread from patient to patient and from patient to nurse. In one Memphis, Tennessee, hospital,

> A man acting as a nurse to his captain, who had gangrene, had small spots of inflammation on his ankle, caused possibly by mosquito bites, which he had rubbed the skin from; he also had scratches on his fingers; gangrene set in at all these points.[11]

Physicians usually isolated patients with hospital gangrene or erysipelas in separate tents or buildings in an attempt to minimize its spread. An army

TABLE 7.1
Hospital Gangrene in Union Forces

Fiscal Year	Cases of Hospital Gangrene
1861 (May and June)	4
July 1, 1861–June 30, 1862	223
July 1, 1862–June 30, 1863	623
July 1, 1863–June 30, 1864	1,611
July 1, 1864–June 30, 1865	135

Note: The year was not specified for forty-six cases.
Medical and Surgical History, Surgical Section, vol. 3, p. 825.

nurse, writing in April 1865, described an isolation unit in the Union hospital at City Point, Virginia:

> To avoid the dangers of a dreadful infection, the gangrene ward was established in an icehouse, apart from the main hospital . . . Here were limbs which could only be cleansed, not dressed, amputations where the flaps had been eaten away, and the flesh was ragged and fallen from the bone; wounds into which the gangrene was making its fearful ravages day by day—a charnel house . . . where the sufferer is past all healing.[12]

The spread of disease from patient to patient, called "hospitalism" in the 1800s, still exists as "nosocomial infections." (The term "nosocomial" is derived from the Greek word for hospital.)

Hospital gangrene destroys tissues by causing blood clotting in the small arteries bringing them blood and nutrients. Hospital gangrene is spread to other parts of the body by the bloodstream. This differs from other types of gangrene, such as frostbite, which usually remain in one area and injure only local blood vessels. In contrast, hospital gangrene continues to spread, progressively involving more tissues. (See Figure 7.1.)

Philadelphia physician S. Weir Mitchell described the fearsomely rapid development of hospital gangrene lesions:

> A slight flesh wound began to show a gray edge of slough, and within two hours we saw this widening at the rate of half an inch an hour, and deepening . . . Instant removal to open air tents, etherization, savage cautery with pure nitric acid or bromin [sic], and dressings of powdered charcoal enabled us to deal with these cases more or less well, but the mortality was hideous—at least 45 percent.[13]

"Etherization" meant administering general anesthesia to ease the patient's pain during the "savage" treatment for this disease.

When hospital gangrene appeared, surgeons often amputated the affected extremity, or re-amputated a residual stump higher on the limb, to try to stop the inexorable progression of the disease. (See Figure 7.2.) A Confederate physician at the prison hospital at Camp Sumter (Andersonville prison) described treating hospital gangrene:

> For a while amputations were practiced in the hospital almost daily, arising from a gangrenous and scorbutic condition, which, in many cases threatened a saturation of the whole system with this gangrenous or offensive matter, unless the limb was amputated. In cases of amputation of that sort, it would sometimes become necessary to reamputate, from gangrene taking hold of the stump again.[14]

BROMINE: AN EXPERIMENTAL TREATMENT FOR HOSPITAL GANGRENE

During the last two years of the war, many surgeons used bromine to treat hospital gangrene, after they heard about a Union surgeon's successful clinical trials with that agent. Middleton Goldsmith, a medical school professor before the war, compared the survival rates of patients with hospital gangrene who had been treated with various antiseptic agents, including bromine, nitric acid, iodine, and carbolic acid. (See Table 7.2.)

Goldsmith obtained much better results when solutions of bromine were applied to the surface and injected deeply into infected areas (usually in patients under general anesthesia) than when he used other compounds. In his report to the Surgeon General, he concluded, "Testimony of these cases will establish the value of bromine in hospital gangrene sufficiently at least for the purpose of challenging investigation."[15]

Goldsmith was sent to facilities having difficulty treating hospital gangrene, where he discussed bromine and "showed surgeons the correct way to apply it and they responded quickly."[16] He reported considerable success with this endeavor, particularly in Nashville and Murfreesboro. Several medical journals and the *U.S. Sanitary Commission Bulletin* printed articles describing the "lively interest" generated by the idea of using bromine, including its use in erysipelas.[17]

TABLE 7.2
Goldsmith's Treatment of Hospital Gangrene

Treatment	Total Cases	Recovered	Died	Required Amputation	% Died
Bromine after nitric acid failed	23	22	0	1	0
Bromine after other remedies failed	8	8	0	0	0
Bromine in any way	152	148	4	0	2.6
Bromine exclusively	27	25	2	0	7.4
Other remedies exclusively	18	7	5	1	27.8
Nitric acid exclusively	13	5	8	0	61.5

Goldsmith M: Bromine in hospital gangrene. *Am Med Times.* 1863;7:121.

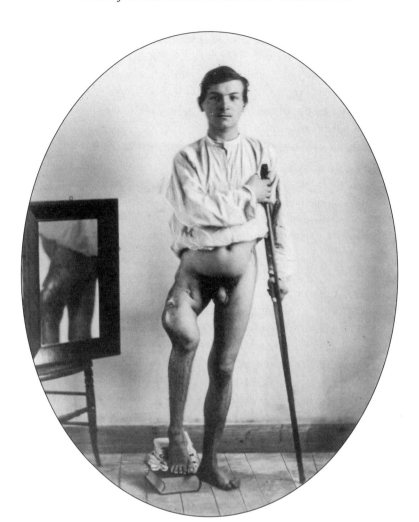

Figure 7.1: Result of Excision of Portion of the Femur (Pvt. John Fredrick, Co. F., 127th NY Vol.), August 15, 1885. This picture illustrates a consequence of the chronic bone infection, osteomyelitis, following a compound fracture caused by a gunshot wound. An attempt to stand on the leg shortly after the injury caused the bend at the seat of the fracture. The ball was removed and the patient was transported to the field hospital, where surgeons decided not to amputate because of the amount of inflammation ("tumefaction") already present. Cold water dressings and splints were applied. Hospital gangrene developed, but was successfully treated with applications of bromine. Examinations in 1873 and 1876 for his pension described a "withered and badly deformed" leg with ulcers, keeping Fredrick largely confined to his bed. (Photo courtesy of the Otis Historical Archives, NMHM, AFIP, No. CP1124.)

One letter from a surgeon reported that since using bromine, "not a case [of erysipelas] has originated." The author continued that it had become unnecessary to isolate cases brought in from other facilities and "so well is its power to prevent spread of erysipelas that even the ward-masters and nurses, who used to dread the effects of being in the wards with erysipelas patients, no longer fear it in the least."[18]

Another doctor reported using bromine prophylactically:

> Nearly every day I have had either cuts, pricks, scratches, or other abrasions on my hands, which are freely exposed in dressing the wounds and in the dead-house [the morgue, where autopsies were performed], with no unpleasant consequences. I have always applied bromine to the denuded surfaces before exposure, and am convinced that the virus of the dead-house, as well as other animal poisons, is entirely destroyed by the action of bromine.[19]

His report is reminiscent of one by a physician from Vienna, Ignac Semmelweis, who advocated washing the hands in chlorine solution to prevent the spread of puerperal sepsis in obstetric cases. This procedure, invented in the late 1840s, was first published in 1860. During the Civil War, at least one physician noted an "apparent affinity [of erysipelas] with puerperal peritonitis."[20] (Puerperal sepsis was later found to be caused by streptococci.)

Confederate surgeons read Goldsmith's article and many adopted the bromine treatment for hospital gangrene. Dr. Joseph Jones, a medical school professor in Augusta, Georgia, first encountered the disease in July 1862. He was both shocked and intrigued by what he recognized as hospital gangrene—a fulminating infection with marked destruction of soft tissues accompanied by discoloration of the affected parts.[21] When additional cases appeared, Jones did his own clinical study of the disease in Confederate armies, hospitals, and prisons. His experiences were similar to those of the Union surgeons. In a lengthy report of his studies at the Andersonville prison, Jones described the spread from patient to patient, the lesions' appearance, and the microscopic findings. He wrote of the futility of treatment, given the dirt and squalor of the prisoners' living conditions and their advanced state of malnutrition:

> Nitric acid and escharotics generally in this crowded atmosphere, loaded with noxious effluvia, exerted only temporary effects. After their application to the diseased surfaces the gangrene would frequently return with redoubled energy; and even after the gangrene had been completely removed by local and constitutional treatment, it would frequently return and destroy the patient.[22]

Some Civil War surgeons reported that after using bromine and similar agents, deaths from hospital gangrene disappeared from their hospitals. Others remained skeptical, apparently considering the treatment a fad. Yet it is not clear that bromine use was actually responsible for decreasing the number of cases of hospital gangrene late in the war.[23] Although many other surgeons used bromine with equal success, Goldsmith's study methods were lacking, since he was not "blinded" to the agents used. Some surgeons reported that they successfully used other substances after they ran out of bromine. One report recorded the successful treatment of Confederate prisoners captured at Gettysburg with a variety of these agents.[24] While the *U.S. Sanitary Commission Bulletin* published several reports discussing bromine's effectiveness, it also had articles describing the successful use of iodine, potassium permanganate, creosote, and other agents. Similar reports were sent to the surgeon general.[25,26]

The incidence of hospital gangrene also might have decreased because, as happens periodically, the *Streptococcus* strain causing it may have spontaneously disappeared. It did, however, still exist in Europe. After the Franco-Prussian War, a Munich hospital recorded that hospital gangrene appeared in 80% of all wounds, and erysipelas was so common that "its occurrence could be regarded as normal." In one year, 11 of 17 amputation patients died of pyemia, and patients with compound (open) fractures were "very rarely to be seen for either the limb was amputated at once, or the occurrence, in a few days' time, of purulent infection, of hospital gangrene, and septicemia rapidly led to a fatal result."[27]

Since the Civil War, hospital gangrene has rarely been reported in the United States. In 1918, beta-hemolytic streptococci was cultured from patients with "necrotizing erysipelas."[28] In 1924, twenty cases of a disease called "streptococcal gangrene" were reported in Peking, China, and the author of the report believed that the etiologic agent was hemolytic *Streptococcus.*[29] Of the outbreaks in the late 1900s, hemolytic *Streptococcus* is the most frequently reported organism, but other bacteria have also been incriminated and a mixture of organisms has been found in many cases. Some recent cases have required amputation, because the gangrene-causing blockages (thrombi) in the blood vessels also prevent antibiotics from reaching the infecting organisms.

During the Civil War, 46% of patients with hospital gangrene died.[30] Today, despite antibiotic therapy and more thorough debridement, up to 20% of patients still die. Civil War medicine doesn't seem so bad after all.

Streptococcal Diseases

By the end of the nineteenth century, physicians knew that both hospital gangrene and erysipelas were caused by the most virulent type of *Streptococcus*, which became known as "group A beta-hemolytic" streptococci. Only some strains of these organisms cause gangrene; most cause erysipelas (skin infection). Erysipelas has remained a common problem, although its severity faded once antibiotics became available to treat it. Bacterial gangrene, on the other hand, became rare after the Civil War; it did reappear as "gas gangrene" (producing gangrene with gas bubbles in tissues) during World War I. Since the 1970s, civilians in the United States and Western Europe have again encountered this disease, which the press promptly dubbed the "flesh-eating virus" or "killer strep."

Now officially called "necrotizing fasciitis," the infection is caused by several organisms and some of them often work together. Streptococci, apparently mutated from the more common benign form, are found in about half of the recent cases.[31] Modern descriptions of necrotizing fasciitis show that the infection usually follows an injury, which can be as minor as a needle stick, an insect bite, a scratch, or, even, blunt trauma that does not break the skin. In some cases, patients do not remember any trauma. The infection spreads rapidly and kills the skin and underlying tissues. Patients initially experience severe pain, but this lessens as the disease progresses and kills nerves, producing numbness or anesthesia which decreases the patient's suffering.

Today, even with antibiotics, necrotizing fasciitis is very difficult to treat, and the fear it has caused indicates how Civil War patients and physicians must have felt when they encountered it. In some modern cases, tissue destruction occurs at the rate of one inch per hour, even faster than in Dr. S. Weir Mitchell's Civil War cases. As they say, sometimes history repeats itself.

CONTROLLING THE SPREAD OF HOSPITAL GANGRENE

Measures by Civil War physicians to control the spread of hospital gangrene and erysipelas show an awareness and understanding of infectious diseases, although the science of bacteriology had not yet been established. Physicians knew that hospital gangrene and erysipelas were contagious, and related, because they saw them appear and spread together from patient to patient, from patient to nurse, and even from patient to visitor. They observed patients

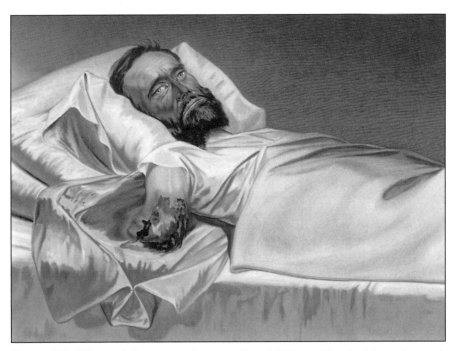

Figure 7.2: "Hospital Gangrene of an Arm Stump." The soldier had been hospitalized at the Naval Academy in Annapolis. Hospital gangrene was a particular problem at that facility. (*Medical and Surgical History*, Surgical Section, vol. 2, plate XV, opp. p. 739.)

who had hospital gangrene in one place develop erysipelas in adjacent areas, such as the other thigh. And nurses developed erysipelas in their cut fingers after they touched gangrenous wounds. As a result, patients with these two diseases were isolated together. In the 1864 *Confederate States Medical and Surgical Journal*, a physician wrote that he was "in charge of the Erysipelas and Gangrene Ward" of the Confederate hospital in Charlottesville, Virginia.[32]

Whenever possible, patients with hospital gangrene were isolated and each had their own supplies for dressing their wounds. For example, in a hospital for released prisoners of war at the Naval Academy in Annapolis:

> Every precaution was taken to prevent the spread of [hospital gangrene] from patient to patient; as soon as it made its appearance in a wound, the patient was immediately removed and placed in a room where there were no wounded . . . Each man had a separate sponge, basin, etc; one nurse was detailed in each ward to dress the wounds of gangrenous patients, and he

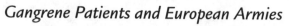

Gangrene Patients and European Armies

Hospital gangrene plagued European military physicians. A manual of surgery published at the outset of the Civil War described appalling epidemics of hospital gangrene during the Crimean War, especially among the French forces. The infection raged "with extraordinary virulence and fatality among the French in the hospitals on the Bosphorus. It also prevailed about the same period within some of the hospitals in the south of France." Dr. Samuel D. Gross described a hospital ship, the *Euphrate*, which went to extremes to prevent the disease from spreading. To effectively isolate patients "in her voyage to the Mediterranean [the crew] was obliged, from this cause alone, to throw sixty men overboard within thirty-six hours!"[33]

was allowed to dress no others; the bedclothes were washed separately, and whitewashing the room was frequently and thoroughly done.[34]

Similarly, at a hospital for captured Confederate soldiers, "each patient was supplied with a sponge for his own use only" and these were washed daily.[35] Another hospital surgeon reported that "each patient was given his own towels, sponges, etc. and no dressings or bandages were used a second time."[36] Dr. Joseph Jones recorded:

> Many of the Confederate surgeons appeared to be aware of the dangers attending the indiscriminate use of sponges, dressings and uncleansed bowls, when erysipelas was present in their wards. When wounds were cleansed with sponges or rags, which had been used on erysipelas patients, it was frequently observed that the disease appeared, and such propagation appeared to be clearly referable to the transference of contagious matter.[37]

Civil War-era literature is filled with discussions of the need for hospital ventilation. Surgeons pointed out that erysipelas seemed to spread in the direction of the wind,[38] an observation that was correct since microorganisms may be scattered by air currents. Others blamed "illy ventilated rooms" in crowded hospitals, although the crowd was more of a problem than the poor ventilation, as experiences with tent hospitals and private-home treatment demonstrated.[39] Tents were well ventilated and had few patients, thus decreasing the opportunity for erysipelas and hospital gangrene to spread. So, it is not surprising that the overall mortality for gunshot wounds was lower when the men were treated in tent hospitals rather than in crowded buildings. During the Franco-Prussian War, tent hospitals were used in imitation of the American experience, and they similarly had a lower mortality.

Soldiers cared for in private homes or while residing in hotels, as officers frequently were, rarely developed hospital gangrene. For example, Maj. Gen. Dan Sickles' leg was amputated within two hours of his being wounded by shrapnel at Gettysburg. He recuperated in a Washington hotel, without complications. He sent his leg, with a calling card, to the Army Medical Museum, where both are still on display.[40]

ANTISEPSIS

Surgeons used agents they called "antiseptics" to decrease the amount of tissue death, called "putrefaction" or "sepsis" (the Greek word for putrefaction), which they thought caused pus in wounds. Despite not knowing that bacteria caused most wound infections, Civil War physicians used antiseptics to reduce their incidence. They observed that using antiseptics decreased the odor from the infected wounds. Since "miasmas" were often characterized by their odors and were believed to be the underlying cause of disease, the beneficial effects of antiseptics seemed obvious.

Observations of Microorganisms

Civil War physicians who studied hospital gangrene lesions using the microscope saw dead tissue with blood vessels in the area occluded with "stagnant blood" (probably a description of the process later called "thrombosis"). While they also saw microscopic organisms, they thought that they were merely opportunistic and a result of the infection, rather than its cause.[41] (This thinking was typical of the era.)

Reporting on his microscopic studies of hospital gangrene, Joseph Woodward described seeing "vibrios" in the lesions. "Vibrio," according to Dunglisen's 1853 dictionary, is a "genus of infusory animalcules which are met with . . . [in] almost all putrescent fluids." In Woodward's original document, which is in the National Archives, the word "vibrio" is crossed out, with the word "bacteria" written above it. The version of his report published in the last volume of *Medical and Surgical History* uses the word "bacteria," but that volume was completed in 1883, after bacteriology was well-established.[42]

Civil War treatments of wound infections included some surprisingly modern approaches, such as using carbolic acid and tincture of iodine. That Civil War surgeons applied carbolic acid to dressings is surprising, since its antiseptic properties had only just been described in 1860.[43] Two years *after* the Civil War, Joseph Lister described it as an essential component of his antiseptic surgery technique.[44]

Maggots and Rats: Nature's Surgeons

According to soldiers' letters, swarms of flies harassed them in every encampment and hospital. Because flies deposited their eggs in any open wound or in wounds covered with the standard moist dressings (apparently, the eggs could penetrate through several layers of moist muslin), maggots rapidly appeared in wounds. Although the maggots caused no pain, they disgusted the volunteer female nurses and their wiggling bothered the wounded men.[45] Clinicians, therefore, used oil of turpentine, petroleum, kerosene, tobacco, chloroform, and antiseptics to kill the maggots when flies were present. In well-run hospitals, strict cleanliness usually prevented their appearance.[46]

Yet, some Civil War surgeons ultimately realized that maggots could have beneficial effects: they painlessly cleansed wounds by digesting and removing dead tissue without injuring healthy tissue. Confederate Surgeon Joseph Jones, for example, reported that "a gangrenous wound which had been thoroughly cleansed by maggots healed more rapidly than if it had been left by itself."[47] In recent times, physicians have rediscovered the ability of maggots to debride wounds, often more carefully than the best surgeon.

In her memoirs, Phoebe Pember noted the skill of rats in removing dead tissues in a wound without damaging healthy tissue or hurting the soldier. "The rat surgeons," she noted, "could have passed the [medical examining] board."[48] A Virginian named Patterson was wounded in the center of the instep of a foot; the wound sloughed, and a large mass of "proud flesh" (newly formed growing tissue, now called "granulation") formed an island in its center. According to Pember,

> The surgeons feared to remove the mass, thinking it was connected to the nerves of the foot and lockjaw might ensue. Patterson was very glum, but [after the rats got to his wound, he] brightened one morning, and he exhibited the foot with great glee, the little island gone, and a deep hollow left, but the wound was washed clean and looking healthy.[49]

Tincture of iodine was also used, and still is. Civil War surgeons even recorded that strong antiseptics, such as iodine, could kill tissues and thus do more harm than good. This clinical principle was forgotten after the Civil War until it was studied during World War I (in part, by Alexander Fleming, who later discovered penicillin).

Civil War physicians also used a variety of traditional poultices to treat wound infections. Usually, they were made of flaxseed or bread.[50] Yeast poultices were used for hospital gangrene, erysipelas, and other suppurating wounds.[51,52] While there are no recorded studies of the effectiveness of these agents, given the widespread occurrence of antibacterial substances in nature, one wonders if they contained some therapeutic factors.

TETANUS

Tetanus, another disease with an extremely high mortality rate, results from infection with *Clostridium tetani*, which is often found in animal feces. In the Crimean War, thirteen cases were diagnosed among the English troops; all the infected soldiers died. During the Civil War, Union forces recorded 509 cases; 89% of these men died.[53] Most of these infections occurred after the soldiers had surgery in temporary field hospitals that had been set up in barns.

Tetanus causes generalized painful muscle spasms. Jaw muscles are often affected first, thus the name "lockjaw." This interferes with patients' ability to swallow and breathe, and is what ultimately kills them. Back, abdominal, and proximal limb muscles also become rigid, and patients' bodies may become so contorted that they are resting only on their heads and feet—a painful position known as "opisthotonus." (See Figure 7.3.)

In 1866, Samuel Gross described opisthotonos:

> [Tetanus] having reached this stage, . . . frequent spasms now occur, convulsing and agitating the whole frame, and greatly increasing the general suffering. The teeth are firmly clenched; the eyes are fixed in their sockets, and have a wild, unnatural expression; the nostrils are expanded; the corners of the mouth are retracted; the countenance has an old, haggard, and withered look; the respiration is laborious and hurried; and the smallest quantity of fluid is unable to descend the fauces and oesophagus.[54]

Aware of the fatal prognosis, Civil War surgeons tried desperately to save tetanus patients. One physician reported that to describe all the types of therapy they attempted "would require a volume."[55] Surgeons anesthetized patients with chloroform to try to relieve the unremitting, intensely painful muscle spasms. While anesthesia gave temporary symptomatic relief, it could

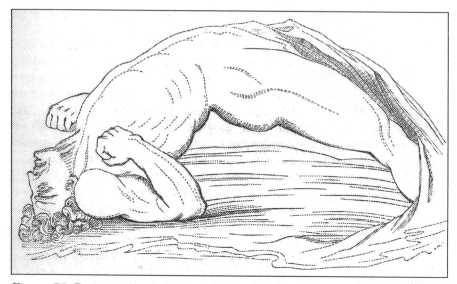

Figure 7.3: Patient with opisthotonos (tetanus). (*SS*, p. 611.)

not halt the inexorable course of the disease. Aware that the disease arose from something in the inflamed wound, surgeons amputated the affected area in 29 cases and, remarkably, they saved 10 of these patients![56]

Even today, physicians must treat tetanus patients symptomatically. There was a great deal of tetanus among British troops in the first year of World War I, but the disease was subsequently prevented by administering the tetanus vaccine that had recently been developed.[57]

Confederate surgeons reported 13 cases of tetanus in 1861, with only 3 deaths. However, the quality of the records from the early days of the war has been questioned, and it is fair to wonder if the diagnosis was correct, given the low mortality rate. In 1862, there were 53 Confederate cases recorded, with 28 deaths (53%). The report in *Confederate States Medical and Surgical Journal* suggests that more cases went unreported to the Surgeon General's Office in Richmond.[58] Fire destroyed the information from subsequent years.

Although gas gangrene is caused by *Clostridium welchii*, an organism related to the one that causes tetanus, there is no evidence that it occurred during the Civil War. Gas gangrene is comparatively easy to diagnose—the bacteria produces bubbles of gas in tissues and occludes the blood vessels, causing rapidly spreading tissue necrosis. Both *C. welchii* and *C. tetani* are present in manure from large farm animals. Gas gangrene was a fearsome problem during World War I, most likely because the fields of Flanders and eastern France were heavily manured. So why didn't it occur during the Civil War? Manure was not used as the primary fertilizer in Virginia and the sites of other major Civil War battles. No manure, no *Clostridium welchii* infection.

REFERENCES

1. Foote S: *The Civil War: A Narrative.* vol. 1. New York: Random House, 1958, p. 323.
2. Lister J: A new method of treating compound fractures, abscesses, etc, with observations on conditions of suppuration. *Lancet.* 1867;1:326 (and subsequent issues).
3. Lister J: On the effects of the antiseptic system of treatment upon the salubrity of a surgical hospital. *Lancet.* 1870;1:4-40.
4. Lister J: A method of antiseptic treatment applicable to wounded soldiers in the present war. *Br Med J.* 1870;2:243-44.
5. Garrison FH: *An Introduction to the History of Medicine with Medical Chronology, Suggestions for Study and Bibliographic Data.* 4th ed. Philadelphia, PA: W.B. Saunders, 1929, p. 832.
6. Dunglisen R: *Medical Lexicon: A Dictionary of Medical Science.* 9th ed. Philadelphia, PA: Henry C. Lea, 1853, p. 732.
7. Harris CR: Report of forty-eight cases of hospital gangrene and hospital erysipelas treated in General Hospital Division No. 1, Charlottesville, VA. from 1st June 1864 to 1st October 1864. *Conf States Med Surg J.* 1864;1(11):183.
8. Baruch S: Two cases of penetrating bayonet wounds of the chest. *Conf States Med Surg J.* 1864;1:133-34.
9. Boyd W: *Textbook of Pathology: An Introduction to Medicine.* 4th ed. Philadelphia, PA: Lea & Febiger, 1943, p. 352.
10. *Medical and Surgical History*, Surgical Section, vol. 3, p. 851.
11. Report of Acting Ass't. Surg. C. H. Cleveland, Church Hospital, Memphis, Tenn. *Medical and Surgical History*, Surgical Section, vol. 3, pp. 843-44.
12. Denney RE: *Civil War Medicine: Care and Comfort of the Wounded.* New York: Sterling, 1994, p. 376.
13. Mitchell SW: On the Medical Department in the Civil War. *J Am Med Assoc.* 1914;62(19):1446.
14. Chipman NP: *The Andersonville Prison Trial: The Trial of Capt. Henry Wirz.* San Francisco: The Author, 1911. Repub.: Notable Trials Library, 1990, p. 127.
15. *Medical and Surgical History*, Surgical Section, vol. 3, p. 836.
16. "Report of Surg. M. Goldsmith," NARA, RG94, Entry #621, File A261.
17. *U.S. Sanitary Commission Bulletin.* 1863;1:195-97, 201.
18. Letter from B. Woodward, M.D. to M. Goldsmith. *Am Med Times.* 1863;6:239.
19. Report of Acting Ass't. Surg. C.H. Cleveland, p. 848.
20. Eve PF: Answers to certain questions propounded by Prof. Charles A. Lee, M.D., Agent of the U.S. Sanitary Comm. relative to the health, etc., of the late Southern army. *Nashville J Med Surg.* 1866 July;1:12-32.
21. Riley HD, Jr.: Joseph Jones, an early clinical investigator. *South Med J.* 1987;80(5):623-29.
22. *O.R.*, Series II, vol. VIII, pp. 588-632.
23. Gillett MC: *The United States Army Medical Department, 1818–1865.* Washington, D.C.: Center of Military History, U.S. Army, 1987, pp. 281-83.
24. Pryer WC: Hospital gangrene in the DeCamp General Hospital. *Am Med Times.* 1864;8:4-6.
25. *U.S. Sanitary Commission Bulletin.* 1863;1:195, 201 and 1864;2:196; also Miller JG: *Am J Med Sci.* 1871;62:573.

26. F. Hinkle, Jarvis General Hospital, Baltimore, November 6, 1863. NARA, RG94, Entry #621, File A263.

27. Walter CW: *The Aseptic Treatment of Wounds*. New York: Macmillan, 1948.

28. Hardzog-Britt C, Riley HD, Jr.: Acute necrotizing fasciitis in childhood. *J Oklahoma State Med Assoc.* 1995;88(9):392-97.

29. Meleney FL: Hemolytic streptococcus gangrene. *Arch Surg.* 1924;9:317-64.

30. Riley HD, Jr.: Medicine in the Confederacy. Part 1. *Mil Med.* 1956 Jan;118(1):53.

31. Letters to the editor. *N Eng J Med.* 1994;331:279-80.

32. Harris, *Conf States Med Surg J*, 1864.

33. Gross SD: *A Manual of Military Surgery or Hints on the Emergencies of Field, Camp and Hospital Practice*. Philadelphia: Lippincott, 1861. Repub: Normal Pub., 1988, pp. 92-93.

34. Pittinos JW: Hospital gangrene as it appeared in St. John's College Hospital, Annapolis, MD. *Am J Med Sci.* 1863 Jul;46:50-56.

35. Pryer, *Am Med Times*, pp. 4-6.

36. Hinkle, NARA, RG94.

37. Jones J: Observations upon the losses of the Confederate armies from battle, wounds and diseases, during the American Civil War of 1861–65, with investigations upon the number and character of the diseases supervening from gun-shot wounds. *Richmond Louisville Med J.* 1870:9:647.

38. Keen WW: Surgical reminiscences of the Civil War. *Transactions of the College of Physicians of Philadelphia*. 3rd Series. 1905;27:95-114.

39. *Medical and Surgical History*, Surgical Section, vol. 3, p. 856.

40. Pinchon E: *Dan Sickles: Hero of Gettysburg and "Yankee King of Spain."* Garden City, NY: Doubleday, Doran & Co., 1945.

41. Woodward JJ: Report of microscopical appearance of hospital gangrene in the Annapolis General Hospital, February 13, 1863. NARA, RG94, Entry #621, File A295.

42. *Medical and Surgical History*, Surgical Section, vol. 3, pp. 830-32.

43. Report by Lemaire in 1860. In: Garrison, *History of Medicine*, p. 832.

44. Lister, *Lancet*, 1867.

45. Hart AG: *The Surgeon and the Hospital in the Civil War*. Gaithersburg, MD: Olde Soldier Books, 1987 (orig. pub. 1902), p. 36.

46. *Medical and Surgical History*, Surgical Section, vol. 3, p. 867.

47. Jordan EL: *Charlottesville and the University of Virginia in the Civil War*. Lynchburg, VA: H.E. Howard, 1988.

48. Pember P: *A Southern Woman's Story: Life in Confederate Richmond*. New York: G.W. Carleton, 1879, p. 61.

49. Ibid.

50. Roberts DJ. In: *The Photographic History of the Civil War*. New York: Review of Reviews, 1970 (orig. pub. 1911), vol. 4B, p. 252.

51. Lee CL: Cases of hospital gangrene at Elmira. NARA, RG94, Entry #621, File A573.

52. Records of Winder Hospital. Eleanor S. Brockenbrough Library, Museum of the Confederacy, Richmond, VA.

53. *Medical and Surgical History*, Surgical Section, vol. 3, pp. 818-19.

54. Gross SD: *System of Surgery*. 4th ed. vol. 1. Philadelphia: Henry C. Lea, 1866, p. 610-11.

55. Cunningham HH: *Doctors in Gray: The Confederate Medical Service*. Baton Rouge: Louisiana State Univ. Press, 1958, p. 237.

56. *Medical and Surgical History*, Surgical Section, vol. 3, p. 819.

57. Dubos RJ: *Bacterial and Mycotic Infections of Man*. Philadelphia, PA: J.B. Lippincott, 1948, p. 366.

58. Sorrel P: Gunshot wounds: Army of Northern Virginia. *Conf States Med Surg J.* 1864;1(10):154.

❧ 8 ❧

Civil War Hospitals

We taught Europe how to build, organize, and manage hospitals.

– Dr. John Shaw Billings

MORE THAN ONE MILLION SOLDIERS RECEIVED CARE in Federal military hospitals during the Civil War. Such a massive medical undertaking was unprecedented; it is one of Civil War medicine's outstanding achievements. Moreover, *fewer than 10% of those patients in Federal hospitals died during the war.*

The Confederates had a similar number of hospitals and the same general results. Mortality figures for Confederate hospitals seem a bit lower, but this may be due, in part, to a different system of record keeping: They counted each patient as a new admission, even when he was only transferred from one unit to another. This practice inflated the admission figures, making it impossible to determine the total number of patients admitted.

With no models to draw on, both sides' Medical Departments devised extensive workable hospital systems. These included mobile field hospitals, evacuation hospitals near the battlefront, temporary depot hospitals at transfer sites, several hundred huge general hospitals in major cities, specialty hospitals, and hospitals for officers.

When existing structures proved unsatisfactory for use as hospitals, medical personnel had to design and build new facilities. They also had to provide the patients they housed with food, medicines, clothing, sanitation, and medical and nursing care. They even invented the type of hospital treatment now called "rehabilitation."

The challenges they faced were immense. Before 1860, the U.S. Army had infirmaries at army posts, but only one, a forty-bed unit at the military post in Fort Leavenworth, Kansas, was considered a hospital.[1] When the war began, the only military hospital in Washington, D.C., was a six-room two-story brick structure on First Street between North B and C Streets that was used for smallpox patients.[2] Civilian hospitals were primarily for the indigent sick, and a few were still evolving from "poor-houses." Those who could afford it received medical, obstetrical, and even surgical care in the home. In some hospitals supported by contributions, such as Massachusetts General Hospital in Boston, patrons' sick servants were entitled to a free bed, since the lady of the house usually preferred not to be burdened with providing care for the help.[3]

THE EVOLUTION OF GENERAL HOSPITALS

At first, lacking adequate hospital facilities, both sides employed a variety of existing structures as hospitals. After a battle, they would appropriate public buildings, hotels, churches, schools, warehouses, mills, and private homes for use as medical facilities. They even used the partially completed Capitol building in Washington as a barracks and hospital: about 2,000 men slept on cots and mattresses lining the halls and in committee rooms and offices. These buildings were woefully inappropriate for the purpose; most didn't have sufficient toilets or facilities for bathing, mortuaries, or adequate heating. Former hotels had tortuous corridors, required extra staffing, and could not be cleaned properly. They also had poor ventilation, which led to pervasive sickening odors.

The small regimental hospitals in training camps during the first year were nearly all tents. Tents were also used for the field hospitals that replaced regimental hospitals. Because they had proven satisfactory in the first major test of their utility at the Battle of Shiloh in April 1862, the Medical Corps was issued large tents that could accommodate eight patients comfortably and be combined to create larger units.[4] When tents, with their superior ventilation, were available, surgeons rarely used existing buildings, even for temporary hospitals. To heat the tents, they devised a way to build the fire outside the tent and divert the smoke so that it would not bother the patients. Advancing enemy forces sometimes overran field hospitals since they were near the front lines. So, to protect the patients and staff, hospitals were identified by special flags: first by solid red flags, then, after 1863, by yellow flags with green numerals.

When permanent hospitals were full, tents were added to create huge complexes arranged in orderly columns and rows. After the Peninsula campaign in mid-1862, the U.S. Sanitary Commission erected about 1,000 tents around White House Landing to serve as hospitals.[5] Tents were also used to isolate patients to prevent the spread of hospital gangrene and erysipelas, and they served as "pest hospitals" for smallpox patients.

Both Union and Confederate armies developed an innovative type of hospital construction. They built pavilion-style general hospitals from wood, with the single-story barracks-like patient wards arranged in columns or rows. These wards formed either a grid or an arc that fanned out from a central administrative facility. (See Figure 8.1.) Originally designed by Dr. John Shaw Billings of the Surgeon General's Office, the typical wards were 150′ long by 25′ wide, with 12′–14′ ceilings.[6] Some of these hospitals remained in use long after the war. In fact, a similar type of construction continued to be used for temporary or semi-permanent military hospitals through both World Wars and into the Vietnam War era.

The hospitals were usually built quickly. For example, a contractor in Philadelphia agreed to provide a functional 2,500-bed hospital in forty days. Satterlee Hospital opened on the appointed date even though it was not entirely complete. Eventually, it was expanded to 3,500 beds.[7] Individual wards usually contained about 60 beds and were fitted with many windows, making them drafty and quite cold in winter.[8] (See Figure 8.2.) Florence Nightingale originated this design after her Crimean War experiences revealed the need for maximum ventilation.[9] Draftiness was considered beneficial most of the time, since it carried away the almost constant and overwhelming odors of putrefaction.

To provide for their patients, hospitals on both sides traded surplus supplies and food for other necessities or delicacies. Hospitals organized their own gardens to grow vegetables. Often the hospital bakery produced extra loaves of bread to barter, and patients produced goods, such as shoes, to trade as well. Convalescent soldiers and volunteers did most of the work in the shops, bakeries, and gardens.[10,11]

Many of the general hospitals functioned during only part of the war, particularly those in relatively remote areas near the major battles. Although the Union Adjutant General's Office archive lists 431 general hospitals, a maximum of 204 were probably operating at any one time.[12] (See Table 8.1.) Hospitals were located from New England to New Orleans and from the Atlantic Ocean to the Missouri River. There were also convalescent centers, sixteen of them near Washington, which held 21,426 beds.[13] In total, about 400,000 hospital beds were available to care for Civil War soldiers.

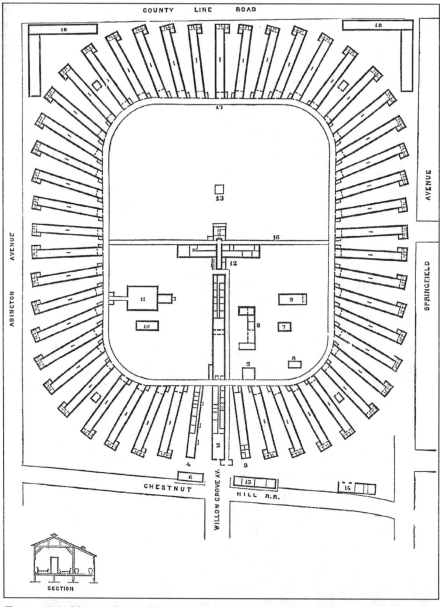

Figure 8.1: Mower General Hospital, Chestnut Hill, Pennsylvania. (1) wards; (2) reception rooms, laundry, etc.; (3) knapsack room, band quarters, etc.; (4) store-rooms, etc., (5) operating room; (6) butcher's shop; (7) guard-house; (8) boiler, coal, etc.; (9) sutler's (10) carpenters' shop; (11) chapel; (12) administration building; (13) ice-house; (14)(15) railroad depots; (16)(17) corridors; (18)(19) L-shaped buildings used as barracks, store-rooms, etc. (*Medical and Surgical History*, Medical Section, vol. 3, p. 933.)

TABLE 8.1

General Hospitals in the Union Army

Fiscal Year Ending	Number of Hospitals	Number of Beds	Average Census
June 30, 1862	151	58,716	9,548
June 30, 1863	182	84,572	45,630
June 30, 1864	190	120,521	55,710
June 30, 1865	204	136,894	71,484

From: Annual Reports of the Surgeon General to the Secretary of War, NARA, Microfilm library; *Medical and Surgical History*, Medical Section, vol. 1.

The greatest concentration of hospitals was in the area around Washington, D.C. During the war, that city had about twenty-eight military hospitals and several more were established nearby, including six in Georgetown and five in Alexandria. The largest were Lincoln and Armory Square Hospitals.[14] Many "temporary" Civil War hospitals were still in use in 1890, including Lincoln and Harewood Hospitals in Washington, Sedgewick Hospital in New Orleans, and Baltimore's Hicks Hospital. Lincoln Hospital held as many as 2,575 beds (including the beds in tents) and treated a total of about 46,000 patients; it still contained 1,240 beds in 1890.[15]

CONFEDERATE HOSPITALS

Confederate Surgeon General Samuel P. Moore wrote that after First Manassas (Bull Run) in July 1861, Richmond was overwhelmed with wounded and sick soldiers. Gen. Joseph Johnston aggravated the situation when, soon after the battle, he cleared all his field hospitals of sick and wounded in anticipation of further fighting. Moore, realizing that he needed additional hospital beds, found that the only suitable structure, the old almshouse, was filled with wounded Union soldiers who had been captured. His only option was to treat the Confederate soldiers in improvised hospitals throughout the city. To accomplish this, he converted private houses, unoccupied wooden buildings, and small tobacco factories into hospitals. In the confusion, the army kept such poor records that they did not know the location of many of their wounded soldiers.

After this experience, the Confederate army quickly adopted a hospital construction plan that was used throughout the war. Their hospitals consisted of numerous small buildings with thirty-two beds each and with passages

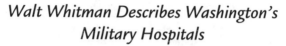

Walt Whitman Describes Washington's Military Hospitals

On December 26, 1863, Walt Whitman wrote a first-person report of the "military hospitals, convalescent camps, etc." in "Washington and the neighborhood" which appeared in the *New York Times*. In it he gave a detailed description of the hospital in the Patent Office:

> that noblest of Washington buildings, . . . [the newly erected barracks being used as hospital wards] each contain sixty men, have a ward-master, a nurse for every 10 or 12 men, ward surgeons generally cover two wards . . . Some of the wards have a woman nurse. Some [hospitals] have over a thousand patients.[16]

Despite the "pitiful sights" and "agony," Whitman concluded the care and concern for the sick was generally good, although there were "tyrants and shysters." He specifically railed against one doctor who enforced unnecessary discipline and banned all amusements for the patients, adding, "In general the officials—especially the new ones, with their straps or badges, put on too many airs."[17]

between the buildings. Limiting each building's size kept men separated into small groups, which minimized the spread of disease. Also, similar to the Federal arrangements, men with hospital gangrene were isolated in tents in an attempt to prevent spread of the disease, with separate "pest houses" for smallpox patients.

The Confederate Medical Department had two major divisions: the general hospital staff and the field hospital surgeons. Although a few transfers did occur between the divisions, in general, the personnel were kept separate. The field staff set up and ran a network of receiving and forwarding hospitals to accommodate soldiers in transit from the battlefields to the general hospitals. These were established at key points, such as where the turnpike running down the Shenandoah Valley met the railroad at Staunton, Virginia. (This route was used by Gen. John Daniel Imboden's ambulance train to evacuate the wounded from Gettysburg.) Wayside hospitals were established along routes used by soldiers who were going home on furlough or who had been discharged because of wounds or sickness.[18]

The Confederate military established at least 154 general hospitals during the war; the majority were in Virginia, North Carolina, Georgia, and

Alabama. When they could not build new hospitals, such as in Charlottes-ville, the Medical Corps would set up general hospitals in a large complex of buildings, including homes, churches, public buildings, and tents. According to the records that still exist, the medical problems and treatments for patients in the major Confederate hospitals were indistinguishable from those of their Union counterparts.[19]

Hospitals were inexpensive to build because they used untreated wood intended for tobacco warehouses (since tobacco was no longer being ship-ped) and the labor was provided by the unemployed factory workers. This permitted both sides to build hospitals rapidly, an important wartime con-sideration. Moore noted that if they had to abandon a hospital, they could replace it at little cost. However, because the Confederate Medical Depart-ment was not independent and had to depend on the Quartermaster and Commissary Departments, there were delays in constructing and furnishing the hospitals. Moore claimed that the Medical Department received the blame for the delays, "which it never deserved."[20]

After consulting with James B. McCaw, a prominent Richmond physi-cian, Moore had a pavilion-style hospital built on Chimborazo Hill, just out-side Richmond. Chimborazo Hospital was spread over forty acres, and, by the end of the war, it had 150 wards with 40–60 patients in each, making it pos-sibly the largest military hospital in the world. Doctors treated about 58,000 sick and 17,000 wounded soldiers at Chimborazo Hospital during the war; only about 9% of the soldiers recorded as being admitted died.

Dr. McCaw was placed in charge of Chimborazo Hospital; it was his job to solve the innumerable problems and keep the large institution running under deteriorating wartime conditions. To do this, he was loaned a nearby farm, "Tree Hill," and the cows and goats raised there provided meat and milk for the patients. A canal boat, *The Chimborazo*, traveled up the James River as far as Lexington and Lynchburg to obtain additional food by bar-tering yarn made from cotton grown on the farm and shoes produced in hospital shops from the skins of animals used for meat. The hospital bakery produced 7,000–10,000 loaves of bread each day, and the grease from its five soup kitchens was mixed with lye (brought through the blockade) to make soap. Many other Confederate hospitals set up bakeries that were larger than needed and traded the excess bread to the local populace for needed food items.[21,22]

Over the course of the war, the Confederacy built six permanent hospi-tal complexes in and around Richmond, providing over 20,000 beds.[23] One of them, Winder Hospital, may have been even larger than Chimborazo.

Figure 8.2: Ward in Carver General Hospital, Washington, D.C., September 1864. The wooden barracks-style construction is evident. Note the surgeons and a hospital steward attending a patient on the left and two women, probably nurses, sitting by a bedside at the right. Two of the men in the picture have had amputations, one of the forearm and the other of the lower leg; the latter is in a wheelchair near the middle of the picture. The soldier on the right is Henry W. Knight of the 6th Maine Volunteers, wearing the cross that was the badge of the Sixth Corps. (Courtesy of NARA, No. 111-B-173.)

Winder opened with 3,000 beds, and quickly grew to at least 4,300 beds divided into five divisions, with an additional tent division. Patients were assigned to the divisions depending on which state they were from. The hospital had 98 buildings, including a huge bakery, warehouses, employees' barracks, a library, and bathhouses. Like Chimborazo, it was also located near the James River and had two canal boats, which it used to transport food grown on its 125-acre farm, often bartering for other goods along the route.

After Surgeon General Moore organized the large military hospitals, he decided to close the innumerable small hospitals that were located mostly in private homes. The quality of the care provided, and the mortality rates, varied greatly among these hospitals, so the decision to close them made sense. To accomplish this easily, a law was passed that all hospitals had to be run by a commissioned officer with a rank not lower than the equivalent of captain.

Among these small hospitals in Richmond was Robertson Hospital, on the corner of Main and Third Streets, run by Sally Louisa Tompkins. Unfortunately, Sally Tompkins was not a captain. With ambulances at her door ready to take the patients away, Tompkins requested help from the Secretary of War. He replied that the only man who could help was Jefferson Davis. When President Davis reviewed her hospital's records, they revealed that her death rate was the lowest of all the hospitals in Richmond and that the number of soldiers who returned to their command was the highest. President Davis immediately gave Tompkins a commission with the rank of captain and ordered her hospital to remain open. The staff cared for over 1,400 sick and wounded soldiers from July 30, 1861, just after First Manassas, to July 13, 1865, two months after Richmond fell.

Although Sally Tompkins has been considered a Confederate heroine ever since, a more thorough review of her hospital's records suggests that her success rate may have been the result of her selection of patients: primarily officers and patients without serious wounds.[24]

HOSPITAL INSPECTIONS

To upgrade the quality of Union military hospitals, the Sanitary Commission quickly began a hospital inspection system soon after the start of the war. Respected private physicians (many were too old or too busy to leave their civilian responsibilities and join the army) volunteered to inspect the military hospitals and make recommendations. Each inspector used 179 questions to document the general health of the men and the sanitary conditions of both the regiment and the hospital. Among these were the state of the latrines, how many changes of underclothing the men had, what they ate, and details such as "Does each man wash his head, neck and feet once a day?"[25]

Even though inspectors arrived unexpectedly at any time of the day or night, the Sanitary Commission reported that

> The Inspectors had been cordially welcomed in almost every Hospital they visited, by the officers in charge. Every facility was afforded them for making a thorough investigation of their condition, and they did not hesitate to point out on the spot deficiencies in the service which met their observation. They found the Surgeons, as a class, faithful, earnest and skillful men, striving, frequently in the face of most serious obstacles, to do their

utmost to relieve the wants of the suffering men under their charge. Many of these Surgeons had left practice in civil life, at a great personal sacrifice, and had entered the Army, from purely patriotic motives. Few of them, it is true, had had any experience in the peculiar labors of Hospital practice, and it was surprising on the whole, how wonderfully nearly all of them had adapted themselves to the exigencies of their new position.[26]

They made their initial inspections in late 1861, when most hospitals were still small infirmaries organized on a regimental basis. In December 1861, the Commission's Executive Secretary, Frederick Law Olmstead, reported that out of 200 regimental hospitals, 105 were considered good, 52 were tolerable, and 26 were bad. He added that supplies and medical equipment generally were poor, the diet was limited, nursing care was bad, attendants were negligent, and there were no nurses on night duty.[27] The first reports summarized the problems inherent in the small regimental hospitals:

> The prominent and obvious defect existing everywhere, but especially observable in the West, was the want of suitable buildings . . . The testimony of all the Inspectors was uniform in regard to the necessity of establishing Hospitals only in buildings specially erected for such a purpose. In their investigations throughout the country, they had found every species of building, from common dwelling-houses, to hotels and churches occupied as Hospitals, and they never failed in their Reports to point out the inherent unfitness of all of them for the purposes for which they were used.[28]

The Value of Hospital Inspections

In a speech to a Chicago physicians' club in 1913, Dr. S. Weir Mitchell emphasized the value of hospital inspections during the Civil War:

> No matter how remote they were, these [hospitals] were subject to frequent ruthless inspections, when a trained man unexpectedly appeared at midnight or in the day, spent twenty-four hours in seeing everything in the hospital, and then with praise or blame sent to the surgeon-general reports which spared no one high or low.

> I am perfectly satisfied that even the best of our city hospitals would be the better for these, sudden inspections by watchful physicians, not of the staff or by ignorant lay managers. Such inspections should fulfill all the exactions of . . . [the] admirable little handbook of hospital management [written by Dr. J. S. Billings during the war].[29]

The inspector-in-chief did point out that suggestions

> with regard to defects and evils found to be existing in any of the Hospitals have, when transmitted . . . to the Surgeon-General, invariably received his immediate and effective attention . . . An inspection of the reports of the different Inspectors, at different and consecutive dates, will also show, in many instances, a very marked and progressive improvement in the condition of the Hospitals inspected.[30]

Initially, the Sanitary Commission performed these inspections without Surgeon General Finley's approval. When William Hammond became surgeon general, he formally requested that they continue. In December 1862, the U.S. Congress established the rank of Medical Inspector General and provided funding for sixteen inspectors. They replaced the Sanitary Commission's volunteer inspectors, while performing similar functions.[31] The Sanitary Commission's relationship with the Surgeon General's Office deteriorated upon the appointment of Hammond's replacement, Joseph K. Barnes, and he refused to allow their inspections to continue after 1864. By then, however, improvements in both sanitation and medical care had reduced the need for such inspections.[32]

SPECIALTY HOSPITALS

While civilian specialty hospitals first opened in the United States in the 1850s, their formation was further encouraged by Civil War medical developments. Both the Union and Confederate Medical Departments set up hospitals in which patients with specific types of injuries could be treated by experienced physicians. In 1863, for example, the Union army established Desmarres Hospital in Washington, D.C. (On August 23, 1864, it was moved to Chicago.) The hospital was "especially set apart for diseases of the eye and ear." Surgeon J. H. Hildreth, U.S. Volunteers, headed the 150-bed hospital and performed eye and throat operations there.[33] Tonsillectomies were also done at Desmarres.[34,35] Near the end of the war, the Confederate army opened an eye hospital in Athens, Georgia, under the command of Surg. Bolling A. Pope.[36]

Interest in nervous system diseases during the Civil War led to the establishment of a special hospital to study nerve injuries. Turner's Lane Hospital in Philadelphia was headed by Dr. S. Weir Mitchell, one of the first U.S. leaders of the field of neurology. Mitchell and his team described many new syndromes, including facial nerve paralysis, causalgia, and phantom limb

The Origin of the Surgeon General's Library

In a speech given long after the war, Dr. S. Weir Mitchell pointed out that the ration provided to the hospitals

> was so liberal that money saved from it was set aside from it to be used for luxuries for the patients. [In addition] flour barrels, bone and fat were eagerly bought. All the coffee grounds were carefully kept and sold to the highest bidder. These were mixed with browned buckwheat or rye, or better than all with sweet potatoes, and then ground up and sold for coffee . . . Tea leaves once used were also sold, [as were] egg-shells [which were ground up for use as] face powders for the ladies. The swill barrel [i.e. refuse] contents, which brought high prices were promptly converted into pigs. I ought to add that at the close of the war there was $80,000 of those unused funds turned in by the hospitals. The surgeon general was allowed to use this money as a basis for the great library of medicine in Washington.[37]

syndrome. They also described abnormalities resulting from bullet wounds to the various autonomic nerves, such as reflex sympathetic dystrophy and Horner's syndrome. Their book, *Gunshot Wounds and Other Injuries of Nerves*, is a classic contribution to this field.[38] The hospital was also the site of original observations on heart disease, including Jacob DaCosta's description of psychogenic cardiac symptoms, called "soldier's heart."[39]

Orthopedic problems dominated the Civil War surgical scene. Special facilities were established to care for patients with fractures that would not heal (non-union), false joints (unhealed fracture sites that developed motion similar to a joint), and chronic dislocations. The Confederates opened orthopedic hospitals in Richmond, Virginia, and Lauderdale Springs, Mississippi. Both sides established hospitals for soldiers who needed artificial legs, unofficially known as "stump hospitals." One such facility opened on October 28, 1862, in what had been St. Joseph's Convent School in Central Park in New York City. Run by the Roman Catholic Sisters of Charity, it was officially referred to as St. Joseph's Hospital (although it was also known as Central Park Hospital).[40] Facilities devoted to maxillofacial injuries and staffed by experienced dentists were also developed.[41]

A convalescent hospital was established near Alexandria, Virginia. Officially called a "Rendezvous of Distribution," it was known unofficially as "Camp Misery." Patients were mainly disabled soldiers still recovering and awaiting reassignment or discharge. It also housed new recruits waiting for their assignments, paroled prisoners of war waiting to be officially exchanged, and captured deserters and stragglers awaiting disposition. *Soldiers' Journal*, the first soldiers' newspaper and a forerunner of the World War II newspaper *Yank*, was started there.[42,43]

The Union had hospitals to care primarily for black troops. In 1863, for example, Tenth General Hospital was established in a large home that the army appropriated in Beaufort, South Carolina. The hospital's staff cared for most of the 146 wounded soldiers from the 54th Massachusetts after their ill-fated attempt (memorialized in the motion picture *Glory*) to take a fort on an island near Charleston.[44] The largest hospital for black troops was at City Point, Virginia, during the siege of Petersburg. According to Miss Helen Louise Gilson, a Sanitary Commission representative who spent three weeks at the hospital, about 3,000 patients were treated, mainly for sickness. She described them as being "patient in their suffering" but vague in regard to their symptoms: nearly all complained of "misery in the breast." The hospital was short of beds, supplies, and nurses. Convalescent soldiers (who were often used as nurses while in military hospitals) from this hospital made poor nurses, since they were unable to read and so could not be trusted with medication.[45]

REFERENCES

1. Mitchell SW: "On the Medical Department in the Civil War." Address to Physicians' Club of Chicago, February 25, 1913. *J Am Med Assoc.* 1914 May 19;62(19):1445-50.
2. Greenbie MLB: *Lincoln's Daughters of Mercy.* New York: G.P. Putnam's Sons, 1944, p. 70.
3. Risse GB: *Mending Bodies, Saving Souls: A History of Hospitals.* New York: Oxford Univ. Press, 1999, p. 347.
4. Gillett MC: *The United States Army Medical Department, 1818–1865.* Washington, D.C.: Center of Military History, U.S. Army, 1987, p. 290.
5. Greenbie, *Lincoln's Daughters of Mercy*, p. 135.
6. Blaisdell FW: Medical advances during the Civil War. *Arch Surg.* 1988 Sept;123(9):1045.
7. Roberts DJ. In: *The Photographic History of the Civil War.* New York: Review of Reviews, 1970, vol. 4B, p. 278.
8. Gillett, *U.S. Army Medical Department*, pp. 230, 251, 290.
9. Nightingale F: *Notes on Nursing and Notes on Hospitals.* London: Harrison, 1859.
10. Bill AH: *The Beleaguered City: Richmond 1861–65.* New York: Knopf, 1946.
11. Greenbie, *Lincoln's Daughters of Mercy*, p. 135.
12. "Records of Adjutant General's Office," NARA, RG94, Entry #626.
13. Roberts, in *Photographic History*, p. 278.

14. "Records of the Adjutant General's Office," NARA, RG94, Entry #626.
15. Burdette HC. In: Freemon FR: *Microbes and Minie Balls: An Annotated Bibliography of Civil War Medicine*. Rutherford, NJ: Fairleigh Dickinson Univ. Press, 1993, p. 160.
16. Whitman W: Report. *New York Times*. December 26, 1863.
17. Ibid.
18. Wheat TA: "Receiving and forwarding hospitals of the Army of Northern Virginia." Presentation at 5th Annual Conference of the Society of Civil War Surgeons, Knoxville, TN: March 21, 1998.
19. Records from Winder Hospital and Records from Lake City Florida General Hospital. Eleanor S. Brockenbrough Library, Museum of the Confederacy, Richmond, VA.
20. Moore SP. In: *Photographic History*, p. 280.
21. Bill, *Beleaguered City*, p. 156.
22. Greenbie, *Lincoln's Daughters of Mercy*, p. 156.
23. Waitt RW: *Confederate Military Hospitals in Richmond*. Richmond, VA: Richmond Civil War Centennial Commission Official Pub. No. 22, 1964; Roberts, *Photographic History*, p. 292.
24. Letter from Robert W. Waitt to the Eleanor S. Brockenbrough Library, Museum of the Confederacy, Richmond, VA, July 27, 1995.
25. U.S. Sanitary Commission documents, New York Public Library, Box 118-119 and others.
26. Stillé CJ: *History of the United States Sanitary Commission: Being a General Report of Its Work during the War of the Rebellion*. New York: Hurd and Houghton, 1868, p. 445.
27. Maxwell WQ: *Lincoln's Fifth Wheel: The Political History of the U.S. Sanitary Commission*. New York: Longmans, Green & Co., 1956, p. 54.
28. Stillé, *United States Sanitary Commission*, p. 444.
29. Mitchell, "Medical Department in the Civil War."
30. Stillé, *United States Sanitary Commission*, p. 446.
31. Munden KW, Beers HP: *The Union: A Guide to Federal Archives Relating to the Civil War*. Washington, D.C.: NARA, 1980, pp. 304-305.
32. Gillett, *U.S. Army Medical Department*, pp. 231-32.
33. *Medical and Surgical History*, Surgical Section, vol. 1, pp. 385-86, 419, and Medical Section, vol. 3, p. 961.
34. Hospital Register, NARA, RG94, Stack area 9W3, Row 3, Compartment 2.
35. *Medical and Surgical History*, Medical Section, vol. 3, p. 896.
36. Cunningham HH: *Doctors in Gray: The Confederate Medical Service*. Baton Rouge: Louisiana State Univ. Press, 1958, p. 215.
37. Mitchell, "Medical Department in the Civil War."
38. Mitchell SW, Morehouse GR, Keen WW: *Gunshot Wounds and Other Injuries of Nerves*. Philadelphia: Lippincott, 1864. Repub.: San Francisco: Norman Pub. Co., 1989.
39. DaCosta JM: On irritable heart. *Am J Med Sci*. 1871;61:17.
40. Hospital Register, NARA, RG94.
41. Hyson JM, Foley GPH: James Baxter Bean. The first military maxillofacial hospital. *Maryland State Dental Association Journal*. 1997;40:77.
42. Greenbie, *Lincoln's Daughters of Mercy*, p. 166;
43. Oates SB: *A Woman of Valor: Clara Barton and the Civil War*. New York: Macmillan, 1994, p. 95.
44. Fox WF: *Regimental Losses in the American Civil War 1861–1865: A Treatise on the Extent and Nature of the Mortuary Losses in the Union Regiments, with Full and Exhaustive Statistics Compiled from the Official Records on File in the State Military Bureau and at Washington*. Albany, NY: Albany Publishing Co., 1889, p. 441.
45. Jayne SF: Report to Sanitary Commission. In: *U.S. Sanitary Commission Bulletin*. 1864;1(21):666.

⌒ 9 ⌒

Treating Disease: Questionable Drugs and "Heroic" Therapies

The improvement which has taken place in medical practice is in the substitution of tonics, stimulants and general management for the drastic cathartics, for bleeding, depressing agents, including mercury, tartar emetic, etc., so much in vogue during the early part even of this century.

– Oliver Wendell Holmes, *Medical Essays*

C IVIL WAR PHYSICIANS HAD A LONG LIST OF DRUGS TO CHOOSE FROM. The Union Army's formulary (supply table) listed more than 131 different preparations.[1] However, most of these drugs were useless at best and harmful too often; very few were effective for treating even the most common diseases. The most valuable drugs were the anesthetics (ether and chloroform), opiates (particularly morphine), and quinine (for malaria). Alcoholic beverages were also considered to be medicinal and, not surprisingly, were the soldiers' most popular remedy. Physicians, desperate to find adequate treatments, also used dietary therapy, and have been accused, incorrectly, of using bloodletting.

THE "PHYSIOLOGICAL APPROACH" TO MEDICAL THERAPY

At the time of the Civil War, Paris was still considered the Western world's leading medical center. Parisian physicians carefully studied diseases and developed their diagnostic skills. But they rarely intervened; instead, they made their patients as comfortable as possible and waited for nature's cure or future, effective treatments.

American physicians rejected this approach, and attempted to both diagnose and treat diseases, while discarding the "heroic" therapies of earlier generations. Physicians learned to administer drugs using a complicated system known as "physiological *materia medica*," and the army medical examining boards carefully tested candidates on these principles.

This approach to drug use fit the contemporary concept of diseases and their treatment, called "therapeutic rationalism," in which physicians applied treatments to symptoms consistent with their broad classifications of diseases. Although the reasoning behind Civil War physicians' use of these agents was based on erroneous concepts—with most treatments being ineffective and some harmful—the system they used was internally logical.

One disease classification, for example, was based on the congestion of blood vessels accompanying inflammation. They thought that this was due to excessive tissue "excitability," which was a characteristic of "sthenic diseases." When a patient had increased body heat (fever), a rapid, bounding pulse, and, often, delirium, physicians said he had a sthenic disease. Civil War physicians considered most of what we know as infectious diseases, such as typhoid fever, as sthenic diseases.

Their therapeutic approach to sthenic diseases was meant to decrease the tissue's excitability, and thus the congestion. In the early 1800s, this was done through bloodletting or cupping and blistering, which were supposed to induce "counter-irritation" by increasing blood flow to the area of skin being treated so that congestion would be reduced elsewhere. By mid-century, the use of bleeding had markedly decreased, but physicians continued to employ cupping and blistering. Mustard plasters and turpentine wraps, also used as counter-irritants, continued to be therapeutic agents well into the twentieth century. Other methods Civil War physicians used to treat sthenic diseases included emetics to induce vomiting and purgatives to draw fluid into the gastrointestinal tract and away from inflamed (excited) sites. They also prescribed meager diets without animal protein.

In contrast to the sthenic diseases, physicians thought that the "asthenic diseases" had deficient tissue excitability, which required stimulation. They considered alcohol a stimulant, and freely administered it, as *spiritus frumenti* (whiskey) and *spiritus vini gallici* (brandy), to patients with such diseases. These "stimulants" were also widely used for "nostalgia," or "home sickness," as they called the depression common in seriously ill young soldiers who were far from their families. Asthenic patients were also given diets rich in animal products and, fortunately, the vegetables and mineral-laden foods they thought were valuable as "tonics."

This diet was particularly beneficial for patients with scurvy, the most important asthenic disease during the Civil War. In its early stages, scurvy was rarely diagnosed; instead, it was considered to be a form of "nostalgia," since it caused weakness, lassitude, and even torpor. When patients presented with scurvy's more advanced symptoms, such as skin hemorrhages and gum changes, surgeons could make an accurate diagnosis and cure it using known antiscorbutics such as potatoes, onions, oranges, and lemons.

COMMONLY USED DRUGS

Civil War physicians also attempted to treat individual symptoms. The most common problems were related to gastrointestinal (stomach and intestine) ailments, but they also tried to treat fevers, wound infections, malaria, and pain. Several potentially harmful medications were used for a variety of purposes, including colchicine, mercury, and turpentine.

Clinicians used a variety of medications to treat nausea, diarrhea, and constipation. These drugs were widely used and relieved some symptoms, but they did little to treat the underlying diseases. In severe nausea, physicians used ipecac to induce vomiting, because they thought patients would feel better if they emptied their stomachs. Belladonna, which contains atropine, effectively calmed intestinal cramps. Soldiers used blackberries to treat chronic diarrhea even if they were not prescribed by a physician, since they could forage for them.[2] When even "the slightest evidence of a scorbutic tendency" accompanied diarrhea, it was treated with a fresh vegetable diet (in Chapter 14, see Causes of Chronic Diarrhea).[3]

Diaphoretics, drugs that induce sweating, were used to decrease body temperature, and included potassium nitrate and Dover's powders, a combination of ipecac and opium. Tartar emetic, a compound containing antimony, was used both to reduce fever and to induce vomiting. Digitalis was used to increase urine flow in feverish patients who became dehydrated, a measure that may have cost some soldiers their lives.[4]

Wound treatments included ways to seal them, stop bleeding, stop infections, and decrease the pain. In a process termed "hermetically sealing," surgeons used "cerate," a waxy substance usually made of beeswax, to cover wounds. "Astringents" were applied to wounds to promote blood clotting and decrease the oozing. Soldiers also received oral doses of astringents with the

Sick Call

A soldier who rose to the rank of major remembered a typical sick call:

> The regular prescriptions were numbered six, nine and eleven, which were blue-pill, quinine, and vinum. We soon learned that "vinum" meant either wine or brandy. I have seen men count from right to left, "six, nine, eleven—six, nine, eleven—six, nine, eleven," and step into the line just where "eleven" would strike. It was a sure thing, since the surgeon gave in regular order, as the men filed past him, something as follows: "Well, what's the matter with you?" "I don't know, Doctor, I've an awful pain in my bowels; guess I've got the chronic diarrhoea." "Let's see your tongue! Give him number six! Next, what's the matter with you?" "I was took with an awful griping pain in my bowels—guess I've got the chronic diarrhoea." "Give him number nine! Next, what ails you?" "I've g-g-got an almighty b-b-bellyache, g-g-guess I've got the chronic d-d-diarrhoea." "Run out your tongue! Give him number eleven!"[5]

unrealistic hope that they would decrease the fluid oozing into the intestines of patients with diarrhea. "Antiseptics" included potassium iodide and potassium permanganate and, late in the war, liquid iodine, bromine, and carbolic acid. The general anesthetics, chloroform and ether, were almost universally used during serious operations, as well as for painful wound treatments and changing dressings. Bromides, a class of sedative, were used to treat epilepsy.

Colchicine, also called colchicum, was used to treat arthritis, although it is effective mainly for gout, a form of arthritis that is uncommon in the military age group and would be minimized by the meager diet of Civil War troops. It is doubtful that this drug was much help. While gout was diagnosed in 506 Union soldiers, no detailed descriptions exist of actual cases in which colchicine was used.[6] There is a record, however, of colchicine being used to treat acute diarrhea, which is surprising since diarrhea is one of the drug's major side effects.[7] It is possible that the drug was used to "cleanse" the intestine. But, since the amount given is not specified, it may represent an example of homeopathy, since that type of treatment is based on using infinitesimal amounts of drugs that cause the symptom being treated ("like cures like").

Unfortunately, mercury was a mainstay of Civil War medical treatment. It was the basis of "blue pills," calomel, and tartar emetic. Mercury is secreted in high concentration in the saliva, producing a metallic taste and causing extensive necrosis of oral tissues. Surgeons repeatedly described this abundant "salivation" in case reports. The resulting loose teeth and necrosis of the gums and jaw were painful and often left permanent disfiguring deformities that made eating difficult. Men died from mercury toxicity, probably due to necrosis extending down the intestinal tract or the poisoning of the kidney tubules. "Blue pills," officially called *hydrargyri pilulae*, contained mercury, licorice, rose water, powdered rose, honey, and sugar. Regimental surgeons routinely carried a huge lump of calomel (mercurous chloride), which they called "blue mass." They tore off lumps and dispensed it indiscriminately to soldiers for diarrhea, dysentery, and typhoid fever. (See Figure 9.1.)

Although calomel caused much harm and little, if any, good, it was a favorite "remedy" of physicians. Surgeon General Hammond decided that mercury was too toxic and provided no benefit, so he banned almost all compounds containing mercury. An uproar ensued after he took this action without prior notification to the field surgeons, and Secretary of War Stanton was able to use this as an opportunity to court-martial Hammond on unrelated charges. Although drugs containing mercury were taken off the army's

Figure 9.1: Hospital knapsack adopted in 1862. Equipment and medication vials were arranged in easily accessible drawers and were less likely to break than in previous models. Size: 16″ high by 12½″ wide by 6″ deep. Fully packed, it weighed almost twenty pounds. (*Medical and Surgical History*, Surgical Section, vol. 3, p. 915.)

supply table, they continued to be available by special request—the usual practice of the time—and continued to be used. By the time Hammond had achieved legal vindication in 1879, he had also obtained medical vindication, since by then there was general agreement on the harmful effects of these mercurial compounds.

Physicians used turpentine topically and orally. Applied to the skin as a counter-irritant, it was supposed to increase blood flow to the skin over a diseased organ and reduce inflammation by withdrawing blood from the affected organ. Along with kerosene and tobacco, surgeons also applied turpentine on and under bandages to prevent wounds from becoming infested with maggots.[8] Turpentine was used orally for chronic diarrhea and, sometimes, typhoid fever. *Medical and Surgical History* notes that it was "pretty extensively employed in the treatment of fluxes both in combination with purgative doses of castor oil and in emulsion."[9] ("Fluxes" was a common term for diarrhea.) European physicians also used turpentine in this fashion. When quinine was in short supply, Confederate physicians tried using turpentine for the intermittent fevers.[10] In fact, it became a favorite remedy among Southern physicians and remained so until about 1906.[11,12] Castor oil, a laxative, was a popular remedy to "cleanse the system," which undoubtedly it did, thereby causing more harm than good given the frequency of diarrhea and dysentery.

QUININE: A REAL CURE

Quinine effectively treats the intermittent chills and fever of malaria, and Civil War physicians used it with reasonable success. Powdered cinchona tree bark, originally extracted by the native population in South America, was also called "Peruvian bark" or "Jesuit powder" in memory of the sixteenth-century Spanish missionaries who first observed its use. The bark's active ingredient, the alkaloid "quinine," was isolated in 1820 by two French chemists. During the Civil War, physicians used both the powdered bark dissolved in water or another liquid and pills of purified quinine sulfate.

The total amount of quinine used by the Union forces was prodigious—at least 19 tons of quinine sulfate and 9½ tons of cinchona bark![13] Physicians prescribed an initial dose of 15–25 grains (equivalent to about 1–1.6 grams) followed by half a dram (30 grains, or 1.5 grams) taken as often as necessary, usually following the onset of each subsequent chill. Those dosages are close to those recommended today, and usually were effective.

Quinine was successfully used to prevent malaria as well as to treat it. Surgeon General Hammond ordered that soldiers in the Vicksburg campaign take quinine daily because "intermittent fevers" were so common.[14] Physicians tried various exhortations and tricks to convince Union soldiers to take quinine preventively (a problem for American physicians in subsequent wars as well). Mixing it with whiskey worked best, and, eventually, they gained some degree of control over malaria. (See Figure 9.2.) Critics have questioned whether Civil War physicians prescribed prophylactic quinine, but its use is well-documented. One surgeon recorded:

> Of one medicine, I should like to speak from personal and long-continued contact. Before the war I had been subject to attacks of malarial fever. At our first winter camp, alarmed at myself, I began to take quinine as a prophylactic in my own case. The hospital steward would put up fifty four-grain powders of quinine; these I carried in my pocket, and took one after each meal, or twelve grains in a day. [Twelve grains would be equivalent to about 0.7 grams, an adequate dose.] There were months in which I certainly did not miss three doses of the medicine. I continued to take the remedy almost continuously for two years and a half, and I never discovered any unfavorable or unpleasant result from it.[15]

The Confederates were equally aware of quinine's value and recorded using it prophylactically.[16] Because of the blockade, they ran low on quinine

Figure 9.2: "Before Petersburg—Issuing Rations of Whisky and Quinine." Quinine was used to prevent as well as to treat malaria. Getting soldiers to take it every day was difficult, but dissolving it in whiskey made the drug much more popular, as this *Harper's Weekly* illustration by A. W. Warren shows.

early in the war. Confederate physicians sought herbs and other botanicals that possessed the same properties as the "Peruvian bark" and tested a variety of natural remedies for malaria, but all proved ineffective. The quinine that was available in the South was not distributed uniformly or even with regard to need, as Maj. Gen. Lafayette McLaws, the Confederate commander in the coastal southeast, reported in August 1864:

> I regret to state that the amount of sickness in this command has been and still is deplorable, and being aware of the great benefit of quinine as a prophylactic, strenuous efforts were made ... by the medical officer in this district, through the proper channels, for a supply of quinine for the District of Georgia, all of which have been totally unsuccessful ... the medical officers have been unable to procure quinine even as a medicine, and officers and soldiers have been sick and suffering for the want of it, at times being entirely without any at all. Under such circumstances it is needless to add that it could not be used as a prophylactic. On the other hand the Third Military District of South Carolina has been superabundantly supplied.[17]

Although quinine was specifically a treatment for malaria, it was also frequently used to treat a variety of febrile diseases and to provide pain relief. Its antipyretic (fever reducing) and analgesic effects are non-specific and weak, but it was the only drug with such effects available until sodium salicylate and antipyrine were introduced after 1875. (Quinine continued to be used for this purpose well into the twentieth century.)[18] Even when supplies were scarce, physicians in both Confederate and Federal hospitals commonly prescribed it to treat fever. Quinine also was used inappropriately to treat other illnesses called "malarial diseases," especially dysentery. Union physician Joseph J. Woodward commented that such errors were "among the most pardonable and least injurious of the therapeutic errors of the Civil War."[19] Such errors had more serious consequences in the Confederacy, since they depleted their meager supplies of quinine, which would have been more effectively used to treat intermittent fevers.

OPIUM AND MORPHINE

During the Civil War, narcotics in the form of opium and morphine were commonly used to treat diarrhea and pain. Opium was an effective treatment for diarrhea, the most common disease affecting armies at the time. Opium was so widely available, usually as a tincture of 10% opium in alcohol called "laudanum," from physicians and in patent medicines that addiction became a problem among soldiers and civilians alike.[20,21]

The most convenient way to store, transport, and administer opium was in pill form. Pill-making machines dated back to 1807, and a machine to make compound tablets, pills containing more than one ingredient, was invented in 1843.[22] Opium was also available as a powder and as laudanum. Morphine, an opium alkaloid, was isolated by a German pharmacist named Sertürner in 1803, but went unnoticed until his second publication in 1816. It was available as a powder or a pill and could be put into solution for injection.

Syringes had been invented in the mid-nineteenth century and were used before the war to administer medications in some hospitals.[23,24] (See Figure 9.3.) However, since there were no sharp needles, surgeons had to make a small incision in the skin to give medicine using a syringe. In the field, surgeons often dusted morphine powder into the wound or pushed it into the injured site with a dirty finger, sometimes moistening it with their saliva to make the powder stick.[25] They found that the amount of powdered morphine that would cling to a moistened fingertip was an appropriate analgesic dose. Dr. Samuel D. Gross advised:

> The endermic application of morphia has been found highly beneficial in neuralgia, chiefly, however, in mitigating pain. It may . . . be sprinkled upon a blistered surface, be inoculated, or, what I greatly prefer, be injected subcutaneously. The operation . . . is executed with a small syringe, having a very slender nozzle, which is inserted into a small puncture preciously made in the skin of the affected parts, the subcutaneous cellular tissue being torn up with a common probe to make room for the reception of a drachm of solution of morphia.[26]

Many have criticized these methods of administering drugs, saying that they contaminated the wounds and caused infection. However, they ignore the fact that using a dirty syringe repeatedly (as it would have been under field conditions) probably would introduce as much infection as a dirty finger.[27,28] In any case, physicians were encouraged to use syringes during the war.[29] Since morphine's effects were more rapid when administered by syringe, its use did increase.

Some have also criticized Civil War physicians for administering opiates topically and orally. They erroneously claim that morphine is ineffective when administered this way. On the contrary, morphine is effective when

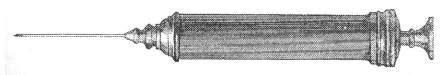

Figure 9.3: Injection syringe. Such syringes were new at the time of the Civil War. (*SS*, p. 621.)

239

The Insertion of Morphine Directly into Wounds

Medical Director Henry Hewit reported on his order regarding the use of morphine in wounds during the Atlanta campaign:

> The insertion of morphine into wounds of the chest, attended by pain and dyspnœa, has been of the utmost advantage. I made the insertion of morphine into all painful wounds a standing order of the medical department, and it has acted so admirably as to enlist every surgeon in favor of the practice. Its good effects are especially remarkable in painful wounds of the joints, abdomen, and chest. From one to three grains are inserted on the point of the finger. I desire especially to call the attention of the profession to this practice, which is simply a generalization of the well recognized application of morphine hypodermically.[30]

taken by mouth, although larger doses are needed because the liver converts much of it to inactive substances before it can act to relieve pain ("first-pass metabolism"). In fact, physicians today effectively use oral morphine preparations. Studies conducted in the early 1900s erroneously suggested that putting opium or morphine directly into a wound was useless, since the drugs worked only after reaching the brain. More recent studies, however, have demonstrated that there are opiate receptors in peripheral tissues which makes topical applications effective.[31,32] In addition, some of the morphine applied to bleeding wounds probably enters the bloodstream and reaches the brain.

Because opiates were among the few drugs that physicians knew were effective, they were used liberally. Union forces used approximately 10 million opium pills and nearly 3 million ounces of opium powder and tinctures to treat almost every illness, including dysentery, stomachache, gallstones, headache, hemorrhoids, tetanus, typhoid fever, syphilis, and neuralgia. Their most common use was to combat diarrhea (opium was by far the most effective remedy) and to relieve the pain of injuries and wounds.[33] Opium was also used for relief of postoperative pain, as well as for causalgia, a painful syndrome that sometimes occurs after nerve injuries, such as in amputations.[34]

Opiates were also used to treat the joint inflammation of acute rheumatism (rheumatic fever) and for pain relief or cough suppression in soldiers with pneumonia, pleurisy, asthma, bronchitis, influenza, and consumption (tuberculosis). Aside from medical ailments, they often were prescribed for the vague symptom of uneasiness, as well as delirium tremens, "insanity," and depression.[35] When Oliver Wendell Holmes criticized the medical profession's overuse of medications, he exempted opium, "which the Creator himself seems to prescribe, for we often see the scarlet poppy growing in cornfields, as if it were foreseen that where there is hunger to be fed there must also be pain to be soothed."[36]

The widespread use of opiates had a predictable downside. By the end of the nineteenth century, narcotic addiction, often called "Old Soldier's Disease," was common. Civil War surgeons have been criticized for creating this epidemic through their liberal use of opium and morphine.[37] Fault was found with the frequency with which they used opiates, the amounts used, and the modes of administration.

While some addiction certainly resulted from these practices,[38] the amount of addiction they caused was negligible compared to the domestic and worldwide addiction problems that developed late in the nineteenth century. A report on rising opium consumption in the United States, published only seven years after the war, did not mention the conflict as a cause of addiction.[39] In fact, veterans who were addicts were not eligible for pensions. The lack of statistics on the number of Civil War veterans who became addicts in the service suggests that the war was simply a convenient event to blame for the late-nineteenth-century addiction epidemic.

Modern studies show that few patients become addicted after getting therapeutic amounts of opiates to relieve severe pain. Therefore, many of the "old soldiers" who became morphine addicts may have been malingerers or had personality disorders. The history of Civil War medicine is disturbing, not only for the enormous loss of life but also for the amount of suffering the soldiers endured. It is important to remember, as Prof. J. J. Chisolm pointed out in his *Manual of Military Surgery* (1864), that the use of morphine "prevented endless suffering on the battlefield."[40]

The United States experienced no increase in opium importation during or immediately following the Civil War. It wasn't until the 1880s that narcotic importation into the United States began to increase. From 1880 to 1889, there was a nine-fold increase in opium importation, the demand peaking in 1895.[41] Civilians could readily obtain narcotics and cocaine directly from a pharmacist without a prescription. Home remedies containing these substances were widely advertised for such problems as children's toothaches and "female complaints." In fact, more women were addicted to opiates than men in the post-war period by a ratio of 3:2.[42] In 1878, researchers noted that "the most frequent cause of the opium-eating habit in females is the taking of opiates to relieve painful menstruation and diseases of female organs of generation. The frequency of these problems in part accounts for the excess of female opium-eaters over males." Extended opium treatments were also used for the vague entity "neurasthenia" in women, contributing to the problem.[43] Respected medical textbooks advocated opiate use for diarrhea and other diseases, including to pacify children as young as one month old.[44,45]

The first restrictions on opiate use in the United States occurred in 1906 with the passage of the Pure Food and Drug Act.[46] In May 1906, an article in the *Journal of the American Medical Association* condemned the widespread use of widely advertised narcotic-containing "remedies." The article listed nostrums containing narcotics, including thirty-one with opium or its derivatives, four with cocaine, and two with cannabis. Opium was present in croup remedies, pneumonia cures, "lung syrup," an expectorant, and teething powders. Morphine was found in teething syrup, preparations called "the infant's friend," and "sneezeless snuff." Heroin was contained in a "soothing syrup" and in an anodyne (pain reliever). A "one-day cough cure" had morphine and *cannabis indica*.[47]

UNION MEDICAL SUPPLIES

Early in the war, Charles Tripler, medical director of the Army of the Potomac, was faced with newly enlisted surgeons from all over the country who had different prescribing habits based on local practices. He ordered that they be allowed to obtain and administer whatever medicines they thought useful. Surgeon General Finley, however, trying to bring some organization into a chaotic situation, countermanded Tripler's order and required his personal approval to use any drugs that were not on the official supply table (formulary).[48] When Hammond succeeded Finley as surgeon general in April 1862, he reversed that order, instructing Jonathan Letterman, Tripler's successor,

> You are authorized to call directly upon the medical purveyors in Washington, Baltimore, Philadelphia, and New York, who will be directed to furnish you with everything you ask for, regardless of supply-tables or forms.[49]

Early in the war, surgeons repeatedly ran out of medical supplies. (See Figure 9.4.) Quartermasters were responsible for obtaining and distributing supplies to the field and hospitals, but they constantly underestimated the need: countless complaints about the medical purveying system resulted. In

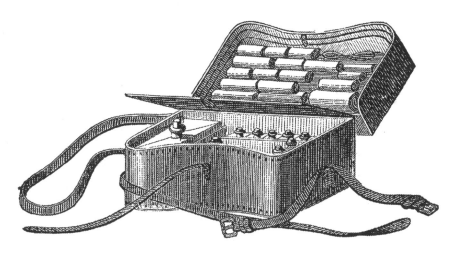

Figure 9.4: The Surgeon's Field Companion carried by surgeons in place of a knapsack. It contained bandages, antiseptics, and medications used in wound treatment. (*Medical and Surgical History*, Surgical Section, vol. 3, p. 915.)

response, Hammond induced the War Department to set up a medical transportation bureau in the Surgeon General's Office. This improved supply distribution, but it was not flawless, particularly when the army had to move quickly and left its huge wagon trains behind. Under these circumstances, medical supplies were delivered last or not at all. During the evacuation of McClellan's army from the peninsula to Washington City and then to Antietam, his medical supplies were left in Virginia. Similarly, when General Meade's army raced to join the fighting near Gettysburg, they arrived well before their medical supply trains. On such occasions, and especially at Gettysburg, the Sanitary Commission was the first to arrive with the needed drugs and medical supplies. (Sanitary Commission officials seemed to have had an uncanny ability to predict where the fighting would take place and to send supplies in a more timely fashion than the army itself.)

There were many medical suppliers, and some who supplied drugs, such as Edward R. Squibb and the Pfizer Company, later developed into major pharmaceutical companies. Before the war ended, medical purveyors could collect supplies from warehouses in principle cities and at about thirty other depots. Nevertheless, after large battles in relatively isolated areas, supplies could run low. For example, when Medical Inspector Edward P. Vollum arrived four days after the fighting had ceased at Gettysburg, he found the demand for antiseptics, tincture of iron, and other drugs so urgent that he purchased some of them at local drugstores and sent the bills to the quarter-master.

Other supply problems arose when a new use was found for a drug normally stocked in small quantities, and demand increased. Such a shortage developed when potassium permanganate, previously little used, was found to be helpful in treating hospital gangrene. Shortages of imported drugs resulted from price variations as the value of the dollar fell against foreign currencies. Speculation on drug prices developed and produced drug brokers, futures options, and attempts to corner the market. By 1863, some pharmaceutical prices had risen as much as 500%. To decrease price fluctuations and to assure the availability and more consistent quality of essential medicines, the army started to manufacture some drugs. This also allowed the re-use of bottles and vials, resulting in considerable cost savings. Union manufacturing facilities, called "laboratories," were set up in the town of Astoria on Long Island (now within New York City) and in Philadelphia. The Confederacy established several similar laboratories.

Since transporting medications was a major problem when the army was on the move, in 1862 they designed a light medicine wagon that traveled with the ambulances. In 1864, the army adopted the Autenrieth wagon, which had one storage case with instruments for capital operations (such as amputations, resections, and trephinations) and another with knives, forceps, and catheters for minor operations. (See Figure 9.5.) In addition, there was increased storage for drugs in drawers and cabinets; shelves lined the main cabinet door so that when it was swung open, the bottles of medicines were immediately accessible.[50] The U.S. pavilion at the 1867 World's Fair (*Exposition Universelle*) in Paris, France, proudly displayed an Autenrieth wagon. Panniers for storing the medicines in the wagons were constantly redesigned to better prevent the contents from jostling. In the field, only 200 hospital stewards, many of whom had been pharmacists before the war, were available to supervise the medicine wagons.[51]

Many soldiers distrusted army physicians, preferring their own home remedies. Sutlers (private entrepreneurs who followed the armies and sold mostly cakes and confections to the soldiers) also stocked widely used patent medicines. On one occasion, President Lincoln urged Surgeon General Hammond to try the patent medicine treatment of a "Dr. Forsha" for gunshot wounds. Hammond obliged, reporting that the concoction was "very irritating and pungent" and aggravated the sufferings of several officers to whom it was administered after the Battle of Cedar Mountain (August 9, 1862).[52]

Figure 9.5: The Autenrieth Wagon was adopted in June 1864 to carry surgical instruments and medications. (*Medical and Surgical History*, Surgical Section, vol. 3, pp. 917-18.)

CONFEDERATE MEDICAL SUPPLIES

In the Confederacy, the chronic scarcity of medicines and medical supplies, primarily due to the Union blockade, received more effort and attention than any other shortage.[53] Federal forces captured a large share of the Confederate Army's medical supplies, so Confederate cavalry seized drugs from Union supply trains at every opportunity: opiates, chloroform, and quinine, along with food, were the most sought-after prizes. Blockade-running along the border with the Northern states was a major means for the Confederacy to obtain drugs, as was the use of houseboats on the rivers running south from Cairo, Illinois, and Paducah, Kentucky. Drugs were small in bulk and fetched a high price when sold at auction to the highest bidder, usually civilians. After 1863, quinine was needed because of the incidence of malaria in the civilian as well as the military populations; it sold for $400 to

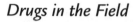

Drugs in the Field

Writing more than fifty years after the war, Charles Beneulyn Johnson, hospital steward of the 130th Illinois Volunteers, remembered the items supplied to regimental surgeons in the field:

> During a campaign our stock of medicines was necessarily limited to standard remedies, among which could be named opium, morphine, Dover's powder, quinine, rhubarb, Rochelle salts, castor oil, sugar of lead, tannin, sulphate of copper, sulphate of zinc, camphor, tincture of opium, tincture of iron, tincture opic, camphorata, syrup of squills, simple syrup, alcohol, whiskey, brandy, port wine, sherry wine, etc. . . . Practically all the medicines were administered in powdered form or liquid state and pills were far from being as plentiful as they are today. The result was that most powders were stirred in water and swallowed . . . The dose, thus prepared, was a bitter one. The bromides, sulfonal, trional, and similar soporifics had not yet come into use, and asafetida, valerium and opium and its derivatives were about all the Civil War surgeon had to relieve nervousness and induce sleep.[54]

$600 an ounce in the Confederacy.[55] Jefferson Davis finally had the Confederate Congress pass a law in early 1864 requiring that blockade-runners' cargoes be comprised of least 50% government supplies, but it was difficult to enforce.[56]

Seeking substitutes for drugs, Surgeon General Moore and the physician-naturalist F. P. Porcher of Charleston published articles in *Confederate States Medical and Surgical Journal* listing indigenous plants that could be substituted for unavailable drugs.[57] The optimism about obtaining active drugs from natural sources was justified. Except for the general anesthetics, all the drugs in use at the time were obtained from plants and other vegetable sources: quinine from the bark of a Peruvian tree; digitalis from the foxglove plant; opium from Asian poppies; belladonna from nightshade plants; colchicine from the Autumn crocus; cerate from beeswax; turpentine from tree sap; as well as innumerable other vegetable remedies of questionable benefit. Unfortunately, most of the new potentially medicinal plants identified in articles and books published during the war proved useless.

Confederate Resentment at the Union Blockade of Medical Supplies

The following footnote to a July 1864 editorial in the *Confederate States Medical and Surgical Journal* called the declaration of medical supplies and equipment as contrabands of war "an atrocious step":

> At a recent meeting of the American Medical Association in Chicago, a distinguished member of the profession made a noble effort to wipe away this disgraceful stain from his country's escutcheon. Dr. Gardner, of New York, introduced a preamble and resolution petitioning the Northern government to repeal their orders to consider medical and surgical appliances as contraband of war. This gentleman showed that such cruelties rebounded on their own soldiers, many of whom, in the hands of rebels, shared the suffering resulting from such a policy, while the act itself was worthy of the dark ages of the world's history.
>
> It will surprise our foreign brethren to know that this learned and powerful tribunal of the medical profession of the North, forgetful of the noble and unselfish teachings of the healing art—blind to all but the gratification of a ruinous hate and ungratified revenge—hissed the benevolent brother from the hall.

Quinine and opium were the most urgently needed drugs during the war and strenuous efforts were made to find plants that would serve as alternatives. Confederates tried to substitute extracts of a variety of tree barks for the Peruvian bark, separately and in combination, but none worked. At the suggestion of Surgeon General Moore, fields of opium-producing poppies were widely planted in the Confederacy, "but very little opium was gathered," and almost all the opium and morphine used was brought in through the blockade.[58] Confederates established drug (called "chemical") manufacturing facilities to produce ether and chloroform, and to research the medicinal properties of various indigenous plants. Such facilities were located in Richmond, Charlotte, and Lincolnton in North Carolina; Columbia, South Carolina; Augusta, Macon, and Atlanta in Georgia; Mobile, Alabama; and Knoxville, Tennessee. In the "Trans-Mississippi," there were similar laboratories in Tyler, Texas, and Arkadelphia, Arkansas.

Surgeon General Moore Suggests a Substitute for Quinine

SURGEON-GENERAL'S OFFICE
Richmond, Va., December 5, 1863

Surg. R. POTTS,
Medical Purveyor, Macon, Ga.:

SIR: Below you will find a formula for a compound tincture of the indigenous barks to be issued as a tonic and febrifuge and substitute as far as practicable for quinine.

Very respectfully, your obedient servant,

S. P. MOORE
Surgeon-General C. S. Army

Dried dogwood bark, 30 parts; dried poplar bark, 30 parts; dried willow bark, 40 parts; whisky, 45 degrees strength; two pounds of the mixed bark to one gallon of whisky. Macerate fourteen days. Dose for tonic and anti-febrifuge purposes, one ounce three times a day.[59]

DIET AS THERAPY

In view of the limited effectiveness of the therapeutic armamentarium, Civil War physicians gave a great deal of attention to dietary approaches to therapy. Medical and surgical textbooks devoted long passages to the diets recommended for each illness. Attending physicians wrote daily diet plans for each hospitalized soldier and special diet kitchens in many hospitals provided the prescribed meals.

One of the Civil War hospital matron's principal roles was to prepare the prescribed food. Although it has been suggested that this was a demeaning task for the Civil War female nurses, diet was an essential therapeutic component, equivalent to medication today, and food preparation was one of the chief nursing duties. Female nurses concentrated on diet therapy when they nursed their own family and believed that they were the experts in preparing special meals. Florence Nightingale's influential 1859 book, *Notes on Nursing*, devotes two chapters to diet and food preparation. In a much-quoted statement, she wrote, "Thousands of patients are annually starved in the midst of plenty, from want of attention to the ways which alone make it possible for them to take food."[60] She emphasized particular foods that nurses should give to people with specific types of problems, such as those with chewing or swallowing difficulties.

One reason that the troops preferred female nurses was the terrible food prepared for hospital patients by soldiers functioning as nurses. Many of the women who wrote memoirs after the war detailed their efforts to find and prepare food for their patients. For example, while visiting military hospitals as a representative of the Soldier's Aid Society of Iowa early in the war, Mrs. Annie Wittenmyer saw the need for special diet preparation. Aligning herself with the Christian Commission, she offered dietary services to the army. Initially based in the West, her program evolved into more than 100 diet kitchens at army hospitals. Soldiers and the military authorities cherished the services these kitchens provided. During the last eighteen months of the war, these diet kitchens provided over 2 million rations.[61]

Phoebe Pember Prepares Chicken Soup and Other Delicacies

Early in her service, Phoebe Pember tried to embellish the chicken soup she made for the patients by adding parsley. One of her patients from a rural area refused to eat it. He said it wasn't like the soup his "mammy" made, but added that he "might worry a little down if it war'n't for them weeds afloatin' round." Mrs. Pember recorded that she was more conservative in her culinary attempts after that.[62]

The meager amount of obtainable meat led the soldier-patients to label one dish "chicken shadow soup"; they claimed it was prepared by boiling water in the shadow of the only chicken available and adding salt and spices.[63] There is also record of the men providing their own delicacies for meals, especially when they could catch a rat or a squirrel. According to Pember, she learned how to prepare them both and found them similar in taste.[64]

"Heroic" Therapies

In the early nineteenth century, "heroic therapy," consisting of vigorous bloodletting, purging (cathartics), and enemas, was the mainstay of medical therapy for almost all diseases. By the 1860s, however, physicians rarely used these measures and Civil War medical records seldom mention them. Most young military physicians had received a formal medical education, which derided its use, and such measures continued to be employed only by older physicians who had apprenticed under doctors trained in the previous century. The end of heroic therapy left a void, however, since there was little effective medical therapy to replace it. As one British physician of the time put it, the only difference between an old and a young physician was that "the former would kill you, the latter will let you die."[65]

Dr. Oliver Wendell Holmes ridiculed his fellow physicians' use of huge drug doses, writing that "If the whole *materia medica* [the available medicines], as now used, could sink to the bottom of the sea, it would be all the better for mankind, and all the worse for the fishes." This statement, which seemed to damn all therapeutic agents, engendered substantial criticism and embarrassed the good doctor. In his defense, he pointed out that he was usually misquoted, with critics often omitting the words "as now used."[66]

Civil War physicians were said to have practiced bloodletting, or venesection, despite information showing that the practice was harmful. In fact, the use of bleeding as therapy began to decline in the 1830s. The dominant clinician in Paris at the time, Francois-Joseph-Victor Broussais (1772–1838), believed that inflammation, primarily in the intestine, caused all disease. He thought that bleeding, especially using leeches, was the best treatment for such inflammation. Broussais's influence was such that France ran out of leeches, causing Parisian doctors to import 33 million leeches annually from Eastern Europe. The popularity of leeches provided an excellent opportunity to determine whether this therapy was effective.

When Dr. Pierre Louis analyzed the effects of bloodletting in pneumonia, he found that no matter when or how often patients were bled, the proportion that survived was always the same. Although Louis never said that bleeding was harmful, his data demonstrated its ineffectiveness. (Louis himself, however, continued to use bloodletting on a very limited basis.)[67] Within a few years of Louis's publishing his paper on bleeding in pneumonia, the number of leeches imported into France had fallen to a few thousand.

In 1836, Dr. James Jackson, Sr., a founder of Massachusetts General Hospital, translated and published Louis's data, publishing similar observations of his own in the *American Journal of the Medical Sciences*. Thereafter, therapeutic bleeding became increasingly less common in the United States.[68,69] In the following decades, other articles appeared that condemned therapeutic bleeding, including British articles reprinted in the *American Journal of the Medical Sciences* in 1847, 1859, and 1860.

In the mid-nineteenth century, all the leading unorthodox sects of medicine—including homeopathy, eclectic medicine, botanic medicine, Thomsonianism, and the Grahamites—opposed heroic therapy in general and bleeding in particular. The harmlessness of their therapeutic systems attracted the lay public, further contributing to venesection's decline among allopathic medical professionals. One prominent physician, Samuel Jackson, alarmed at how quickly this traditional method was disappearing, wrote in 1854, "We are threatened with a general hematophobia."[70]

How much bloodletting did army physicians do during the Civil War? The Confederate manual of military surgery opposed venesection as "the treatment of the old school which recent experience does not uphold."[71] Out of about 6.5 million recorded cases of illness and wounds treated in Union hospitals, *Medical and Surgical History* lists only four patients in whom bleeding was considered as therapy. Of those four, surgeons only bled two of

Bleeding and the British Royal Family

Bloodletting was far from an exact science. The amount of blood removed varied widely, as illustrated by the treatment received by two members of the British royal family.

In 1820, the Duke of Kent, a son of George III and the father of Princess (later Queen) Victoria, became ill, apparently with pneumonia. His physicians treated him with venesection followed by cupping and still more bleeding, and extracted 120 ounces (seven pints) of blood. Not surprisingly, his condition deteriorated. Dr. William Maton, who had been caring for King George III, was called from London. Maton criticized the Duke's physicians for not bleeding him enough! They then cupped and bled the Duke some more, after which he died.

The same month, immediately after succeeding to the throne, King George IV, the Duke's brother, fell ill. He was bled and 150 ounces (nearly 9½ pints) of blood was extracted. He lived for another ten years; the bloodletting was credited with saving his life.[72]

them. In one instance, the patient's dyspnea improved, and the case description suggests that he had congestive heart failure, which can be relieved, at least temporarily, by venesection. In fact, patients with that condition continued to be bled occasionally, often with significant improvement in their condition, until powerful diuretic drugs became available in the mid-1900s. The other patient who was bled had pneumonia, for which bloodletting had previously been the main form of treatment; no improvement was noted.

The following discussion in *Medical and Surgical History* reveals that surgeons were aware of the deleterious effect of venesection, also called "general depletion," particularly on exhausted, or "adynamic," soldiers:

> On one point there was unanimity—general depletion was rarely employed as an antagonist to the febrile state. Medical officers realized the adynamic influences that affected the troops and declined, in a disease which is so frequently fatal by asthenia [generalized weakness], to purchase temporary relief at the expense of an impoverishment of an already deteriorated blood.[73]

Therapeutic bleeding did not completely end in the United States. After the Civil War, European immigrants familiar with bloodletting often requested it, contributing to its perpetuation. An often-quoted Old English adage, "A bleeding in the spring/ Is physic for a king," referred to one of the favorite and enduring uses of venesection as a "tonic" to prevent illness in healthy people.[74] Medical textbooks continued to mention bleeding, but there was a progressive decrease in advocacy between 1830 and 1890. In his 1873 textbook, Austin Flint, one of the leaders of American clinical medicine during and after the Civil War, did not advocate bleeding at all.[75] Samuel D. Gross, a major figure in American surgery, told students at Jefferson Medical College in 1867, "The divorce is complete . . . Taking the practice of the present-day as [the] standpoint, I cannot see why such a sanguinary operation should ever have been necessary."[76] But others did not reject the practice as completely. An 1870 article warned that, although it was wise for the profession to give up its extensive use of bloodletting, medicine had probably "gone to the opposite extreme."[77]

Cupping and blistering, painful procedures long used as treatments for pneumonia, were considered "local bleeding," that is, they caused blood to accumulate in the skin in the area where the treatment was applied and thus were also considered anti-inflammatory measures. Since these ineffective procedures were still advocated by William Osler in 1892 (and were used well into the twentieth century), Civil War physicians clearly were not behind the times when using these measures.

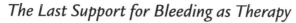

The Last Support for Bleeding as Therapy

In the first edition of his textbook, *The Principles and Practice of Medicine* (1892), the renowned physician-educator, William Osler, surprisingly advocated bleeding for several conditions, including some forms of heart disease, pulmonary edema, sunstroke, arteriosclerosis, pneumonia, and emphysema. Osler included this passage on the treatment of pneumonia:

> In many cases the question comes up at the outset as to the propriety of venesection. The reproach of Van Helmont, that "a bloody Moloch presides in the chairs of medicine," cannot be brought against the present generation of physicians. During the first five decades of this century the profession bled too much, but during the last decades we have certainly bled too little. Pneumonia is the disease in which a timely venesection may save life. To be of service it should be done early. In a full-blooded, healthy man with high fever and bounding pulse, the abstraction of from twenty to thirty ounces of blood is in every way beneficial, relieving the pain and dyspnea, reducing the temperature, and allaying the cerebral symptoms, so violent in some instances. Unfortunately, in a majority of the cases, bleeding is now used at a late stage in the disease.[78]

REFERENCES

1. Smith GW: *Medicines for the Union Army: The United States Army Laboratories during the Civil War.* Madison, WI: American Institute for the History of Pharmacy, 1962, p. 2.
2. Pullen JJ: *The Twentieth Maine: A Volunteer Regiment in the Civil War.* Philadelphia, PA: Lippincott, 1957.
3. Woodward JJ: *Outlines of the Chief Camp Diseases of the United States Armies as Observed during the Present War.* Repub: San Francisco: Norman, 1992, p. 253.
4. Evans BA: *A Primer of Civil War Medicine: Non-Surgical Medical Practice during the Civil War Years.* Knoxville, TN: Bohemian Brigade, 1997, p. 57.
5. Small AR. Quoted in: Wiley BI: *The Life of Billy Yank: The Common Soldier of the Union.* Baton Rouge: Louisiana State Univ. Press, 1952, p. 138.
6. *Medical and Surgical History*, Medical Section, vol. 1, tables c, cxI.
7. Case Books of the General Hospital in Lake City, Florida. Eleanor S. Brockenbrough Library, Museum of the Confederacy, Richmond, VA.
8. Jordan EL: *Charlottesville and the University of Virginia in the Civil War.* Lynchburg, VA: H.E Howard, 1988.
9. *Medical and Surgical History*, Medical Section, vol. 2, pp. 816-921.
10. Case Books of the General Hospital, Lake City, FL, Eleanor S. Brockenbrough Library.

11. Calhoun JT: Offhand sketches of an army surgeon's experiences during the Great Rebellion. *Med Surg Reporter.* 1863;9:279.
12. Adams GW: Confederate medicine. *J South Hist.* 1940;6:151-88.
13. Steiner PE: *Disease in the Civil War: Natural Biological Warfare in 1861–65.* Springfield, IL: C.C. Thomas, 1968, p. 22.
14. Freemon FR: The Siege of Vicksburg, 1863: how medicine affected the outcome. *Bull NY Acad Med.* 1991 Sept-Oct;67(5):429-38.
15. Hart AG: *The Surgeon and the Hospital in the Civil War.* Gaithersburg, MD: Olde Soldier Books, 1987, p. 7.
16. Logan S: Prophylactic effects of quinine. *Conf States Med Surg J.* 1864;1(4):81-83.
17. Letter from Maj. Gen'l L. McLaws, August 30, 1864. *O.R.* Series I, vol. XXXV/2, pp. 617-18.
18. Goodman LS, Gilman A: *The Pharmacological Basis of Therapeutics.* 2nd ed. New York: Macmillan, 1956, p. 1200.
19. Churchman JW: The use of quinine during the Civil War. *Johns Hopkins Hosp Bull.* 1906;17:175-81.
20. *Medical and Surgical History*, Medical Section, vol. 2.
21. Cummings HT: Article VIII. Report on Pharmacy. *Transactions of the Maine Medical Association, 1866–68.* Portland, ME: Steven Berry Printer, 1869, p. 47.
22. Stabler-Leadbetter Apothecary Shop Museum, Alexandria, VA.
23. Maury RB: Hypodermic injections in the treatment of disease. *Am J Med Sci.* 1866 Oct;52:371.
24. Howard-Jones N: A critical study of the origins and development of hypodermic medication. *J Hist Med Allied Sci.* 1947;2:201-49.
25. Samuel D. Gross, M.D., *System of Surgery.* vol. I. 4th ed. Philadelphia, PA: Henry C. Lea, 1866, p. 621.
26. Franchetti MA: Trauma surgery during the Civil War. *South Med J.* 1993;86(5):556.
27. Adams GW: *Doctors in Blue: The Medical History of the Union Army in the Civil War.* Dayton, OH: Morningside Press, 1985, p. 54.
28. Brooks SM: *Civil War Medicine.* Springfield, IL: C.C. Thomas, 1966, pp. 65, 68.
29. Chisolm JJ: *A Manual of Military Surgery for Use of the Surgeons in the Confederate Army.* Columbia, SC: Evans & Cogswell, 1861. Repub.: Morningside Press, 1992, p. 188.
30. Report of Surg. Henry S. Hewit, U.S. Army, Medical Director, January 1865. *O.R.*, Series I, vol. XXXVIII/2, p. 530.
31. Hedner T, Cassuto J: Opioids and opioid receptors in peripheral tissues. *Scan J Gastroenterol Supp.* 1987:130:27-46.
32. Joris JL, Dubner R, Hargreaves KM: Opioid analgesia at peripheral sites: a target for opioids released during stress and inflammation? *Anesth & Analg.* 1987;66:1277-81.
33. Courtwright DT: Opiate addiction as a consequence of the Civil War. *Civil War Hist.* 1978;24:101.
34. Mitchell SW, Morehouse GR, Keen WW: *Gunshot Wounds and Other Injuries of Nerves.* Philadelphia, PA: Lippincott, 1864. Repub.: Norman Pub. Co., 1989.
35. Kandall SR: *Substance and Shadow: Women and Addiction in the United States.* Cambridge, MA: Harvard Univ. Press, 1996, pp. 20-23.
36. Holmes OW: Currents and counter currents in medical science. *Medical Essays, 1842–1882.* Boston: Houghton Mifflin, 1883, pp. 173-208.
37. Courtwright, *Civil War Hist*, 1978.
38. Earle CW: The opium habit: a statistical and clinical lecture. *Chicago Med Rev.* 1880;2:442-6.
39. Musto DF: *The American Disease: Origins of Narcotic Control.* New Haven, CT: Yale Univ. Press, 1973, pp. 251-52.
40. Chisolm, *Manual of Military Surgery*, p. 188.
41. Quinones MA: Drug abuse during the Civil War (1861–1865). *Int J Addict.* 1975;10(6):1007-20.
42. Ibid.

43. Kandall, *Substance and Shadow*, p. 24.
44. Osler W: *Principles and Practice of Medicine*. 1st ed. New York: Appleton Century Crofts, 1892, p. 403.
45. Holt LE: *The Diseases of Infancy and Childhood*. New York: Appleton, 1897, p. 51.
46. Kandall, *Substance and Shadow*, p. 23.
47. Ibid., p. 41.
48. Smith, *Medicines for the Union Army*, p. 4.
49. Ibid., p. 5.
50. Duncan LC: *The Medical Department of the United States Army in the Civil War*. Gaithersburg, MD: Butternut Press, 1985, p. 355.
51. Smith, *Medicines for the Union Army*, p. 9.
52. Ibid., p. 7.
53. Massey ME: *Ersatz in the Confederacy: Shortages and Substitutes on the Southern Home Front*. Columbia: Univ. South Carolina Press, 1952, pp.115-23.
54. Johnson CB. Quoted in: Commager HS: *Blue and Gray*. vol. 2. Indianapolis, IN: Bobbs-Merrill, 1950, p. 195.
55. Massey, *Ersatz in the Confederacy*, p. 120.
56. McPherson JM: *Battle Cry of Freedom: The Civil War Era*. Oxford: Oxford Univ. Press, 1988, p. 380.
57. Indigenous remedies of the South. (editorial) *Conf States Med Surg J*. 1864;1:104-8.
58. Massey, *Ersatz in the Confederacy*, p. 121.
59. Letter from Surgeon General Moore to Surg. R. Potts, December 5, 1863. *O.R.* Series IV, vol. II, p. 1024.
60. Nightingale F: *Notes on Nursing and Notes on Hospitals*. London: Harrison, 1859. Repub.: Classics of Medicine Library, 1982.
61. Wittenmyer A: *A Collection of Recipes for the Use of Special Diet Kitchens in Military Hospitals*. Mattituck, NY: J.M. Carrol, 1864 (repub. 1983).
62. Pember P: *A Southern Woman's Story: Life in Confederate Richmond*. New York: G.W. Carleton, 1879. (Repub.: Mockingbird, 1987, p. 21.)
63. Robertson JI: *Soldiers Blue and Gray*. Columbia: Univ. South Carolina Press, 1988, pp. 153-54, 165.
64. Pember, *Southern Woman's Story*, p.62.
65. Johnson P: *The Birth of the Modern World Society 1815–1830*. New York: Harper-Collins, 1991, p. 746.
66. Holmes, *Medical Essays*, p. xv.
67. Holmes, *Medical Essays*, pp. 258-59.
68. Louis P: Researches in the effects of blood-letting in some inflammatory diseases. *Am J Med Sci*. 1836;18:102.
69. Jackson J: Letter to Pierre Louis. *Am J Med Sci*. 1836;40:233-34.
70. Bryan LS, Jr.: Blood-letting in American medicine, 1830–92. *Bull Hist Med*. 1964;38(5):516.
71. Chisolm, *Manual of Military Surgery*, p. 296.
72. Woodham Smith CBF: *Queen Victoria: From Her Birth to the Death of the Prince Consort*. New York: Knopf, 1972.
73. *Medical and Surgical History*, Medical Section, vol. 3, p. 808.
74. Bryan, *Bull Hist Med*, 1964.
75. Flint A: *A Treatise on the Principles and Practice of Medicine*. Philadelphia, PA: Henry C. Lea, 1873.
76. Bryan, *Bull Hist Med*, 1964.
77. Sullivan RB: Sanguine practices: a historical and historiographic reconsideration of heroic therapy in the age of Rush. *Bull Hist Med*. 1994;68(2):211.
78. Osler, *Principles and Practice of Medicine*, p. 530.

∾ 10 ∾

Epidemic Diseases in Recruits

. . . we began to feel the scourge of new regiments. Disease became almost universal. We had but a single medical officer and he was tasked beyond his strength. One hundred and fifty or two hundred men were prescribed for every morning, aside from those so ill as to be in the hospital.

– Surgeon George T. Stevens, 77th New York Volunteers

"EVERYTHING EXCEPT TEETHING, NETTLE-RASH, AND WHOOPING COUGH"

THE FIRST YEAR OF THE CIVIL WAR can truly be called the end of innocence for all the states, as well as physicians, politicians, and the military. The expectation of a "ninety-day war" quickly disappeared— replaced by the horror of innumerable deaths. Over the course of the war, disease caused roughly *two-thirds* of the 600,000-plus deaths among the troops. Both armies were composed almost entirely of new recruits, who were particularly susceptible to most diseases. During the war's first terrifying year, newly inducted soldiers gathered in camps, and diseases began to appear and spread rapidly. Confederate Gen. John Brown Gordon wrote about recruits:

> It was amazing to see the large number of country boys who never had the measles. They ran through the whole catalogue of complaints that boyhood and even babyhood are subjected. They had everything except teething, nettle-rash, and whooping cough. I rather think some of them were afflicted with the latter disease."[1]

And they were. Physicians sometimes called these epidemic diseases a form of "crowd poisoning," a logical concept given that they thought that "miasmas" were the etiologic agents of infectious diseases.

Frightened and demoralized troops on both sides suffered from the lack of both hospital facilities and effective treatments for their ills. Their letters home, many of which appeared in newspapers, upset their families and caused a commotion in the press. Both the Union and the Confederate Medical Departments were condemned for their ineptitude and, despite enormous improvements, this image persisted throughout the war.

From a modern viewpoint, the mortality figures for disease are distressing, but they were considered commendable at the time. Joseph Woodward reported in *Army and Navy Journal* that the mortality rates from disease for the first full year of the war were lower than those in any previous American war and those of the recently fought Crimean War. (The first issue of *Confederate States Medical and Surgical Journal* summarized Woodward's report in their section devoted to medical news from foreign sources.)

Woodward noted that, during the war's first year, disease killed 50 of every thousand soldiers (5%), while the death rate from wounds and "injuries of every kind" was 17 per thousand (1.7%). In contrast, the annual death rate from disease in the U.S. Army during the prior eighteen peacetime years was 24 per thousand (2.4%) and during the Mexican War (1846–48), it was 110 per thousand (11%). He noted that 232 of every thousand British soldiers (23.2%) died from disease each year during the Crimean War (1853–56).[2] Unfortunately, this information was published too late to affect the public's perception; in any case, it would have offered little solace.

While the most widespread diseases throughout the war were diarrhea and dysentery, initially, measles and typhoid fever were the most dangerous threat to recruits and they continued to devastate newly inducted soldiers throughout the war. Pneumonia and "consumption" (tuberculosis) decreased in frequency in the later years, while scurvy and smallpox occurred episodically. Malaria was prevalent during the summer and early fall, particularly in coastal areas and along Southern rivers.

What contributed to the high incidence of disease in recruits? The main causes were inadequate pre-enlistment screening, the lack of immunity to diseases, inexperienced physicians, and poor sanitation. Because the war was expected to be brief, no one thought it important to exclude men with illnesses. Physicians simply had to state that the men were well enough to march and carry a gun. Later, particularly after the draft was instituted in 1863, physicians had to perform thorough pre-enlistment examinations.

Because most new soldiers were from rural areas, few had developed immunity to even the common epidemic infections. Complicating the situation were the inexperienced medical personnel, haphazard mechanisms for surgeon appointments in the hastily organized armies, and the incompetence of the first Union surgeons general.

A major factor contributing to disease in the camps was an abysmal lack of sanitation (this continued until line officers learned to appreciate its importance). In part, this resulted from the confusion and chaos when the military tried to apply regulations and procedures designed for an army of

A British Comment on American Mortality Rates

Even early in the war, the British were favorably impressed by the Union Army's medical experiences. An 1862 editorial in *Lancet*, a prestigious British medical journal, summarized an account by the U.S. Sanitary Commission's actuary:

> The annual death rate of the Volunteer Army, to that period, was estimated . . . at 65 per 1000 of strength. The annual mortality of the British Army throughout the Crimean War was 227 per 1000 [a figure slightly lower than that given by Woodward]—the maximum rate being 1173 (January, 1855); the minimum, 72 (June, 1854).

The editorial went on to point out that even when the death rate in the Crimea had fallen to its lowest point, "the mortality did not fall below the annual average of 124 per 1000!"

The editorial concluded:

> well might [the author of the report] claim for the United States Volunteers, in the midst of a disastrous war, a supremacy of health-conditions above the forces of the chief European nations in active service.

The editorial's author, aware of the disastrous military events of the Peninsula campaign and Second Bull Run, could not resist adding,

> We will not pause to inquire how it came to pass that forces characterized by such unrivaled health efficiency . . . should have proved so unfortunate in the field.[3]

(The period covered is shorter than that covered in Joseph Woodward's report, which explains the differences in the statistics.)

about 15,000 men scattered on frontier posts to a huge army gathered into a few large camps. The incidence of most diseases decreased as sanitation and military discipline improved, and most of the men acquired immunity to the common illnesses. (See Figure 10.1.)

Apart from its historical importance, there are still lessons to be learned from the epidemiological information from the Civil War. The advent of vaccines and antibiotics and improved sanitation has, in developed countries, eliminated most of the diseases that plagued Civil War soldiers. However, they still occur among populations that are thrust into wartime conditions without advanced medical resources.

While the facts compiled in *Medical and Surgical History* are among the best and most detailed of that era, several factors limit the general applicability of the information. First, as the authors themselves point out, physicians must have made diagnostic mistakes, particularly before improved screening eliminated many incompetent physicians from service. Second, only those illnesses affecting males in late adolescence and early adulthood are included, so the statistics are not representative of the entire population. Third, crowding, exposure, exertion, malnutrition, and the psychological stresses of wartime conditions modified these diseases, increased their frequency, and aggravated their manifestations. Finally, since the armies only collected data from men who were hospitalized or relieved from duty, they never recorded the incalculable number of milder cases of every illness seen in the twice-daily sick calls.

RECRUITS

In the early months of the war, when citizens were bursting with patriotism and sure that the conflict would be short-lived, pre-enlistment screening ranged from perfunctory to non-existent. This accounts for some of the illness seen in the first year. Governors were anxious to fill quotas, and pressured the physicians they had appointed to give recruits only a superficial examination. Condemning this practice, an 1862 editorial in *American Medical Times* bemoaned the poor inspection of volunteers, pointing out that examining surgeons were often paid a "per caput fee" based on the number of men who enlisted in the regiment. A physician-examiner thus aimed "to increase the numbers which he daily passes." *The British Medical Journal* considered this editorial important enough to quote shortly after its initial publication.[4]

Figure 10.1: The 96th Pennsylvania Infantry Regiment, during a drill at Northumberland in the fall of 1861. The tents in the background are typical of a regimental camp at that time. The tiny stream in the foreground was probably both the water supply and the mechanism of waste disposal for the camp. The lack of concern about sanitation in such camps fostered the spread of diseases; diarrhea, dysentery, and typhoid fever were especially frequent during this period. (Courtesy of NARA, No. 111-B-487.)

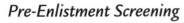

Pre-Enlistment Screening

One regimental surgeon recalled screening recruits in the early days of the war:

> The cry was that the war would be over in ninety days, and regimental and company officers urged acceptance of every available man. The surgeon could not but be affected by the constant calls to fill up regiments and get [them] to the front as soon as possible. Under this pressure men were passed who proved utterly unfit for military service, and when put on ordinary steady duty, and especially on the march, with a soldier's impediments, they were soon in hospital or convalescent camp.[5]

Medical Director Charles S. Tripler's voiced his opinion about the inadequate screening of recruits:

> During the months of October, November, and December [1861] 3,939 men were discharged from the Army of the Potomac upon certificates of disability. Of these 2,881 were for disabilities that existed at the time the men were enlisted . . . It seemed as if the army called out to defend the life of the nation had been made use of as a grand eleemosynary institution for the reception of the aged and infirm, the blind, the lame, and the deaf, where they might be housed, fed, paid, clothed, and pensioned, and their townships relieved of the burden of their support.[6]

MEDICAL SCREENING

While early recruiting examinations were inadequate, later recruits received careful and complete physical examinations. The amount of illness among the troops early in the war prompted the surgeon general to order regimental surgeons to reexamine soldiers in their units. They accomplished this task with the assistance of the Sanitary Commission, and, in July 1862, the Commission reported to President Lincoln that "at least 25 percent of the volunteer army raised last year was not only utterly useless, but a positive encumbrance and embarrassment."[7] Before the 1863 draft, physicians received detailed instructions concerning the examination of recruits; as a result, many men were rejected for health reasons. The instructions made clear that "the examining surgeons will bear in mind that the object of the

Government is to secure the services of men who are effective, able-bodied, sober and free from disqualifying diseases."[8]

By the second year of the war, the Union army had improved their pre-enlistment physical exams and the results were impressive. Starting in 1863, stringent examinations eliminated large numbers of recruits and draftees (or their paid substitutes) due to physical illnesses. The rejection rates for the drafts called in July 1863, March 1864, July 1864, and December 1864 varied between 257 and 314 per thousand recruits examined. Records of their medical examinations reveal a picture of the general health of 1,014,776 American men at the time, and also provide an assessment of American physicians' ability to detect disease.[9] (There are no similar statistics for the rejection of Confederate recruits, although they were also subjected to a stringent examination.) Comparing the Union results with recruit rejection rates in Great Britain, France, and Belgium shows similar rates of rejection, indicating that the health of young American males was similar to that of European draftees of similar ages.[10] These statistics appeared in *The*

Orders on the Examination of Recruits

United States army regulations, modified and issued in 1863, included the following instructions to surgeons:

1297: In passing a recruit the medical officer is to examine him stripped; to see that he has free use of all his limbs; that his chest is ample; that his hearing, vision, and speech are perfect; that he has no tumors, or ulcerated or extensively cicatrized legs; no rupture or chronic cutaneous affection; that he has not received any contusion, or wound of the head, that may impair his faculties; that he is not a drunkard; is not subject to convulsions; and has no infectious disorder, nor any other that may unfit him for military service.

1298: Medical officers attending recruiting rendezvous will keep a record (Form 14) of all the recruits examined by them. Books for this purpose will be procured by application to the Surgeon-General, to whom they will be returned when filled.

1299: As soon as a recruit joins any regiment or station, he shall be examined by the medical officer, and vaccinated when it is required.[11] [Vaccination was required if there was no scar documenting previous vaccination.]

War of the Rebellion: A Compilation of the Official Records of the Union and Confederate Armies, a 178-volume publication of the U.S. War Department published between 1880 and 1901 (hereafter referred to as *Official Records*).

As Table 10.1 shows, hernias were the most common reason for rejecting recruits, followed by the loss of the four front teeth. Men without those teeth could not bite off the ends of their cartridges to load their rifles—a significant disability during a battle. Loss of sight and disease of the eyes were surprisingly common, whereas complete deafness and purulent drainage from the ear (otorrhoea) were less common. Most ear disease would have been due to chronic middle ear infections, which were widespread before antibiotics, as were perforations of the eardrum and an associated chronic mastoiditis. The reasons for the high incidence of loss of sight are not as clear, although trauma and infections may have played a role.

Heart disease was well-known; it was one of the most frequent reasons for medical discharge among both black and white troops. With proper physicals, 1.9% of recruits and draftees were rejected for heart disease.[12] Most of the heart disease was probably rheumatic valvular disease, which results from episodes of rheumatic fever (known as "acute rheumatism" to Civil War physicians). Interestingly, the incidence of rheumatic valvular disease, and the ability of physicians to detect it, from the Civil War to World War II apparently didn't change. During World War II, 96,000 U.S. draftees out of 2 million (2.4%) were rejected because of heart disease, and about half of them had rheumatic valvular disease.[13] This figure is nearly identical to that from the Civil War. The incidence of rheumatic fever rapidly decreased after 1945 when antibiotics became available to civilians.[14]

"Rheumatism or chronic pain," meaning chronic arthritis, was also a reason for rejection. Among Union recruits, 4.7 men per 1,000 were rejected for this reason. The number of recruits with chronic arthritis may have been greater, however, since other reasons for rejection—such as "deformities of hands and fingers" and "deformities of feet and toes"—could have been the result of rheumatoid arthritis, chronic reactive arthritis, trauma, or infection.

The term "curvatures of the spine" suggests rickets, a common condition in the late 1800s, particularly in urban areas.[15] Lateral curvature of the spine (scoliosis) was known to be rickets' main manifestation, but this association was not stressed in Civil War literature. Originally described in England, rickets was a well-known disease in northern Europe; on the Continent, it was often called "the English disease." Spinal disease was the most common reason for rejection in Great Britain in the early 1860s. Since they were not differentiated, it is not possible to tell how many of the cases of curvature of

TABLE 10.1

Number Rejected Per 1,000 Recruits Examined for Diseases and Infirmities in the Union Army and Great Britain*

Cause of Rejection	Union Army 1863	Great Britain 1860	1861
Hernia	34.28	11.79	14.89
Loss of teeth	23.60	9.52	7.76
Diseases of the heart	18.59	12.86	25.52
Diseases of the eyes (myopia included)	17.80	28.75	28.52
Deformity and deficient size of chest and curvature of the spine	14.00	25.30	55.67
Varicocele	10.88	13.39	23.52
Epilepsy	9.31	—	—
Varicose veins	7.10	28.63	40.79
Diseases of the ears and deafness	6.60	3.10	4.51
Imbecility	4.99	2.20	0.50
Myopia	3.54	—	—
Hemorrhoids	3.17	5.00	5.88
Stammering	2.00	1.31	1.63
Diseases of the skin	1.80	5.54	8.63
Diseases of the brain and spinal cord	0.98	12.86	0.62
Diseases of the nose and mouth	—	0.77	1.63

*According to the original table, "This comparison is as complete as the different classifications in the English . . . returns will admit."

O.R. Series 3, vol. 3, p. 1054.

the spine were rickets and how many were another process, such as spinal tuberculosis (Pott's disease).

FARM BOYS AND CITY SLICKERS

Most Union and Confederate recruits were from rural areas, with "urban" being defined as a community of 2,500 or more. When they enlisted, 48% of the Union soldiers identified themselves as farmers or farm workers.[16] Both Union and Confederate observers were surprised to find that young men from rural areas were not as healthy and were less able to withstand the physical rigors of army life as their counterparts from the cities.[17] As one Confederate physician wrote, "Townsmen contrasted favorably with countrymen."[18]

Part of the reason for this was rural soldiers' lack of exposure to the epidemic diseases that those from urban areas usually acquired in childhood. Soldiers from rural areas succumbed more easily to measles and similar epidemic diseases in both armies, particularly early in the war. This lack of acquired immunity, however, is not the entire explanation. Dr. Albert Gaillard Hart recorded his personal observations on the military capabilities of soldiers from rural and urban areas:

> It was at first supposed that men from the rural districts, with their regular habits and well-developed muscles, would prove enduring soldiers, while the city recruits of less robust build, and with more or less irregular habits, would fare ill. The recruits were a great surprise; it proved that steady farm work had not developed good legs for drilling and marching. On the other hand, the man from the city was less affected by irregular meals, labor, and sleep. He was better prepared to look out for his own comfort on the field, and proved to have more adaptation to the exigencies of the service . . .
>
> [I] soon had the surprising experience of seeing the stalwart six-footers, the pride of their companies, ambitious men, who gave every energy to the work, among the first to give out entirely, go to hospital, and perhaps never rejoin the regiment. At the same time [I] would see the slender "counter-jumper," or the disreputable, snug-built "bummer," carry his gun, accoutrements, knapsack, and rations, without flinching, on every march and in every battle.[19]

CHILDREN

The age of some enlistees contributed to the amount of illness. Both young children and the elderly (the average male's life-expectancy was about forty-five years) were more susceptible to disease and injury than were other soldiers. While about 80% of the soldiers in both armies were between eighteen and twenty-nine, many were under the minimum age of eighteen or over the maximum age of forty-five.[20] Union soldiers' average age was twenty-five. Both sides, however, unofficially enlisted volunteers younger than sixteen years old, and about 300 soldiers were less than thirteen. Boys as young as ten are known to have served as drummers and couriers, and at least 25 were under ten years of age.[21] In 1863, Walt Whitman commented, "I am more and more surprised at the very great proportion of youngsters from fifteen to twenty-one in the army. I afterwards found a still greater proportion among the Southerners."[22]

Women in the Ranks

Because of the lax examinations early in the war, at least 400 women served in the Union army disguised as men. For example, Private Albert

Cashier joined the 95th Illinois Infantry in August 1862 and served for over three years. He participated in many campaigns, including those at Vicksburg, the Red River, and Mobile. Cashier continued to wear men's clothes until 1911, when, after fracturing his leg in an automobile accident, "he" was found to be Jennie Hodgers, born in Belfast in 1844. She continued to receive a soldier's pension and, at her death in 1915, she was buried with full military honors.[23]

Jennie Hodgers seated on the right.

An officer who served in the Confederate army as Samuel Blalock was one of at least two wives who saw considerable field service with their husbands. She was discovered to be Mrs. L. M. Blalock only after she was captured and imprisoned on Johnson's Island in Ohio and gave birth. A note in the *Sandusky* (Ohio) *Register* of December 12, 1864, read:

> One day last week one of the rebel officers . . . on Johnson's Island gave birth to a 'bouncing boy.' This is the first instance of the father giving birth to a child that we have heard of.[24]

Women's roles in the war are further discussed in Chapter 16.

Photo by Spencer H. Watterson.

Since the minimum age for enlistment in the Union army was eighteen, underage boys who wanted to remain truthful would write "18" on a piece of paper and put it in their shoe. Then, when asked their age, they would respond truthfully, "I'm over 18."[25] The official age range for the Confederate army at the beginning of the war was eighteen to twenty-nine but, as in the Union army, there were many exceptions. Late in the war, Confederate authorities lowered the minimum age to sixteen. Private John Mather Sloan, of the 9th Texas, was only thirteen when he received an official commendation from Gen. Pierre G. T. Beauregard after a battle at Farmington, Mississippi, in which Sloan lost a leg.[26] The youngest Confederate soldier on record was Charles C. Hay of Alabama, age eleven.[27]

Aside from their propensity to become ill, most youngsters were not useful soldiers. Maj. Albert Gaillard Hart, a Union surgeon in an Ohio regiment, recorded his experiences with young enlistees:

> Many boys at sixteen and seventeen, calling themselves eighteen, were accepted. As was to have been anticipated, these boys were most of them a dead weight on the service. The men who did almost the whole of the marching and fighting in my regiment were between nineteen and forty."[28]

Both sides recorded the lack of military value of adolescents. In 1862, a medical journal, lamenting the inadequacy of the "inspection of recruits," quoted Napoleon III as saying, "I demand a levy of 300,000 men; but I must have grown men."[29]

The Drummer Boy of Shiloh (and Chickamauga)

Johnny Lincoln Clem, born August 13, 1851, in Newark, Ohio, ran away from home to join the army in 1861. Several Ohio and Michigan regiments explained that they were not "enlisting infants," but he followed the 22nd Michigan, acting as an unofficial drummer boy. Officers donated money so that he received a private's pay ($13/month). When his drum was smashed at Shiloh, he was written up in the newspapers as "Johnny Shiloh, the smallest drummer."

At Chickamauga, he rode on an artillery caisson with a cut-down musket, and won fame again when he shot a Confederate officer who chased after the caisson, shouting, "Surrender, you damn little Yankee!" Johnny was then officially enlisted in the army and served as a courier. He was wounded twice.

After the war, his application to West Point was turned down for lack of education, but he appealed to President Ulysses S. Grant, who appointed him directly to second lieutenant in December 1871. In 1903, he became a colonel and assistant quartermaster general. He retired in 1916 with the rank of major general.[30]

THE EPIDEMICS

Illnesses quickly spread through the ripe environment of military camps on both sides. The troops lived in very close quarters and the diseases repeatedly spread from man to man. Measles and mumps, now considered relatively benign, left thousands dead in their wake. Lung infections constantly plagued the men. Typhoid, typhus, and *Meningococcus*, always serious diseases, exacted enormous tolls at a time when effective treatment was at least a century in the future. When infections did not kill, nature did. Sunstroke, almost in epidemic proportions, also decimated the troops.

Besides decreasing the number of men available for duty, sick soldiers tied up personnel and other resources for their care, and the resulting deaths demoralized the rest of the unit. Measles contributed to General Lee's failure to recapture Virginia's western counties in August 1861. Lee never mentioned illness among his troops in his official reports, but, in a letter to his wife on September 1, 1861, he accurately described the problem:

> We have a great deal of sickness among the soldiers, & now those on the sick list would form an army. The measles is still among them, though I hope [it] is dying out. But it is a disease which though light in childhood is severe in manhood, & prepares the system for other attacks. The constant cold rains, mud, &c., &c., with no shelter but tents, have aggravated it. All these drawbacks, with impassable roads, have paralyzed our efforts.[31,32]

These, then, are the killer epidemics.

MEASLES AND MUMPS

Measles and mumps quickly became epidemic in recruit camps on both sides. There were 67,763 cases of measles recorded in white Union troops, with 4,246 deaths (6%). Among the black troops, there were 8,555 cases with 931 deaths (11%). The incidence of measles (per thousand men per year, based on the mean strength of the Union army during the war years) was twice as high in the black troops. Black soldiers' isolation during slavery, which minimized their exposure to crowds and common childhood illnesses was a possible reason for this.

As troops acquired immunity after the war's first year, the incidence of measles decreased markedly. Almost no cases of measles were recorded among the Union troops during the year that began July 1, 1865, when the army was demobilizing, and not recruiting.

Measles appear to have been more prevalent among Confederate recruits. Again, this was probably because fewer had acquired immunity, since most soldiers came from rural areas. Measles was so rampant that it affected the Confederate military effort early in the war. As one senior physician noted,

> Measles prevailed extensively in the new regiments, specially those from the country, and greatly impeded their organization. It so diminished the effectiveness of the troops and proved so fatal in camp that companies, battalions, and whole regiments had to be temporarily disbanded and the men sent home.[33]

The 12th North Carolina's surgeon saw 800 out of the 1,200 men who had enlisted in his regiment in the early months of the war come down with measles.[34] Captain Alfred Bell, of the 39th North Carolina, reported in April 1862 that 6 out of every 7 men in his newly formed regiment were ill. It was

Measles in World Wars I and II

Measles was again a problem among recruits in the American armies of the twentieth century, and the observations from those wars may explain the relatively high mortality from the disease during the Civil War. In World War I, approximately 102,000 U.S. soldiers contracted measles, and 2,370 (2.3%) of them died. However, bacterial cultures showed that almost all the deaths were due to streptococcal infections that caused bronchopneumonia or lobar pneumonia.[35]

Streptococcus infections apparently were even more frequent and more virulent during the Civil War, judging from the frequency of erysipelas and hospital gangrene, which are caused by that organism. There were also a large number of cases of acute rheumatism caused by streptococci-induced acute rheumatic fever among Civil War troops.

During World War II, measles was less frequent than in the Civil War (60,809 cases, with only 33 deaths). Still, the incidence of measles was highest among soldiers during their first two months in camp and in recruits from rural areas. For example, at Camp Pike in Arkansas, which drew men from the predominantly rural areas of the surrounding states, measles afflicted 165 men per 1,000 per year. However, at Camp Dix, New Jersey, which drew recruits from New York City and Philadelphia, measles afflicted only 7.3 men per 1,000 per year.

Mumps also occurred among recruits in both world wars, as it had in the Civil War. During World War I, 237,000 cases were recorded; during World War II, there were 103,055.[36]

so bad that Confederate authorities tried to withhold recruits from active duty until they were "put through the measles."[37]

Mumps was almost as common as measles among white Union troops (48,128 total cases, which was 23 cases per 1,000 men per year) and even more prevalent among the black troops (12,186 cases, which was 86 cases per 1,000 men per year). Unlike measles, mumps caused few fatalities in either group (72 deaths in white soldiers, 12 deaths in black units). For reasons that are unclear, many soldiers considered mumps a "fashionable disease." When the disease struck an encampment, men would tie up their jaws with a bandage to decrease the pain from inflamed parotid glands when they chewed.[38]

Acute Respiratory Tract Infections

Colds, officially called "epidemic catarrh," also spread rapidly among recruits. Physicians noted that they knew which tents contained recruits because of the amount of coughing.[39] Since a large variety of respiratory viruses causes colds, sick recruits often spread their infections to veterans who had not yet been infected by these new agents. As a result, adding fresh troops often actually decreased the number of effective men in veteran units. Exposure to inclement weather and lack of adequate clothing and blankets also increased the incidence of these infections among the men. Respiratory tract infections were common throughout the war, and particularly during the winter of 1864–65, which was the harshest weather of the era.

The case descriptions demonstrate that all kinds of illnesses were called "colds" (a phenomenon that still occurs). According to official records, epidemic catarrh was diagnosed 144,266 times and acute bronchitis 191,363 times in Union troops.[40] Bronchitis remained widespread throughout the war on both sides, and some physicians correctly surmised that the smoke from the omnipresent campfires aggravated the problem.

Pneumonia, one of the most feared "killer" diseases, was also pervasive early in the war. All too often, pneumonia developed following a "cold," bronchitis, or measles. Since these predisposing diseases were rampant among new recruits, the frequency of pneumonia decreased as the war continued. However, in Northern prison camps late in the war, pneumonia caused the most deaths among the Confederate POWs (see Chapter 15, *Prison Camps*). Malnutrition and a lack of adequate clothing during the worst winter weather of the century were contributory factors.

Among white soldiers contracting pneumonia, 24% died. Not until almost eighty years later, after the introduction of sulfa drugs and penicillin, did this mortality rate change significantly. For example, for every 1,000 cases of acute lobar pneumonia seen at Massachusetts General Hospital between 1822 and 1889, the mortality rate averaged 25%; during the last ten years of that period, from 1880 to 1889, it was 28%.[41] A review of pneumonia therapy in the 1930s showed a 34.2% mortality rate among cases receiving standard therapy and a 17.7% mortality rate among those given serum therapy. It seems valid to conclude that the treatment given by Civil War physicians was no worse than expected for their time.[42]

Surprisingly, there were no recorded outbreaks of influenza among Civil War troops, despite reports of epidemics of disease called "influenza" in the civilian population before and during the war. For example, a physician at Pennsylvania Hospital described an outbreak in Philadelphia that appeared from early December 1860 until March 1861, reappeared in 1863, and persisted to the time of his report in January 1864. He specifically mentioned some malignant forms of the disease.[43] The intermittent episodes, timing, and severity in some cases resemble influenza as we know it today.

TYPHOID FEVER

Feared and often fatal, typhoid fever was one of the most terrible epidemic diseases in the 1800s. Typhoid is an intestinal infection that is spread by ingesting food or water contaminated with the bacteria called *Salmonella*

General Robert E. Lee Confronts Disease in Recruits

The problem of sickness led General Lee to write to Secretary of War Randolph on October 8, 1862, three weeks after the Battle of Antietam (or, as he would have called it, Sharpsburg):

The medical director reports that . . . about 4,500 . . . sick from this army are now accumulated in Winchester, and they are principally, if not altogether, the conscripts and recruits that have joined since we have been stationary. They are afflicted with measles, camp fever, &c. The medical director thinks that all the conscripts we have received are thus afflicted, so that, instead of being an advantage to us, they are an element of weakness, a burden. I think, therefore, that it would be better if the conscripts be assembled in camps of instruction, so that they may pass through these inevitable diseases, and become a little inured to camp life.[44]

typhi. Such contamination was usually widespread in army camps, and caused huge epidemics. During the Civil War, the were 75,418 cases in white Union soldiers and 27,058 (36%) of them died. Black troops encountered the disease at a comparable rate, and the Confederate records that exist indicate a similar experience.

The disease was at its peak during the first full year of the war (July 1, 1861, to June 30, 1862). During that period, 5.9% of Union soldiers (based on the army's mean strength that year) were diagnosed with typhoid fever; 2% of the entire army died from it. The next year, when there was still active recruitment, 4.9% of the men reportedly had typhoid fever and 1.7% died. In subsequent years, the incidence of typhoid fever averaged about 1.5% of the army's mean strength, and less than 1% died. There are no exact statistics on the incidence of disease in Confederate troops during this period, but anecdotal reports from physicians and commanders suggest a similar experience.

Patients with severe typhoid experience fever and severe generalized malaise as the bacteria spreads through the body. These patients usually develop transient red skin lesions called "rose spots" and have diminished mental function. Paralysis of wall muscles in the bowel can lead to intestinal dilatation, distending the abdomen; nineteenth-century physicians described this phenomenon as "adynamia." Diarrhea or constipation may occur, and perforation of the intestine can lead to death. Typhoid can also cause bronchitis, leading to pneumonia.

Physicians could not make a definitive diagnosis of typhoid until the twentieth century, when bacteriologic and serologic tests became available. Civil War physicians, however, described their typhoid fever cases and recorded autopsy findings which demonstrate that their diagnoses were correct. Many of the cases in *Medical and Surgical History* contain detailed descriptions of the characteristic features of the disease, such as "rose spots" on the chest and abdomen. In addition, autopsy reports reveal characteristic pathologic findings, such as enlarged intestinal lymphoid follicles ("Peyer's patches") and, often, perforation through one or more of these follicles. (See Figure 10.2.)

When typhoid was first recognized as a separate disease in the 1830s, it needed to be distinguished from another epidemic disease characterized by delirium: typhus. "Typhus" is derived from a Greek word meaning "smoke" or "stupor," referring to the mental clouding of delirium, and typhoid was given a name that stressed this resemblance to typhus. Typhoid was undoubtedly far more common than the incidence figures indicate, since only very

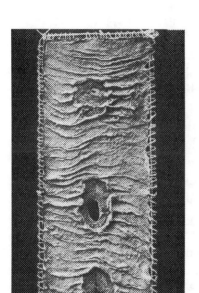

Figure 10.2: Specimen of the small intestine, mounted in the fashion of the time, showing the complication of typhoid: perforation (in this case, multiple perforations) of the intestine through the lymphoid follicles known as Peyer's Patches. (*Medical and Surgical History*, Medical Section, vol. III, facing p. 382.)

severe, fully developed cases were labeled with this diagnosis. The occurrence of delirium was a major criterion for making that diagnosis: it is an ominous prognostic sign and its use probably accounts for the high mortality among patients diagnosed with typhoid fever during the Civil War. Even today, when the definitive diagnosis of typhoid fever can be made using bacteriologic or serologic criteria, delirium remains an ominous prognostic indicator.

There were no effective treatments for typhoid. Physicians attempted to treat the symptoms using analgesics and quinine (as an antipyretic), and tried to find a palatable, appropriate diet for sufferers. Occasionally, these measures did some good. However, some physicians prescribed calomel for typhoid fever, causing mercury poisoning in many of the patients.

Typhoid Carriers and Immunity

We now know that people can be infected with typhoid without having any symptoms. Likewise, roughly 2% to 3% of typhoid fever patients become chronic carriers of the organism, which they excrete in their feces. Given the extremely poor sanitation in Civil War encampments, the flies that plagued all campsites, and virtually no opportunity for handwashing, veterans who were chronic typhoid carriers must have easily spread the organisms, and the disease, to susceptible recruits. The situation was the same in hospitals, particularly early in the war when sanitation was little better than in the camps. Many volunteer female nurses, who generally came from well-to-do families, were exposed to typhoid for the first time. Typhoid fever ended the nursing career of Louisa Mae Alcott (author of *Little Women*), whose father came to Washington and took her home. Miss Alcott survived her illness, but her supervising matron, Hannah Ropes, died of the disease.[45,46]

Typhoid in Confederate Recruits

Despite the absence of detailed data, evidence suggests that the incidence of typhoid fever was extremely high among Confederate recruits. On August 7, 1861, Brig. Gen. John Magruder, reporting on the evacuation and burning of Hampton, Virginia, stated:

> The sickness among the troops in the Peninsula is grave, both in extent and character, all diseases taking more or less a typhoid character, and many deaths occurring—at Yorktown about two a day. Some idea may be formed of its effects when I state that the Fifth North Carolina Regiment, composed of twelve companies and over 1,000 strong, is now less than 400 for duty . . . Typhoid has been so prevalent and fatal at Jamestown Island as to make the withdrawal of the men from that post necessary.[47]

Civil War physicians knew that typhoid fever survivors had immunity from further attacks.[48] As Dr. Joseph Jones pointed out, "Typhoid fever is most likely to attack recruits, and as a general rule affects the individual but once during his lifetime."[49] And, in an 1866 U.S. Sanitary Commission document, Alfred Stillé wrote, "Typhoid protects against subsequent attacks as perfectly as smallpox."[50] Both mild cases of typhoid fever that remained undiagnosed and cases that remained asymptomatic would have resulted in immunity.

This acquired immunity caused the incidence of typhoid fever to decrease markedly as the war progressed, even when sanitation was at its worst, such as in the prison camps during 1864 and 1865 (discussed in Chapter 15, *Prison Camps*). Dr. Joseph Jones investigated typhoid fever in Camp Sumter, the Confederate prison near Andersonville, Georgia, where sanitation was probably the worst of the war. He noted that few prisoners had typhoid fever—slightly more than 1% of the Union patients treated in the hospital—although the incidence among the Confederate guards was much greater:

> This difference appears to be due in a measure to the fact that the Confederate forces were composed of reserves between the ages of sixteen and eighteen and forty-five and fifty-five years, and had been but recently collected together for service. They were raw troops who had not as yet

passed through the diseases of camp. On the other hand, the Federal prisoners had passed through most of the diseases incident to raw troops, as measles and typhoid fever.[51]

Comparisons of typhoid's incidence (and other medical experiences) between the American Civil War and the Franco-Prussian War of 1870–71 are problematic because of the differences in the diagnostic terms used. In addition, there is no decent data for disease in the French army (and that for the wounded is incomplete). In Germany, typhus was usually called "exanthematous typhus" to emphasize the characteristic rash. Germans used the term "typhus abdominalis" for what British and American physicians called typhoid fever. To further complicate matters, some European, British, and American physicians used "enteric fever" for typhoid, although it was not included on the official list of diagnoses during the Civil War.[52]

Typhoid Pneumonia

Civil War physicians occasionally used the term "typhoid pneumonia" in case records. At times it referred to lung diseases occurring as part of typhoid fever, while it was also used when the intestines (and the belly) distended in patients with lobar pneumonia in a lower lobe of the lung. Pneumonia inflames the pleura (lung covering) that is in contact with the diaphragm and may irritate the abdominal organs, causing abdominal pain and partially paralyzing the intestines. Since intestinal and abdominal swelling were characteristic of typhoid fever, these findings led to the term "typhoid pneumonia." Lobar pneumonia (officially called "inflammation of the lungs") was usually due to the *Streptococcus pneumoniae*; its occurrence in Civil War troops is covered in the next chapter.

REMITTENT, CONTINUED, AND TYPHOMALARIAL FEVERS

Civil War physicians also diagnosed patients with "remittent," "continued," and "typhomalarial" fevers. Some of these cases probably were unrecognized instances of mild typhoid fever.

"Remittent fever" was the most-used term in the official list of diagnoses, with a total of 286,490 cases recorded among the white Federal troops; it occurred with about equal frequency in black troops. Physicians used the term "continued fever" in 1861 and 1862, during which time they diagnosed 11,898 cases. Both "remittent fever" and "continued fever" had relatively low case-fatality rates of about 1%. Undoubtedly, a variety of different diseases was included in these categories, making these terms the nineteenth-century equivalent of the modern term "fever of unknown origin."

In July 1862, the Union army abandoned the term "continued fever" when Dr. Joseph Woodward introduced the diagnostic term "typhomalarial fever."[53] (The term "typhomalarial fever" remained controversial and Confederate physicians never used it.) "Typhomalarial fever," which was diagnosed in 49,871 cases, had a much lower mortality rate than typhoid fever, averaging 8.1%. (Data for the black troops are discussed in Chapter 12.)

Many soldiers with "typhomalarial fever" actually had mild typhoid fever. In his book *Camp Diseases*, Woodward's description of "typhomalarial fever" includes every manifestation of typhoid except delirium.[54] The International Medical Congress of 1876, held before medical bacteriology was accepted, defined the term as the simultaneous occurrence of typhoid fever and malaria. Since chills and fever can occur in both diseases, it may have been difficult to tell which was the correct diagnosis in some patients, leading to popularity of the combined term. In some cases, physicians may have diagnosed typhomalarial fever when the two diseases actually occurred simultaneously, a likely occurrence as both were so common.[55,56]

After the Civil War, physicians continued to use the term "typhomalarial fever" for several decades until bacteriological diagnosis of typhoid fever rendered the term obsolete. As late as the Spanish-American War in 1898, the Typhoid Commission, assigned to investigate a severe typhoid outbreak among recruits, found that malaria and typhoid fever were often confused with each other clinically (bacteriological diagnosis was not yet routine).[57]

TYPHUS

Also known as "typhus fever," this group of diseases is caused by *Rickettsia* species. The illnesses are characterized by sudden onset of prostration, severe headaches, a generalized rash, high fever, and progressive neurological involvement. The epidemic form thrives in crowded, unsanitary conditions. At the time of the Civil War, typhus was widespread in Europe, and many American physicians were familiar with it since it was a major problem during the European wars. Soldiers also knew the disease, because many were immigrants from Europe.

It is surprising that typhus was rarely diagnosed among Civil War troops, since lice transmit the disease and the men were covered with lice and fleas. Outbreaks of typhus were often named for the locale in which they occurred, such as "jail fever" or "ship fever." The term "spotted fever" was occasionally used and it could have meant typhus in some instances. An outbreak of "spotted fever" occurred after troops were transported by ship, but no large epidemics were diagnosed as typhus. Complications include broncho-pneumonia and nephritis.

MENINGITIS AND MENINGOCOCCEMIA

Until the era of antibiotics, bacterial meningitis, infection of the membranes lining the brain and spinal cord, was usually fatal. Although almost any organism that infects the central nervous system can cause meningitis, the most common is *Neisseria meningitidis*, which still causes deadly outbreaks. This organism spreads rapidly through the bloodstream, giving rise to tiny hemorrhagic blisters in the skin. These lesions spawned the term "spotted fever." A few of the Civil War cases called "spotted fever" that had a high mortality rate may have been caused by *N. meningitidis*. Even with anti-biotics, mortality continues to be high, because the disease can overwhelm infected individuals before they can receive effective treatment.

"Inflammation of the membranes of the brain" and "inflammation of the brain" were the official terms used for meningitis during the Civil War, but physicians also used "cerebrospinal meningitis" as a diagnosis. Among the white Union troops, there were 2,037 cases called "inflammation of the brain" or "inflammation of membranes of the brain," with a mortality rate of 99%.[58] As with many other diseases, it occurred predominantly in the first two years of the war. Among black troops, 415 cases were diagnosed, with a mortality rate of 89%.

One outbreak of meningitis among Confederate recruits resembles episodes seen in recruit camps during recent wars. During the winter of 1862–63, when the 22nd North Carolina was encamped on the Rappahan-nock River below Fredericksburg, four cases of meningitis occurred in close succession within the same company; three of the men died. All but one of the men "were conscripts and had been in the camp but a short time, per-haps little more than a month."[59] The three dead soldiers were two brothers and their brother-in-law.

Other diseases produce small visible hemorrhagic lesions and thus could also be called "spotted fever." One is the rickettsial disease Rocky Mountain spotted fever (named for the locale in which it was first recognized), which is currently more common in the east coast states—the sites of the Civil War campaigns. Rickettsial diseases could have accounted for some of the ill-nesses called "spotted fever" during the war. However, these diseases rarely occur as major outbreaks or epidemics, and they are not particularly charac-teristic illnesses of recruits in military settings. Typhus is also a rickettsial disease that produces similar skin hemorrhages. Concerned that accurate diagnoses might not be made, *Confederate States Medical and Surgical Journal* printed an article that discussed the differential diagnosis of typhus and cerebrospinal meningitis.[60]

SUNSTROKE

When infectious organisms didn't kill new recruits, sometimes nature did. Sunstroke, severe overheating of the body, was another highly lethal illness that primarily affected recruits. Case descriptions reveal that physicians had a good understanding of the problem, how to prevent it, and how to treat it. Nevertheless, 269 Union soldiers died of sunstroke during the war, an astonishing number given that it was totally avoidable.

Civil War physicians clearly attributed sunstroke to overheating plus dehydration. They noted the rapid onset of sunstroke when dehydration had progressed to the point at which perspiration ceased, and they described the manifestations in detail, including the occurrence of convulsions. Treatment was appropriate: they attempted to cool and rehydrate the men, although they were unsuccessful if they delayed too long. They also noted that bloodletting was neither recommended nor used.[61] Sunstroke's classification in the tables of diseases under "Diseases of the Nervous System" provides further evidence that they understood the basic nature of the problem.

Sunstroke occurred almost entirely during May, June, July, and August. There were proportionately more cases in the Army of the Potomac than in the Western armies. The cases almost always developed when the troops were on a forced march or during laborious fieldwork. About 90% of the cases during a given month occurred on one particular day.[62] We now know that this is typical—it would have been a day with both a high temperature and excessive humidity, so that sweating would be useless as a cooling mechanism.

Old soldiers, it seems, knew how to prevent sunstroke. They would drop out of the march, lie in the shade, disrobe, and drink as much water as was available until they cooled. Raw recruits were more likely to try to continue to march until they fell by the wayside, sometimes dying as a result. The case-fatality rate was just under 4% among all the white recruits and veterans, but it was 11% among the black soldiers, a large proportion of whom were always recent recruits. During the same period, there was a 50% fatality rate among civilians, probably because few of them knew how to prevent sunstroke.

REFERENCES

1. Gordon JB: *Reminiscences of the Civil War*. New York: C. Scribner's Sons, 1905, p. 49.
2. Woodward JJ: Mortality rates of the U.S. armies during the year ending June 1862. *Conf States Med Surg J.* 1864;1(1):11.
3. Editorial. *Lancet.* 1862 Nov. 22;1:571.
4. *Br Med J.* 1862 Sept. 13;1:287.
5. Hart AG: *The Surgeon and the Hospital in the Civil War*. Gaithersburg, MD: Olde Soldier Books, 1987, p. 8. (orig. pub. 1902)
6. Report of Surg. Charles S. Tripler, Medical Director of the Army of the Potomac, on the operations of the medical department of that Army from August 12, 1861 to March 17, 1862. *O.R.* Series I, vol. V, p. 82.
7. Wiley BI: *The Life of Billy Yank: The Common Soldier of the Union*. Baton Rouge: Louisiana State Univ. Press, 1952, p. 23.
8. Instructions for the Physical Examination of Recruits, April 21, 1863. *O.R.* Series III, vol. III, p. 91.
9. *O.R.* Series III, vol. V, p. 679.
10. Correspondence, Orders, Reports; Returns of the Union Authorities from January 1 to December 31, 1863. *O.R.* Series III, vol. III, p. 1054.
11. U.S. Army: *Regulations of the Medical Department of the Army*. Washington, D.C.: GPO, 1861. Reprinted: Bohemian Brigade, 1989, p. 313.
12. Report of R.H. Coolidge, Medical Inspector, U.S. Army. *O.R.* Series III, vol. III, p. 1054.
13. Markowitz M, Kuttner AG: *Rheumatic Fever: Diagnosis, Management, and Prevention*. Philadelphia, PA: W.B. Saunders, 1965, p. 4.
14. Stollerman GH: *Rheumatic Fever and Streptococcal Infection*. New York: Grune & Stratton, 1975, p. 65.
15. Rosen G: *Preventive Medicine in the United States, 1900–1975: Trends and Interpretations*. New York: Prodist, 1977, p. 5.
16. Fox WF: *Regimental Losses in the American Civil War 1861–1865: A Treatise on the Extent and Nature of the Mortuary Losses in the Union Regiments, with Full and Exhaustive Statistics Compiled from the Official Records on File in the State Military Bureau and at Washington*. Albany, NY: Albany Pub. Co., 1889, p. 62.
17. Wilkinson W: *Mother, May You Never See the Sights I Have Seen: The Fifty-seventh Massachusetts Veteran Volunteers in the Army of the Potomac, 1864–1865*. New York: Harper & Row, 1990.
18. Eve PF: Answers to certain questions propounded by Prof. Charles A. Lee, M.D., Agent of the U.S. Sanitary Commission, relative to the health, etc., of the late Southern army. *Nashville J Med Surg*. NS, July 1866;1:12-32.
19. Hart, *Surgeon and the Hospital*, p. 8.
20. Fox, *Regimental Losses*, p. 62.
21. Roberts DJ: Medical Service in the Confederacy. In: *The Photographic History of the Civil War*. New York: Review of Reviews, 1970 (orig. pub. 1911), vol. 4A, p. 232.
22. Whitman W: *Walt Whitman's Memoranda during the War (&) Death of Abraham Lincoln*. Bloomington, IN: Indian Univ. Press, 1962 (reproduced in facsimile), p. 8.
23. Faust PL: *Historical Times Encyclopedia of the Civil War*. New York: Harper & Row, 1986, p. 119.
24. Wiley BI: *Confederate Women*. Westport, CT: Greenwood, 1975, p. 142.
25. Robertson JI: *Soldiers Blue and Gray*. Columbia: Univ. South Carolina Press, 1988, p. 25.
26. Davis WC: *Rebels and Yankees: Fighting Men of the Civil War*. New York: Thomas Yoseloff, 1959, p. 17.
27. Robertson, *Soldiers Blue and Gray*, p. 25.
28. Hart, *Surgeon and the Hospital*, p. 9.

29. Editorial. *Am Med Times.* August 30, 1862, p. 123.
30. Faust, *Encyclopedia of the Civil War*, p. 145.
31. Lee RE: *The Wartime Papers of Robert E. Lee.* New York: Da Capo Press, 1987, p. 69.
32. Lee RE: *Recollections and Letters of General Robert E. Lee.* Garden City, NY: Garden City Pub., 1926, p. 471.
33. Eve, *Nashville J Med Surg*, 1866.
34. Buist JR: Some items of my medical and surgical experience in the Confederate army. *Southern Practitioner.* 1903:574-81.
35. U.S. Army Medical Service: *Internal Medicine in World War II.* vol. 2. (Havens WP, ed.) Washington, D.C.: Office of the Surgeon General, Dept. of the Army, 1961, pp. 32-33.
36. U.S. Army Medical Service, *Internal Medicine in World War II*, vol. 2, p. 35.
37. Wiley BI: *Life of Johnny Reb: The Common Solider of the Confederacy.* Indianapolis: Univ. Indiana Press, 1943, p. 244.
38. Cunningham HH: *Doctors in Gray: The Confederate Medical Service.* Baton Rouge: Louisiana State Univ. Press, 1958, p. 215.
39. Haskell JC: *The Haskell Memoirs.* New York: Putnam, 1960, p. 132.
40. *Medical and Surgical History*, Medical Section, vol. 1, Tables C, CXI.
41. *Transactions of the American Climatological Association.* 1889;6:41-43.
42. Cecil RL: Present status of serum therapy in pneumonia. *Bull NY Acad Med.* 1939;15:104-15.
43. Levick JJ: Remarks on an epidemic of influenza. *Am J Med Sci.* 1864;47:65-80.
44. *O.R.*, Series I, vol XIX/2, p. 657.
45. Alcott LM: *Hospital Sketches.* (Jones, BZ, ed.) Cambridge, MA: Harvard Univ. Press, 1960.
46. Brumgardt JR: *Civil War Nurse: The Diary and Letters of Hannah Ropes.* Knoxville: Univ. Tennessee Press, 1993.
47. Report of Brig. Gen. John B. Magruder, C. S. Army. *O.R.* Series I, vol. IV, Chapter 8, p. 573.
48. Stillé A: Typhoid fever. In: *United States Sanitary Commission Documents.* New York: Hurd & Houghton, 1866.
49. Jones J: Medical history of the Confederate states army and navy. *South Hist Soc Papers.* 1892;20:109-66.
50. Stillé, Typhoid fever, 1866.
51. Jones J: Observations upon the diseases of the Federal prisoners confined in Camp Sumter, Andersonville. *O.R.*, Series II, vol. 8, pp. 582-632.
52. Footnote. *Br Med J.* 1871;1:101.
53. Woodward JJ: *Outlines of the Chief Camp Diseases of the United States Armies as Observed during the Present War. A Practical Contribution to Military Medicine.* Philadelphia, PA: J.B. Lippincott, 1863. Repub: Norman, 1992, pp. 77-149.
54. Ibid., p. 77.
55. Smith DC: The rise and fall of typhomalarial fever, I. Origins. *J Hist Med Allied Sci.* 1982;37(2):191.
56. Smith DC: The rise and fall of typhomalarial fever, II. Decline and fall. *J Hist Med Allied Sci.* 1982;37(3):287.
57. U.S. Surgeon General's Office: *Report on the Origin and Spread of Typhoid Fever in U.S. Military Camps during the Spanish War of 1898.* Washington, D.C.: GPO, 1904.
58. *Medical and Surgical History*, Medical Section, vol. 1, Tables C, CXI.
59. Robinson PG: Four cases of cerebro-spinal meningitis. *Conf States Med Surg J.* 1865;2(2):33.
60. Moses GA: Epidemic cerbro-spinal meningitis. *Conf States Med Surg J.* 1864;1(8):113.
61. *Medical and Surgical History*, Medical Section, vol. 3, p. 857.
62. Ibid., pp. 853-54.

∾ 11 ∾

Nature's Scourges: Epidemic Diseases on Parade

It is very evident from Surgeon Blair's report that, if the command be left much longer in its present exposed, unprotected, and unprovided condition, the ordinary military commanders will be relieved soon of the further care of very many of the men, as they will have been placed by Generals Rheumatism, Diarrhea, Pneumonia, and Typhoid Fever beyond the reach of further human care.

– Brigadier-General Thomas J. Wood

CIVIL WAR SOLDIERS SUFFERED GREATLY from a variety of infectious diseases that were, at the time, very common. We still experience some of them, such as the diarrheal illnesses. Others, such as malaria and yellow fever, have become rare in North America, and the world is now free of smallpox. During the Civil War, though, these diseases decimated both the civilian and military population.

DIARRHEA AND DYSENTERY

Among the medical problems suffered by Civil War troops, acute "diarrheal diseases" were by far the most common—as they have continued to be among armies up to the present time. Soldiers' diets and abysmal sanitary practices, as well as food spoilage, almost inevitably led to acute diarrhea, with its loose stools and frequent bowel movements. The miserable quality of the cooking didn't help; an attempt to designate men as cooks failed miserably. Most soldiers did their own cooking alone or as part of a small group. They usually fried their rations in lard, leading to physicians' fears of "death by frying pan."

Rations provided by both the army and unscrupulous vendors were of poor quality. And without refrigeration, any fresh food rapidly spoiled. This exacerbated the problem, resulting in what we now recognize as staphylococcal food poisoning. In one incident of probable food poisoning, two regiments suddenly became ill following their consumption of a "delicious pudding."[1] Even foraging for fresh fruit wasn't safe; soldiers contracted diarrhea after eating unripe fruit. When the men shared their rations, as they often did during campaigns when they were issued several days-worth of rations at a time, they also shared their diarrhea.

Civil War physicians generally used the terms "diarrhea" and "dysentery" to mean the same thing. Some used "dysentery" to mean an urgent need to defecate; to others it meant blood in the stools. The authors of *Medical and Surgical History* could not clarify this ambiguity and used the diagnostic terms the surgeons submitted. Recognizing the confusion, however, they combined the two diagnoses when discussing this illness. Among Union troops, there were 1,528,098 reported cases of acute diarrhea and dysentery. Among Confederate soldiers, each of whom had five or six illnesses a year, diarrhea and dysentery were the most common.[2]

Fortunately, in view of their extremely high rate of occurrence, acute diarrhea and dysentery were relatively benign diseases. Compared to most other diseases, they had low case-fatality rates (the percentage of individuals with a disease who died). Of those with acute diarrhea, only 3 men of every 1,000 afflicted died and for those cases labeled "dysentery," 17 of every 1,000 men died. Together they caused a total of 7,007 deaths among Union forces. Soldiers suffering from diarrhea or dysentery had to attend to their "urgent calls of nature," and literally became sitting ducks. However, many men were undoubtedly saved from being shot by the unwritten rule (honored by both sides) not to shoot a man while he was in that position.

The reported incidence of acute diarrhea and dysentery was highest in the war's first months, and peaked again during the beginning of 1863 when black soldiers began their service. For most of the war, however, the incidence of diarrheal diseases remained fairly constant, despite major improvements in sanitation. There was a small seasonal variation, with the highest incidence in summer and the lowest in winter. But not all cases were reported. Diarrhea was such a constant feature of army life that soldiers often did not report their

Quicker than the Trots

Soldiers had many names for diarrheal diseases. Southern troops simply called it "the Confederate disease."[3] Union soldiers in the East, for example, called diarrhea "The Virginia Quickstep," while the Western army called it the "Tennessee Trots." (The name changed to match the state they were in.)[4]

So badly did disease drain the Confederates' effective strength that when General Halleck's Union troops cautiously approached the Confederate base at Corinth, Mississippi, General Beauregard surreptitiously withdrew his ailing men from the area.[5] Surprised Union forces entered the town without a fight. Unfortunately, they used the same contaminated water supply and developed the same diseases. They called their diarrhea "the Evacuation of Corinth."

illness. For those who did, regimental physicians did not keep a record of their complaint unless they were ill enough to require hospitalization or removal from duty. Thus, there was a much higher incidence of diarrhea among Civil War soldiers than was officially recorded.

Acute diarrhea (and other diseases) had a profound effect. For example, enteric diseases were rampant for a few weeks after the Battle of Shiloh, the first huge conflict. Over two days, even though more men were killed and wounded at Shiloh than in the total of all previous wars the United States had fought, more soldiers died of disease immediately before and after the battle than during the fighting.

While the acute diarrheal diseases caused relatively few deaths, "chronic diarrhea" and "chronic dysentery" caused more fatalities than any other disease during the war: Of soldiers suffering from chronic diarrhea, 162 of every 1,000 died; for chronic dysentery, 126 of every 1,000 died. (See Chapter 14, *Chronic Diarrhea.*)

Civil War physicians treated diarrhea following practices of the time. They did not have intravenous and specific oral rehydration fluids or modern antibiotics. Their most effective, and most often administered, treatments were opiates (narcotics), usually in an alcoholic solution such as tincture of opium or paregoric, or as pills. (For constipation, physicians administered calomel, known as "blue mass.") A variety of other medicines were used, including turpentine.[6] A Confederate surgeon stated that during sick call,

> diagnosis was made by intuition, and treatment was with such drugs as we chanced to have in the knapsack. . . . On the march my own practice was further simplified, and was, in fact, reduced to the lowest terms. In one pocket of my trousers I had a ball of blue mass, in another a ball of opium. All complainants were asked the same question, "How are your bowels?" If they were open, I administered opium; if they were shut I gave a plug of blue mass.[7]

Today, many infectious agents are known to cause acute diarrhea/dysentery—and all probably did so during in the Civil War. These agents undoubtedly included *Salmonella, Shigella, Campylobacter, Escherichia coli*, among other causes of "traveler's diarrhea."

USE OF THE TERM "CHOLERA"

Cholera was called "Asiatic cholera" at the time of the Civil War, and it was the most deadly epidemic disease during the nineteenth century. However, there were no outbreaks of the true cholera in the United States during the war.

Civil War physicians did occasionally used the term "cholera" or "*cholera morbus*" to mean severe diarrhea, usually with vomiting, in their case records. The death rate for patients with the illness identified by these terms was relatively high: 10 deaths per 100 cases.

North America first suffered from cholera during the second pandemic of 1826–37. A fourth pandemic began in 1863, but it mainly affected Latin America and Asia.[8] Immediately after the war, the government established a quarantine blockade to prevent "the Asiatic cholera, now devastating the shores of the Mediterranean," from entering the United States.[9] The adjutant general reported that:

> Well-grounded apprehensions of the appearance of Asiatic cholera as an epidemic early in the present [fiscal] year [which began July 1, 1865] required prompt action for the protection of our troops. A rigid military quarantine was established on the southern Atlantic Coast and sanitary precautions enforced. The adoption of these measures availed to control or eradicate the disease at the recruiting depots and forts where it appeared before it assumed its usual alarming epidemic form; and official recognition has been given to the meritorious services of medical officers whose fidelity, energy, and skillful administration succeeded in averting or diminishing the horrors of widespread pestilence.[10]

JAUNDICE

Epidemic jaundice, another disease spread by poor sanitation, was common during the Civil War, but few deaths were recorded. Most recognized cases were probably due to viral hepatitis, a relatively benign disease. During the second year of the war, about 50 of every 1,000 men became jaundiced; only about half this number were diagnosed in subsequent years. However, everyone with hepatitis does not become jaundiced, so there may actually have been many more cases than were recognized.

While improved sanitation may have contributed slightly to the decrease, it is more likely that virtually all veteran soldiers had been exposed to the disease and acquired immunity by the third year. In support of this theory, jaundice was not a common problem in the prisons, where sanitation was abysmal.

TUBERCULOSIS AND SCROFULA

Nineteenth- and early-twentieth-century Americans feared tuberculosis of the lungs ("consumption"), which became more prevalent as people gathered in large cities and large groups. It became an increasingly common cause of death in the pre-antibiotic era. Army physicians diagnosed it from the cough (especially if blood-streaked), weight loss, and by examination of the chest. Men with advanced cases could be spotted easily and they were rejected from service, even at the start of the war, as being unable to stand the rigors of military life. But many men in the early stages of the disease enlisted and were accepted for service. Once in the army, their tuberculosis (TB) progressed as a result of their exposure to stress, inclement weather, malnutrition, and other common diseases (especially measles). For white troops, tuberculosis became the most frequent reason for medical discharge from the army after gunshot wounds (see Table 11.1). Compounding the problem was the fact that tuberculosis was not thought to be contagious; infected soldiers were not isolated and the disease could spread to their comrades.

The incidence of TB in white troops peaked in the second year of the war. By the time of the 1863 army draft, many men were rejected due to consumption and the number of cases fell as fewer infected men were enlisted and soldiers with the disease were discharged (or died).

While consumption was diagnosed only slightly more often among black soldiers than among the white troops, black troops suffered more from another form of TB: scrofula. Often called "the King's Evil" in prior centuries,

TABLE 11.1
Medical Discharges from the Union Army (1861–66)*

Reason	Number of Soldiers Discharged	
	White Troops	Black Troops
Gunshot wound	33,458	751
Consumption	20,403	592
Chronic diarrhea	16,185	302
Debility	14,500	540
Rheumatism	11,799	874
Heart disease	10,636	161
Amputation	5,832	327

*Compiled from the certificates of disability.
Medical and Surgical History, Medical Section, vol. 1, pp. 646, 716.

physicians had used the term "scrofula" to mean any of a variety of lumps, including those of plague (buboes). While Civil War physicians occasionally used the term for any enlarged lymph nodes, they generally used "scrofula" to mean tuberculosis of the lymph nodes, mostly in the neck. As these nodes expanded, the caseous or cheesy pus characteristic of TB exuded through breaks in the overlying skin. Scrofula affected more than five times as many black soldiers as it did white soldiers. Why was that?

There are two possible explanations for the high incidence in blacks. First, the blacks, as slaves, may have had more exposure to the disease. Twentieth-century researchers found that scrofula primarily developed after drinking unpasteurized milk from cows infected with bovine tuberculosis, and that cattle in the United States were commonly infected. The high frequency of scrofula in the black troops might mean that while in slavery, blacks were given milk from sickly cows. Around the time of the Civil War, there were many more cattle in the South in relation to the population than in the North, although fewer were dairy cattle. Tellingly, Southern dairy cows were described as "starvelings" and produced less milk per head than those in the North, suggesting they might have been sick.[11]

The second reason is that black troops may have been infected with an atypical type of tubercle bacillus. These organisms, usually found in the soil, are especially common in the southeastern states. They frequently cause the painless lymph node swelling that is characteristic of scrofula.

During the Civil War, about 7 out of every 1,000 black soldiers died of tuberculosis each year. For comparison, in 1867, only 3.4 black civilians died each year for every 1,000 living in Charleston, South Carolina. By 1876, however, the black civilian death rate rose to 7 per 1,000, the same as in the black soldiers. During this same period, the death rate from tuberculosis among the white civilians in Charleston was about 2 per 1,000 each year. The greater susceptibility of blacks than whites to tuberculosis was well-documented in the later nineteenth and early twentieth centuries.[12,13]

MALARIA

With almost a million cases recorded among Union forces alone, malaria, officially called the "intermittent fevers," was second in frequency only to diarrhea and dysentery (see Table 11.2). The incidence of malaria varied with the region soldiers occupied and the season of the year. Once acquired, malaria naturally recurs. So, gradually, an increasing number of soldiers began suffering from recurrent malaria. The typical chills and fever of malaria became so common that one soldier wrote home saying that if the Union forces could synchronize their chills, they could shake the rebels into submission.[14]

Most soldiers with malaria would improve and appear normal for one or more days between the bouts of shaking chills (rigors) and high fevers. This unusual pattern, appropriately, gave rise to the official diagnostic term of "intermittent fevers." The disease was classified according to the frequency of chills: "quotidian" when chills occurred once daily, "tertian" for chills

TABLE 11.2
Incidence of All Intermittent Fevers (Malaria)
(July 1, 1861–June 30, 1865)

	Total Number of Cases	Number of Cases per Thousand Men per Year*	Total Number of Deaths
White Troops	838,619	1,794	3,996
Black Troops	78,866	1,237	764

*Note: The incidence per thousand men per year was derived from the total number of cases, divided by the average yearly strength for four years in white troops and two years in black troops. Additional cases, not included in the table, occurred after July 1, 1865, bringing the total number of recorded cases to 1,028,750. *Thus, malaria accounted for almost 16% of the 6.5 million episodes of illnesses recorded among Union soldiers.*

Medical and Surgical History, Medical Section, vol. I, numerous tables.

every other day, and "quartan" for chills every third day. (This nomenclature, based on the days between chills, seems confusing. It was originally introduced in the Hippocratic era and counted the day of a chill both as the first day of a new cycle and also the last day of the prior cycle.)

Contemporary observers thought that the Confederate forces had a higher incidence of malaria than the Union armies. This belief might be explained by the higher percentage of soldiers from areas where the disease was endemic. General Ulysses S. Grant's Western forces had the highest incidence of malaria of any Union army. The number of cases in Grant's troops peaked in June, July, and August of 1863; physicians identified, respectively, 116, 136, and 130 malaria cases per thousand troops *per month*. This was just before and after the fall of Vicksburg, during which time the men were exposed to the swamps along the Mississippi River.

The rarest and most malignant form, "congestive intermittent fever," must have been what is today termed "falciparum malaria." It was diagnosed in 2.1% of the cases in black troops and 1.2% in the white troops. This deadly variety caused the bulk of the fatalities from malaria (86% of the deaths among the black troops, 79% among the white forces). Even today, with modern antimalarial drugs, it remains the most difficult to treat and the most deadly.

SMALLPOX

While smallpox occurred throughout the war, a major pandemic struck the United States in 1863, causing widespread disease in both armies. Clara Barton reported that in 1863, the disease swept through the Union forces on Hilton Head Island and the surrounding occupied areas.[15] Consistent with their belief that smallpox was contagious and that isolation or quarantine was necessary to minimize the spread of the disease, whenever possible the medical corps established separate hospital units, sometimes called "pest houses," for infected soldiers. Fear of the disease motivated more people in the United States to be vaccinated during that autumn and the following winter (1863–64), than had ever been immunized in a comparable period of time.[16]

Black troops suffered disproportionately from smallpox. While 5.2 out of every 1,000 white soldiers became infected each year, 35.1 out of every 1,000 black soldiers acquired the disease. During the most severe epidemic period (July 1, 1863 to June 30, 1864), the incidence among white troops only rose to 7.4 cases per 1,000, while black troops, then in their first year of active service, suffered at more than eight times that rate—61.1 cases per

1,000 men. This much higher incidence among the black soldiers suggests both that they had not been vaccinated when they were slaves, and that the policy of vaccinating newly enlisted troops without vaccination scars was not enforced in this group. After the war, a prominent physician in Mobile, Alabama, recorded that

> a large proportion of them [the former slaves] had never been vaccinated, scarcely any vaccinated, and they therefore afforded an unprecedented amount of material for the disease. Fully nine out of ten of the deaths from smallpox have been among the Freedmen.[17]

In May and June 1861, shortly after President Lincoln issued his call for volunteers, army physicians reported a relatively large number of smallpox cases without any fatalities.[18] Since the disease had a high case-fatality rate during the rest of the war, these early cases were most likely misdiagnosed: rather than smallpox, they were probably chickenpox. (Measles and mumps became epidemic—and were diagnosed—among the newly militarized recruits, but other childhood diseases, such as chickenpox, pertussis, and whooping cough, must also have been common. Neither was listed in the official records of diagnoses and thus no records were kept of their frequency, but one Confederate commander recognized that whooping cough had infected his troops.)[19]

Smallpox Vaccination

To prevent epidemics, the army's policy was to vaccinate all recruits who had not already had smallpox or a vaccination prior to entering active duty. Unfortunately, this was not always enforced. Additionally, some of those who had been vaccinated had received inactive vaccine. Civil War soldiers feared both smallpox and the vaccination to prevent the disease. It is easy to understand their fear of smallpox, since its case-fatality rate was 20% to 40%. But it is harder for us today to understand why vaccination generated so much fear.

The fear of vaccination was understandable given the sources of vaccine in the mid-nineteenth century. Vaccines were often ineffective and could themselves cause illness. In civilian life, children were first vaccinated with material taken directly from a lesion on the udder of a cow or a calf infected with cowpox, which was caused by a virus similar enough to smallpox to confer immunity. (See Figure 11.1.) Liquid obtained from the children's lesions, called "lymph," was then inserted into adults' arms by making deep, painful gouges with a knife, which, of course, was not sterilized. Liquid from the adults' lesions was then used to inject others. In the army, soldiers often vaccinated each other.

Figure 11.1: Private Leander E. Villers, photographed when recovering from small-pox. Note the numerous lesions on the face. The innumerable scars left by smallpox probably contributed to the popularity of beards. (Courtesy of Chris Jordan Collection at USAMHI.)

The lack of sterility often resulted in severe local infections which often caused death from "blood poisoning." In her memoirs, hospital matron Phoebe Pember gave an excellent portrayal of the complications that could develop after vaccination:

> They were dreadfully afflicted objects, many of them with sores so deep and thick upon arms and legs that amputation had to be resorted to save life. As fast as the eruption would be healed in one spot, it would break out in another, for the blood seemed entirely poisoned.[20]

Pember also noted that the poor nutritional status of some of the Confederate soldiers was a predisposing factor.

While the army often instituted mass vaccinations after a smallpox epidemic had begun, some of the "lymph" obtained from soldiers actually contained virulent smallpox virus, rather than cowpox—this accelerated the epidemic. Syphilis was another feared complication of vaccination, since it could be transmitted through the "lymph" taken from soldiers with active syphilis. Several outbreaks of syphilis were recorded following troop vaccinations. In one such episode, the military effectiveness of a Union militia unit in Missouri was seriously impaired, as their colonel reported: "The command at La Fayette is so weakened by syphilis (from vaccination) that they cannot furnish many men for scouting purposes."[21] Some Civil War surgeons appropriately blamed this on "spurious vaccination," meaning complications arising after "indiscriminate vaccination and revaccination from arm to arm."[22]

It was difficult to obtain enough "vaccine matter" for the large number of men. When smallpox appeared in Fayetteville, Arkansas, for example, a Confederate colonel described his plans for acquiring an adequate quantity of the vaccine (and revealed his misunderstanding of the nature of the cowpox [*vaccinia*] virus):

> I have also issued orders to all the surgeons of my brigade to save all reliable vaccine matter . . . The medical director of the division is also using his efforts to obtain reliable matter from the inoculation of the cow with real small-pox virus. I trust that with precaution the disease will be arrested at once.[23]

Smallpox Vaccination in One Regiment

After the war, Surgeon Albert Gaillard Hart described his efforts to protect his newly formed regiment of volunteers from Ohio against smallpox:

> While at our camp of rendezvous, in September 1861, my commanding officer, after much urging on my part, issued an order for the vaccination of the entire regiment. This was bitterly opposed by the men at the time, but they afterwards fully appreciated its value. It was thoroughly enforced, and many complete vaccine pustules and a multitude of incomplete ones resulted. The old Jennerian virus was used, bovine virus not having been introduced at that time. The result was complete immunity from smallpox on the part of the regiment, after repeated exposure, where regiments around us, not revaccinated, suffered severely from the disease.[24]

[Presumably, by "Jennerian virus," Hart meant material originating in a cow lesion but subsequently passed from arm to arm. After the turn of the century, pharmaceutical companies began to prepare vaccine material, taking it directly from calves under sterile conditions to produce relatively clean vaccine that had not been passed from arm to arm.]

SMALLPOX IN THE PRISONS

Smallpox plagued prisons on both sides of the conflict despite their policy of vaccinating all prisoners who lacked the appropriate scars. The ineffective vaccines did not prevent the disease from recurring every time a new group of prisoners arrived.[25] Smallpox was particularly pervasive at the Federal prison near Alton, Illinois. In July 1863, the acting surgeon general suggested the use of cleanliness, disinfection, and isolation, in addition to vaccination. The prison's director finally got permission to purchase a lot two miles from the prison, where he could isolate diseased prisoners. Over the strenuous objections of area residents, he set up a "pest hospital" in tents and used contract physicians to care for the sick prisoners. The situation improved.[26]

New prisoners were constantly brought into many prisons despite smallpox outbreaks. After the war, this practice resulted in accusations of "biological warfare." The charge was raised during a post-war Congressional Committee inquiry into the treatment of Union prisoners of war (POWs) by the Confederates. Former Confederates made similar claims against the Union, asserting that at Camps Alton, Morton, Douglas, and Chase (located in Illinois, Indiana, and Ohio), the "inhuman practice of putting our prisoners into camps infected by smallpox prevailed. It was equivalent to murdering many of them by the torture of a contagious disease."[27] In fact, if an effective, potent vaccine had been available, the measures that were taken would have controlled the disease. And, while accusations and counteraccusations were unrestrained, there is no evidence that anyone on either side intended to harm the prisoners.

When Federal prisoners arrived at Chimborazo Hospital, they received smallpox vaccinations of the same material used on Confederate soldiers, and many subsequently developed complications. After the war, Confederate medical officers were blamed for purposely using "spurious vaccine," equivalent to the modern charge of using "biological warfare." In reality, the same complications also occurred among Confederate troops. Captain Henry Wirz, the commandant of the Confederate prison camp at Andersonville, was convicted in the only "war crimes" trial resulting from the Civil War. One of the accusations against Wirz concerned the deaths that followed prisoners' smallpox vaccinations. Wirz and the Confederate medical staff denied that the complications resulted from a purposeful use of contaminated vaccine. Apparently, the vaccine used was of ordinary, that is, poor, quality.

When Confederate Surgeon General Moore asked Dr. Joseph Jones to look into the problem of "spurious vaccination," he found that vaccine material contaminated with infectious syphilis and malnutrition among those

President Lincoln Gets Smallpox

On November 19, 1863, after giving what became known as the "Gettysburg Address" while dedicating the National Cemetery at Gettysburg, President Lincoln developed a severe headache during his train ride back to Washington. He arrived at the White House around 1 A.M. and went to bed complaining of "pain in head and back, fever and general malaise." Two days later, a rash appeared. Lincoln's family doctor diagnosed the illness first as a cold, later as "bilious fever," and then, after the rash appeared, as "scarlatina." Smallpox was diagnosed only after Dr. van Bibber was called in from Baltimore to consult.

Since the president's rash was "small and widely scattered," and no doubt because they wished to minimize the gravity of the situation (a type of "spin control" that presidents' doctors would repeatedly use in subsequent administrations), Lincoln's doctors said he was suffering from "varioloid." That term usually described a mild case of smallpox that appeared in previously vaccinated people whose immunity had waned sufficiently to allow a mild illness to develop. There is no mention anywhere, however, of Lincoln ever having been vaccinated. Mild though his rash apparently was, the president was ill until mid-December.

Meanwhile, the White House was placed under what one person on the staff called "penetrable quarantine." The president worked on his annual message to Congress and continued to see selected people, including members of his Cabinet, when he felt well enough. Some among the ever-present crowd of office seekers reportedly fled the White House when they found out which disease Mr. Lincoln had. Others, mindful that the president "could appoint [them] today and die tomorrow," were more persistent. Referring to the still-filled waiting room in the White House, the president remarked to a visitor, "There is one good thing about this. I now have something I can give everybody."[28]

immunized caused many of the complications. In the prisons, he found that the widespread scurvy was often to blame. (The medical aspects of the trial are discussed further in Chapter 15, *Prison Camps*.) Later, Jones wrote: "In 1863, I examined about two hundred cases of spurious vaccination in the general hospitals of Richmond, Virginia, collected chiefly from General Lee's army, and traced the abnormal manifestations to chiefly secondary syphilis and scurvy."[29]

TREATING SMALLPOX

Although no treatment for smallpox existed, Civil War-era physicians tried their best. An 1864 report on smallpox among Confederates imprisoned at Rock Island, Illinois, described the disappointing results of the treatments recommended in the medical literature. The author, Dr. R. M. Lackey, gave the standard therapy used for all diseases: open the bowels and give an emetic, if there is much nausea, "to assist in freely unloading the stomach," Dover's powders (which contained opium) for restlessness and insomnia, and "quinine, iron, wine egg-nogg [sic] and nourishing diet." The article reported his results when he tried these treatments on smallpox.

Dr. Lackey recorded that the skin lesions often became infected with erysipelas (due to streptococci), and he would treat them with "local and constitutional use of iodine and bromine." These treatments were thought to be effective against erysipelas and hospital gangrene during the war and were widely used for the next fifty years. Dr. Lackey noted that a large proportion of the men had ostensibly been vaccinated and he concluded that "the virus furnished the Medical Department of the [Union] Army is often worthless and harmful."[30] (Treatment for smallpox is no longer needed, since a United Nations vaccination program has eliminated the disease worldwide.)

YELLOW FEVER

Ever since its first appearance in the Western Hemisphere during the seventeenth century, yellow fever epidemics occurred with distressing regularity in U.S. coastal cities, particularly in Southern ports. Yellow fever reappeared almost every summer, and was one of the most feared epidemics of the time. These epidemics killed from 20% to 50% of those taken ill; often 10% to 20% of a city's populace died of the disease. Although Union officers worried that troops occupying Southern ports would be exposed to the devastating disease, only a few small outbreaks occurred. This spared both the local citizens and the invading Yankee troops. During the entire war, 1,355 yellow fever cases were diagnosed among Union troops, with 436 deaths.[31]

Yellow fever is a form of fulminating viral hepatitis characterized by severe jaundice (the skin coloration gave the disease its name), hemorrhages, and the excretion of large amounts of protein in the urine. It is transmitted from person to person in urban areas by a species of mosquitoes, *Aedes aegypti*. Outbreaks usually began in cities after a ship arrived carrying infected passengers. Typically, the ship had stopped in the West Indies, the

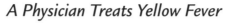

A Physician Treats Yellow Fever

Assistant Surgeon W. F. Cornick described his yellow fever treatment, used during an outbreak in North Carolina:

> As soon as the patient is attacked with symptoms of fever he is placed to his chin in a hot bath containing four to eight ounces of mustard until he gets into a profuse perspiration or complains of being faint; he is then put in bed and between blankets and fifteen to twenty grains of calomel are administered, followed in four hours by an ounce or two of castor oil. By the time the oil has had a good effect his pulse as a rule has become almost natural, though in many cases quite frequent. I then give him ten grains of quinine every hour until he has taken two doses, after which five grains every two hours until he complains of ringing in the ears or other indications of the action of the remedy. I also give sweet spirits of nitre to keep the kidneys in good working order, from the derangement of which we have so much to fear. Should the patient after this complain of gastric uneasiness I give, as a preventative of black vomit, one drop of creosote in the form of a pill; this has been attended with the happiest results, sometimes even after black vomit has made its appearance. If the patient complains of much uneasiness about the stomach I generally resort to sinapisms, which will in most instances give relief. After this he is treated upon general principles.[32,33]

site of the most frequent epidemics. After a few weeks, cases would begin to appear among the city's residents. When news of an epidemic broke, people would flee, often leaving behind a ghost town without enough healthy residents to care for the sick and bury the dead. Fleeing refugees often were denied admission to nearby towns, since their citizens were afraid of developing the disease themselves.

No effective treatment for yellow fever existed. *Medical and Surgical History* reports some use of the "water cure," or hydropathic medicine, that was popular at the time, as well as some attempts at symptomatic relief. The most feared complication was for the kidneys to shut down, now called "hepatorenal syndrome," an ominous development that usually leads to death.

NEW ORLEANS AND YELLOW FEVER

New Orleans was severely affected by yellow fever before the Civil War, with outbreaks occurring in late summer almost every year. The epidemics increased steadily in intensity and virulence, and reached their peak during the 1850s. In 1853, for example, between 8,000 and 9,000 people died of yellow fever. Severe epidemics also occurred in 1854 and 1855; in 1858, another 5,000 people died from "the yellow jack."

To the surprise of citizens of New Orleans, there was almost no yellow fever in the city during the war. During 1861, Union ships blockaded the entrance to the Mississippi River, an effective form of quarantine. In April 1862, Union forces under Adm. David Glasgow Farragut forced their way past the forts guarding the entrances to New Orleans and, by yellow fever season, the Union army occupied the city.

After the "Crescent City" fell, a Union physician wrote: "the Southern press at once endeavored to soothe the feelings of the people by assuring them that they had an ally in Yellow fever, which would soon drive the Union army from the soil of Louisiana."[34] Locals knew that visitors were more susceptible to the disease than they were, probably because many of them had survived previous epidemics and acquired immunity. General Benjamin Butler recorded that

> the rebels are relying largely on yellow fever to clear out northern troops . . . whom they had learned from experience were usually the first victims of the scourge . . . [I heard] that in the churches prayers were put up that the pestilence might come as a divine interposition on behalf of the brethren.[35]

The native population did their best to keep Yankee soldiers in fear of yellow fever. Within hearing of Union officers, they would speak of previous epidemics; and even measured soldiers at random, explaining that there was a contract to provide 10,000 coffins. Children playing in the street would chant, "Yellow jack will grab them up and take them all away." As a result, Gen. Butler was deluged with requests using every possible excuse for transfers or leaves.[36]

General Butler and his medical officers were justifiably worried that yellow fever would return and decimate their forces. The chief surgeon of Admiral Farragut's fleet, Dr. Jonathan M. Foltz, sent Butler a letter urging "a strict quarantine and positive non-intercourse with ports where yellow fever existed." Butler had already appointed a physician as his own quarantine officer with the following instructions: "In this matter your orders shall be absolute. Order off all you may think proper, and so long as you keep yellow fever away from New Orleans your salary shall be [paid]. When yellow fever appears in this city, your pay shall cease."[37]

The quarantine meant that all vessels entering the river were required to stop below the quarantine station for inspection. If yellow fever was thought to be on board, the vessel was held for forty days (the classic term from which the name "quarantine" was derived, dating from the era of the plague epidemics in fourteenth-century Europe). Any vessel that had been in ports afflicted by yellow fever was kept in quarantine for the full forty days, regardless of the inspection findings. To enforce these restrictions, General Butler ordered that any ship that tried to evade the quarantine should be fired on.

Butler instituted other measures to keep out the "seeds" of contagion. Based on the "miasma" theory of disease origin, he ordered that any debris and decaying animal matter in the streets be cleaned up to prevent spreading disease. The French market near the waterfront was particularly filthy: for decades, spoiled produce and refuse from butcher shops had been thrown on the street and ground into the dirt. Butler ordered the market scrubbed and washed until it was clean and free of odors. He also saw to it that the drains and ditches in the city were cleaned, the streets were flushed by the water works, and a system of refuse collection was established. (See Figure 11.2.) The sanitary regulations were strictly enforced and violators threatened with imprisonment. While mosquitoes were not suspected as disease vectors, these sanitary measures had the unplanned effect of decreasing areas where mosquitoes could breed, thus diminishing the likelihood of yellow fever, malaria, and dengue fever.

No "Thank You" for General Butler

Benjamin Franklin Butler, a lawyer and legislator from Massachusetts, was the first politician President Lincoln appointed to the rank of major general. After New Orleans was captured, he was made military governor of Louisiana. His policies and harsh reaction to insults directed at Union troops led the locals to call him "Beast Butler."

He bragged about his success in keeping yellow fever out of New Orleans, but residents of the city refused to give him any credit. They attributed the absence of the disease to divine intervention, saying (in Creole) that God was merciful and would not send them both General Butler and yellow fever at the same time.[38]

Figure 11.2: Cartoon showing General Benjamin Butler reporting to President Lincoln after his tour of duty in New Orleans. His success in preventing a yellow fever epidemic in that city was attributed to his cleaning up the filth in the markets along the riverfront. (*HW*)

Butler thus combined quarantine and sanitary measures, the two theories of disease prevention that had been practiced for centuries. These measures remained in force throughout the Union occupation and no yellow fever appeared in New Orleans during the war. In 1864, Union physician George M. Sternberg wrote that Southerners had believed the Union occupation of

New Orleans would be temporary because of the disease but "two summers have now passed, and their hopes have been disappointed."[39] Interestingly, Sternberg later became an early leader in the field of bacteriology in the United States and, as surgeon general, appointed the army commission headed by Dr. Walter Reed that firmly established the mosquito's role in the etiology of yellow fever after the Spanish-American War.

New Orleans' first post-war yellow fever epidemic in occurred in 1867, and epidemics recurred until 1905, when knowledge of the mosquito's role in transmission led to effective preventive measures.[40,41]

OUTBREAKS IN OTHER CITIES

Yellow fever did appear in some port cities occupied by Union forces during the war, including Galveston, Pensacola, Key West, and New Bern. A small outbreak occurred in Hilton Head, South Carolina, and the surrounding areas after troops from the 7th New Hampshire arrived from Key West, where the disease had been introduced by a ship from Havana.[42] Union Maj. Gen. Ormsby M. Mitchel, who had been an internationally famous astronomer, mathematician, and lecturer before the war, succumbed to the Hilton Head epidemic after leading an expedition inland to interrupt the Charleston-to-Savannah railroad. He died of yellow fever on October 30, 1862, after an illness of only four days.[43] Confederates in Charleston and Wilmington also noted some yellow fever cases during the war years, thus documenting the incomplete nature of the blockade, but the outbreaks were limited, which suggests that *Aedes* mosquitoes were not present to act as vectors to spread the disease.

Occasionally, yellow fever determined how the war should be fought. For example, a serious outbreak of yellow fever occurred in Wilmington, North Carolina, in the summer and fall of 1862, despite the Federal blockade. The skipper of the USS *Victoria* reported on September 17 that "the yellow fever is prevailing at Wilmington. There have been 15 deaths. It was introduced by the steamer Kate, from Nassau." On November 29, Lt. W. S. Cushing, the skipper of the USS *Helzel*, reported that "the yellow fever has nearly disappeared in Wilmington." Finally, on December 8, U.S. Navy Comdr. William A. Parker notified Maj. Gen. J. G. Foster, commander of the U.S. Army forces in the Department of North Carolina, that the end of the yellow fever epidemic made the time right for an attack on Wilmington. "In my opinion," he stated, "the present moment is the best time to attack Wilmington and the adjacent forts. . . . The yellow fever has entirely disappeared."[44]

Military Intelligence from the Newspapers

General Lee frequently scanned Northern newspapers obtained from captured soldiers within a day or two of publication, usually correctly interpreting what he read in them.

In the spring of 1863, Lee read in Northern papers of a yellow fever outbreak in North Carolina, and mistakenly thought that the news was planted in the papers to mislead Confederate commanders about the intentions of Union forces.

Lee wrote to Jefferson Davis on June 25, 1863:

> I have observed that extracts from the Northern journals contained in the Richmond papers of the 22nd instant, state that yellow fever has appeared in New Berne [sic], and that in consequence the Federal troops are being moved back to Morehead City. If in fact the fever is in New Berne, it would tend of itself to prevent active operations from that point. But as I have never heard of the disease being in that city, and as it does not generally break out so early in the season, even in localities which are subject to it, I am disposed to doubt the truth of that statement, and regard it as a cover for the withdrawal of the enemy's forces for some other field.[45]

Another epidemic of yellow fever occurred in Union-occupied New Bern in September, October, and November of 1864. (The name of the town usually was spelled "Newbern" at the time of the war.) It attacked 571 Union soldiers, causing 278 deaths (48.7%) among the troops stationed there, a typical fatality rate for the disease.[46]

THE FEDERAL AND CONFEDERATE NAVIES

Yellow fever constantly threatened sailors who visited ports with the disease. During the war, the usual late summer-early fall yellow fever outbreaks struck the Caribbean and Eastern Atlantic islands, including Bermuda, Nassau, Havana, Puerto Rico, Haiti, the Virgin Islands, and the Windward Islands. Yellow fever markedly altered naval strategies in the Civil War as the sailing plans of both Federal and Confederate ships were constantly altered by reports of disease at ports they intended to visit. On August 23, 1864, the commander of the USS *Cuyler* reported that when he arrived at Bermuda in search of the Confederate raider *Tallahassee*, he

> [anchored] outside of the harbor of St. George, sending in a boat with Lieutenant Commander Norton and Acting Assistant Paymaster Wright to communicate and gather all possible intelligence. At noon the boat returned with the U.S. Consul on board, and reported yellow fever raging with great violence on shore, many deaths occurring daily. Mr. Norton very properly returned on board at once upon receiving this intelligence, without entering the town. Upon their return on board, I at once got underway and stood out to sea, the consul returning to the shore in the pilot boat . . . On account of the ravages of yellow fever, the consul declared the blockade-running business from Bermuda to be at an end for the season.[47]

The consul reported that due to the epidemic, the blockade-runners had transferred their base of operations to Halifax, Nova Scotia.

Similarly, Commander S. Nicholson, captain of the USS *Galatea*, wisely chose an anchorage in Haiti that minimized the likelihood of "miasmas" bringing yellow fever to his ship. It was an effective strategy in that it minimized the chance of mosquitoes, and thus yellow fever, reaching his vessel. On November 28, 1864, he wrote to the secretary of the navy:

> While at Cape Haitien I learned that a number of cases of yellow fever (mostly fatal) had recently occurred among the French shipping in port . . . it is confined entirely to the French vessels in port, and was brought there by them from some of the Windward Islands; but for security I anchored well clear and to windward of all shipping.[48]

The following year, yellow fever affected the sailing plans of Capt. Charles S. Boggs of the USS *Connecticut* in the Caribbean. He reported from Cape Haitien on March 6, 1865, that "It was my intention to have proceeded hence via St. Johns [San Juan], Puerto Rico, to St. Thomas for coal, but the U.S. consul at this place informs me that the yellow fever is raging at that port; consequently, I shall not visit St. Thomas."[49]

When yellow fever appeared at Union-occupied Key West, naval forces in ports further north enforced strict quarantines. On August 16, 1862, Maj. Gen. David Hunter, army commandant at Hilton Head, advised the commander of the South Atlantic Blockading Squadron, Adm. Samuel F. DuPont:

> Admiral: I have lately received information that yellow fever of a malignant type prevails at Key West. As vessels from that place are likely to seek to enter this port, I deem it of the last importance that rigid quarantine regulations be established and enforced, and I respectfully invite your

cooperation in securing that end. I shall detail a medical officer who will be instructed to board every vessel seeking to enter this port from the South, and shall require all vessels amenable to my authority to observe such quarantine as that officer may recommend.[50]

Admiral DuPont replied two days later, "I need hardly add that I shall cooperate with you most earnestly in carrying out your views on this important subject."[51]

There was at least one outbreak of yellow fever aboard a Confederate ship, the CSS *Florida*. (The same vessel that eventually became one of the most successful and feared of the raiders that preyed on Federal shipping.) On August 17, 1862, at the height of yellow fever season, a newly built British ship, the *Oreto*, sailed from Nassau in the Bahamas and was turned over to Confederate naval Lieutenant John Newland Maffitt at Green Key. He recommissioned the ship as the CSS *Florida*, but yellow fever immediately appeared in members of the crew. Maffitt and most of the crew became desperately ill, and at least one person died. Having no pilot on board, he decided to risk sailing past the Federal blockade off Mobile during daylight. A Federal ship challenged them, and Maffitt at first hoisted British colors, but then hauled them down and, sailing into Mobile Bay, outran his pursuers. In January 1863, the ship, with a new crew, set out on its legendary twenty-month tour to destroy Federal shipping.[52]

In a few instances, individual yellow fever cases appeared on American ships during or shortly after visiting a port affected with the disease. Since yellow fever occurs in huge epidemics, a single case probably indicates that the crew member became infected while visiting ashore, developed the disease after reboarding the ship, but did not bring any mosquitoes capable of spreading the disease with him. Without *Aedes aegypti* aboard, no new cases would appear.

REFERENCES

1. Macfarlane C. Quoted in: Steiner PE: *Disease in the Civil War: Natural Biological Warfare in 1861–65*. Springfield, IL: C.C. Thomas, 1968, p. 19.
2. Jones J: Medical history of the Confederate states army and navy. *South Hist Soc Papers*. 1892;20:109-66.
3. Foote S: *The Civil War: A Narrative*. vol. 1. New York: Random House, 1958, p. 664.
4. Wiley BI: *The Life of Billy Yank: The Common Soldier of the Union*. Baton Rouge: Louisiana State Univ. Press, 1952, p. 136; and Robertson JI: *Soldiers Blue and Gray*. Columbia: Univ. South Carolina Press, 1988, p. 150.
5. Foote, *Civil War*, vol. 1, pp. 381-86.
6. *Medical and Surgical History*, Medical Section, vol. 2, pp. 816-21.
7. Adams GW: Confederate medicine. *J South Hist*. 1940;6:151-88.

8. Evans RJ: Cholera in nineteenth-century Europe. In: Ranger TO, Slack P, eds.: *Epidemics and Ideas: Essays on the Historical Perception of Pestilence.* Cambridge: Cambridge Univ. Press, 1992, p. 151.

9. Jos K. Barnes, Surgeon General, to Hon. E.M. Stanton, Secretary of War. In: Annual Report of the Secretary of War for FY 1865. NARA, Microfilm M997, pp. 894-97.

10. Townsend ED. In: *O.R.* Series III, vol. V, p. 1034.

11. Gates PW: *Agriculture and the Civil War.* New York: Knopf, 1965, pp. 7-8.

12. Mays TJ: Human slavery as a prevention of pulmonary consumption. *Trans Am Climatological Assoc.* 1904;20:192-97.

13. Zinsser H: *Infection and Resistance.* 2nd ed. New York: Macmillan, 1918.

14. Wiley, *Life of Billy Yank,* p. 142.

15. Oates SB: *A Woman of Valor: Clara Barton and the Civil War.* New York: Macmillan, 1994, p. 193.

16. Gillett MC: *The United States Army Medical Department, 1818–1865.* Washington, D.C.: Center of Military History, U.S. Army, 1987, p. 278.

17. Nott JC: Smallpox epidemic in Mobile during the winter of 1865-6. *Nashville Med Surg J.* N.S. 1867;2:372-80.

18. *Medical and Surgical History,* Medical Section, vol. 1, Table III.

19. Gordon JB: *Reminiscences of the Civil War.* New York: Charles Scribner's Sons, 1905.

20. Pember P: *A Southern Woman's Story: Life in Confederate Richmond.* New York: G.W. Carleton, 1879.

21. Report of Col. John F. Williams, *O.R.* Series I, vol. XXXIV/4, p. 567.

22. Cunningham HH: *Doctors in Gray: The Confederate Medical Service.* Baton Rouge: Louisiana State Univ. Press, 1958, p. 201.

23. Report of Col. Louis Hebert to Maj. Gen. Sterling Price, January 22, 1862, *O.R.* Series I, vol. VIII, p. 738.

24. Hart AG: *The Surgeon and the Hospital in the Civil War.* Gaithersburg, MD: Olde Soldier Books, 1987 (orig. pub. 1902).

25. Report of Capt. H.W. Freedley. *O.R.* Series II, vol. V, p. 150.

26. Multiple reports. *O.R.* Series II, vol. VI, p. 104.

27. Report of Joint Select Committee of Congress appointed to investigate the condition and treatment of prisoners of war, March 3, 1865. *O.R.* Series II, vol. VIII, p. 348.

28. Hopkins DR: *Princes and Peasants: Smallpox in History.* Chicago: Univ. Chicago Press, 1983, p. 281.

29. Jones J: Observations upon the losses of the Confederate armies from battle, wounds and diseases, during the American Civil War of 1861–65, with investigations upon the number and character of the diseases supervening from gun-shot wounds. *Richmond Louisville Med J.* 1870;9:650.

30. Lackey RM: Some practical observations on smallpox vaccination. *Am Med Times.* 1864;8:236.

31. *Medical and Surgical History,* Medical Section, vol. 1, Tables 100, 111.

32. Mustard plasters are a mixture of mustard and flour applied on a cloth to the abdomen or chest to induce redness, and were considered a form of "counter-irritation."

33. *Medical and Surgical History,* Medical Section, vol. 3, p. 678.

34. Sternberg GM: Is yellow fever endemic in New Orleans? *Am Med Times.* 1864;8:197.

35. Butler BF: Some experiences with yellow fever and its prevention. *N Am Rev.* 1888;147(384):525-41.

36. Carrigan JA: Yankees vs. yellow jack in New Orleans, 1862–66. *Civil War Hist.* 1963;9:248-60.

37. Foltz CS: *Surgeon of the Seas: The Adventurous Life of Surgeon General Jonathan M. Foltz in the Days of Wooden Ships.* Indianapolis: Bobbs-Merrill, 1931, p. 253.

38. Carrigan, *Civil War Hist,* 1963.

39. Sternberg, *Am Med Times,* 1864.

40. Duffy J: Yellow fever in the continental United States during the nineteenth century. *NY Acad Med Bull.* 1968;44(6):687-701.
41. Carrigan, *Civil War Hist,* 1963.
42. Horner GRB: Notice of the yellow fever as it occurred at Key West and in the U.S. East Gulf Blockading Squadron in 1862. *Am J Med Sci.* 1863;46:391-98.
43. Smiley TT: The yellow fever at Port Royal, SC. *Boston Med Surg J.* 1863;67:449-68; Mitchel FA: *Ormsby Macknight Mitchel: Astronomer and General.* Boston: Houghton Mifflin, 1887.
44. *Navy O.R.,* Series I, vol. VIII, p. 263-64.
45. Lee RE: *The Wartime Papers of Robert E. Lee.* New York: Da Capo Press, 1987, p. 532.
46. Annual Report of Surgeon General Joseph K. Barnes, to Hon. E.M. Stanton, Secretary of War, for fiscal year 1865. (pp. 894-97 of Annual Report of Secretary of War). NARA, Microfilm 997, reels 12, 13.
47. *Navy O.R.,* Series I, vol. III, pp. 161-62.
48. Ibid., pp. 381-82.
49. Ibid., p. 447.
50. *Navy O.R.,* Series I, vol. XIII, p. 264.
51. Ibid,
52. Musicant I: *Divided Waters: The Naval History of the Civil War.* New York: Harper Collins, 1995, pp. 335-43.

๑ 12 ๑

Disease Among the Troops: Real, Imagined, and Imitated

During the winter [1862–63], when Hooker was in command . . . the head-quarters of the Army of the Potomac was a place to which no self-respecting man liked to go, and no decent woman could go. It was a combination of barroom and brothel.

— Charles Francis Adams, III, Captain, Union Army

MANY ILLNESSES AND HEALTH PROBLEMS AFFECTED CIVIL WAR TROOPS in addition to epidemic infectious diseases. For example, acute rheumatism, a serious disease at the time, was extremely common. Sexually transmitted diseases and psychiatric illnesses, problems observed in modern wars, were present. There were also the typical behavioral problems, often called "malingering," that are universal in wartime armies. This wide variety of maladies, some devastating and others simply annoying, plagued Civil War soldiers and confounded Civil War physicians.

ACUTE RHEUMATISM (ACUTE RHEUMATIC FEVER)

Civil War troops were devastated by "acute rheumatism" also known by the modern term "rheumatic fever." Union forces alone reported 155,049 cases. Between July 1, 1861, and June 30, 1865, 61.7 white soldiers out of every 1,000 suffered from the disease each year. Blacks were diagnosed at almost twice this rate, 111.3 cases per 1,000 soldiers per year. While this seems like an outlandishly high incidence for a disease that is now rarely seen in the United States, even as late as World War II, soldiers still suffered from rheumatic fever at about the same rate as during the Civil War.[1]

Although nineteenth-century physicians sometimes used the term "rheumatism" to describe generalized aches and pains, as well as non-inflammatory types of arthritis, Civil War physicians usually meant "acute rheumatic fever" when they used that diagnosis.

At the time of the Civil War, acute rheumatic fever was a serious disease that caused swelling, warmth, tenderness of major joints (hips, knees, ankles, shoulders, elbows, and wrists), and severe pain, especially with movement. It was especially common during the winter months, and generally lasted one or two months. As a contemporary medical textbook described, rheumatic fever was so devastating to the patient that it had to be differentiated from paralysis. With paralysis, the author wrote, the patient does not move the extremity because of lack of muscle function; in cases of rheumatism, "they dare not move" the extremity because it is too painful to do so.[2] However, by the mid-1960s, this disease as seen in the United States had become less intense, with milder symptoms and a shorter duration.

Rheumatism, generally meaning joint inflammation, was classified as a "constitutional" disease, a concept similar to today's concept of inherited susceptibility. (It is now known that inheritance is indeed a factor in the development of some rheumatic diseases.) But, Civil War physicians did not recognize the external precipitating causes of "acute rheumatism," such as sore throats. (It was almost a century before the relationship of antecedent streptococcal infection to rheumatic fever was unequivocally established.)

The only treatments available during the war were to give opiates for the severe joint pain and quinine or potassium iodide for their mild anti-inflammatory effect. Various baths and compresses were used, since they also had mild analgesic and anti-inflammatory actions. The first really effective anti-inflammatory agents, salicylates such as aspirin, would not be available for another decade.

Acute rheumatic fever affects internal organs as well, especially the heart. The sac around the heart often becomes inflamed (pericarditis). But the most serious, and long-lasting, effect is the inflammation of the heart's valves. This often leads to abnormal heart function and heart failure, and the most common form of heart disease detected in Civil War pre-enlistment physical examinations and the most frequent cause of medical discharges. The Union army listed valvular heart disease (3,778 cases) and acute inflammation of the pericardium (1,319 cases) diagnoses as separate entities. While it was not until 1889 that Dr. Walter Butler Cheadle fully described the nature of rheumatic fever, including the life-threatening involvement of the heart, Civil War physicians clearly knew that heart disease was associated with acute rheumatism.[3] Pericarditis and valvular pathology were both described in fatal cases of acute rheumatic fever, and physicians documented that "death [of patients with rheumatism] was generally due to an implication of the heart."[4]

Rheumatic fever rarely affects the brain. When it does, it produces Sydenham's chorea, also known as "St. Vitus's Dance." This form of chorea (involuntary writhing movements) occurs during the episode of rheumatic fever, usually after the joint inflammation has subsided. It is not a serious problem unless it is accompanied by other manifestations of rheumatic fever. It was not generally recognized as a result of rheumatic fever before the 1800s, but, by 1850, the connection between chorea and rheumatism was widely accepted. Some authorities, however, continued to question this relationship until well into the twentieth century.[5]

While Sydenham's chorea did occur in Civil War soldiers—it was observed at Turner's Lane Hospital in Philadelphia, which was devoted to nerve injuries and related diseases—there is almost no mention of it in the medical literature of the war. No cases were included in the tables in *Medical and Surgical History*, possibly because no one was hospitalized or relieved from duty because of this illness, and it is not clear whether Civil War physicians associated it with acute rheumatism. There are records of medical discharges for men with chorea, however. A total of 187 white and 5 black soldiers were discharged with "Surgeon's Certificates of Disability" listing this diagnosis during the war. It is possible that some cases of chorea were also misdiagnosed as malingering or epilepsy.

CHRONIC RHEUMATISM

Prolonged joint disease, or "chronic rheumatism," struck 105,853 white soldiers (46.6 cases per 1,000 men annually) and 10,956 black soldiers (81.6 cases per 1,000 men annually). Although the men had to demonstrate significant disability to be discharged, 11,503 white Union soldiers and 499 black soldiers had the diagnosis listed on their Certificates of Medical Discharge.

Unlike "acute rheumatism," the syndrome of "chronic rheumatism" was a vague entity, and many of the cases probably were really prolonged acute rheumatic fever. Although *Medical and Surgical History* acknowledges that acute rheumatism "sometimes passes into" the chronic form, it does not specify what justified calling it "chronic." Acute rheumatic fever, however, almost never leads to chronic, deforming, or disabling arthritis. A small number of the "chronic rheumatism" cases probably were rheumatoid arthritis, since the physicians described swollen finger joints and other deformities associated with this disease. Many of the "chronic rheumatism" cases, though, occurred in outbreaks, unlike the pattern of rheumatoid arthritis. There is, however, another possibility.

There is good reason to believe that many cases of "chronic rheumatism" were either a disease now called "reactive arthritis," or, with the addition of a few other clinical features (primarily urethritis and conjunctivitis), "Reiter's syndrome." Reactive arthritis can resemble acute rheumatic fever, with inflammation of one or more large joints, and it is usually very prolonged. In some chronic reactive arthritis cases, permanent deformity of joints and muscle atrophy can occur, often with the shortening of muscle groups, causing joint contractures. The disease follows some venereal infections and many intestinal diseases, particularly after various forms of dysentery. The endemic dysentery among Civil War troops makes reactive arthritis a likely explanation for the large number of chronic rheumatism cases, including the sudden epidemics.

The occurrence of spinal arthritis also supports this theory. While the spine is commonly involved in reactive arthritis, it is rarely affected in acute rheumatic fever. "It was common enough during the Civil War," Dr. Joseph Woodward wrote, "for patients afflicted with diarrhea and dysentery . . . to complain of rheumatic pains in the back and limbs."[6] Arthritic pain in the spine joints, called "lumbago," was mentioned in many soldiers' case histories, although it is not known how many cases occurred over the course of the war, since lumbago was not on the list of diagnoses. However, for the first year (ending July 1, 1862), 4,269 cases of lumbago were reported to the Federal Surgeon General's Office, in addition to 26,257 cases of acute rheumatism and 14,219 cases of chronic rheumatism.[7]

Few biographies of Robert E. Lee mention his illnesses, but the famous general did have episodes of diarrhea, as well as "lumbago," which were severe but transient.[8] In a letter written on October 23, 1863, Lee mentioned to Lt. Gen. Leonidas Polk that "I have been for more than a month a great sufferer from rheumatism in my back, so that I can hardly get about."[9] These episodes suggest that Lee had reactive arthritis affecting the spine, but that it did not become chronic. There is also good evidence that he had acute rheumatic fever and developed rheumatic valvular heart disease, which played a major role in his final illness after the war.[10,11]

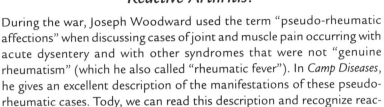

Was Pseudo-rheumatism Actually Reactive Arthritis?

During the war, Joseph Woodward used the term "pseudo-rheumatic affections" when discussing cases of joint and muscle pain occurring with acute dysentery and with other syndromes that were not "genuine rheumatism" (which he also called "rheumatic fever"). In *Camp Diseases*, he gives an excellent description of the manifestations of these pseudo-rheumatic cases. Tody, we can read this description and recognize reactive arthritis:

> The most characteristic group of the cases belonging under the heading of pseudo-rheumatism contains most of the *sore backs* and *weak backs* which have been so common among the troops since the breaking out of the war.
>
> The disease begins with malaise, languor and general indisposition to exertion. By-and-by vague pains make their appearance in various parts of the body. These pains are sometimes acute and cutting, sometimes dull and heavy, but very often do not at first amount to more than a sense of soreness in the parts affected.
>
> They may be located in any part of the body, but their most common seat is in the thighs and legs, and in the small of the back. The last is especially the characteristic seat of the disorder, and is more uniformly involved than any other portion of the body . . .
>
> As the disease progresses, the pain becomes more severe, and, if it is seated in the back or the lower extremities, the patient becomes quite unfit for duty. Sometimes he is confined to bed, but most frequently he hobbles about with the aid of a stick. [Original italic][12]

In addition, the discussion of diarrhea and dysentery in *Medical and Surgical History* includes a complete review of the medical literature and Thomas Sydenham's description of rheumatism that occurred in association with a dysentery epidemic in London in 1672. One of the authors quoted in *Medical and Surgical History*

> regarded this form of rheumatism as similar in its symptoms and progress to gonorrheal rheumatism, the chief difference being that the latter is usually limited to a single joint, or at most two, while dysenteric rheumatism involves several, either simultaneously or in succession.[13]

These clinical observations accurately describe the syndromes of gonorrheal arthritis and reactive arthritis, respectively, as they are now known.

Civil War physicians were puzzled by the low mortality rate from acute rheumatism among soldiers. In the civilian population, the mortality rate was over 3%, but among the troops, the mortality was less than one-tenth that number. Surprised by the difference, physicians tried adding the cases with deaths from the forms of heart disease they associated with acute rheumatism-pericarditis and endocarditis—but the total mortality was still low.[14] In retrospect, it seems likely that much of the rheumatism, both acute and chronic, was not rheumatic fever but reactive arthritis, which does not cause heart disease or death. Inclusion of these cases in the total cases of acute rheumatism could account for the lower proportion of non-fatal cases in the military population, since reactive arthritis is much less frequent in civilian populations.

TONSILLITIS

We now know that almost all cases of acute rheumatic fever occur following streptococcal throat infections. If the tonsils are present, the term "tonsillitis" is used. Yet tonsillitis was recorded in only about 66,000 soldiers, about one-third the frequency of diagnosed acute rheumatism. There are two likely explanations for this discrepancy. First, many throat infections probably went unrecorded, since most soldiers were seen at Sick Call and were not relieved from duty or referred to the regimental or larger unit hospitals. Second, many of the cases of acute rheumatism probably were not acute rheumatic fever, but actually were acute reactive arthritis, which is not associated with tonsillitis. With this in mind, the discrepancy between the recorded frequency of pharyngitis or tonsillitis and that of acute rheumatism is less marked.

SCARLET FEVER AND BRIGHT'S DISEASE

Apart from rheumatic fever, other diseases now known as sequelae of streptococcal infections were surprisingly rare in Civil War troops. One example is scarlet fever, which results from distinct strains of streptococci that produce a specific exotoxin. Scarlet fever is easy to diagnose with its distinctive rash, yet only 696 soldiers developed the disease.

Also relatively easy to diagnose was Bright's disease, the term used in the 1800s and early 1900s for kidney disease, especially glomerulonephritis. It was diagnosed in only 1,807 cases. Since most cases of acute glomerulonephritis also are caused by infection with certain strains of streptococci (often the same ones that produce scarlet fever), the rarity of this disease in Civil War troops is surprising.

Some of the 9,454 cases listed as "inflammation of the kidneys" may have been a form of Bright's disease. Although most of these cases, including many of the 154 deaths, were probably bacterial kidney infections (pyelonephritis), some were undoubtedly post-streptococcal glomerulonephritis. It is clear from a variety of case reports that examinations of the urine, including microscopic examination, were done frequently. In a few of the case histories, urinalyses revealed albumin and, upon microscopic examinations, red cells, fat globules, and even uric acid crystals were found.[15] (Uric acid crystals are hard to visualize even with modern microscopes.) These cases, which were called "inflammation of the kidneys," were probably glomerulonephritis. In some cases, patients also had massive generalized edema, suggesting they had the form of Bright's disease later called "nephrotic syndrome." However, even after adding these cases to the number actually diagnosed as Bright's disease, the total is surprisingly small. We now know that only specific streptococcal strains cause acute kidney complications, although many strains can cause rheumatic fever. Thus, it seems likely that the nephritogenic strains of *Streptococcus* were rare during the Civil War.

SEXUALLY TRANSMITTED DISEASES

Syphilis and gonorrhea were common among Civil War troops. Many hospitals had separate wards to treat venereal diseases, which were classified as "enthetic," a term meaning "arising from within." That syphilis was spread through sexual contact had been known since its initial appearance in Europe about 1495, and was known of gonorrhea since Old Testament times. During the Civil War, a diagnosis of "gonorrhea" was used for all forms of urethral discharge. (Subsequently, microbiologists found that other sexually transmitted infections have similar discharges, but until long after the Civil War all of them were called gonorrhea.)

Gonorrhea was diagnosed in 102,893 soldiers during the Civil War, and 79,589 soldiers were diagnosed with syphilis. Physicians diagnosed only the primary and secondary forms of syphilis that cause typical superficial lesions affecting the skin and mucous membranes and generalized glandular enlargement. As described by Dr. Samuel D. Gross,

> when the patient is in an exhausted, irritable condition, [syhpillitic lesions] are very apt to become severely inflamed, . . . often spreading with immense rapidity, both in diameter and depth. The system generally actively sympathizes with these sores; the skin is dry and hot, the pulse small, quick, and

frequent, the appetite impaired, the sleep destroyed, and the loss of flesh and strength excessive . . . Its very appearance, in fact, usually at once stamps its character. In the first place, it is ordinarily circular or oval, and of an excavated shape, with hard, everted edges, and a foul surface, destitute of granulations and of healthy discharge; the surrounding parts are indurated, and generally somewhat discolored, the tint often resembling that of copper.[16]

Only 123 deaths were attributed to syphilis and 6 to gonorrhea during the entire war among white troops; 28 were attributed to syphilis and 1 to gonorrhea among black troops. As a result, the disease was little feared. Civil War physicians did not know about the devastating late (tertiary) forms of syphilis that affect the nervous and cardiovascular systems. Such complications appear in a minority of cases and usually take years to develop. Cases recognizable as tertiary cardiovascular syphilis (such as widespread alteration of the ascending aorta with aneurysm formation and rupture) are described in *Medical and Surgical History*, but the diagnosis of syphilis is not mentioned.[17] There is no way of knowing the number of men who died years later from late complications of the syphilis they contracted during the war.

Only 426 men with venereal disease were hospitalized; the remainder must have been relieved from duty, at least temporarily, to receive treatment. A total of 80 cases of "suppurating bubos" (lymph glands in the inguinal area that have become purulent and broken through the skin, discharging pus) were reported, 77 of these had the primary diagnosis of syphilis and 3 had the primary diagnosis of gonorrhea.[18] Since neither of these diseases causes suppurating bubos, the soldiers probably suffered from other venereal diseases which produce such lesions (such as those now called "chancroid" or "lymphogranulom venereum") that were unknown at the time.

Syphilitic skin lesions were usually treated by applying compounds containing mercury. This therapy had been used for 300 years and had some beneficial effect. But its lack of lasting benefit is best summarized by the classic graffiti found in a London men's room and recorded by James Boswell: "A night with Venus, a lifetime with Mercury."[19] Other "remedies" for syphilis and gonorrhea included poke roots or berries, wild sarsaparilla, sassafras and jessamine. To cure stubborn gonorrhea, they used "silk weed root put in whiskey and drank, giving at the same time pills of rosin from the pine tree, with very small pieces of blue vitriol."[20] Eventually, the symptoms would subside spontaneously and the last (ineffective) treatment that had been administered was credited with the "cure."

SAFE SEX IN TENNESSEE

The Union troops occupying Nashville were plagued by sexually transmitted diseases. The local commander, Brig. Gen. R. S. Granger, reported that at one point in June 1863, he was "daily and almost hourly beset" by regimental commanders and their surgeons requesting that he devise a way to rid the city of diseased prostitutes. The provost marshal, Lt. Col. George Spalding, failed in an attempt to round them up, place them aboard a steamer, and ship them to some other city because no other city would accept them. Spalding then instituted a licensing system with frequent "inspection" and hospitalization "of those likely to disseminate disease." The inspection fee was fifty cents, "for the purposes of defraying the expenses of said hospital."[21] Infected prostitutes were hospitalized, treated, and released only when evidence of the disease had cleared. Initially, few prostitutes reported and many left the city rather than submit to the licensing system, but the plan gradually gained popularity. By January 1864, 300 were registered and 60 were found to be diseased, the number of licensees eventually rising to 456 "white cyprians" and 50 "colored prostitutes."[22]

General Hooker and Prostitutes

When he assumed command of the Army of the Potomac in February 1863, General Joseph Hooker introduced several measures designed to improve troop morale. He increased furloughs, instituted badges to identify units, and is said to have encouraged prostitutes to visit the encampments, including his headquarters. Nevertheless, there appears to have been no significant increase in the incidence of syphilis and gonorrhea in the Army of the Potomac during that period.

Still, Hooker's name became associated with prostitution. A book on Washington City (as Washington, D.C. was called during the Civil War) noted that there were an estimated 5,000 prostitutes in the city during the war, that one red-light district was known as "Hooker's headquarters," and that a brothel was named "Hooker's Division."[23]

Etymologists, however, have evidence that the use of the word "hooker" as slang for "prostitute" antedated the Civil War. This usage apparently increased considerably after the war, though, probably due, in part, to the general's proclivities.[24]

These preventative measures significantly decreased the incidence of venereal disease among the troops in Nashville. For example, Surgeon W. H. Chambers wrote,

> During the winter, spring and summer of 1863 I had generally from 10 to 20 officers under treatment at one time for nearly the whole of the three periods, whereas for the past six months I do not prescribe for one in a month. [As of December 31, 1864,] of the 2330 cases treated in the male venereal disease wards of this hospital only 31 contracted the disease in this city.[25]

Chambers treated 107 prostitutes for primary syphilis, 30 for "soft chancre occurring synchronously with secondary syphilis," and 4 for gonorrhea. He explained that "the average number of days each case of primary syphilis was treated is eleven (11), whereas cases of secondary nature remain in the hospital 38 days. Gonorrhea was treated an average of 10 days." Two prostitutes died in the hospital, "one from consumption the other from smallpox."[26] He added that when the program was first instituted, many "of the women were "exceedingly filthy in their persons and apparel and obscene and coarse in their language, but this soon gave place to cleanliness and propriety."[27] He claimed that the women who were examined and treated were pleased with the system and did not want it discontinued.[28] The medical officers were of the opinion that many "of the better class of prostitutes" were drawn to Nashville by the relative protection from venereal disease in the city.[29]

A similar system was instituted in Memphis beginning in September 1864. " 'Street walking,' soliciting, stopping or talking with men in the street" was banned, and registered women were admitted to a female ward of the "new City Hospital" for any disease. The program, largely administered by the city government, successfully decreased the amount of venereal disease.[30]

Since no effective treatment for either syphilis or gonorrhea existed at the time, the decrease in venereal diseases associated with treating prostitutes was probably due to their enforced segregation during periods of infectivity. Syphilis, in particular, is transmitted only when there are superficial lesions on the genitalia, mucous membranes, or skin. Enforced isolation during the periods when visible lesions could be detected on examination would have minimized the spread of the disease.

Venereal disease, and gonorrhea in particular, causes strictures of the urethra. Civil War surgeons recorded 2,581 cases of organic stricture of the urethra, with 8 deaths and 247 medical discharges.[31] They believed that almost all of these cases were due to venereal disease, not trauma. *Medical and Surgical History* specifies that efforts were made to relieve the strictures and includes illustrations of the metal catheters and dilators used for the purpose. It does not mention whether anesthesia was given when these instruments were used—one can only hope that it was.

PSYCHIATRIC PROBLEMS

Although psychological problems did not figure as prominently in Civil War literature as it does in modern wars, they must have been quite common.[32] The usual diagnostic terms used were "nostalgia" and "homesickness," which were described as a "temporary feeling of depression," including lack of appetite and weight loss.[33,34] During the war years, 5,016 white and 281 black soldiers were admitted to hospitals with "homesickness": the rate of occurrence in the two groups was similar (slightly over 2 per 1,000 men per year).

In World War I, British and American physicians used the term "shell shock" for this type of problem, although the French term, *tristesse sombre* (dark sadness), seems a better description of the depressive symptoms depicted among Civil War soldiers. The Civil War soldiers hospitalized with this problem were not just what we would now call "homesick," but probably had major depression—often accompanying another serious disease. Common homesickness, as might be expected, was widespread during periods of inactivity, particularly in the evening when listening to the bands that were a part of many regiments. Soldiers wrote that if the band played "Home Sweet Home" there usually wasn't a dry eye in the regiment. These feelings were least common during active campaigning. Commanders realized that providing diversion during periods of prolonged encampment helped mitigate the problem. They arranged various forms of entertainment, including musicians and "prestidigitators." The men also created their own diversions, including sports such as baseball and snowball fights, which could become major battles fought with military strategy and deadly intensity. Card games and dice were ubiquitous and exotic games, such as louse jumping contests, were invented.

Civil War physicians recorded that "some derangement of health, as a rule, preceded the mental phenomena,"[35] without mentioning specific diseases. Hospitalized men whose physical disease was doing poorly were often particularly depressed, and with good reason. Visits by family members were extremely difficult and rare, although volunteer female nurses tried to compensate. At times, physicians could find no underlying disease but watched men die from what they diagnosed as "nostalgia"; sixty-seven deaths were attributed to this cause. In retrospect, it seems likely that tuberculosis and scurvy, which cause fatigue, lassitude, and other symptoms similar to those of depression, may have been important components in some of these cases, and any underlying disease would certainly exaggerate feelings of depression (and vice-versa).

Acute psychotic episodes were described in an indeterminate number of soldiers. Often the symptoms became chronic psychoses with delusions and hallucinations. Union soldiers who developed persistent psychotic symptoms were hospitalized, many at the Government Hospital for the Insane in Washington (later known as St. Elizabeth's). Overall, 2,410 white and 193 black soldiers were diagnosed as insane. Eighty white and 4 black solders' deaths were attributed to insanity (although many could have been from encephalitis or other organic diseases). Insanity was the basis for discharge in 869 white and 34 black cases.[36] Despite the availability of the Hospital for the Insane, Union soldiers were often hospitalized in local institutions, especially those in the Western theater of action. Confederate policy specified the hospitalization of insane soldiers in any available asylum. No central facility was established for the purpose.[37]

After the war, many veterans described persistent hallucinations and delusions of being in imminent danger of being shot, consistent with what is now called "post-traumatic stress disorder." After discharge, wild uncontrollable behavior by some of these men led to commitment to mental hospitals; and many killed themselves.[38]

MALINGERING

Soldiers seeking to avoid duty were a constant problem, particularly early in the war when discipline was the worst. During battles, shirkers feigned injuries and interfered with the evacuation of the wounded when they crowded into ambulances. During the Peninsula campaign, for example, malingerers displaced wounded men from hospital ships, trains, and horse-drawn ambulances. The appearance of the Sanitary Commission's ambulance boats led to "a wild rush for them by [the] sick, wounded, deserters and malingerers."[39] Later, guards were posted to prevent malingerers from supplanting the wounded.

General Grant's constantly moving army in May and June of 1864, coupled with the hordes of wounded in the Battles of the Wilderness and Spotsylvania, created confusion in a well-functioning evacuation system. Malingerers compounded it after the battles by congregating at Fredericksburg, the main depot for collecting and transporting the wounded northward. By this time, veteran army physicians were wary of malingerers, so the shirkers would seek out inexperienced contract physicians, many of whom were volunteers with the Sanitary Commission. These doctors were more easily impressed by the malingerers' "bloody bandages and judicious limping."[40]

Soldiers quickly learned how to feign disease and bamboozle new regimental surgeons. Examinations during sick call consisted primarily of looking at the tongue and Dr. Albert Gaillard Hart recorded in his memoir:

> At our rendezvous, on three successive mornings, men reported sick, complaining of backache and headache, and with a very heavily coated tongue, but without other symptoms. Thinking it might prove an oncoming fever, I excused the first and second lots, and then saw that they were "old-soldiering the surgeon." Long afterwards one of the men explained the trick. The camp was surrounded by rose-bushes in bloom, and a liberal chewing of rose-leaves a little before sick call produced the effect I saw on the tongue. This is but an illustration of innumerable devices to mislead the surgeon and get excused from duty or escape the battlefield.[41]

The manner in which physicians handled soldiers they believed to be shirking led to many accusations of callousness in both soldiers' and nurses' letters home. In some instances, the physician was clearly wrong about the severity of the soldier's illness and, when their letters appeared in newspapers at home, these episodes contributed to the public's widespread view that Civil War doctors was heartless and cruel.[42] For example, soldiers in the early stages of scurvy were often diagnosed as malingering when, in fact, they were malnourished. But, they were in the minority of those designated as malingerers.

The malingerers' main goal was to receive a Medical Certificate of Discharge. Since joint pain and a limp are easy to feign, many pretended to have chronic rheumatism. Thus, doctors had to differentiate malingering from true chronic rheumatism. This was often difficult. The form of "chronic rheumatism" that was most common during the Civil War—reactive arthritis—can lead to deformities, including atrophy and shortening of muscles, which limits joint movement. A test was devised to determine whether muscle contractures were real or faked. The soldier was given chloroform or ether to establish if the shortened muscle was being voluntarily restricted and could be stretched during sleep. Fortunately, not much anesthetic was needed for such tests; there is no record of any fatalities. (This test is similar to a technique used during and after World War II that used intravenous sodium amytal [truth serum] to diagnose and treat "war neurosis.") Anesthesia was also used to diagnose many other forms of malingering.

Malingering

In his 1863 painting "Playing Old Soldier," Winslow Homer humorously recorded an episode of malingering that was described in the *Army and Navy Journal* of 1863:

> A surgeon of a New York regiment in General Davidson's brigade was much puzzled during the winter of 1861, to account for so many of the men having coated tongues. It was almost a distemper in the regiment. After much diligent inquiry, he discovered that among the privates was a druggist who furnished for a trifle his comrades with a white mixture, which they applied to their tongues whenever desirous of getting off from duty. The discovery was not made, however, until nearly the whole regiment had deceived him at one time or another.[43]

The faking of paralysis and other nerve injuries was of special interest to the staff at Turner's Lane Hospital in Philadelphia. In contrast to reports from European armies, they rarely saw self-induced disease in Civil War troops. Rather, American soldiers would "exaggerate maladies of trifling character or feign diseases outright." In their publications, they described feigned lameness, paralysis, epilepsy, blindness, deafness, vomiting, pain, insanity, chronic rheumatism, and aphonia (inability to talk). The ethical issue of using anesthesia to uncover malingerers troubled these physicians, who nevertheless used it for that purpose while documenting its utility and safety.[44]

Dr. William W. Keen, assigned to treat the malingerers at Turner's Lane Hospital, suggested that the expression *in vino veritas* be applied to the use of anesthesia to detect feigned disease. He described testing blindness in one eye by "etherizing" the man and covering the good eye with adhesive plaster. On awakening, the man could not resist reaching out for some offered whiskey. In another instance, a man feigning aphonia (not being able to speak) recovered from the anesthesia and found himself answering questions. He immediately recovered his equanimity and fell on his knees before the surgeons, exclaiming "Thank you doctors! You have restored my voice!" More difficult to test were the men who could pretend to be fully asleep from the ether and were able to keep up the pretense of a paralyzed limb or a joint contracture.[45]

Epilepsy was also a favorite illness among malingerers during the war. Great efforts, including the use of anesthesia, were made to exclude feigned epilepsy before discharging soldiers with this diagnosis.[46] Many men with epilepsy were not discharged, instead they were assigned to the Veterans Reserve Corps for hospital duty. Epilepsy was diagnosed in 8,619 white Union soldiers (with 323 deaths) and in 813 black soldiers (with 56 deaths). There was no effective treatment for it except general anesthesia.

"SOLDIER'S HEART"

Heart symptoms often accompany anxiety, but the physical stresses of a soldier's life can also reveal underlying heart abnormalities. Given the limited diagnostic tools available (no electrocardiograms or radiographs) during the Civil War, the true cause of many soldiers' cardiac ailments baffled their physicians, who argued over the etiology.

Dr. Jacob DaCosta, who also worked at Turner's Lane Hospital in Philadelphia, is credited with the first description of "soldier's heart" or "stress heart," a form of what today is considered psychogenic heart disease. Of the 300 cases DaCosta studied, most men had episodes of palpitation and shortness of breath, and some developed evidence of cardiac hypertrophy but not dilatation.[47] DaCosta considered the findings a "functional disorder" and attributed them to "cardiac muscular exhaustion."[48] Other physicians agreed, noting that the excitement of battle and "double quick" marching caused the syndrome of irritable heart.

Surgeons described many "functional" cases that must have had considerable cardiac pathology. These included soldiers with "fits of fluttering cardiac action" and "cardiac irritability," pulse rates of 120 to 150 with occasional shortness of breath, coughing up of blood (hemoptysis), fainting, "valvular murmurs," friction rubs, and enlargement of the heart by percussion. Physicians did observe, however, that symptoms in these cases often were precipitated by "cardiac overexertion" due to mental stress, thus pointing out that psychological factors can aggravate organic disease.[49] Undoubtedly, in some cases with "fluttering cardiac action," there were cardiac arrhythmias, but methods of diagnosing such arrhythmias did not exist. Some of DaCosta's cases include descriptions which suggest the presence of cardiac hypertrophy (enlargement of the heart muscles). Such changes could have resulted from high blood pressure, but since there were no instruments to measure blood pressure, he could not make that diagnosis.

While the term "functional disorder" eventually came to indicate a psychogenic etiology, DaCosta used the term to mean a true functional, that is, physiological, abnormality.[50,51] Of the cases he labeled "irritable heart," however, while they may have included some organic syndromes, many of his case descriptions seem to indicate a psychogenic basis and today probably would be labeled a form of "stress syndrome."

In 1864, another military physician, Henry Hartshorne, also described the heart disease he saw in his patients. He reported that endocarditis and pericarditis were infrequent in the patients he treated, that valvular disease (without evidence of ventricular hypertrophy) occurred occasionally, and that palpitations occurred with anemia and after a variety of stimuli, including "nervousness" and "abuse of alcohol."[52] These observations are compatible with today's knowledge of heart disease and document good clinical observations and appropriate interpretation by Civil War physicians.

During the war, 10,516 white and 100 black soldiers were discharged due to heart disease. Discharges due to valvular disease or "soldier's heart" were not separated out, but available records show that physicians did recognize various types of cardiac pathology. Valvular heart disease was diagnosed in

Postmortem Observations Suggestive of Clots in the Lung (Pulmonary Embolism)

Pulmonary emboli (obstruction of a pulmonary artery by a clot) most likely occurred in some patients described in Civil War medical reports, especially in those with hemoptysis and fainting. Some of these patients died suddenly, a phenomenon consistent with massive pulmonary emboli. Civil War-era physicians were unaware of this pathologic phenomena. However, some autopsy reports describe the changes expected with pulmonary embolism.

Following a series of autopsies he conducted, Surgeon M. K. Taylor of Keojuk, Iowa, speculated on the existence of such pathology. He described many instances of

> dilatation and thinning of the walls of the right ventricle with incompetency of the tricuspid valve, . . . nine-tenths of those affected [in this fashion] had suffered some obstruction to the free circulation of blood at no very remote period.[53]

His description suggests changes in the right side of the heart caused by obstruction of blood flow in the lungs (pulmonary heart disease or *cor pulmonale*). This syndrome was not clearly delineated until the next century.

3,574 whites and 325 blacks; most undoubtedly resulted from rheumatic fever. Civil War physicians clearly were skilled at using a stethoscope to detect this form of heart disease.

ALCOHOLISM

Military physicians were very tolerant of soldiers' use of alcohol. They would hospitalize only men who suffered severe effects such as delirium tremens.

Records indicate that only 4,625 Union soldiers were hospitalized or relieved from duty for inebriation; of these, 98 died. Of the 3,284 soldiers admitted for delirium tremens, 423 died—a lower percentage than in modern times. Among Federal soldiers, alcoholism was most common in the area around Washington, and was most frequent at the beginning and at the end of the war.[54]

Many army physicians were themselves accused of alcoholism, particularly in some of the post-war autobiographical works of women who served as matrons, many of whom were later prominent in the temperance movement. Dorothea Dix, for example, who organized female nursing services for the Union army at the beginning of the war, strongly advocated national prohibition. She was so convinced that alcoholism was a major problem among physicians that she tried to have doctors ordered to abstain from alcohol for the duration of the war.[55] Many other observers, however, reported that abuse of alcohol was, if anything, less common among physicians than among other Civil War army personnel. There are no figures available to help judge which reports are more accurate. Physicians did, though, have easy access to alcohol, since *spiritus frumenti* (whiskey) and *spiritus vini gallici* (brandy) were standard medical supplies.

SKIN DISEASES

During the war, almost 200,000 Federal soldiers were hospitalized for various types of dermatological disorders. Insect bites and secondary skin infections resulting from scratches were common. Fleas and lice plagued all Civil War soldiers, typified by the saying that "officers and men scratched alike." Although regulations required men to bathe once a week, no one obeyed that order. Consequently, the men were covered with dirt, scratches, and bites: it is not surprising that "army itch" was one of the most common medical problems recorded during the war.

Soldiers' initial reaction to lice infections was embarrassment until the men realized they were ubiquitous. They periodically boiled their clothes to get rid of the lice. A favorite putdown was "Go boil your shirt!" equivalent to "Go jump in the lake!" "Hunting graybacks" (lice) was a constant diversion and, when bored by inactivity, the men held "vermin fairs" and louse-jumping contests.[56] According to one officer's letter, General William T. Sherman was so "concerned that the fleas and lice would carry off his army" after a long march that he ordered the ranks to stop so that the men could divest themselves of the pests.[57]

Civil War physicians recognized that scabies was a frequent cause of "camp itch." Scabies is a highly communicable skin disease caused by the itch mite, *Sarcoptes scabiei*. It can spread readily among soldiers crowded together in a tent or other shelter. The medical literature discussed the relationship of scabies to "the itch," and most authors concluded that many cases of itch actually were scabies. Although there was no separate entry for scabies on their diagnostic list, they placed "itch" under the parasitic diseases. Among Union troops, 31,947 men were relieved from duty or hospitalized for treatment of "the itch."[58] Confederate hospital records also listed numerous admissions for itch.

Assistant Surgeon (and future Surgeon General) George Sternberg described the cause of the "itch" in 1866:

> The soldier catches the disease by sleeping with a comrade who is covered with the eruption or in blankets which are filled with acari [mites] and their ova, and the disease is at once started from many different centers. The little acarus squats upon a new recruit with every prospect of a long life and large family, and burrows away, undisturbed by soap or sulfur, until every square barley-corn of the poor soldier's skin is like a New York tenement house—full inside and out.[59]

Physicians used a variety of treatments for the itch. The most-needed treatment—cleanliness—could rarely be implemented, but a wash consisting of sulfur and lime was considered effective. The author of an article in *Confederate States Medical and Surgical Journal*, titled "On the treatment of camp itch," claimed to have had great success using an ointment made from the inner bark of the elder tree, lard, and sulfur flour. The author recommended that patients wear the same underclothing for one week, since it would soak up the ointment and avoid the trouble of reapplication.[60]

Scratching the "itch," as well as breaks in the skin from other causes, inevitably led to more serious skin infections. Over 130,000 Union soldiers experienced skin infections, including abscesses, boils, and carbuncles. Only 199 deaths resulted from these deep skin infections, especially surprising given how devastating wound infections were at that time. The explanation is probably that such deep skin infections were less likely to be contaminated with devastating streptococci, unless they were acquired in a hospital.

Civil War physicians also used the nonspecific diagnostic category of "skin diseases." These probably were minor or chronic skin problems (such as prickly heat in the summer) that led to scratching, abrasions, or thickening of the skin that progressed to an "eczematoid condition." While 35,168, Union soldiers with this diagnosis were relieved from duty or hospitalized, only 5 died.

COMPARISON OF DISEASE IN BLACK AND WHITE TROOPS

Black regiments, sometimes called the "Corps d'Afrique," were organized and began active service in the Union army in July 1863. In general, there was more disease with a higher mortality rate among the black troops. Many black soldiers had recently been slaves, thus the data on their illnesses reveals information about their health during slavery. Further, the statistics reveal the increased susceptibility of black men to certain diseases; these epidemiological patterns became more obvious later in the century. Table 12.1 shows the total number of illnesses recorded and the total number of deaths from illness among the two groups of soldiers. Table 12.2 looks at this data another way: the number of sick men per 1,000 men per year and the number of deaths due to illness per 1,000 men per year.

The lower incidence of diagnosed illnesses but the higher rate of deaths among black troops may mean that most of their illnesses were treated by regimental surgeons, so the men were not relieved from duty or admitted to hospitals. Generally, black soldiers were hospitalized with other soldiers, although in some areas, such as during the Siege of Petersburg near City Point, Virginia, black troops were put in separate hospitals. It is difficult to determine whether the medical treatment given to black soldiers was less effective, but that is certainly a possibility. On the other hand, the drugs available made little difference to outcomes and the medical treatment of all disease was generally ineffective.

TABLE 12.1
Recorded Illness and Death during the War

	White*	Black**
Total Illnesses	5,579,526	470,122
Total Deaths	161,188	23,465
Fatality Rate	2.9%	5.0%

*July 1, 1861 to June 30, 1865
**July 1, 1863 to June 30, 1865
Source: *Medical and Surgical History*, Medical Section, vol. 1.

TABLE 12.2
Recorded Illness and Death per 1,000 Soldiers per Year

	White*	Black**
Number of Illnesses	2,138	1,475
Number of Deaths	103	123

*July 1, 1861 to June 30, 1865
**July 1, 1863 to June 30, 1865
Source: *Medical and Surgical History*, Medical Section, vol. 1.

Wound treatment, however, did make a difference. As Table 12.3 shows, the percentage of the wounded who died after admission to field hospitals was the same for both groups over the entire war. This suggests that the medical care given to both groups may have been comparable. The mortality from wounds, however, was not constant throughout the war. When mortality data for the white troops are compared only for the two years that they overlapped with service by the black troops (July 1, 1863, to June 30, 1865), white soldiers had an average mortality rate of 12.6%, a significant difference from their mortality rate for the entire war. (The changes in mortality rate from wounds during the war are discussed in Chapter 3, *Civil War Surgery*.)

Table 12.4 shows the relative incidence of a variety of diseases in black soldiers as compared to white soldiers. Although racial differences in the incidence of many of the diseases in this table have been discussed previously, two are worthy of comment: intestinal worms and anemia. Worms were diagnosed infrequently, but were prevalent among black soldiers. Early in the twentieth century, it was established that intestinal worms were widespread in the southeastern states and that black soldiers presumably had acquired them while still slaves. Anemia was almost twice as common among black soldiers; in the twentieth century, anemia was found to be a frequent result of hookworm (another intestinal parasite) infestation, which was prevalent in the same area.

VARIATIONS IN DEATH RATES

The death rate varied considerably among the roughly 2,000 Union regiments that served for part or all of the war.[61] (A fully staffed regiment had about 1,000 men, but few were fully staffed.) Analysis of the data by regiment reveals no clear patterns, except that the 32 black regiments are among those

TABLE 12.3
Number of Recorded Wounds and Deaths of the Wounded

	White*	Black**
Number of Wounded	229,119	6,466
Number of Deaths	32,731	922
Fatality Rate	14.3%	14.3%

*For July 1, 1861 to June 30, 1865
**For July 1, 1863 to June 30, 1865
Source: *Medical and Surgical History*, Medical Section, vol. 1.

TABLE 12.4
Incidence of Selected Diseases in White and Black Troops

| | No. of Cases/Year/1,000 Mean Strength | | Ratio of |
Disease	Black*	White**	Black/White Cases
Smallpox	36.9	5.7	6.5
Scrofula	15.0	2.8	5.4
Scurvy	66.0	1.3	5.1
Night blindness	11.0	2.8	3.9
Inflammation of the lungs	113.0	29.0	3.9
Mumps	86.0	23.0	3.7
Inflammation of pleura	46.0	15.0	3.1
Intestinal worms	4.5	1.6	2.8
Measles	65.0	32.0	2.0
Acute bronchitis	149.0	78.0	1.9
Anemia	19.0	10.0	1.9
Acute rheumatism	117.0	67.0	1.8
Chronic rheumatism	86.0	51.0	1.7
"Intermittent fevers"	619.0	401.0	1.5
Valvular heart disease	2.6	1.7	1.5
"Typhomalarial fever"	44.0	29.0	1.5
Tonsillitis	41.0	28.0	1.5
Acute dysentery	145.0	108.0	1.3
Consumption	8.4	6.3	1.3
Acute diarrhea	701.0	533.0	1.3
Remittent fever	165.0	130.0	1.2
Chronic diarrhea	75.0	79.0	1.0
Syphilis	25.0	31.0	0.8
Typhoid	28.0	35.0	0.8
Jaundice	35.0	33.0	0.8
Gonorrhea	33.0	42.0	0.8
Inebriation	0.1	2.2	0.1

*July 1, 1863 to June 30, 1865
**July 1, 1861 to June 30, 1865
Source: *Medical and Surgical History*, Medical Section, vol. 1.

that lost the most men. Four of the thirteen regiments that had over 500 total deaths were black regiments. In those four regiments, from 85% to 100% of the deaths were from disease. Although some black regiments had heavy battle losses, in general, the black regiments had a higher percentage of deaths due to disease than did white regiments. The numbers for black regiments may be slightly skewed, however, because most blacks remained in the military during 1866, which was a period with little, if any, fighting but with a great deal of disease.

Of all Union regiments, the 5th Colored lost the most men: 829 men died, of whom 128 were either killed in battle or died of wounds; the rest died of disease. Contributing to these losses was their participation in the Mine Explosion (Battle of the Crater) during the Siege of Petersburg, as well as in the capture of Fort Fisher and the Carolinas campaign. The regiment was mustered out of service relatively early, on September 20, 1865.

Among white Union regiments, the 3rd Tennessee Cavalry had the highest percentage of casualties from disease. Although the regiment saw a lot of fighting, 98% of their 546 casualties were from disease. Organized on January 27, 1863, it participated in a variety of expeditions in northern Alabama and Mississippi until September 25, 1864, when most of the regiment was captured. The remaining men fought in the Battle of Nashville on December 15–16, 1864. In all likelihood, most of the regiment's men who died from disease were in prison camps at the time.[62]

CASE-FATALITY RATES OF MAJOR DISEASES

One of the most surprising and puzzling phenomena of Civil War medicine is the progressive rise in case-fatality rates (the percentage of individuals with a disease who died) from almost all the major diseases over the course of the war. Better sanitation and preventive measures and the acquired immunity of veteran soldiers resulted in a decreased incidence of most major epidemic diseases. But even as the total numbers of cases and of deaths fell, the case-fatality rate increased continuously during the war. For example, the case-fatality rate for typhoid fever among white Union soldiers during May and June of 1861 was 17.5%. During the first full year (July 1, 1861 to June 30, 1862), the rate was 25.7%; it subsequently rose each year and reached 59.5% of the diagnosed cases during the last year of fighting.

Table 12.5 summarizes the data for white troops only, since they served for the entire war. The table includes all those diagnostic categories listed in *Medical and Surgical History* in which 2,500 or more deaths occurred.

TABLE 12.5

**Case-fatality Rates for Diseases that Caused 2500
or More Deaths in White Union Troops**

| | *Fiscal Year** | | | | |
	1860	1861	1862	1863	1864
Average number of soldiers	41,556	288,919	659,955	675,413	645,506
% in general hospitals**	0	3.3	6.9	8.2	11.1
Typhoid fever	17.5%	25.7%	32.6%	44.0%	59.5%
"Typhomalarial fever"	N.U.†	N.U.	5.0	9.9	11.2
Consumption	10.1	22.2	35.0	42.7	67.1
Pneumonia	.2	19.5	22.6	25.2	30.8
Chronic diarrhea/dysentery	1.3	3.5	11.6	17.3	23.6
Smallpox and varioloid	2.2	30.1	32.8	43.4	42.7
Remittent fever	0	0.9	1.3	1.2	1.6
Acute diarrhea/dysentery	0	0.3	0.4	0.5	0.6
Congestive intermittent fever‡	2.8	16.2	25.8	27.0	25.8
Measles	0.3	2.6	7.5	7.3	11.0
Other "zymotic diseases"	0	0.5	2.8	2.3	2.1
% deaths from all causes (including wounds) among hospitalized soldiers	0.4	2.8	3.0	2.8	3.4

*The figures for 1860 were collected only during May and June of 1861, since the augmentation of the strength of the army with volunteers began at that time. The other figures represent the entire twelve-month fiscal year, which extended from July 1 of the year given to June 30 of the next year.

**The term "general hospital" refers to institutions which accepted men from any army unit, and does not include brigade, division, or corps hospitals in the field; the data for deaths include all deaths in all the hospitals in the Union army.

† N.U. = not used as a diagnostic term until fiscal 1862.

‡ "Congestive intermittent fever" was the term used for the most serious form of malaria, probably the disease later shown to be caused by *Plasmodium falciparum*.

Source: *Medical and Surgical History*, Medical Section, vol. 1.

What explains the increasing percentage of deaths from each of the major diseases? Was the pattern the result of a change in diagnostic criteria? The available evidence does not support such a contention. For example, when the term "typhomalarial fever" was first used in late 1862, replacing the term "continued fever," the diagnosed cases had a fatality rate of 5%. The change in terminology might have meant that milder forms of typhoid were diagnosed as typhomalarial fever, leaving only the more serious cases with a higher fatality rate to be actually diagnosed as typhoid. This would account for an increased case-fatality rate for typhoid. However, the case-fatality rate for typhomalarial fever also rose each year, reaching 12.1% in the last year of the war. This makes it unlikely that an increasing proportion of the milder cases of typhoid were called typhomalarial fever in the later years. A similar increase in case-fatality rates occurred with measles, pneumonia, smallpox, and pulmonary tuberculosis ("consumption"), the most deadly wartime diseases, even though the incidence and total number of cases of each disease fell every year. There is no evidence that the diagnostic criteria changed for any of those diseases over the course of the war.

Could the increased number of soldiers sent to general hospitals in the later years of the war have altered case-fatality rates? It is possible that patients with diseases of greater severity were being transferred to these hospitals, while milder cases were retained in the base or field hospitals. However, such a phenomenon cannot explain the increase in the fatality statistics, since the recorded deaths include both those in field hospitals and in general hospitals. Throughout the war, line officers discouraged the transfer of men to general hospitals. If men stayed in the field hospitals, they returned to their units when they recovered. When men were sent to general hospitals in another city, the regiment rarely saw them again. The increasing number of cases in general hospitals may be partly the result of the increasing number of men with prolonged disabilities or in slow recovery from suppurating gunshot wounds. Moreover, the enormous number of wounded from the later military campaigns required the rapid transfer of the sick and wounded from field hospitals to general hospitals, to free up beds for new casualties.

The most probable explanation for the progressively higher case-fatality rates is the soldiers' increasingly poor nutritional state. Kept in the field for long periods and fed mainly what was easily transportable, soldiers suffered from ever more nutritional deficiencies as the war continued. Many Civil War physicians wrote about the link between malnutrition and the increased susceptibility to diseases. They were reluctant, for example, to vaccinate men afflicted with scurvy because they knew that they were more likely to have complications.[63] In *Camp Diseases*, Joseph Woodward observed:

> Besides these simpler cases of scorbutic disease, there can be no doubt that the same tendency has complicated diseases generally throughout the army . . . and has even modified the results of wounds and injuries, interfering with the healing process, and increasing the mortality of traumatic cases of every kind.[64]

The authors of *Medical and Surgical History* concluded that scurvy was "a formidable ally of the continued fevers." They noted that the same pattern was observed during the Crimean War and quote an observer who wrote that

> typhus was at that time (winter of 1854–55) raging fiercely, and I am convinced that . . . certainly the cause of its great mortality was the scurvy. . . . [the manifestations of scurvy include] sloughing ulcers, gangrene of the mouth, general dropsy and chronic diarrhea.[65]

These are symptoms that suggest the soldiers suffered from generalized malnutrition. The possible role of scurvy in wound healing and Civil War surgeons' observations that it increased the frequency and mortality from wound infections are discussed in Chapter 6, Scurvy and the Mortality Rate from Gunshot Wounds.

Civil War physicians blamed the extremely high fatality rates in prisons, particularly at Andersonville, on the prisoners' malnutrition and, specifically, on scurvy. Although exposure to inclement weather and lack of adequate protective clothing and blankets clearly contributed to the frequency of respiratory tract infections, especially in Northern prisons, malnutrition must have had a contributory role. As one Confederate surgeon reported on October 17, 1864,

> The character of disease now prevailing is of that class most commonly produced by vicissitudes of weather—such as catarrh, bronchitis, pneumonia, rheumatic affections, and glandular swellings. These causes of disease are more active on systems debilitated from want of sufficient food, &c.[66]

After the war, Dr. Joseph Jones discussed the importance of scurvy in amplifying the severity and mortality of other diseases:

> By the official reports of the medical officers of both the English and French armies, during the Crimean War, it was conclusively shown that . . . scurvy and a scorbutic condition of the blood increased to a fearful degree the mortality, not only of gunshot wounds, but of all diseases, and especially of pneumonia, diarrhea and dysentery. I have recorded numerous incontrovertible facts to show that the scorbutic ulcers and hospital gangrene, and the accidents from vaccination arising at Andersonville, were by no means new in the history of medicine, and that the causes which induced these distressing affections have been active in all wars and sieges, and amongst all armies and navies.[67]

Medical Inspector Frank Hastings Hamilton lamented the fact that commanders often disregarded the need to provide vegetables for their troops. (The increased fatality rate from chronic diarrhea when it was combined with scurvy is addressed in Chapter 14.) After a visit to Union's Army of the Cumberland, under General Rosecrans, in April 1863, he noted that scurvy was associated with increased deaths from disease:

> So long as men are not dying in considerable numbers directly from scurvy, they [the commanders] manifest no alarm; for they have never been able to understand that, to some extent, all men must be scorbutic who have been excluded such length of time from vegetables; that the rheumatic pains, the bloody discharge from the bowels, the tender gums, the short breath, the irregular action of the heart, the obstinate ophthalmiae, the sudden deaths of patients suffering under diarrhea, the speedy exhaustion of men in the trenches and on the march, were all the result of impoverished blood; that the frequency, rapidity, and fatality of typhoid pneumonia were due in great measure to the same cause.[68]

We now know that malnutrition increases the susceptibility to a variety of diseases, especially infections. In the early 1900s, long before it was learned that malnutrition affects specific immune mechanisms, the effect of an inadequate diet was observed in cases of tuberculosis. Malnutrition, and particularly the lack of meat, was shown to increase the incidence of and mortality from tuberculosis in England, France, and individual African tribes. Data obtained from occupied countries during both World Wars, especially Denmark and the Low Countries, revealed that malnutrition increased the death rate not only from tuberculosis but also from other diseases.[69] Studies on the survival rates of prisoners of war confirmed these findings. The relationship between vitamin A deficiency and an increase in the frequency, severity, and mortality of infections has also been noted. In fact, the most observable symptom of Vitamin A deficiency, night blindness, was increasingly diagnosed as the Civil War continued.[70-74]

The regional variations in mortality from disease throughout the war support the correlation between malnutrition and the increasing frequency and severity of disease. The differences in the case-fatality rates were sometimes marked, and they paralleled the increased incidence of diagnosed scurvy and night blindness in the regions. This was especially true for typhoid fever, pneumonia, and tuberculosis found in the Union forces within the Central Region from July 1863 to June 1865. (In general, the Central Region included Virginia west of Harper's Ferry, the Shenandoah Valley, the newly formed state of West Virginia, Maryland west of the Monocacy River, Ohio, Indiana, Illinois, Tennessee, Missouri, Arkansas, the Gulf states, Michigan, Wisconsin, Minnesota, Iowa, and the Northwest territories.)

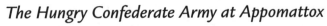

The Hungry Confederate Army at Appomattox

Confederate forces were often short of food, and it is highly likely that they suffered increased disease from malnutrition, as General Lee repeatedly pointed out in his reports to Richmond. Grant's strategy before Petersburg of shifting forces to the west to cut rail lines, and thus obstruct the delivery of supplies to Lee's army, forced the general to capitulate after his army was increasingly depleted by disease and desertion. Fortunately, the first thing Grant did after the surrender was signed at Appomattox was to provide food for Lee's men. In his memoirs, General Grant provided a moving description of his actions in the McLean House when he met with General Lee:

> General Lee, after all was completed and before taking his leave, remarked that his army was in a very bad condition for want of food, and that they were without forage; that his men had been living for some days on parched corn exclusively, and that he would have to ask me for rations and forage. I told him "certainly," and asked for how many men he wanted rations. His answer was "about twenty-five thousand:" [sic] and I authorized him to send his own commissary and quartermaster to Appomattox Station, two or three miles away, where he could have, out of the trains stopped, all the provisions wanted. As for forage, we had ourselves depended upon the country for that.[75]

REFERENCES

1. Rammelkamp CH, Wannamaker LW, Denny FW: The epidemiology and prevention of rheumatic fever. *Bull NY Acad Med.* 1952;28:321-24.
2. Watson T: *Lectures on the Principles and Practice of Physic: Delivered at King's College London.* Philadelphia, PA: Lea & Blanchard, 1845, p. 925.
3. Cheadle WB. Quoted in: Stollerman GH: *Rheumatic Fever and Streptococcal Infection.* New York: Grune & Stratton, 1975, p. 8.
4. *Medical and Surgical History,* Medical Section, vol. 3, pp. 830, 860.
5. Stollerman, *Rheumatic Fever and Streptococcal Infection,* p. 8.
6. *Medical and Surgical History,* Medical Section, vol. 2, p. 406.
7. Woodward JJ: *Outlines of the Chief Camp Diseases of the United States Armies as Observed during the Present War. A Practical Contribution to Military Medicine.* Philadelphia: Lippincott, 1863. Repub.: Norman, 1992, p. 318.
8. Davis B: *Gray Fox: Robert E. Lee and the Civil War.* New York: Holt, Rinehart & Winston, 1956, pp. 254, 315.
9. Lee RE: *The Wartime Papers of Robert E. Lee.* New York: Da Capo Press, 1987, p. 614.

10. Riley HD, Jr.: Robert E. Lee's battle with disease. *Civil War Times Illus.* 1979;12-22.
11. Welsh JD: *Medical Histories of Confederate Generals.* Kent, OH: Kent State Univ. Press, 1995.
12. Woodward, *Camp Diseases,* p. 319.
13. *Medical and Surgical History,* Medical Section, vol. 2, p. 408.
14. *Medical and Surgical History,* Medical Section, vol. 3, p. 829.
15. Ibid., pp. 881-83.
16. Samuel D. Gross, M.D., *System of Surgery.* vol. I, 4th ed. Philadelphia, PA: Henry C. Lea, 1866, p. 315.
17. *Medical and Surgical History,* Medical Section, vol. 3, p. 868.
18. Ibid., p. 891.
19. Lowry TP: *The Story the Soldiers Wouldn't Tell: Sex in the Civil War.* Mechanicsburg, PA: Stackpole, 1994, p. 103.
20. Cunningham HH: *Doctors in Gray: The Confederate Medical Service.* Baton Rouge: Louisiana State Univ. Press, 1958, p. 211.
21. *Medical and Surgical History,* Medical Section, vol. 3, p. 893.
22. Ibid., p. 894.
23. Leech M: *Reveille in Washington 1860–65.* New York: Harper & Bros., 1941, pp. 261-71.
24. Lowry, *Story the Soldiers Wouldn't Tell,* p. 147.
25. Report of W.H. Chambers, Surg., USV, NARA, RG94, Entry #621, File A435.
26. Ibid.
27. Medical and Surgical History, Medical Section, vol. 3, pp. 885, 894-5.
28. Chambers, NARA, RG94.
29. *Medical and Surgical History,* Medical Section, vol. 3, p. 894.
30. Ibid., pp. 895-96.
31. *Medical and Surgical History,* Surgical Section, vol. 2, p. 386.
32. Dean ET, Jr: *Shook Over Hell: Posttraumatic Stress, Vietnam, and the Civil War.* Cambridge, MA: Harvard Univ. Press, 1997, p. 46.
33. *Medical and Surgical History,* Medical Section, vol. 3, p. 884.
34. Anderson DL, Anderson GT: Nostalgia and malingering in the military during the Civil War. *Persp Bio Med.* 1984;28:156-66.
35. *Medical and Surgical History,* Medical Section, vol. 3, p. 885.
36. *Medical and Surgical History,* Medical Section, vol. 1.
37. Dean, *Shook Over Hell,* p. 123.
38. Ibid., pp. 66-67.
39. Greenbie MLB: *Lincoln's Daughters of Mercy.* New York: G.P. Putnam's Sons, 1944, p. 140.
40. Gillett MC: *The United States Army Medical Department, 1818–1865.* Washington, D.C.: Center of Military History, U.S. Army, 1987, p. 250.
41. Hart AG: *The Surgeon and the Hospital in the Civil War.* Gaithersburg, MD: Olde Soldier Books, 1987, (orig. pub. 1902), p. 10.
42. Maxwell WQ: *Lincoln's Fifth Wheel: The Political History of the U.S. Sanitary Commission.* New York: Longmans Green, 1956, p. 56.
43. *Army and Navy Journal.* 1863;1:314.
44. Keen WW, Mitchell SW, Morehouse GR: On malingering, especially with regard to simulation of disease of the nervous system. *Am J Med Sci.* 1864;48:367-94.
45. Keen WW: Surgical reminiscences of the Civil War. *Transactions of the College of Physicians of Philadelphia.* 3rd Series. 1905;27:95-114.
46. Keen et al., *Am J Med Sci,* 1864.
47. *Medical and Surgical History,* Medical Section, vol. 3, p. 885.
48. Ibid., p. 862.
49. Ibid., p. 863.
50. DaCosta JM: On irritable heart. *Am J Med Sci.* 1871;61:17.
51. *Medical and Surgical History.* Medical Section, vol. 3, p. 863.

52. Ibid., p. 862.
53. Ibid., p. 864.
54. Ibid., pp. 890-91.
55. Marshall HE. Quoted in: Freemon FR: *Microbes and Minie Balls: An Annotated Bibliography of Civil War Medicine.* Rutherford, NJ: Fairleigh Dickinson Univ. Press, 1993, p. 204.
56. Robertson JI: *Soldiers Blue and Gray.* Columbia: Univ. South Carolina Press, 1988, pp. 154-5.
57. Ibid., pp. 153-54.
58. Records of the Winder Hospital. Eleanor S. Brockenbrough Library, Museum of the Confederacy, Richmond, VA.
59. Sternberg G: *Medical and Surgical Reporter.* Philadelphia: 1866, vol. XIV, p. 298.
60. Chambers SR: On the treatment of camp itch. *Conf. States Med Surg J.* 1865;2:10.
61. Fox WF: *Regimental Losses in the American Civil War 1861–1865: A Treatise on the Extent and Nature of the Mortuary Losses in the Union Regiments, with Full and Exhaustive Statistics Compiled from the Official Records on File in the State Military Bureau and at Washington.* Albany, NY: Albany Pub. Co., 1889, p. 1.
62. Ibid.
63. *Medical and Surgical History*, Medical Section, vol. 3, pp. 625-27.
64. Woodward, *Camp Diseases*, p. 61.
65. *Medical and Surgical History*, Medical Section, vol. 3, p. 622.
66. *O.R.*, Series I, vol. XLI/4, p. 1003.
67. Jones J: The treatment of prisoners during the War between the States. *South Hist Soc Papers.* 1876;1(3):177.
68. Hamilton FH. Quoted in: *Am J Med Sci.* 1863;46:411-32.
69. Dubos R, Dubos J: *The White Plague.* New Brunswick, NJ: Rutgers Univ. Press, 1952, pp. 140-1.
70. Sommer A: Vitamin A status, resistance to infection and childhood mortality. *Ann NY Acad Sci.* 1990;587:17-23.
71. West KP, Howard GR, Sommer A: Vitamin A and infection; public health implications. *Ann Rev Nutr.* 1989;9:63-86.
72. Twining et al.: Neutrophil cathepsin G is specifically decreased under vitamin A deficiency. *Biochim et Biophys Acta.* 1996;1317:112-18.
73. Cohen BE, Elin RJ: Vitamin A-induced resistance to infection. *J Infec Dis.* 1971;129:597-600.
74. Underwood BA: Blinding malnutrition: a preventable scourge. *Int Child Health.* 1992;3:64.
75. Grant US: *Personal Memoirs of U.S. Grant.* vol. II. New York: C.L. Webster, 1885–86, pp. 494-95.

～ 13 ～

Scurvy and Other "Dietic Diseases": Desiccated Vegetables and Deteriorating Health

I ate a lot of desiccated vegetables yesterday and they made me the sickest of my life. I shall never want any more such fodder.

– Sergeant Cyrus Boyd, Fifteenth Iowa Infantry

MALNUTRITION AFFECTED THE HEALTH OF CIVIL WAR SOLDIERS, and thus the fighting strength of the armies. Diseases due to dietary deficiencies, such as scurvy, and the wounds, infections, and illnesses aggravated by malnutrition decreased the number of soldiers available at critical junctures. Surgeons advised the military commanders about improving the soldiers' diets, but the advice was often ignored.

Civil War physicians knew that some minerals plus a variety of nutrients, including those they called "albuminous, fatty, and saccharine," were required for a healthy diet. While the role of micronutrients, such as vitamins, was not yet understood, the Federal Surgeon General's Office listed "dietic disease" (their term for malnutrition) as a major category in their disease classification. However, they recognized only three "dietic diseases": scurvy, delirium tremens, and inebriation. Since the last two are related to excessive alcohol consumption, scurvy was the only disease caused by dietary deficiency recognized. This "dietic" disease had a large impact on soldiers' health, increasing the severity of other illnesses and the mortality rate from treated gunshot wounds.

Despite attempts to provide soldiers with an adequate diet, scurvy was common in both the pre-war U.S. Army and all armies during the Civil War. Physicians recognized that when they diagnosed a few cases of scurvy in a unit, the disease was actually widespread, since they could only diagnose it in its advanced forms. Due to its many debilitating effects, scurvy had a major impact on the military effectiveness of some units, a fact well documented during the war. The data collected by the Federal Surgeon General's Office indicate that the frequency of scurvy increased as the war went on, with some major outbreaks. Night blindness, listed under "eye diseases" during the Civil War, was later shown to be due to vitamin A deficiency. This dietary deficiency disease also became more frequent over the course of the war.

UNION TROOPS' DIET

Soldiers always gripe about their food, but Civil War troops clearly had a lot to complain about. They subsisted on a monotonous diet that rarely included fresh vegetables. "Soft bread" was a delicacy and soldiers treasured it whenever it was available. Hardtack, a tough biscuit, was the main staple. It was often so stale that it was barely chewable even after being soaked in boiling water. (See Figure 13.1.) The cases containing hardtack were labeled "B. C.," which stood for "brigade commissary," although the men insisted it referred to the date the biscuits were manufactured.

Soldiers called the biscuit "skillygalee" when it had been soaked in water and fried in pork grease. If they could crush it before soaking, it became "hellfire stew" and soup made of hardtack, salt pork, and anything else available was named "lobcourse."[1] When hardtack was infested with worms, soldiers considered it "so much gain," since the worms added to their meager meat ration. Yet they preferred to eat infested hardtack, called "worm castles," at night so they didn't have to look at the critters. Although they complained about it and even made up songs describing it, soldiers generally liked hardtack. Confederates did not have hardtack; they normally used coarsely ground cornmeal for baking bread.

The basic army ration was increased by an Act of Congress on August 3, 1861, that stipulated the following:

> A ration is the established daily allowance of food for one person. For the United States Army it is composed as follows: Twelve ounces of pork or bacon, or one pound and four ounces of salt or fresh beef; one pound and

Figure 13.1: "Hard Tack" by Winslow Homer (1864) depicts the difficulty soldiers had chewing hardtack. (The Metropolitan Museum of Art, Harris Brisbane Dick Fund, 1947. [47.91.25] All rights reserved. The Metropolitan Museum of Art.)

six ounces of soft bread or flour, or one pound of hard bread [hardtack], or one pound and four ounces of corn-meal; and to every one hundred rations, fifteen pounds of beans or peas, and ten pounds of rice or hominy; ten pounds of green coffee or eight pounds of roasted (or roasted and ground) coffee, or one pound eight ounces of tea; fifteen pounds of sugar; four quarts of vinegar; one pound and four ounces of adamantine or star candies; four pounds of soap; three pounds and twelve ounces of salt; four ounces of pepper; thirty pounds of potatoes, when practicable, and one quart of molasses . . . Desiccated compressed potatoes or desiccated compressed mixed vegetables, at the rate of ounce and a half of the former and one ounce of the latter, to the ration, may be substituted for the beans, peas, rice, hominy or fresh potatoes.[2]

At the time of the Civil War, the term "bacon" was used for most of the meat from a hog, except the ham. Each hog typically weighed about 200 pounds and was expected to supply 100 pounds of bacon.[3] The meat was usually smoked or salted to preserve it. When soldiers bought meat from purveyors, it was old, tough, and very salty beef or pork, so they called it "salt horse" or "salt junk." Fresh meat was provided occasionally from herds of cattle that moved with armies.[4] There was no attempt at meat preservation in the field, and, if not immediately consumed, fresh meat became infested with maggots unbelievably fast. One soldier describes infestation occurring "in twenty minutes after it was killed, before it was cut up to be delivered."[5] It was often eaten rare, still quivering, roasted on sticks or bayonets or, most commonly, fried in lard. (The soldiers tended to fry everything over their small fires.) The cattle were usually scrawny from enduring long marches and poor forage. During the Siege of Petersburg, for example, Grant's army had a large herd of cattle near the supply base at City Point, but men of one Massachusetts regiment described the cows as so thin, "it would take a dozen cows to make a decent shadow."[6]

Soup made from beans or peas was common and one soldier recorded that "the bean soup was good, but with some cooks it was made so thin that men used to say there was one bean to a quart of water."[7] Soldiers' nutritional intake was not helped by the nearly ubiquitous coffee, which they considered indispensable. Whenever soldiers took even a few minutes break from a march, most immediately began boiling water for coffee. Commissary officials, therefore, tried to ensure that coffee was always available, even if there was no other food.[8] The Confederates rarely had real coffee and used all sorts of beans and nuts as substitutes. When they could trade with Union soldiers, they usually wanted only coffee in exchange for their tobacco.

The food allotment for each company was based on the original roster. Partly because the complement of men shrank from the toll taken by disease and combat and partly because some men didn't eat their allotment, a company's ration often exceeded its needs. The surplus could be sold, and the proceeds used to form a "company fund" to buy items that were not issued, such as milk, butter, seasonings, and utensils. Vegetables were often purchased with these funds, but the demand was always greater than the supply.[9]

Sutlers accompanied the armies almost everywhere, usually following the paymaster. They sold delicacies such as pies and cakes, as well as paper and pencils for writing letters home, all usually at exorbitant prices. The men condemned the sutlers, referring to them as vultures and to their products as "pizen cakes." But, overall, sutlers did not contribute much of value to the nutritional needs of the army.[10]

CONFEDERATE FOOD SUPPLIES

From the war's outset, Confederate armies were hungry much of the time, and they occasionally were near starvation. There were many reasons for this lack of food; one was the personality of the commissary general, Col. Lucius Bellinger Northrop. Fellow Confederates considered Northrop a "sour pus" and accused him of being more interested in paperwork (even then called "red tape") than in getting food supplies to where they were needed. Complaints about Northrop's job performance finally led to his resignation on February 13, 1865, but many factors actually limited his ability to provide adequate rations (see Biographical Box, p. 342).[11]

Before the war, the Southern states did not produce enough food for their own use. When the war began, farmers switched from raising cotton, which they couldn't sell because of the blockade, to growing food crops. Throughout the war, food was available, and even abundant, in some parts of the Confederacy, despite the lack of manpower on the farms. For example, Sherman's army ate very well when they marched through Georgia (November and December 1864), although they didn't bring any rations. The same held true for Grant's army during the Vicksburg campaign (May 1863) after they crossed the Mississippi and attacked eastward to take Jackson. In fact, Grant's men became so glutted with rich food that on one occasion, they actually protested not getting their usual fare by chanting the word "hardtack" as the general rode past. That night, Grant arranged for them to feast happily on hardtack, beans, and coffee instead of "all that turkey and sweet potatoes."[12] Soaring prices, however, made Southern farmers unwilling to sell food to the Confederate army for less than they could get in the marketplace.

With the fall of Vicksburg, the Confederate government was cut off from the allied states west of the Mississippi (the area called "Trans-Mississippi" during the war). Federal occupation of progressively larger portions of the Confederacy meant there was less land available for farming, so procurement agents had an increasingly difficult time obtaining food for their army.[13] In Georgia, however, political differences between Governor Joseph Brown and President Jefferson Davis kept the army's food supplies low.[14]

The South's decrepit transportation system, especially the railroad, also limited Northrop's ability to provide food for Confederate forces. In contrast to the Federal railroad, which under Herman Haupt ran spectacularly well through most of the war, the Confederate system was chaotic. One reason was that different railroad gauges were used in different states, so valuable time and energy were wasted transferring goods to new cars when crossing state

Col. Lucius Bellinger Northrop (1811–1894)

An 1833 graduate of West Point, Lucius Bellinger Northrop served in the prewar U.S. Army with Jefferson Davis, an acquaintance from the Academy. During the Seminole War in 1839, he accidentally shot himself in the leg and became partially disabled. While on long-term sick leave, he studied medicine; first through an apprenticeship and then at a formal medical school. When South Carolina seceded, he was practicing medicine in Charleston.

He finally resigned his U.S. Army commission and traveled to Montgomery, Alabama, where Confederate President Jefferson Davis commissioned him a lieutenant colonel and initially appointed him as acting commissary general. Northrop continued in this post through almost the entire war because Davis' choices for permanent commissary general refused to accept the post.

Northrop was never promoted higher than colonel because the Confederate Congress blamed him for the army's food shortages and considered him peevish, condescending, secretive, and intolerant of suggestions. Confederate Congressman Henry Stuart Foote of Tennessee—a foe of everything Jefferson Davis advocated—was a particularly ardent enemy. Addressing the issue of inadequate food supplies for prisoners of war in December 1863, Foote said, "if the Yankee prisoners had not got enough, it was the fault of the Commissary-General, Mr. Northrop, and his way of doing business. This man has been a curse to the country."

Foote called him "a pepper doctor from South Carolina . . . [who] should be dragged from his position." ("Pepper doctor" probably meant "botanic doctor," and was meant as an insult.) However, Foote's attempts to dismiss Northrop from office were unsuccessful.[15]

In retrospect, Northrup did rather well under the circumstances, which included a shortage of funds, skyrocketing prices, and transportation difficulties. Jefferson Davis remained a special friend and protected Northrop from critics. But Davis finally yielded, and Northrop resigned in February 1865. After the war, Northrop was imprisoned for several months on the suspicion that he willfully starved prisoners, but he was never tried or convicted. He bought a farm near Charlottesville, Virginia, where he spent the remainder of his life.[16-18]

lines. In addition, the railroad's deteriorating rolling stock could not be replaced, since most of it had come from the North before the war. Another problem Northrop faced was that the transport of troops and military supplies received priority over transporting food.[19]

Although some Confederate commanders, such as Braxton Bragg, did not consider feeding the troops a high priority, Robert E. Lee constantly struggled with the secretary of war to improve his men's rations, particularly during the last two years of the war.[20] During the spring of 1863, Lee wrote to the secretary of war:

> Their ration consists of 1/2 pound of bacon, 18 ounces of flour, and 10 lbs. of rice to each 100 men, every third day, with a few peas and a small amount of dried fruit occasionally as could be obtained. This may give existence to troops who are idle but certainly will cause them to break down when called upon for severe exertion.[21]

The western Confederate forces ate better than did Lee's Army of Northern Virginia for most of the war, in part because there was more available forage. Fighting in the thoroughly picked-over territory of Virginia, by October 1864, Lee's men were getting bacon only one day in four. In contrast, Gen. Joe Johnston's army, which faced Sherman in northern Georgia (considered "the West"), received meat from beef cattle sent across the Mississippi by the thousands through much of 1864.[22]

SCURVY

Since the Crusades (and maybe much earlier), physicians recognized that soldiers commonly suffered disastrously from scurvy. Before the nineteenth century, they differentiated "land scurvy" from the disease that affected sailors, which was often confused with syphilis or blamed on the salt air. By the time of the Civil War, however, it was understood that the two varieties of scurvy were identical and that fresh vegetables played a role in the prevention of scurvy.

In 1753, British naval surgeon James Lind published his classic work on the use of citrus fruits to treat and prevent scurvy. Physicians in the early 1800s found that a number of foods other than citrus fruits, such as onions and fresh green vegetables, were also antiscorbutic (antiscurvy agents). These foods, later found to contain large amounts of vitamin C, were called "specifics." ("Specifics" were drugs that were particularly effective for a certain disease, with little or no effect on other diseases. For example, they noted that lemon juice "supplies something to the blood which is essential to its healthy properties," a good description of the later theory of nutritional deficiency diseases.) About the same time, they realized that "farinaceous seeds, such as wheat, barley, oats and rye," lacked antiscorbutic properties.[23] Wild vegetables were picked whenever possible; at one fort, wild artichokes, which are edible from the beginning of April, were reported to be particularly effective for treating scurvy. Despite this knowledge, scurvy remained a major problem within the military through World War I.[24]

Potatoes were also found to be very potent antiscorbutics, especially raw potatoes. (This is because Vitamin C is heat-labile, and much of it is destroyed during cooking.) Therefore, army physicians correctly prescribed raw potatoes when symptoms of scurvy were severe. According to the testimony of Dr. John C. Bates, a contract surgeon at Andersonville prison:

> There was in my ward a boy of 15 or 16 years, in whom I had a particular interest. . . . He would often ask me to bring him a potato, a piece of bread, a biscuit, something of that kind, which I did; I would put them in my pocket and give them to him. I would sometimes give him a raw potato, and as he had the scurvy, and also gangrene, I would advise him not to cook the potato at all, but to eat it raw, as an antiscorbutic.[25]

During the 1800s, there were many theories on what caused scurvy. Scientists made numerous attempts, using modern scientific concepts, to establish a chemical basis for the disease. During the Civil War, their studies concentrated on substances that could be measured at the time, such as the vegetable acids, citric acid, and phosphorus. Although off the mark in terms of later knowledge, researchers had moved into the modern scientific era, far from earlier theories of contagion, miasmas, and exposure to salt air.

Before the Civil War, the army had difficulty supplying fresh vegetables to frontier troops, thus the soldiers suffered terribly from scurvy, particularly in late winter when their vegetable supplies were depleted. From 1843 to 1861, the annual incidence of scurvy in the American army was 26.3 cases per 1,000 mean strength; about twice the average annual incidence among white Union troops during the Civil War. Describing a pre-war scurvy outbreak at Council Bluffs, a surgeon reported that "neither small-pox nor Asiatic cholera, in their most malignant forms, was so dreadful as this outbreak of scurvy."[26]

To combat the problem of scurvy in the frontier army, Congress passed a law before the war that mandated use of a canned preparation known as "desiccated, compressed mixed vegetables." Devised to conserve shipping space, it supposedly contained string beans, turnips, carrots, beets, and onions compressed into dry cakes or bricks one-inch thick and up to one-foot square. Soldiers, though, claimed that the cakes consisted mainly of roots, leaves, vegetable tops, and stalks. When soaked in water, the cakes expanded to an awesome size. Usually, they were boiled extensively to make them chewable, but if too large a cake was used, it swelled out of the pan

"Limeys"

After Dr. (Sir) Gilbert Blane became a commissioner on the Sick and Hurt Board of the British Admiralty, he convinced the navy that James Lind's findings on the link between diet and scurvy were important. Thus, beginning in 1795, lemon and lime "water" (i.e., juice) were stocked aboard naval vessels. By the end of the Napoleonic Wars in 1815, the Royal Navy had issued 1.6 million gallons of lemon juice, giving a ration to each man every morning. The terms "lemon" and "lime" were used interchangeably by the British during the 1800s, and so British sailors became known as "limeys."

In the 1900s, physicians realized that the lemon/lime juice could be ineffective in treating scurvy. The old method of preparing, storing, and shipping the lemon juice involved heating the juice, and this resulted in the loss of vitamin C content. (Vitamin C is heat-labile.) However, Lind and others, especially Capt. James Cook in his mid-1700 Pacific voyages, had demonstrated that fresh vegetables of all types could preserve sailors' health during long stretches at sea. The Royal Navy, therefore, brought supplies of vegetables to the ships on blockade duty. This probably prevented more scurvy than the use of lemon juice.

The measures taken to prevent scurvy were credited with doubling the Royal Navy's manpower, since they no longer had to bring warships into port every two or three months to "refresh" the crew. For example, Admiral Nelson's men had been at sea for about two years when they met and defeated the French at Trafalgar, aborting Napoleon's plans to invade England—Napoleon invaded Russia instead.[27]

and overflowed into the fire, causing a fiasco.[28] They tasted awful and Civil War soldiers despised them, calling them "desecrated vegetables" or "baled hay."[29] Considering the way they were prepared and cooked, they probably had little or no vitamin C left anyway.

The British Army issued a similarly unworkable regulation to the one substituting desiccated mixture for fresh vegetables. This regulation resulted in a devastating incidence of scurvy among the British troops in the Crimea. The British War Department, despairing of shipping the necessary volume of fresh vegetables to the army in Bulgaria and later in the Crimea, instead commanded the men to go to the nearest town and buy fresh vegetables whenever they received their pay and were given leave. But, through most of the war, the only nearby town was Balaclava, where "no green vegetables could be obtained at any price."[30] The result was an incidence of scurvy which would have eliminated the entire British Expeditionary Force in less than a year were it not for replacements and a new order that made lime juice and potatoes freely available.[31]

During the Civil War, physicians appear to have recognized the first symptoms of scurvy after soldiers went two to three months without foods now known as sources of vitamin C (ascorbic acid). The same pattern was seen on long sea voyages in earlier centuries, when scurvy appeared after two to three months at sea without fresh vegetables. Recent studies suggest that the body stores enough vitamin C to last up to about six months. The discrepancy may have been because Civil War soldiers (and sailors in earlier centuries) initially had lower vitamin C stored than the modern test subjects. During the war, the incidence rate of scurvy varied, and it reached epidemic proportions several times. After the war, the army again had problems supplying troops with a diet containing antiscorbutics and the incidence of scurvy in the post-war army rose well above wartime levels.

Transporting enough vegetables for the large number of men in the field posed a significant problem. The space required was prohibitive, especially when all supplies had to be carried by wagons over narrow rough roads. Commissary officials tried to ship potatoes, onions, turnips, and similar vegetables; they provided oranges and lemons when they could. However, food had to compete for space with other supplies, including fodder for the horses used by the artillery, the cavalry, and to pull the Commissary Department's wagons. Vegetables often spoiled during shipment, before they could be used.[32]

As early as July 1861, in his initial report as the executive secretary of the Sanitary Commission, Frederick Law Olmstead recorded his concern about scurvy:

> There seemed to be an abundance of such food—beef and pork—as the Subsistence Department was permitted by law to furnish, but under the regulations no green vegetables could be issued and of course none were provided. The consequence was that the army was generally believed to be in great danger of decimation by scurvy.[33]

SCURVY'S MANIFESTATIONS

Civil War physicians described scurvy's clinical manifestations in impressive detail, documenting the effect of malnutrition on the soldiers' health and on their ability to function. The first symptoms were usually lassitude, an

How to Prepare the Desiccated Compressed Mixed Vegetables

Both Dr. Charles Tripler and Dr. Jonathan Letterman, the successive Army of the Potomac medical directors between 1861 and 1863, believed that desiccated compressed mixed vegetables were useful in preventing scurvy, but only if they were prepared as a soup. In November 1861, while the Army of the Potomac was training near Washington, Tripler wrote to the chief of staff:

> [the] soup requires three and one-half hours for its preparation; volunteers will not take so much trouble unless it is enjoined upon them by positive order, and also made the duty of the company officers to see that it is done. Cold weather and the want of vegetable food are almost sure to engender scurvy.[34]

The following November, Letterman still advocated the use of the vegetable concoction. In an extensive discussion of proper food preparation for the army, he described a similarly impractical method of cooking:

> The desiccated vegetables should be steeped in water for two hours, and boiled with the soup for three hours; . . . and half a ration of desiccated vegetables previously soaked in cold water for an hour, with a few small pieces of pork, adding salt and pepper, with water sufficient to cover well the ingredients, and stewed slowly for three hours, will make an excellent dish. . . . The secret in using the desiccated vegetables is in having them thoroughly cooked. The want of this has given rise to a prejudice against them which is unfounded; it is the fault of the cooking, and not of the vegetables.[35]

Neither medical director discussed the practicality of their suggestions when dealing with a large army of volunteers, most of whom prepared their own food. They also did not explain how they could be implemented in an army subjected to long exhausting marches.

apparent laziness, and indisposition to do assigned tasks, which were described as "muscular debility and depression of the spirit." Tissue changes soon became apparent, with a "sallow appearance, puffy, tender and bleeding state of the gums, with a tendency for the teeth to become loose." Small hemorrhages appeared in the skin, and doctors observed excessive bleeding from wounds and a need for an increased number of sutures during surgery.

Pains and aches were common; they were often the predominant symptom, since bleeding also occurred in muscles and joints.[36]

Some soldiers also had superficial ulcerations on their feet and toes; liver-colored patches on their arms, legs, and chest; ulcerations on their legs; or "suppurative inflammation of wounds, [and] foul state of the socket after extraction of a tooth." Others had "derangement of the bowels" and they tended to relapse after they stopped treatment with remedies such as lemonade.[37] If patients did not receive food containing vitamin C, the disease worsened: the weakness became prostration and the hemorrhagic areas were more extensive in the skin and the organs, impairing function and eventually causing death.

During the Civil War, physicians attributed only 771 deaths directly to scurvy: there were more than 46,000 scurvy cases diagnosed in the Federal army. Civil War physicians correctly recognized that there were "subclinical" manifestations of scurvy (i.e., symptoms, but not enough to make a definitive diagnosis). They concluded,

> Such subclinical scurvy probably explains complaints of some commanders about the attitude of units which were generally out of keeping with the general spirit and effectiveness of most units in both armies. . . . [Furthermore,] it is usually considered that if one man in a command is affected with well developed signs of scurvy many other men of that command, all of whom have been subject to the same dietary, will be more or less disabled, although they may not be borne on the sick-report. This assumption is indisputable.[38]

It was also correct.

As with all diseases, diagnoses were recorded only when men were relieved from duty or were sent to a hospital with the fully developed advanced disease. In many instances, men were described as having the "scorbutic taint" but were not relieved from duty or hospitalized. A variety of vague diagnostic terms such as "debility" were used (especially in the Confederate army). During the early stage of tiredness and lethargy, many men were accused of malingering. This subclinical form of scurvy was thought to be responsible for "lack of morale" and a general "poor attitude." Sanitary Commission reports noted:

> A soldier becomes worthless without any obvious evidences of disease. He complains of weakness, hebetude [sic], loss of appetite, disinclination to exertion, is slow and torpid in intellect, has palpitations of the heart and soreness of the muscles, and suffers from pseudo-rheumatic and neuralgic pains.[39]

Physicians often used the term "cachexia," meaning severe generalized weakness and debility, to describe the physical state of men affected by scurvy, whether or not the disease was severe enough to be diagnosed. Scurvy was thought to explain many symptoms usually attributed to other diseases. One of these was "scorbutic rheumatism," which referred to pains and aches in the extremities. Physicians believed these symptoms were caused by scurvy, and they were probably correct, since the disease causes hemorrhages in muscles, in joint tissues, and along bones (i.e., in or under the periosteum). Diarrhea, especially when fatal, was also associated with scurvy.

The incidence of scurvy among Confederate forces was probably similar to or higher than in the Union army. The Confederate Medical Department often used the Latin *debilitas* to describe the weakness and debility associated with the early stage of scurvy before the characteristic diagnostic hemorrhages appeared.[40]

SCURVY DURING THE PENINSULA CAMPAIGN

The first and largest scurvy epidemic occurred early in 1862 during the initial major campaign in the East. In April, Assistant Surgeon E.S. Dunster reported scurvy among McClellan's forces, and the epidemic became increasingly severe. Tripler questioned the diagnosis, since the men had received adequate supplies of desiccated vegetables and potatoes. When he investigated, however, he found that the men "very generally refused to use the desiccated vegetables; the chief commissary had an abundance of them and could not get rid of them. Even potatoes had been suffered to rot upon his hands and in the camps."[41] Hammond, the newly appointed surgeon general, quickly ordered supplies of lime juice.

Tripler had notified McClellan's chief of staff of the "proper" cooking method for the desiccated vegetables, but his method proved impractical due to the prolonged preparation time required and the army's almost continuous maneuvering and fighting. In his report, Tripler stressed that he had "requested the Adjutant-General to compel the men to use desiccated vegetables, and to make and use soup daily." He indicated that he felt trapped by the army regulations, which he ruefully quoted:

> Paragraph 1202, General Regulations, confines the issue of anti-scorbutics to the sick, and then they are to be paid for out of the hospital fund. I think, however, that potatoes have been made part of the ration by act of Congress. It is certain that vegetables are absolutely necessary to prevent scurvy, and if, as in our present circumstances, they cannot be purchased by the men, the Subsistence Department must supply them, or the men

will become scorbutic. I have ordered a supply of lemons and cream of tartar from White House [the location of the army's supply base in the Peninsula at the time] to Sumner's corps. I have also telegraphed to Colonel Clarke to issue, if possible, potatoes, dried apples, pickles, and desiccated vegetables to the men.[42]

Tripler futilely tried to defend himself from criticism by adding,

The means, then, of preventing scurvy have always been ready for issue in the subsistence department. The responsibility for its occurrence rests with those who have neglected to use these means. I think stringent orders necessary to compel regimental officers to see that their men are provided with and habitually use these necessary articles.[43]

Tripler believed that the army was relatively healthy and that the 50,000 cases of diarrhea and dysentery during his tenure were to be expected. Despite his predictions and efforts, he was criticized for the outbreak of scurvy, as well as for the chaotic care of the casualties, especially after the Battle of Fair Oaks. Subjected to "much censure and abuse," as he described it, Tripler requested a transfer. He was replaced by Dr. Jonathan Letterman on July 4, 1862.[44]

Letterman quickly became convinced of the presence of scurvy and reported to Surgeon General Hammond:

Scurvy had made its appearance before [the army's] arrival [on the peninsula], the seed of which had doubtless been planted some months previously. . . . The disease is not to be dreaded merely by the numbers it sends upon the reports of sick. It goes much farther. The causes which give rise to it undermine the strength, depress the spirits, take away the energy, courage, and elasticity of those who do not report themselves sick and yet they are not well. . . . It has affected the fighting powers of the army, and much more than was indicated by the numbers it has sent upon the reports of the sick.[45]

To counter the outbreak of scurvy on the peninsula, Letterman requisitioned potatoes, onions, cabbage, tomatoes, squash, beets, and fresh bread, even though they were not called for in army regulations. By August 16, he noted that the disease had disappeared:

A true idea of the improvement that took place could not be conveyed in writing, as there was so much in appearance, in the life and vivacity exhibited by the men in their slightest actions, even in the tone of the voice, which conveyed to one's mind the impression of health and spirits, of recovered tonicity of mind and body and of the presence of vigorous and manly courage.[46]

Letterman's actions controlled the episode of scurvy on the peninsula.

The overall incidence of scurvy in the Union army increased throughout the war. Table 13.1 shows the reported incidence of scurvy and of night blindness, a disease we now know to be caused by vitamin A deficiency.

Major outbreaks of scurvy were reported among Union troops during the Peninsula campaign and the sieges of Atlanta, Vicksburg, and Petersburg. Confederate forces also suffered greatly from scurvy, but detailed data on incidence rates are not available.

Scurvy and night blindness were much more common among black soldiers, implying that black troops had even less fresh vegetables in their diet (see Table 12.4). Many black regiments were assigned to garrison duty in forts; this would have limited their opportunities to forage.

TABLE 13.1

Incidence of Scurvy and Night Blindness in White Troops, Union Army

(Recorded Cases per 1,000 Men per Year)

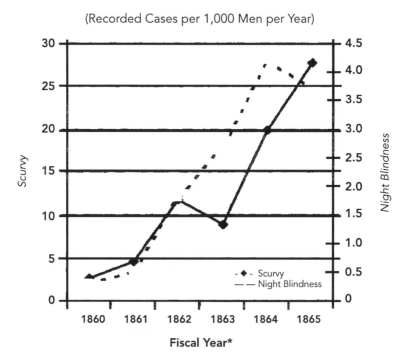

Fiscal Year*

*Data for FY 1860 is from May and June 1861. Other FY run from July 1 of year given through June 30 of following year.

FORAGING

Soldiers on both sides quickly learned that they had to forage for anti-scorbutics to avoid coming down with scurvy. Although all armies officially prohibited foraging during most of the war, soldiers learned that this was the best way to obtain meat and fresh vegetables. When foraging was limited, as it was during prolonged sieges or in the prison camps, scurvy became rampant.

Blackberries, which soldiers correctly considered medicinal, were a favorite of foragers. In his memoirs, General Sherman referred to the importance of blackberries to the troops, stating, "I have known the entire skirmish line, without orders, to fight a respectable battle for the possession of some old fields full of blackberries."[47] Surgeon Hewit, medical director of the Army of the Ohio, reported that from May 1 to September 8, 1864, "Scorbutus [scurvy] . . . existed as a rather vague cachexia rather than a definite disease. It was antagonized [prevented] in the early part of the summer by an abundance of blackberries, and later by green corn, sorghum, cane juice, and vegetables."[48]

The effect of foraging is dramatically exemplified by the Union troops that suffered through the siege of Chattanooga. On limited rations and unable to forage during the siege, in November 1863, many of them were hurriedly sent to Knoxville to relieve Gen. Ambrose Burnside's men, who were being besieged by Confederate Lt. Gen. James Longstreet. Division Medical Director W. W. Blair reported that

> Notwithstanding the limited clothing and shelter, the health of the command continued good, and in many instances, owing to the complete change in diet, for we were compelled to subsist upon food collected from the country through which we marched, there was a marked improvement in health.[49]

As the war dragged on, the poorly provisioned Confederate army often tried to rely on foraging to supplement their diet. In a March 1863 letter to Confederate Secretary of War James A. Seddon, General Lee mentioned an order to forage for wild plants to combat scurvy among his men before the spring campaign:

> The troops of this portion of the army have for some time been confined to reduced rations, . . . I do not consider it [the food available] enough to continue them in health and vigor, and I fear they will be unable to endure the hardships of the approaching campaign. Symptoms of scurvy are appearing among them and, to supply the place of vegetables, each regiment is directed to send a daily detail to gather sassafras buds, wild onions,

---

Descriptions of Foraging

A Union physician:

> The author has seen a whole regiment at a halt, break ranks for a turnip field, and devour the succulent roots raw; green ears of corn have also been treated in the same way.[52]

Robert E. Lee, about Gen. John Bell Hood's troops:

> Ah, General, when you Texans come about, the chickens have to roost mighty high.[53]

Chorus of a favorite song among Confederate soldiers:

> Just before the battle, the general hears a row,
> He says, "The Yanks are comin' boys, I hear their rifles now!"
> He turns around in wonder, and what do you think he sees,
> The Georgia Militia, eating goober peas.*[54]

*"Goober peas" were peanuts.

---

garlic, lamb's quarter, and poke sprouts; but for so large an army the supply obtained is very small.[50,51]

There is no data on the actual incidence of scurvy in Lee's army, but it is known that the nutritional state of his troops was of constant concern to the general. Foraging was an inadequate supplement to the rations Commissary General Northrup provided, largely because the troops were fighting in the same area most of the time and the fields were thoroughly picked over. Although the local citizens tried to help the soldiers, the fact that they fought mostly in home territory hampered the Confederates. When Lee's men invaded Maryland and Pennsylvania, where less fighting had taken place, their foraging was much more successful.

Sherman's army took along very little food when they left Atlanta to begin their March to the Sea in late 1864. They expected to live off the land, so search parties were sent out to collect food each day and the men ate luxuriously. They enjoyed turkeys, ducks, sheep, and hogs, along with corn, sweet potatoes, turnips, rice, and other vegetables. Scurvy, which had been prevalent during the Atlanta campaign, disappeared from the ranks during the march.[55]

SCURVY IN THE NAVY

Although the navy had virtually eliminated scurvy by the mid-1800s, there were some outbreaks during the Civil War. Scurvy became an ongoing problem during blockade duty, as ships had to stay at sea for extended periods without fresh provisions. Some naval officers also observed scurvy on merchant ships returning from long voyages, and they provided them with fresh vegetables from their own stores. For example, Commander Napoleon Collins of the U.S. steam sloop *Wachusett* reported that on August 20, 1864, while hunting Confederate raiders off Bahia, Brazil,

> On our way from Rio de Janeiro . . . in latitude 20° 12′ S., longitude 37° 26′ W., we fell in with the American ship *Princess* of Boston, R. Crowell, master, with a cargo of guano, 108 days from Baker Island, Pacific Ocean, bound to Liverpool. Three of her crew had died, five more were unfit for duty from scurvy, and all the remainder were suffering more or less with the same diseases.
>
> We supplied her with 50 pounds of desiccated potatoes, 50 pounds of desiccated assorted vegetables, and some medicines; also eight men to assist in working her into this harbor.[56]

At the very beginning of the hostilities, scurvy developed among the crew of a ship blockading the eastern Gulf. Apparently, the U.S. frigate *Sabine* had been at sea anticipating the conflict for some months and, in April 1861, Captain Adams wrote to the secretary of the navy,

> I regret to inform you that the scurvy has broken out on board the *Sabine*, and in the opinion of the surgeon is likely to spread. She ought to go immediately to some place where fresh meat and vegetables for the crew can be had.[57]

Captain Adams became increasingly concerned and, on May 1, 1861, he added,

> I must beg leave respectfully to call your attention to the circumstances of this ship's company. They are getting very much discontented at the length of the cruise. The scurvy is increasing among them and they have had no fresh meat for more than three months.[58]

There was also scurvy aboard the famous ironclad USS *Monitor*, shortly after its clash with the Confederate ironclad CSS *Virginia* (previously the USS *Merrimac*) in Hampton Roads, Virginia. On July 28, 1862, Commodore Charles Wilkes, commander of the James River Flotilla, wrote to the assistant secretary of the navy, "We need the fresh provisions very much. The scurvy has shown itself on board the *Monitor*."

On January 17, 1862, Gideon Welles, Federal secretary of the navy, wrote to the treasury secretary requesting permission for the Southern Atlantic Blockading Squadron to purchase provisions from the Southerners:

> SIR: The crews of some of our vessels at Port Royal and in that vicinity are suffering from scurvy, and I therefore have the honor to request that license may be granted to responsible parties who desire it, and who you are satisfied will not abuse it, to trade with those vessels, under the provision of the act of July 13, 1861, taking them fresh supplies and such other articles as you may think advisable.[59]

After Rear-Admiral John A. B. Dahlgren assumed command of the South Atlantic Blockading Squadron on August 9, 1863, he reported the need for more antiscorbutics in the sailors' rations:

> I am admonished by the daily recurrence of disability among the men, ... Scurvy is now added to the list of diseases and to-day the fleet surgeon recommends the return of the *Marblehead* to the North, because to remain here would break down the whole of the crew.
>
> I would therefore respectfully submit to the Department a recommendation to add certain articles of diet to those already provided by the regular ration:
>
> 1. Fresh vegetables daily, whether the meat be fresh or salt; potatoes, cabbage, onions, lemons, etc.[60]

Admiral D. G. Farragut, commander of West Gulf Squadron off New Orleans, also found that scurvy was a problem for his blockading fleet, even after the city's capture in April 1862. On June 6, 1862, he wrote to the secretary of the navy about one of the ships in his squadron: "The crew of the *Santee* is seriously affected with scurvy, and she must be relieved by the first vessel I can get for the purpose, but at present I have none."[61] Another ship in that squadron was similarly affected the following year. On July 23, 1863, Commodore H. H. Bell, while patrolling off Galveston, reported: "I regret to observe that there are several cases of scurvy occurring on board the *Brooklyn* and other vessels of this blockade. Supplies of fresh provisions and vegetable are much wanted."[62]

A month later, Frederic S. Hill, a young lieutenant in command of the bark *William G. Anderson,* had to explain why he took his ship off station while along the coast of Texas:

> SIR: Yours of August 25 [1863], asking my reasons for leaving my station, is at hand. I forwarded by Lieutenant-Commander Dana a letter to you, stating my reasons, which were as follows: Finding my men exhibiting evidences of scurvy, I ran down (80 miles) from Corpus Christi one night to this place to obtain some limes and other anti-scorbutics, purposing an immediate return the same day.[63]

These reports show that scurvy was a recurring problem in the U.S. Navy during the Civil War. Although the treatment was well known, the means to obtain the necessary antiscorbutics were not always available because of practical, military considerations. Nevertheless, there is no evidence of any death because of scurvy on military vessels, primarily because the necessary steps were taken to halt any disastrous outbreaks.

NIGHT BLINDNESS

During the Civil War, night blindness was classified as an eye disease rather than a "dietic disease." Officially called "nyctalopia," it was rarely diagnosed in the early years of the war, but the rate of occurrence increased as the war progressed.[64] Civil War physicians recognized that night blindness often accompanied scurvy, as evidenced by the discussion of both as "dietic disease" in *Medical and Surgical History*. Although the authors recorded that "sporadic cases of night-blindness occurred but no general tendency to night-blindness has been recorded as connected with the scorbutic taint," in the same paragraph they describe an outbreak of night blindness during Sherman's Atlanta campaign, when scurvy was especially widespread.

Surgeon J. C. Norton, who was in Sherman's army, reported "its [scurvy's] extensive prevalence in summer of 1864 in the 3rd Div. of 4th Army Corps." The first case of night blindness he saw appeared on

> May 8, 1864, after a hard day's march from Ringgold to Buzzard's Roost, Georgia . . . After this several other cases occurred, and as the campaign advanced the diseases appeared to rage as an epidemic. Some regiments had to lead thirty or forty blind men every night.[65]

Confederate physician Robert J. Hicks mentioned a dietary factor as the cause of night blindness in the Army of Northern Virginia:

> A man who could see well during the day complained at nightfall that he could not see, and like a blind man, walked holding the arm of a comrade . . . It was considered . . . due to the meagre diet, the want of vegetables.[66]

Hicks was correct, since vitamin A, like vitamin C, is obtained primarily from fresh vegetables. In contrast to vitamin C, however, vitamin A can be stored in body tissues and, thus, it usually takes longer for a deficiency to occur. Some Union physicians recorded that furloughs (leaves from the army) cured night blindness. Although this probably resulted from an improved diet while at home, many Civil War military physicians erroneously felt that it supported the contention that night blindness was a form of malingering.

Like scurvy, night blindness undoubtedly was more common than the official records show. Since the cause was unknown and the men were able to fight with their units during the day, the bulk of the cases would have been seen and treated at "Surgeon's Call" rather than relieved from duty or hospitalized, so the diagnoses would not have been recorded. It seems clear from the case descriptions that relatively few soldiers were relieved from duty for this problem and that many more cases occurred than were reported.

Sixty years later, night blindness was shown to be an early manifestation of vitamin A deficiency. More fully developed symptoms described in the twentieth century include changes in the skin (roughening and increased scaliness) and in the lining of the respiratory and intestinal tracts. Changes in the bronchial lining bring about a loss of normal cells on the surface; they are replaced with cells that fail to secrete a type of mucus that helps prevent infection. As a consequence, bronchitis and pneumonia can result from a deficiency of vitamin A, and it has been called the "anti-infection vitamin." Gastrointestinal abnormalities also occur, but their exact relationship to this nutritional deficiency is less clear. Progressive eye changes can ultimately lead to loss of the normal surface covering, with scarring and permanent blindness. While there is no record that Civil War troops suffered these permanent eye changes, vitamin A deficiency probably contributed to the incidence and severity of infections of the lungs and, perhaps, the intestine.

VARIATIONS IN THE INCIDENCE OF SCURVY AND NIGHT BLINDNESS

Although Civil War physicians had only a rudimentary understanding of nutrition, they knew enough to prevent malnutrition. So why did the cases of malnutrition increase as the war progressed? First, men were kept in the field for long periods—up to four successive years—with erratic supplies of fresh food and, particularly, a lack of fresh vegetables. Second, military commanders disregarded the surgeons' advice. They considered ammunition more important than fresh vegetables, unaware that the food would preserve their army's fighting ability. Third, transportation disruptions during the war made delivering fresh vegetables to the armies difficult.

Dr. Frank Hastings Hamilton, professor of surgery at Bellevue Medical College in New York and an intermittent volunteer medical inspector for the surgeon general, clearly understood the medical consequences of generalized malnutrition in an army, as well as the attitude of military commanders:

It need scarcely be said, . . . that no government ever provided more liberally for the wants [of] its soldiers in respect to food. We are convinced, however, that the principal reasons why the troops have not had fresh vegetables in greater abundance are, that the commissaries and commanding officers have either not known the true condition of the matters, or they have been ignorant of what would be the consequences. Whatever explanation we may adopt, the fact remains, that owing to an insufficiency of vegetable food the armies of the United States have been, a large proportion of the time, in imperfect health, and often scorbutic.[67]

Hamilton supported his conclusions by describing major episodes of malnutrition in Union armies. In one instance,

[In] the Army of the Potomac, under Major-General McClellan, . . . soon after the Battle of Fair Oaks [May 31 and June 1, 1862], scurvy began to manifest itself and continued to increase until we left the peninsula. For a period of five or six months probably not one full ration of fresh vegetables had been issued to the troops. In the latter part of August, a few days before we left Harrison's Landing on the James River, vegetables were supplied in abundance; but they came too late to put the army in condition for another advance upon Richmond.[68]

Hamilton stated that when the peninsula was abandoned, many men were too weak to march to the transports for transfer back to the Washington area. The surgeons of the 4th Corps turned over 2,000 men in this condition to the Sanitary Commission. Hamilton wrote,

In about the same ratio . . . all the other corps were depleted. Most of these men, we believe, were in some degree scorbutic. It is our confident belief that 20,000 men might have been saved to General McClellan's army during this unfortunate campaign, if the men had been furnished at all times with a reasonable amount of fresh vegetables.[69]

McClellan always felt he did not have enough men to move aggressively against the Confederate defenders of Richmond. Such an increase in the army's fighting capacity might well have made a difference militarily if McClellan had had the ability and the will to take advantage of it.

During General Sherman's Atlanta campaign, the incidence of scurvy and night blindness progressively increased in his troops. The basic reason again was difficulty in transporting sufficient antiscorbutic vegetables to the troops. Sherman's army engaged in frequent battles against Gen. Joe Johnston's defending Confederate forces, as the two armies constantly maneuvered near the single-track rail line from Chattanooga to Atlanta. Sherman documented this in his memoirs:

I now recall the extreme anxiety of my medical director, Dr. Kittoe, about the scurvy, which he reported at one time to be spreading and imperiling the army. This occurred at a crisis about Kennesaw [June 1864], when the railroad was taxed to its utmost capacity to provide the necessary ammunition, food and forage, and could not possibly bring us an adequate supply of potatoes and cabbage, the usual anti-scorbutics.[70]

WOMEN FIGHT SCURVY

Women who contributed to the war effort were particularly concerned with providing the soldiers with fresh vegetables. Most were mothers who knew the importance of a good diet to health. They formed innumerable ladies' aid societies, most of which became affiliated with the U.S. Sanitary Commission or one of its branches.

Once scurvy appeared in epidemic form during the Peninsula campaign (June 1862), Sanitary Commission members focused some of their efforts on obtaining the fruits and vegetables that the army could not provide. Lemons and oranges were known to be the most effective in combating scurvy, but they could not be provided in sufficient quantities. Multiple methods were used to mobilize the public in this effort. Mary A. Livermore, president of one of twelve aid societies of Chicago and, later, a leader of the Western Sanitary Commission, focused her energy on obtaining potatoes and onions—two known antiscorbutics—for the troops in the West. She arranged talent shows sponsored by local aid societies with the charge for admission being a potato or an onion. School children competed to bring the most potatoes. Signs and slogans appeared, such as "Don't send your sweetheart a love letter. Send him an onion."

Aid societies sent wagons door-to-door to gather potatoes and onions from storekeepers, farmers, and housewives, and then ensured that the supplies collected would begin their journey to the troops. Livermore, for example, arranged for General Grant to provide the shipping if the women would see that the boats were manned. This was how Mrs. Hoge, from the Sanitary Commission's Western Branch, became commander of the "potato fleet."

Livermore also organized a huge Sanitary Fair in Chicago to raise money for the Commission's efforts and to ship vegetables to the troops. To demonstrate support, the City of Chicago (population 110,000) closed so its citizens could attend the fair on October 27, 1863. Chicago residents watched a parade that included 100 wagons laden with potatoes, onions, cabbage, beets, barrels of cider, and kegs of beer. Spectators cheered and helped unload the produce into Sanitary Commission storage rooms. Newspapers printed

Figure 13.2: "Soldiers' Depot–Dining Room." [New York City] Facilities such as these were maintained by the Sanitary Commission in the North and by local women's groups in the South to provide accommodations, meals, and refreshment for soldiers on furlough or during transfers. (Courtesy of the Museum of the City of New York. © Museum of the City of New York. Reprinted with permission.)

human-interest stories, such as the gift of five barrels of potatoes by six young girls who had grown the vegetables themselves.[71,72] For fourteen days, parades of foodstuffs arrived: chickens, calves, loads of hay, apples, bags of beans, pots of butter, bundles of socks, mechanical products, and other gifts for soldiers or items to be sold to raise money. Again, Livermore arranged for the transportation of the food and treats to the soldiers in the field.

SCURVY IN EUROPEAN MILITARY UNITS DURING THE 1860S AND 1870S

During the time of the Civil War, and more than 100 years after British naval physician James Lind had documented the role of oranges and lemons in the treatment and prevention of scurvy, the British Navy still experienced outbreaks of the disease. According to an 1864 report, Her Majesty's Ship *Dreadnought* (whose name came to designate a whole class of vessels) had eighty-six cases of scurvy in one year.[73]

The French were afflicted with scurvy in the Franco-Prussian War. After the siege of Paris, the health of the troops was given as the main reason for the capitulation in January 1871. Physicians' advice to the French military commanders about how to prevent scurvy may have been muddled, an hypothesis supported by a debate on the subject held at the National Academy of Medicine in Paris in 1874. One of the main protagonists was Dr. Jean-Antoine Villemin, a prominent physician-scientist and the first to show that tuberculosis was contagious by transmitting it to animals. Villemin thought that all disease was contagious, even scurvy, and he would not accept a dietary deficiency as a cause of disease among the French troops:

> Scurvy is due to their being overworked, short of sleep and ... [living in] cold, damp and poorly ventilated quarters ... Provisions were relatively good ... the bread was white, the meat, though mainly horse was fresh, the wine ration was not reduced for a long time and was then supplemented with brandy; in a word there was no appreciable privation.[74]

Villemin attacked the concept that James Lind had found the cause of scurvy, as opposed to simply a treatment and preventative for the disease (which was all Lind had actually claimed), stating, "Certainly fresh vegetables and lemon juice have a certain curative value, but do we, just because quinine can cure malaria, conclude that the cause of malaria is a deficiency of quinine?"[75] By comparison, Union surgeon Joseph Woodward, in his book on *Camp Diseases* (1863) said "the leading cause of scurvy may be designated by a single word as camp diet."[76]

REFERENCES

1. Robertson JI: *Soldiers Blue and Gray*. Columbia: Univ. South Carolina Press, 1988, p. 69.
2. *Medical and Surgical History*, Medical Section, vol. 3, pp. 711-12.
3. *O.R.*, Series I, vol. XXXV/2, p. 606.
4. Bellard A: *Gone for a Soldier: The Civil War Memoirs of Private Albert Bellard: from the Alec Thomas Archives*. Boston: Little Brown, 1975, p. 119.
5. Robertson, *Soldiers Blue and Gray*, p. 67.
6. Wilkinson W: *Mother, May You Never See the Sights I Have Seen: The Fifty-seventh Massachusetts Veteran Volunteers in the Army of the Potomac, 1864–1865*. New York: Harper & Row, 1990, p. 206.
7. Bellard, *Gone for a Soldier*, p. 119.
8. Robertson, *Soldiers Blue and Gray*, p. 66.
9. Maxwell WQ: *Lincoln's Fifth Wheel: The Political History of the U.S. Sanitary Commission*. New York: Longmans Green, 1956.
10. Robertson, *Soldiers Blue and Gray*, p. 66.
11. Moore JN: *Confederate Commissary General Lucius Bellinger Northrop and the Subsistence Bureau of the Southern Army*. Shippensburg, PA: White Mane Pub., 1996, p. 275.
12. Foote S: *The Civil War: A Narrative*. vol. 2, New York: Random House, 1958, p. 383.
13. Gates PW: *Agriculture and the Civil War*. New York: Alfred A. Knopf, 1965, p. 126.
14. Parks JH: *Joseph E. Brown of Georgia*. Baton Rouge: Louisiana State Univ. Press, 1977.
15. Records of the First Confederate Congress (Fourth Session), Wednesday, December 9, 1863. *Southern Historical Society Papers*. 1953, New Series, vol. 12. (Old Series, vol. L.) p. 24.
16. Faust PL, ed.: *Historical Times Encyclopedia of the Civil War*. New York: Harper & Row, 1986, p. 538.
17. Moore, *Confederate Commissary General*, p. 295.
18. Foote, *Civil War*, vol. 2, p. 162.
19. *O.R.*, Series 1, vol. LI/2, p. 122. In: Moore, *Confederate Commissary General*, p. 74.
20. Lee RE: *The Wartime Papers of Robert E. Lee*. New York: Da Capo, 1987, pp. 418, 672, 698, 773, 886, 890.
21. "General R.E. Lee to James A. Seddon, Sec'y of War, April 17, 1863." *O.R.*, Series I, vol. XXV/2, p. 730.
22. *O.R*, Series I, vol. XLVI/2, p. 1222.
23. Watson T: *Lectures on the Principles and Practice of Physic: Delivered at King's College London*. Philadelphia, PA: Lea & Blanchard, 1845, pp. 1047-48.
24. Carpenter KJ: *The History of Scurvy and Vitamin C*. Cambridge, MA: Cambridge Univ. Press, 1986, pp. 117, 172, 186.
25. Chipman NP: *The Andersonville Prison Trial: The Trial of Capt. Henry Wirz*. Sacramento, CA: The Author, 1911, pp. 126-27.
26. *Medical and Surgical History*, Medical Section, vol. 3, p. 683.
27. Carpenter, *History of Scurvy and Vitamin C*, pp. 117, 172, 186.
28. Wilkinson, *May You Never See the Sights I Have Seen*, p. 205.
29. Robertson, *Soldiers Blue and Gray*, pp. 65-72.
30. Lawson G: *Surgeon in the Crimea: The Experiences of George Lawson Recorded in Letters to His Family 1854–1855*. London: Military Book Society, 1968, p. 156.
31. Cantlie N: *A History of the Army Medical Department*. vol. 2. Edinburgh: Churchill Livingston, 1973.
32. Report of Col. Henry F. Clarke, U.S. Army, Chief, Commissary of Subsistence, on operations from August 1, 1861, to November 9, 1862. *O.R.* Series I, vol. XI/1, p. 171.
33. Stillé CJ: *History of the United States Sanitary Commission: Being a General Report of Its Work during the War of the Rebellion*. New York: Hurd & Houghton, 1868, p. 85.
34. *O.R.*, Series I, vol. V, p. 664.
35. *O.R.*, Series I, vol. XIV, p. 351.
36. *Medical and Surgical History*, Medical Section, vols 1 and 3, various pages.
37. Ibid.
38. *Medical and Surgical History*, Medical Section, vol. 3, pp. 683-84.

39. U.S. Sanitary Commission, Flint A, ed.: *Contributions Relating to the Causation and Prevention of Disease, and to Camp Diseases, Together with a Report on the Diseases, etc. among the Prisoners at Andersonville, GA.* New York: Hurd & Houghton, 1867, p. 283.
40. Breeden JO: A medical history of the later stages of the Atlanta campaign. *J South Hist.* 1969;35:31-59.
41. *O.R.*, Series I, vol. XI/1, p. 207.
42. Ibid., p. 186.
43. Ibid., p. 207.
44. *O.R.*, Series IV, vol. I, p. 186.
45. *O.R.*, Series I, vol. XI/1, p. 211.
46. *Medical and Surgical History*, Medical Section, vol. 3, p. 688.
47. Sherman WT: *Memoirs of General William T. Sherman.* (2 vols.) New York: Appleton, 1875, p. 392.
48. *O.R.*, Series I, vol. XXXVIII, Part 2, p. 530.
49. *Medical and Surgical History*, Medical Section, vol. 1, p. 292.
50. Lee, *Wartime Papers*, p. 418; and Davis B: *Gray Fox: Robert E. Lee and the Civil War.* New York: Holt, Rinehart & Winston, 1956, pp. 181-82.
51. *O.R.*, Series I, vol. XXV/2, p. 687.
52. Woodward JJ: *Outlines of the Chief Camp Diseases of the United States Armies: As Observed during the Present War.* San Francisco: Norman, 1992, p. 66.
53. Foote, *Civil War*, vol. 2, p. 237.
54. Ladies Christian Commission: *Soldier's Songbook.* Bath, ME: U.S. Christian Commission, 1852.
55. Davenport H: Such is military: Dr. George Martin Trowbridge's letters from Sherman's army 1863-1865. *Bull NY Acad Med.* 1987;63(9):844-82.
56. *Navy O.R.*, Series I, vol. III, p. 191.
57. *Navy O.R.*, Series I, vol. VII, p. 598.
58. Ibid.
59. *Navy O.R.*, Series I, vol. XII, p. 490.
60. *Navy O.R.*, Series I, vol. XIV, p. 432.
61. *Navy O.R.*, Series I, vol. XVIII, p. 540.
62. *Navy O.R.*, Series I, vol. XX, p. 407.
63. Ibid., p. 483.
64. Robertson, *Soldiers Blue and Gray*, p. 69.
65. *Medical and Surgical History*, Medical Section, vol. 3, p. 706.
66. Hicks: *Richmond Med J.* 1867;3:35. Quoted in: *Medical and Surgical History*, Medical Section, vol. 3, p. 707.
67. Hamilton FH: *A Treatise on Military Surgery and Hygiene.* New York: Balliere Bros., 1865, p. 81.
68. Ibid.
69. Ibid.
70. Sherman, *Memoirs*, pp. 391-92.
71. Greenbie MLB: *Lincoln's Daughters of Mercy.* New York: G.P. Putnam's Sons, 1944, pp. 82, 148-51, 186.
72. *Medical and Surgical History*, Medical Section, vol. 3, p. 698.
73. Scurvy in the mercantile marine. *Lancet.* 1864;2:299-300. This note blamed the development of scurvy on "poor sanitary practices" as well as "spurious lime juice." The latter was probably accurate since some varieties of limes have low levels of vitamin C, a problem that continued to cause medical disasters well into the 1900s.
74. *Parisian Bull Natl Acad Med.* 1874. Quoted in: Carpenter, *History of Scurvy and Vitamin C*, p. 127.
75. Ibid.
76. Woodward, *Camp Diseases*, p. 62.

∾ 14 ∾

Chronic Diarrhea: It Takes Good Guts to Be a Good Soldier

Bowels are of more consequence than brains.

— Maine Commandery, Military Order of the Loyal Legion of the U.S.
(MOLLUS), 1898. Quoting an oft-repeated wartime assertion.

C HRONIC DIARRHEA CAUSED MORE DEATHS than any other disease during the Civil War. From the start of the war through demobilization, 27,558 soldiers died of the disease (typhoid fever was a close second with 27,056 deaths), and it was one of the main causes of medical discharge from the Union army, following only gunshot wounds and consumption (see Table 11.1). Available data suggests that all troops, black and white, Union and Confederate, suffered equally from chronic diarrhea. A leading Southern physician opined that no Confederate soldier had a fully formed stool during the entire course of the war.[1]

There was no clear definition of "chronic diarrhea" that distinguished it from the common, almost ubiquitous acute diarrhea that affected most soldiers intermittently. Chronic diarrhea, however, was far more serious than simply having loose stools. Case descriptions indicate that the syndrome called "chronic diarrhea" was characterized by prolonged, severe, daily diarrhea with frequent liquid or unformed stools, accompanied by weight loss, severe weakness, and wasting, often progressing to emaciation. Many of the descriptions of chronic diarrhea resemble the syndrome called "malabsorption" today. "Chronic dysentery," a term used in fewer cases and even less clearly defined, probably was used when there was also blood in the stools.

Chronic diarrhea was so prevalent and caused so much disability that among Civil War troops, it was said that a man "had to have good guts to be a good soldier." In fact, "guts" eventually came to mean soldierly qualities, particularly bravery, and the first literary use of this slang term was in the 1880s.[2] Dr. Joseph Jones stated:

> Chronic diarrhea and dysentery were the most abundant and the most difficult to kill among army diseases; while . . . typhoid fever diminished, chronic diarrhea and dysentery progressively increased, and not only destroyed more soldiers than gunshot wounds, but more soldiers were permanently disabled and lost to the service from these diseases than from the disability following the accident of battle.[3]

CAUSES OF CHRONIC DIARRHEA

Civil War physicians strove to understand and treat chronic diarrhea. They performed numerous autopsies and carefully studied specimens sent to the museum established in the Surgeon General's Office. One entire volume of *Medical and Surgical History*'s three huge medical volumes is devoted to the subject. It was listed as a "miasmatic" disease, along with the major infectious diseases, but physicians of the time never understood its nature or its multiple causes. In fact, many illnesses produced chronic diarrhea, but one can suggest the most probable causes based on present-day knowledge of intestinal diseases.

Civil War physicians recognized that both nutrition and infection may have played a role in chronic diarrhea's etiology. For example, in 1862, Dr. H. H. Gardner of the Army of the Cumberland wrote in the *American Medical Times*:

> [chronic diarrhea] has two distinct causes—scurvy and miasmatic influences. . . . If the cause be scurvy, there is great danger of its becoming chronic. Now your calomel and quinine will do no good, and may do much mischief. Opiates may be called for; but the main dependence is on fresh meat and vegetables. Potatoes, green apples, peaches, and pears, if they can be obtained and used as food will soon cure it. . . . One word in regard to climate. Many have recovered on being sent North to their homes; yet I do not think that climate has much to do with their recovery. They go home, live on fresh vegetables, and soon recover. *The same would happen here, were the diet the same* . . . With plenty of these [fresh vegetables], we need have little fear of scurvy or of *"chronic diarrhea," which is but another name for the same disease.*[4] [Original italics]

Although infections that Civil War surgeons would have called "miasmatic" must have caused many chronic diarrhea cases, Dr. Gardner, among others, rightly observed that nutrition might have caused some, and perhaps most, of the cases.

One of the infectious causes was what we now know as intestinal tuberculosis. Although Civil War physicians didn't consider the disease to be related to pulmonary tuberculosis, which they called "consumption," autopsies on some chronic diarrhea patients revealed intestinal ulcerations with "tubercles" in the mesenteric lymph nodes. While the records also noted the presence of pulmonary (lung) lesions in these cases, surgeons did not realize that the diarrhea was probably due to disseminated tuberculosis. The cases of intestinal tuberculosis, however, account for only a small percentage of the soldiers with chronic diarrhea.

AMEBIASIS

Amebiasis, which can occur in epidemic outbreaks, may also have been the source of some chronic diarrhea. Amebae were found in many of the areas where the troops camped and fought. Since fecal contamination of water or food spreads amebiasis, it most likely affected Civil War soldiers. However, physicians did not know this until 1875, when infection with amebae (*Entamoeba histolytica*) was shown to cause chronic diarrhea.

Although autopsy reports frequently noted changes commonly seen with amebiasis, particularly ulceration of the mucosal lining of the colon, few showed corroborative evidence, such as liver abscesses. Of the 396 cases of chronic diarrhea showing intestinal ulceration at autopsy, only 16 had liver abscesses and of these, just 6 had a single abscess, which suggests the possibility of amebiasis. Amebiasis is unlikely in the 10 cases having multiple abscesses.

The authors of *Medical and Surgical History* analyzed the occurrence of liver abscesses in association with "chronic dysentery" in detail. Their literature review emphasized a geographic variation, with single hepatic abscesses noted in "tropical dysentery" and multiple abscesses found in cases occurring in temperate climates such as in France and England. Since amebiasis occurs primarily in warmer climates and usually causes only solitary liver abscesses, tropical dysentery was probably mainly amebiasis. They did not conclude that "tropical dysentery" was the disease they observed, but some cases, especially those with single liver abscesses, probably were. Amebic dysentery was a considerable problem in American troops in North Africa during WWII, and also in the troops in Vietnam.

Yet, after men with chronic diarrhea were discharged, there were no reports of similar diseases occurring or spreading in their home communities (as would be expected to occur, especially given the rudimentary sanitation of the time).[5] This evidence leads one to suspect that there were no specific infectious causes, such as amebiasis, of chronic diarrhea, at least as a widespread phenomenon.

IMMUNE DEFICIENCY

When patients with deficient immune systems are infected with organisms that ordinarily cause transient symptoms, severe or prolonged disease, such as chronic diarrhea, often results. Since malnutrition can cause immune deficiency, this may have been the cause of some Civil War soldiers' chronic diarrhea. Among the organisms that cause chronic diarrhea in immuno-compromised individuals today are parasites that are spread by the fecal-oral route, such as *Cryptosporidium, Isospora,* and *Giardia.* However, these organisms primarily affect the small intestine, while the pathology in the autopsied cases reported in *Medical and Surgical History* was mostly in the large intestine. Other more common causes of bacterial dysentery today, such as *Salmonella* (non-typhoid), *Shigella, Campylobacter,* and invasive *Escherichia coli,* rarely cause chronic diarrhea in healthy individuals but may have been causes in malnourished Civil War soldiers.

Civil War physicians microscopically examined the stools of patients with chronic diarrhea in search of "pus corpuscles" and disease-causing microorganisms. They reported seeing pus corpuscles, as well as bacteria in the form of "cocci in chains," "bacilli," and budding yeast, which they called "torula." They did not think that the presence of these microorganisms was meaningful, since similar organisms could be found in stools from normal individuals.[6] The presence of pus cells suggests an infectious component to the etiology, but physicians at the time could not distinguish between normal intestinal flora (the bacteria normally found in stools) and pathogenic organisms. Such a distinction was about twenty years in the future.

While inflammatory bowel diseases (mainly ulcerative colitis and Crohn's disease, also known as granulomatous enteritis) are important causes of chronic diarrhea in the United States today, they are too infrequent to have significantly contributed to the incidence of chronic diarrhea during the Civil War. These diseases cause pathologic changes in the colon, but they are not contagious and do not occur as epidemics. Civil War physicians did not know about these diseases, but autopsies on some Civil War soldiers with chronic diarrhea showed intestinal changes that resemble the characteristic abnormalities seen in these syndromes: narrowing of the terminal ileum due to thickening of the intestinal lining or extensive ulceration of the colonic mucosa. However, in the reproductions of the microscopic examinations (and recent reexamination of the same slides still accessible in the Army Medical Museum), no lesions are recognizable as granulomatous enteritis, although there are the non-specific pathologic changes seen in those diseases. Some descriptions of the pathology in the contemporary medical literature mention ulcerations extending through the thickness of the wall of both the small and large intestine,[7] changes rarely seen in the cases of inflammatory bowel disease today.

Many pension applications and descriptions of individual soldiers' health after the war mention persistent chronic diarrhea that continued after their discharge from the military, although there is no information about its frequency. Since there are no reports of outbreaks of diarrhea or dysentery in veterans' family members or communities, there is no evidence to suggest an infectious etiology. It is unlikely that diarrhea caused by malnutrition would persist after discharge and the men's return to a more usual diet. Although some form of chronic inflammatory bowel disease is suggested by such cases, there is not enough information to warrant further discussion of the disorder in these men.

CHRONIC DIARRHEA AND MALNUTRITION

Civil War surgeons repeatedly emphasized the connection between diarrhea and scurvy, noting the therapeutic effect of fresh vegetables on bowel complaints. Although twentieth-century literature on scurvy rarely mentions chronic diarrhea, clinicians in previous centuries routinely observed it, calling it "scorbutic diarrhea." For example, British naval surgeon James Lind, who, in the mid-1700s, showed that citrus fruits prevented and treated scurvy, called chronic diarrhea the "scorbutic flux."[8] During the Crimean War, physicians described an association of scurvy with "scorbutic dysentery."[9] Civil War physicians noted that deaths from scurvy usually occurred in men who also had chronic diarrhea, and that deaths from chronic diarrhea usually occurred in the men with concomitant scurvy. Both scurvy and chronic diarrhea were ubiquitous, and the leading causes of death, in most prisons. (See Chapter 15, *Prison Camps*.)

Civil War surgeons repeatedly emphasized the association of diarrhea and scurvy. A severe outbreak of scurvy during the Atlanta campaign prompted one Federal surgeon to state:

> Diarrhea has persistently followed us, and has disqualified more [men] from active duty than all other diseases together. The cause seems to have been scorbutic to a great extent . . . Nor could this cause be removed for some time, owing to the difficulty of obtaining supplies of vegetables, &c., but as soon as the berries were sufficiently ripened, and fruit in a condition to cook, large quantities were consumed, and the scorbutic symptoms rapidly diminished until the present time, when no complaints are made and but few indications of the disease can be found.[10]

The association of scurvy and diarrhea and the response of both to treatment with a diet rich in vegetables suggest a nutritional cause in many chronic diarrhea cases. Because folic acid (a B vitamin) and vitamin C are in many of the same foods and have similar solubility in water and sensitivity to heat, people who are deficient in one vitamin are often deficient in the other. For example, a form of anemia observed in some patients with scurvy ("the megaloblastic anemia of scurvy") was thought to be due to vitamin C deficiency, but careful investigation showed it to be the result of concomitant folate deficiency.[11]

Deficiencies of other B vitamins can also cause diarrhea, a notable example being pellagra. Pellagra was known in Europe, particularly in northern Italy, for more than 100 years before it was recognized in the United States. The patient presents with weakness, weight loss, skin changes (especially in traumatized areas, such as areas exposed to the sun, including the forearms, face, and neck), and severe intractable chronic diarrhea. Severe mental changes, sometimes including dementia, are also characteristic. Before its nutritional cause (a deficiency of nicotinic acid, a B vitamin) was discovered, there was no effective treatment for pellagra; therefore, it had a high mortality rate. For example, between 1900 and 1940, it caused about one million deaths in the United States, predominantly in the southeastern states.

Did pellagra cause the devastating chronic diarrhea during the Civil War? While American physicians who had studied in Europe knew of pellagra, no one believed it existed in the United States before the epidemic in the early 1900s.[12] Yet, one contract physician, W.J.W. Kerr, believed, in retrospect, it might have plagued at least some soldiers during the Civil War. Along with Dr. Joseph Jones, he studied diseases among the prisoners at Andersonville, completing many autopsies himself. Kerr witnessed the start of an American epidemic of pellagra in 1905. After observing pellagra cases in Alabama, Kerr wrote that some of the illness he had seen at Andersonville was probably due to pellagra, especially among those with chronic diarrhea.[13]

Dr. Kerr's observation may have been correct. In the 1900s in the South, pellagra occurred in people who subsisted on little more than cornmeal, the dietary staple of the Andersonville prisoners. Moreover, the prisoners exhibited pellagra's four "D's": dermatitis, diarrhea, dementia, and, finally, death. Although these symptoms could have been due to other causes, Kerr's observations reemphasize the fact that Civil War soldiers with scurvy and chronic diarrhea had multiple nutritional deficiencies.

Both prisoners and physicians noted the relationship between scurvy and diarrhea, not only at Andersonville, but also in other prisons with high death rates, such as the northern prison at Elmira, New York. A prisoner at Elmira noted that "close on the heels of the scurvy epidemic came an even larger outbreak of diarrhea."[14] One contract physician at Andersonville recorded that

> the diarrhea seemed to be a symptom of scurvy, not the ordinary camp diarrhea seen in our army. The men got better as soon as they got better treatment [in the hospital] and fresh vegetables. Fresh vegetables increased our ordinary diarrhea . . . a good many [men] were idiotic and demented.[15]

Although dementia is one of the cardinal manifestations of pellagra, under those conditions, there were many other possible causes.

When the Andersonville prisoners were freed and taken to Union hospitals, physicians recorded that all the returned prisoners who were scorbutic suffered from diarrhea.[16] These observations support the hypothesis that much of the chronic diarrhea, and especially its fatal form, was related to malnutrition, possibly concomitant vitamin B and C deficiencies.

Andersonville physicians, unknowingly, also documented the association of scurvy with other forms of malnutrition. For example, they noted a connection between scurvy and "dropsy," because both increased in frequency almost simultaneously.[17] ("Dropsy" meant the accumulation of fluid in tissues that today we call "edema.") These cases must have resulted from protein malnutrition, which decreased the concentration of albumin in the serum, allowing fluid to leak into the tissues. Such edema is also prominent in another form of malnutrition that occurs in epidemic form, beriberi, although this was not specifically diagnosed.

Civil War soldiers with chronic diarrhea frequently observed that blackberries had a beneficial medicinal effect. Blackberries contain both ascorbic acid and folic acid, but have more of the latter vitamin.[18] One possible explanation, which was only recognized recently, is the disease called "tropical sprue." Its symptoms include chronic diarrhea, malabsorption of essential nutrients, and edema. It is thought to be caused by a bacterial infection of the intestine, and it is also associated with a vitamin deficiency. Tropical sprue often responds to treatment with folic acid (such as in blackberries) or an antibiotic, or both.[19] Some Civil War soldiers may have had a similar form of chronic diarrhea, with malnutrition making them more susceptible to an infectious component (as seems to be the mechanism causing tropical sprue).

Dr. Joseph Woodward conducted the most extensive studies of chronic diarrhea during the Civil War. His conclusion, written in 1863, summarizes physicians' knowledge about the relationship between chronic diarrhea and malnutrition:

> Originating chiefly among troops in camps, the disease evidently stands in some definite relationship to the usual conditions of camp life. Of these, it would appear most intimately connected with the diet, and this relationship is of such a kind that chronic diarrhea becomes more and more common and fatal as the constitutional manifestations which result from camp diet approach more and more to the condition of recognizable scurvy, a most important point to be considered in connection with the hygienic treatment of this disease. As a consequence it has more than once happened on a grand scale, during the present war, to see a sudden and palpable diminution in the amount of diarrhea follow the liberal issue of potatoes and onions to an army in which the tendency to scurvy was exhibiting itself in a manner too evident to be overlooked.[20]

TREATMENT OF CHRONIC DIARRHEA

Physicians tried a host of drugs to treat chronic diarrhea. Opiates, which suppress bowel activity, were useful and became a mainstay in all cases; similar modern preparations, such as paregoric (tincture of opium) and other narcotic-containing compounds, are still used. Oil of turpentine and glycerin were also widely used. One accepted treatment consisted of "nourishing food that is easily assimilated, plenty of eggs, tender beef steak, mutton chops, good stale bread, sweet milk."[21] Although this list does not include fresh vegetables, the diet would not have been limited to these items, with the milk and eggs being especially beneficial. The diet presumably helped, since these recommendations were published in the *U.S. Sanitary Commission Bulletin* and widely dissemination to other physicians.

The connection between chronic diarrhea and scurvy, as well as the effective treatment of both by fresh vegetables, were observed as early as the Peninsula campaign of 1862. Surgeon J. F. Dyer of the 19th Massachusetts reported that in his command:

there were 19 cases of pronounced scurvy and 100 cases of the scorbutic taint and many of diarrhea which [he] attributed to the causes of scurvy, in as much as it was controlled when the patients had access to a free supply of vegetables.[22]

Similarly, a surgeon from the 20th Massachusetts documented:

In many other instances the scurvy taint was only apparent in its modification of other diseases. Thus a large number of the diarrheas were characterized by massive hemorrhage and a peculiar intractability when treated by ordinary methods, yet they yielded readily to vegetable acids and antiscorbutics when they could be procured.[23]

Generally, vegetables and fruits are harmful to patients "suffering from fluxes" ("fluxes" was a popular term for diarrhea). However, the authors of *Medical and Surgical History*, after making that point, stated:

abundant testimony has . . . [shown] the benefit derived from the use of fruits and vegetables in the fluxes of the Civil War, and like effects may be anticipated whenever diarrhea or dysentery is complicated by the scorbutic taint . . . [Scurvy is] even more prone to occur in military practice in times of war than in civil life, because a tendency to the scorbutic condition is so frequently present, even when no symptoms express its existence, and a shorter time is therefore required for the development of scorbutic phenomena by unsuitable diet than would be required under ordinary circumstances.[24]

As an examination of the Medical Section of *Medical and Surgical History* illustrates, army physicians repeatedly confirmed that chronic diarrhea failed to respond to any of the usual treatments, except for temporary improvement with opiates. Fresh vegetables were the only treatment that helped in many cases. Knowing that vegetables usually aggravated ordinary diarrhea, they wrote that they were surprised at the beneficial effect in chronic diarrhea. For example, after his August 1863 inspection of the Army of the Cumberland, Dr. Frank Hastings Hamilton stated,

I have noticed everywhere in the department that the free use of berries, peaches and green corn, with other fruits and vegetables, although the fruits were seldom ripe when eaten, has had a salutary effect upon the mucoenteric affections. If they have occasionally increased or produced a diarrhea, they have also cured or prevented many more.[25]

Likewise, in April 1865, Medical Inspector Smart of the Army of the Potomac reported:

During the remainder of the month [March 1865] . . . diarrhea, the prevailing disease, became very obstinate, and was accompanied with very great and rapidly increasing prostration, resembling the disease as seen during the Peninsular campaign of 1862. The fatigues of recent active service, the bad water in the Second Division, but more than all, I believe to be the origin of this, the lack of vegetables. Since camp near Hatcher's Run was broken up until the present time only one or two rations of potatoes have been issued, and none of any other vegetables, except to a portion of the command a small quantity of beans. This has been all, a quantity insufficient to prevent the occurrence of scorbutic symptoms.[26]

The fruits and vegetables many Civil War physicians recommended as treatment for chronic diarrhea were also used for scurvy. These included lime or lemon juice, potatoes, onions, leeks, squashes, pumpkins, carrots, turnips, spinach, cabbage, tomatoes, and "lettuce, if tender and fresh." "Mother" Mary Ann Bickerdyke, the favorite nurse and matron of Grant's and Sherman's troops, foraged for plants of medicinal value for her "boys"; she even made a blackberry cordial to treat diarrhea.[27]

When food became abundant, chronic diarrhea would improve throughout the entire army. During their March to the Sea, "Sherman's bummers" sustained the army by foraging. (The term "bummer" was applied to the men officially assigned as foragers in Sherman's army, a task that was rotated among the troops daily; thus it came to be applied to all of Sherman's troops in Georgia. The soldiers liked the name because they thought it frightened the Southerners.)[28] They ate better than any other troop had during the war, and sweet potatoes, a good source of vitamins C and A, were a particular favorite. For the duration of the march, scurvy and night blindness almost completely disappeared among these men, and the incidence of chronic diarrhea was reduced to half its earlier incidence.

Undoubtedly, there were many causes for the chronic diarrhea among Civil War soldiers. To use a modern term, there was a "multifactorial etiology." Numerous physicians' observations during the war clearly point to nutrition as a factor in many cases. Certainly this was the case for those men whose diarrhea was associated with scurvy and whose diarrhea responded to treatment with fresh vegetables.

The facts that physicians linked deaths from chronic diarrhea to concomitant scurvy and attributed the cure to treatment with fresh vegetables, strongly suggest more than a accidental relationship. On the other hand, diarrhea was so universal among Civil War soldiers that whenever a soldier was ill, he inevitably also had diarrhea or dysentery.

REFERENCES

1. Eve PF: Answers to certain questions propounded by Prof. Charles A. Lee, M.D., Agent of the U.S. Sanitary Commission, relative to the health, etc., of the late Southern army. *Nashville J Med Surg*. NS, 1866;1:12-32.
2. Partridge E: *A Dictionary of Slang and Unconventional English: Colloquialisms and Catch-Phrases, Solecisms and Catachreses, Nicknames, Vulgarisms, and Such Americanisms as Have Been Naturalized*. 3rd ed. New York: Macmillan, 1950, p. 363.
3. Riley HD, Jr.: Medicine in the Confederacy. Part 2. *Mil Med*. 1956;118(2):144-53.
4. Gardner HH: Chronic diarrhea. *Am Med Times*. 1862;5:107-8.
5. Gillett MC: *The United States Army Medical Department, 1818–1865*. Washington, D.C.: Center of Military History, U.S. Army, 1987, p. 279.
6. *Medical and Surgical History*, Medical Section, vol. 2, p. 278.
7. *U.S. Sanitary Commission Bulletin*. 1864 Jan. 1;5:156.
8. Lind J: *A Treatise on the Scurvy*. London: S. Crowder, 1772. (Repub.: Classics of Medicine Library, 1980, pp. 210-13.)
9. Carpenter KJ: *The History of Scurvy and Vitamin C*. Cambridge, MA: Cambridge Univ. Press, 1986, p. 114.
10. Report of Surg. Charles S. Frink, U.S. Army, Surg. in Chief. Third Division, 23rd Army Corps, September 10, 1864. *O.R.*, Series I, Vol. XXXVIII/2, p. 695.
11. Zalusky R, Herbert V: Megaloblastic anemia in scurvy with response to 50 mcg. of folic acid daily. *N Eng J Med*. 1961;265(21):1033-38.
12. Osler W: *The Principles and Practice of Medicine*. New York: Appleton Century Crofts, 1892.
13. Kerr WJW: Pellagra and hookworm at Andersonville. *Conf Veteran*. 1910;18:69.
14. Robertson JI: The scourge of Elmira. *Civil War Hist*. 1962;8(2):184-201.
15. Chipman NP: *The Andersonville Prison Trial: The Trial of Capt. Henry Wirz*. Sacramento: The Author, 1911.
16. Report of Acting Surg. S. J. Radcliffe, *Medical and Surgical History*, Medical Section, vol. 3, p. 44.
17. *O.R.*, Series II, Vol. VIII, p. 614.
18. Bollet AJ: Scurvy and chronic diarrhea in Civil War troops. were they both nutritional deficiency syndromes? *J Hist Med Allied Sci*. 1992;47(1):49.
19. Spies TD: *Experiences with Folic Acid*. Chicago: Yearbook Pub., 1947, p. 76.
20. Woodward JJ: *Outlines of the Chief Camp Diseases of the United States Armies as Observed during the Present War. A Practical Contribution to Military Medicine*. Philadelphia, PA: J.B. Lippincott, 1863. Repub: Norman Pub., 1992, p. 253.
21. *U.S. Sanitary Commission Bulletin*. 1864 Jan. 1;5:156.25.
22. *Medical and Surgical History*, Medical Section, vol. 3, p. 687.
23. Ibid.
24. *Medical and Surgical History*, Medical Section, vol. 2, p. 678.
25. Ibid., p. 96.
26. *O.R.*, Series I, Vol. XLVI/1, p. 704.
27. Denney RE: *Civil War Medicine: Care and Comfort of the Wounded*. New York: Sterling, 1994, p. 298.
28. Faust PL, ed.: *Historical Times Encyclopedia of the Civil War*. New York: Harper & Row, 1986, p. 95.

~ 15 ~

Prison Camps:
The Most Appalling Story

In truth, these men at Andersonville were in the condition of a crew at sea confined on a foul ship, upon salt meat, and unvarying food, and without fresh vegetables. Not only so, but these unfortunate prisoners were like men forcibly confined and crowded upon a ship tossed about on a stormy ocean— without a rudder, without a compass, without a guiding star, and without an apparent boundary or end to their voyage.

— Dr. Joseph Jones, 1876

WHILE DEATHS IN CAMPS AND ON THE BATTLEFIELD CLAIMED MANY LIVES, perhaps the worst place to be during the Civil War was in a military prison. About 10% of all the deaths among Civil War soldiers occurred in military prisons. Nearly 23,000 Union soldiers died in Confederate prisons, an appalling 18% of the approximately 127,000 prisoners. The absolute numbers were even worse up north: more than 26,000 Southern prisoners of war (POWs) perished in Northern prisons—the best estimates being 12% of 220,000 prisoners.[1] The majority of these deaths were due to disease, so the factors that affected prisoners' health and survival in the prisons are fundamental to understanding the Civil War's medical history.

The health of prisoners was a minor problem in the first years of the war. Captured soldiers were paroled on their word of honor not to return to combat until officially exchanged. Designated "exchange officers" met often

377

to exchange lists of prisoners, trading them using formulas based on each soldier's rank. These formulas established how many men of lower rank would be equivalent to each officer grade. The trades themselves were very civilized. For example, Union boats, sailing under a flag of truce, picked up freed prisoners at City Point on the James River and took them up the Chesapeake Bay to Annapolis or further north. In the West, Confederate prisoners were taken on Union transports from Cairo, Illinois, to Vicksburg.[2] Those men not paroled were usually exchanged after only limited confinement. Makeshift prison facilities were used early in the war to house the prisoners until they could be exchanged. One of the largest, and most notorious, was Libby Prison in Richmond, a converted tobacco warehouse used despite its lack of ventilation, water, exercise space, and sanitary facilities. (See Figure 15.1.)

Serious problems with food supplies and waste disposal arose almost immediately in these improvised prisons, and became much more severe as the war progressed. Officials on both sides expressed concern for their prisoners' health, not only for humanitarian reasons but also because they could only exchange living prisoners for their own soldiers. However, as the war continued and many prisoners were held for long periods before exchange, the shortages of medical supplies and food became more and more severe. By the fall of 1863, Federal prisoners returning from Richmond were suffering from severe malnutrition. Many of these men died, most of chronic diarrhea, with pneumonia and "debility" nearly as common. Some released prisoners, particularly those captured at Gettysburg, complained that their captors had not treated their wounds, so physicians and nurses were subsequently stationed on the ships used to transport the returnees.

The prisoner exchange system began to collapse late in 1863, and exchanges ceased completely in March 1864, when Grant became the Union army's supreme commander. He reasoned that since Confederate forces were dwindling and Union strength was peaking, the exchange of prisoners would only replenish the Confederate army and prolong the war. Large prison camps with long-term housing suddenly became necessary, and both sides hastily erected them.

Neither Union nor Confederate forces took adequate care of their prisoners, and sometimes they were the victims of retaliation. Reports of the starvation and suffering in some Southern camps, particularly at Camp Sumter in Andersonville, Georgia, led Union officers to purposely starve their prisoners. Defending this unconscionable behavior, some Union officials claimed that they were simply making certain that Confederate prisoners were not

Figure 15.1: View of Libby Prison, a converted tobacco warehouse in Richmond used to house Federal prisoners, mostly officers, until exchanged. Photograph by Matthew Brady after the fall of Richmond in April 1865 shows Union troops outside the building where many may have been imprisoned at one time. (Meredith R: *Mr. Lincoln's Camera Man: Matthew B. Brady.* Garden City, NY: Dover Press, 1946.)

eating better than were their compatriots in the field. As a result, the number of all prisoners who died of starvation and disease rapidly rose to such shocking levels that it is pointless to speculate on which prisoners fared worse.

Numerous books and articles describe the appalling suffering in these camps, clearly one of the war's darkest and most disturbing chapters. It is no wonder that most Civil War literature treads lightly on this bitter aspect of our nation's history.

ANDERSONVILLE: THE MOST DISEASE-RIDDEN CONFEDERATE PRISON

The first prisoners arrived at Camp Sumter on February 24, 1864. The prison was located near the city of Andersonville in southwestern Georgia because, at that time, it was far from any threat of Union raids. The stockade was originally designed for 10,000 men but, by July 1864, it held 29,998 prisoners. No shelter was prepared for the captured soldiers before their arrival.[3] After they arrived, the Union prisoners placed their makeshift huts and crude shelters according to personal whim, with no rows or streets to provide access to Stockade Creek, the sole source of water.

Officials also intended to use the lower end of the creek for waste disposal, however, the order to use only this area was not enforced. A latrine was built along on the bank of the stream so that the flowing water could flush the waste out of the camp. Unfortunately, there was inadequate current to do this except for a brief time after heavy rains. Moreover, the latrine was located upstream of many prisoners' water supply. The camp commandant, Capt. Henry Wirz, had planned to build two dams to accumulate enough water so that opening them twice daily would flush the waste, but lack of tools prevented their construction.

Compounding the problem, the prison guards—two companies of Confederate soldiers—located their camp about a quarter-mile upstream of the stockade. They also used the stream for washing and bathing, and their latrines overflowed into the creek whenever there were heavy rains. The cooking facilities for the stockade, located just above the camp, also contaminated the water. The prisoners, disgusted by the creek water's smell and appearance, used any tools they could find or fashion to dig wells as far from the stream as possible.

Prisoners were horrified by the conditions they found on arrival. Few had tents and their Confederate captors issued them no clothing. Only tiny amounts of soap were available, so the prisoners were extremely dirty. The whole prison reeked with an overpowering stench, largely due to lack of discipline regarding latrine use. One medical inspector stated that he "observed men urinating and evacuating their bowels at the very tent doors, and around the little vessels in which they were cooking their food."[4]

INADEQUATE RATIONS

The official ration for the inmates included a quarter-pound of "bacon" (actually smoked or salted pork) or one pound of beef, as well as peas, beans, rice, and vinegar or molasses. The commandant could not issue most of these items, however, because there were not enough buckets to carry them. Bread was made from crudely milled cornmeal and consisted, as one inmate wrote,

> fully of one-sixth of husk . . . is almost unfit for use and [is] increasing dysentery and other bowel complaints . . . If the meal, such as it is now, was sifted the bread rations would fall short fully one-quarter of a pound.[5]

The bakery and cookhouse were finally completed in May, but the cooking facilities remained grossly inadequate—prisoners drew cooked and uncooked rations at random. Rations that were cooked were smaller portions: an Ohio sergeant complained that the first day he drew cooked rations, he received only a small piece of cornbread and two bites of meat. When their ration came cold and raw, a lack of firewood within the stockade made it almost impossible for prisoners to cook it.

Sgt. Eugene Forbes of the 4th New Jersey wrote in his diary on May 30 that his day's ration consisted of "one-third of a loaf of bread, and a piece of bacon about the size of a penny spongecake, one tablespoon of mush." A Vermont private recorded his Sabbath meal was "1/2 cup of Boiled Rice no meat or bread or meal to go with it." The cornbread contained "ground cob and all." The hungry men killed low-flying birds and ate them immediately; captured rats were considered a delicacy. Even the inadequate food ration was sometimes eliminated: when guards, and especially Wirz, were angered, a frequent punishment was loss of a day's rations.[6]

Brigadier General John H. Winder, the provost marshal in Richmond, assumed responsibility for Andersonville in June 1864, and for all prisons in Georgia and Alabama in July. Winder believed that eating more food would decrease the prisoners' rate of death—a correct assumption since malnutrition was the main cause of death. His strenuous efforts to improve the prisoners' diet put him in constant conflict with Col. Lucius Northrop, the Confederate commissary general, who was then struggling just to find enough food for their soldiers. Once, when Winder tried to get a ten-day supply of prisoners' rations as a stockpile to make up for the unreliable food supply, Colonel Northrop reportedly was outraged, since the troops in the field were restricted to one day's rations. In several instances, after Winder paid for inmates' necessities with his own money, Northrop sarcastically responded that Winder must not know where to apply to get the rations paid for.[7]

It didn't help that both men were strict disciplinarians with a fondness for red tape, or that they each had personalities that made them numerous enemies and impaired their effectiveness. Political pressures also interfered with any efforts to improve the prisoners' lot. For example, the *Richmond Whig*, an influential newspaper and an implacable foe of Jefferson Davis, criticized the Confederate president for being too soft on the imprisoned soldiers.[8]

VERMIN AND DISEASE

Insects tormented prisoners even more than other soldiers. They were so common that "skirmishing" for lice, also called "graybacks," provided prisoners with recreation. Similar to the later "flea circus" hoaxes, they bragged about the feats their lice could perform and claimed to be training them for exhibition at the next "vermin fair." Despite the vermin, there was no typhus or yellow fever at Andersonville. There was plenty of malaria, however, and, like all Civil War soldiers, inmates suffered from "the itch," most due to scabies.

Smallpox was as much a problem in the prisons as it was in army camps. Prisoners without vaccine scars were vaccinated, but the resulting pustules usually ulcerated and became infected. Because of the prisoners' malnourished state and the ubiquitous contamination with microorganisms, many became gangrenous. While some amputations were performed to try to stop the spread of gangrene, deaths often followed the surgery.

The high number of amputations and deaths following smallpox vaccination led to accusations that prison doctors had deliberately used poisonous, or "spurious," vaccines. One smallpox episode was a major factor in the postwar investigation of Andersonville and in the trial of Captain Wirz. In summarizing Wirz's case, the Federal prosecutor stated:

> These facts, drawn from reliable and recognized medical authorities, will enable the court and the world to appreciate in some degree the heartlessness and implacable cruelty of the rebel authorities at Andersonville, in persistently compelling prisoners of war to be vaccinated.[9]

It should be noted that during the trial, it was not mentioned that similar problems with contaminated and ineffective vaccine existed in both the Confederate and Union armies.

ANDERSONVILLE'S "HOSPITAL"

Andersonville prison's "hospital" was appalling. The chief surgeon blamed the high death rate from disease on hospital conditions, including its location within the stockade (later it was moved out). Only some of the tents had bunks, and those had vermin-filled bedding and two occupants each. Many hospitalized prisoners lay on bare ground in the tents, and about 300 had no shelter at all. Paroled prisoners did most of the nursing, and they provided no comfort to their fellow prisoners. Hospitalization was considered by prisoners to be a death warrant.[10]

The Confederate adjutant general in Richmond sent Col. Daniel T. Chandler to inspect the prison at Andersonville. At morning report on August 2, 1864, he found fifteen doctors caring for 5,010 sick prisoners within the prison stockade, and an additional 1,305 prisoners in the prison hospital. (Because of overcrowding, only extremely sick men were hospitalized.) Thirteen additional surgeons handled the daily six-hour sick call for the prisoners in the main stockade. Each squad sergeant reported at the outside gate with prisoners from his unit who were ill. Physicians prescribed whatever medicines were available, and the squad sergeants picked them up and gave them to the men.

Colonel Chandler called the prison "a disgrace to civilization." He offered numerous suggestions for improving the prisoners' lot, including issuing clothing and soap and reducing the number of prisoners held there. He condemned Winder and recommended "substitution in his place of someone who unites both energy and good judgment with some feelings of humanity." Concerning the prison's commander, Capt. Henry Wirz, Chandler wrote that he was "entitled to commendation for his untiring energy and devotion to the discharge of the multifarious duties of his position." The assistant adjutant general forwarded Chandler's report to the Confederate secretary of war with the comment, "The condition of the prison at Andersonville is a reproach to us as a nation."[11] During Wirz's post-war trial, the prosecution used Chandler's description of prison horrors, but omitted the praise for Wirz.[12]

On August 6, the prison's chief surgeon, Isaiah H. White, submitted a request to Winder for better hospital facilities, including barracks with adequate ventilation, more food, and medicines. He emphasized the need for proper sanitation and cleanliness in both the hospital and the stockade, and asked that the creek be widened and deepened and that Confederate soldiers be prevented from contaminating it above the stockade. He also requested that proper latrines be located where prisoners would not have to wade through mud and feces to use them. None of these protests and requests made to local authorities or to Richmond resulted in action.

In fact, Winder had already tried unsuccessfully to obtain the material to construct facilities such as barracks. Despairing of ever improving the terrible, and embarrassing, situation, he repeatedly requested the release of at least the sick prisoners, without exchange. The Confederate official in charge of exchanges, Col. R. O. Ould, urged that his requests be turned down. The secretary of war concluded that "Winder's request was worse than the evil," and ordered him to carry on in the best manner possible.[13] In February 1865, Winder "again urge[d] paroling the prisoners and sending them home," without success.[14]

It is impossible to say how much of the horror in the prison was due to Winder's ineptitude and how much was due to the dwindling fortunes of the Confederacy. It is clear, however, that running a large POW camp was more than the government in Richmond could handle, consequently senior Confederate officials just ignored the disaster occurring at Andersonville.

In November 1864, Winder became commissary general of all prisons located east of the Mississippi. This brought the prison in Florence, South Carolina, under his control. The overall mortality was 22% at Florence, as bad as that of Andersonville. When he took over, the 12,400 Union prisoners at Florence were dying at the rate of 220 per week. Winder succeeded in lowering that rate to 35 per week.[15] Even so, when Winder died suddenly in February 1865 while on a visit to Florence prison, the prisoners celebrated. He was buried with military honors but his grave was left unmarked, because Union forces under Sherman were approaching the site.[16]

Confederate Surgeon Joseph Jones, upon "hearing of the unusual mortality amongst the Federal prisoners," suggested to Surgeon General Moore that a medical inspector be sent to Andersonville to investigate. Moore appointed Jones, who spent several months in Andersonville examining sick prisoners, inspecting records, and doing autopsies. He prepared a report but, by then, the fall of Richmond was imminent and Jones never submitted it. As a result, it was not destroyed when the Surgeon General's Office was consumed in the fire after the capital's evacuation. Dr. Jones kept it at home in Augusta; he mentioned it to visiting Northern physicians after the war and it was subpoenaed for the trial of Captain Wirz. His observations were published in the *Official Records* and in *Medical and Surgical History*.[17,18]

In describing the camp conditions that he believed produced disease, Jones blamed "the accumulation of the sources of disease, as the increase of excrement and filth of all kinds, and the concentration of noxious effluvia."

The waters of the creek in the stockade, "loaded with filth and human excrement, . . . emit[ted] an intolerable and most sickening stench."[19] He stated that dying men brought into the hospital from the stockade were covered from head to toe with their own excrement, their skin black from smoke and filth.[20] He observed:

> millions of flies crawled over everything and covered the faces of sleeping patients and crawled down their open mouths, and deposited their maggots in the gangrenous wounds of the living and in the mouths of the dead. Myriad mosquitoes also infested the tents, and many of the patients were so stung by these pestiferous insects that they appeared as if they were from a slight attack of measles.[21]

Jones mentioned that paroled prisoners working as hospital attendants stole money, rations, and clothing from the sick and the dead, conducting a brisk trade with the guards.

DEATHS AT ANDERSONVILLE

According to Jones, 9,479 Andersonville prisoners (23.3% of those confined) died between February 24, 1864, when the prison was opened, and September 21, 1864. Monthly mortality increased from 3.8% of the average number of prisoners in March to 9.1% in August. Jones ascribed the "chief causes" of death to "diarrhea, dysentery, scurvy, and hospital gangrene."

The Confederate troops guarding the prison did not fare well either. During July and August, 64.4% of the command reported sick, with a two-month mortality rate of 2.3%. (During the same period, it was 15% among the prisoners.) After the war, Chief Surgeon I. H. White wrote, somewhat inaccurately,

> A strong point illustrating the position that the sickness among the prisoners was from causes which the Confederate authorities could not control, is the fact that the Confederate guards, officers and surgeons were attacked by the same maladies, and that the deaths among them were about as numerous, in proportion to their numbers, as among the prisoners themselves.[22]

The most frequent causes of death listed in the prison death register were diarrhea and dysentery—together they caused 50% of the deaths in the six-month period that Jones studied (March 1 to September 1, 1864). He attributed 28% of those deaths to scurvy and thought (correctly) that a scorbutic condition rendered many prisoners easy prey to other diseases. He also felt that many of the deaths listed as being due to other causes could actually be attributed to diarrhea and scurvy.

The scurvy, Jones believed, was due to "the effects of salt meat and an unvarying diet of corn-meal, with but few vegetables and imperfect supplies of vinegar and sirup [sic]." Based on his survey, he estimated that 9,501 of the prisoners were afflicted with scurvy and concluded that it was responsible for nine-tenths of the mortality, "either directly or indirectly." Many prison guards, who were officially given the same diet as the prisoners, also developed scurvy.

During the time that Jones worked at the prison, he made other diagnoses, mostly of phenomena that are recognizable now as manifestations of malnutrition. For example, anasarca (generalized fluid accumulation now

Malnutrition among U.S. Soldiers in World War II Prison Camps

During World War II, observers documented nutritional causes of diarrhea in prisoners of war. Allied prisoners of war commonly developed severe nutritional deficiencies. In a survey of one group of recovered allied military prisoners (RAMPs) at the end of the war, the average period of imprisonment by the Germans was 143 days. Eighty-seven percent of this group had diarrhea during their incarceration, 15% "most of the time," and another 14% "frequently." Night blindness was also common among these recovered prisoners.

Almost all the American prisoners held by the Japanese during World War II suffered from malnutrition. Most had beriberi, a result of severe deficiency of vitamin B1 (thiamin) that occurs in people on a diet of polished rice and no vegetables; the disease appeared regularly after three months of imprisonment. In a study of survivors of the Japanese prison camps, the incidence of symptoms suggestive of beriberi was as high as 98% in one group, and an unequivocal diagnosis of beriberi was made in 66% of another group of freed prisoners. The "dry" form of beriberi, which is characterized mainly by painful neuropathy, was associated with diarrhea. Of the American servicemen who were prisoners of the Japanese, 37.2% died, as opposed to 1% of the POWs held in Germany. Even though the German prisoners had been in captivity for a much shorter period, about 25% needed hospitalization and nutritional rehabilitation after recovery.[23] The occurrence of diarrhea in these malnourished POWs is reminiscent of the problem of chronic diarrhea in the prison camps of the Civil War.

known to result from low serum proteins, i.e., hypoalbuminemia, and caused by overall protein depletion) was recorded in 1,510 prisoners and was blamed for 315 deaths. "Debilitas" was diagnosed in 875 prisoners, of whom 168 died.

Jones made a special study of hospital gangrene in prisoners, mentioning that

> the smallest injury, as a splinter running into the hand or foot, the blistering of the skin from the hot sun, or abrasions of the skin in scratching a mosquito bite, were often followed by the most extensive and alarming gangrenous ulceration.... [Amputations] did not arrest hospital gangrene; the disease almost invariably returned. Almost every amputation was followed by death, either from the effects of gangrene or from the prevailing diarrhea and dysentery.[24]

Jones blamed the hospital gangrene on "noxious exhalations," which he assumed extended for a considerable distance, since "Confederate soldiers . . . who did not enter the stockade . . . were in several instances attacked with hospital gangrene."[25]

He also noted that scurvy and hospital gangrene frequently existed in the same individual. Similarly, Dr. Frank Hastings Hamilton observed in Union troops that "in such cases vegetable diet . . . would remove the scorbutic condition without curing the hospital gangrene."[26] These observations fit our current understanding of the etiology of "hospital gangrene," namely that it probably was an aggressive bacterial infection, presumably most often streptococcal, which malnutrition made more frequent and more severe. Once established, these infections would have been too potent to respond to nutritional therapy alone.

Typhoid fever was diagnosed in 472 prisoners, with 185 deaths. It was almost three times as frequent among guards as it was among prisoners, although the guards' case-fatality rate was slightly lower. As Jones pointed out, the Confederate guards were recently enlisted and either very young or relatively old, and most were being exposed to the diseases they encountered for the first time. Jones specifically observed that typhoid fever was mainly a disease of recruits and that it affected an individual only once. He stated:

> The absence of typhoid and typhus fevers amongst all the causes which are supposed to generate these diseases appeared to be due to the fact that the great majority of these prisoners . . . had been subject to the same bad influence, and those that had not had the fevers before either had them during their [earlier] confinement in Confederate prisons or else their systems from long exposure were proof against them.[27]

THE TRIAL OF CAPTAIN WIRZ

In the postwar trial of Andersonville's Commandant, Henry Wirz, charges of inadequate rations and poor medical care figured prominently. He was also accused of personally beating, torturing, and, even, murdering prisoners in cold blood.

Wirz was born in Switzerland in 1822, where he trained as a homeopathic physician. He subsequently obtained M.D. degrees from medical colleges in Paris and Berlin. When the war started, he was practicing medicine in Louisiana, and he enlisted in the Confederate army as a private. During the Battle of Seven Pines, his right arm was badly shattered but not amputated. He was then promoted to captain "for bravery on the field of battle," but, as he was unfit for battle, he was assigned to General Winder's staff as acting adjutant-general in August 1862.[28] After serving at prisons in Richmond and Tuscaloosa, Wirz was appointed as the commandant at Andersonville in April 1864. He was promoted to major shortly before the war ended.

After Winder's death, Wirz was left alone to face the post-war wrath of Union authorities and the public. He was vilified in the press as the "Demon of Andersonville," a "human monster." No convincing proof of any act of brutality was presented at his trial, but he definitely was harsh in his manner and speech—one Rebel soldier described him as "the profanist man I ever saw."[29]

Prosecutors accused Wirz of purposely starving the prisoners. (See Figure 15.2.) Much was made of his refusal to permit Southern women to take vegetables into the stockade for the starving, scurvy-ridden prisoners. It was actually Winder who, convinced that the countryside was full of traitors, had blocked the petitions because of an excessive fear of a prison revolt.

The defense claimed that the prison guards received the same rations as the prisoners. This testimony was ridiculed in light of the obvious malnutrition among the prisoners (ignoring the evidence of scurvy Joseph Jones found among the guards). In their statements, the officers of the guard, as well as their regimental surgeons, made clear that many guards received supplementary rations from home and from local citizens. Thus, the guards had the equivalent of foraging to supplement their diet. Dr. F. G. Castlen, surgeon of the 3rd Georgia Reserves, added: The men [the guards] had an opportunity of getting things from home to prevent it [scurvy]. There was no difficulty in that respect at all . . . any man in the regiment could send home and get things.[30]

One of the guards, First Lieutenant John F. Heath, described their diet:

> We received in my regiment a pound and quarter of meal, very coarse at that, generally. Once in a while a third of a pound of bacon. At other times

388

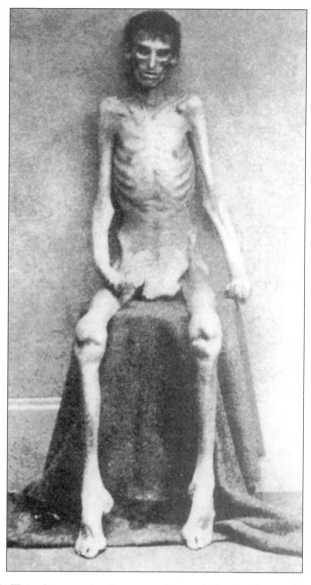

Figure 15.2: This photograph of a gaunt, almost skeletal, prisoner from Anderson-ville was taken when the prisoners arrived at a special facility for freed prisoners of war at Annapolis. (The Naval Academy was moved to Newport, Rhode Island, when the war began.) The publication of drawings based on these pictures led to mass revulsion and a desire for revenge upon the Confederate authorities responsible for the maltreatment of Federal prisoners. The photographs were instrumental in setting the psychological atmosphere that led to the trial and execution of Capt. Wirz. *(PHCW)*

a pound of beef, and that very poor, and when we did not get bacon or beef, we got a little sorghum, a kind of molasses made out of Chinese cane.[31]

He asserted that his men drew the same rations from the commissary as the prisoners, but failed to mention that the guards drew first, undoubtedly getting the best of whatever was available. He noted that the guards also had additional sources of food: "I had to send home for provisions to live on, and to buy what I could through the country . . . I could not tell how long I could have lived on the rations without having other provisions."[32]

Although there were some officers held within Andersonville's main stockade, most were housed in a separate officer's prison. Nutrition among the officers who were prisoners seems to have been substantially better than that of the regular soldiers, mainly because of the money that officers usually carried. The testimony of Capt. Wilson French, who was imprisoned at Andersonville, supports the contention that food was available in the area around the prison but that it was not provided to the prisoners. During the Wirz trial, French described the diet in the officers' prison:

> The quality of rations served out was very poor and the quantity was not sufficient to sustain life . . . Had we not been allowed to buy provisions, we would have starved there . . . We never had any difficulty in getting vegetables . . . my mess [eight men] used to buy from two to four bushels of sweet potatoes a week at the rate of fifteen dollars of Confederate money per bushel . . . Turnips we bought at twenty dollars a bushel . . . We bought meat and eggs and biscuit. There seemed to be an abundance of those things. That sergeant [Wirz's chief sergeant] used to come down with a wagon-load of potatoes at a time.[33]

These comments support a view widely held at the time of the war that food was available in much of the Confederacy but that government authorities failed to make it accessible to the soldiers, prisoners, or guards. They also document the importance of foraging, of one type or another, to the health of Civil War troops.

The court found Captain Wirz guilty, and he was sentenced to death. Many later commentators viewed the hanging of Wirz as a miscarriage of justice. His defenders believed that he had fallen prey to Northern politicians and journalists who "waved the bloody shirt," as well as to some Southerners who used him as a scapegoat for the embarrassment of Andersonville.

ELMIRA: THE MOST DISEASE-RIDDEN FEDERAL PRISON

The worst Federal prison was probably the one at Elmira, New York. Like Andersonville, it was established hastily without adequate preparation. On

May 15, 1864, the commander of the local army training camp, Col. Seth Eastman, was given notice to set aside space for prisoners who would arrive in five days.[34] Described as a "perfect pest-hole," Confederate prisoners called it "Hell-mira." Overall, 12,123 prisoners were sent to Elmira and 2,963 died, the rate of 24.4% being slightly higher than at Andersonville. Sanitation was almost as great a problem as at Andersonville: effluent from latrines drained into a pond inside the camp's boundary that was fed by a stream with inadequate flow for proper drainage.

Food supplies were woefully inadequate, although officials initially claimed that food was available and of good quality. The prisoners lacked fresh vegetables and scurvy was rampant. At one time, scurvy affected 2,000 prisoners; diarrhea/dysentery killed almost 1,400.[35] However, the Union

A Confederate Soldier Remembers Elmira

Gragg's *Illustrated Confederate Reader* contains this description of life at Elmira:

> There were nearly 10,000 prisoners at Elmira at one time, sometimes less and sometimes more. During the winter those who came from the South felt the cold exceedingly and died from pneumonia. Our clothes were poor . . .

> There were many cases of pneumonia and measles and thousands of us were afflicted with the stubborn diarrhea. The poor fellows died rapidly, despondent, homesick, hungry and wretched. I have stood day after day watching the wagons carry the dead outside to be buried, and each day for several weeks sixteen dead men were taken through the gate. While the prison was occupied by us, which was about one year, it was estimated that 3,000 men died. The physicians were very good, but it was impossible to save all.

> At one time scurvy was among us. There were not many deaths, but it caused much suffering. I was among the victims. It frequently attacked the mouth and gums, which became so spongy and sore that portions could be removed with the fingers. Others became afflicted in their limbs, the flesh became spotted and the pain was almost unbearable. The remedy was raw vegetables and a medicine called "chalk mixture."[36]

(The vegetables were effective—the "medicine" was not.)

authorities, including Surgeon General Barnes, General Halleck, and Secretary of War Stanton, made no effort to improve the prisoners' diet. Instead, they agreed to give Confederate prisoners a diet that was not any better than they would receive from their own army in the field.[37] In addition, on August 18, Federal Commissioner of Prisons Col. William Hoffman decided to retaliate for the conditions at Andersonville. He restricted the prisoners' diet to only bread and water; by September 11, scurvy was reported. Some vegetables were added in October and some meat in December, but it was of very poor quality; apart from this, the prisoners were kept on bread and water. Compounding the problem, many men were too weak to get to the mess hall and those who did were not allowed time to eat. The men hunted rats, but hundreds of prisoners died of starvation—25 a day in December, according to one inmate.

Weather also affected prisoners' health; the winter of 1864–65 was one of the coldest in memory. Pneumonia probably killed more Confederate prisoners (in all prisons) than any other disease. Compounding this, Col. Hoffman limited the amount of clothing prisoners were issued. For example, on July 25, 1863, he wrote to the surgeon in charge of De Camp General Hospital (on Davids' Island in Long Island Sound) where wounded prisoners from Gettysburg were hospitalized: "I think it proper to remind you that only such [clothing] as is absolutely necessary will be issued. Men in hospital at this season of the year require [very little clothing]."[38] He sent another letter in August, pointing out that his intention was "not only to save expense to the Government but also that these prisoners might not be returned to the rebel army in better condition for service than when they were captured." (He anticipated a resumption of prisoner exchanges, as did most people.) Some kindly New Yorkers (many with Confederate sympathies) brought gifts of food and clothing to the prisoners but, Hoffman added, "No contributions of clothing for prisoners of war will be received other than the prescribed articles."[39]

During the winter of 1864–65, temperatures at Elmira reached −10° to −15° for long periods. Many of the prisoners were housed in tents but, late in the winter using mostly prison labor, barracks were completed. The barracks were made of green lumber and were insufficient for the winter wind and cold. Colonel Tracy finally got permission to install two small stoves in each barracks, and the men clustered around them, jostling to get close to the fire. Colonel Hoffman still would not allow much clothing: he insisted that any clothing prisoners' families sent would be issued only if it was gray, and most of it was burned. Half-naked prisoners stood ankle deep in the snow to answer roll call. To alleviate the problem, the Confederate government allowed a shipment of cotton to be sent north and sold; the proceeds were used to buy clothes for the prisoners. The death rate at Elmira peaked in February and March 1865, when almost 5% of the camp's 9,000 prisoners died each month—most of pneumonia worsened by malnutrition.

In October 1864, a special exchange of very sick prisoners occurred. Many of the 1,200 soldiers who were sent south for exchange, however, died en route. This led to criticism that the doctors were inhumane for choosing men too sick to endure the trip. A Federal medical inspector agreed; his report stated:

> proper care does not appear to have been exercised by the medical officer at Elmira in the examination of the prisoners for transfer, for it is not possible that so short a journey could have brought about the condition in which these sick were found on their arrival at this point.[40]

Medical officers accused Col. Benjamin Franklin Tracy, the prison camp's commander, of interfering with the hospital's management and making it difficult to care for sick prisoners. Late in 1864, Col. William Hoffman investigated and concluded that not only the commandant but also the doctors were incompetent. At Hoffman's prodding, Tracy improved drainage and accommodations in the camp.

When an outbreak of smallpox occurred at Elmira, as it did at Andersonville and other prisons, there was a great delay in getting vaccine. Many

A Contrast: The Best Federal Prison

The best Federal prison was Johnson's Island in Ohio, which opened in 1862 on 360 acres near Sandusky. The prisoners' better health was attributed to good quality water, excellent "drainage" (meaning of sewage), and a good diet. Johnson's Island primarily housed officers while Elmira was limited to enlisted men.

The single Union army surgeon at Johnson's Island could not get contract surgeons to help because of the facility's isolated location and the low pay ($80 a month). He was aided, though, by Confederate surgeons who had served as line officers and were therefore not released as were other doctors. The incidence of illness from all causes was 35.4 per 1,000 men per year, less than one-fifth the rate at the next-most-healthy prison.[41]

prisoners were cared for in their quarters or in special tents because the hospital facility became overcrowded. By mid-March 1865, 1,700 of the 6,000 prisoners were sick with smallpox. One inspector described their condition as "pitiable." The pond in the prison flooded easily and, on the night of March 10, 1865, the Chemung River inundated the smallpox hospital established along its bank. Between 200 and 300 patients had to be removed on rafts. The official report emphasized that no lives were lost and no one escaped.[42]

The end of war and the warmer weather brought some improvement before the prison was closed on July 5. It was demolished one month later. The prison hospital was closed when the last prisoner left on September 27, 1865. Ultimately, the outcome of the war determined the fate of each prison's commander: Tracy became secretary of the navy while Wirz, the commandant of Andersonville, was hanged.

CARE OF WOUNDED PRISONERS

While health care within Civil War prison camps is an extremely disturbing episode in our history, the medical care of wounded men captured during battle is a different story. With few exceptions, both sides treated captured wounded about as well as they did their own men. After Antietam, Letterman summarized the attitude on both sides, saying, "Everything [was] done to alleviate their sufferings that was done for our own men. Humanity teaches us that a wounded and prostrate foe is not then our enemy."[43]

The care given to the Confederate wounded by the Union army was described in Letterman's official report:

> Immediately after the retreat of the enemy from the field of Antietam, measures were taken to have all the Confederate wounded gathered in from the field, over which they laid scattered in all directions, and from the houses and barns in the rear of their lines, and placed under such circumstances as would permit of their being properly attended to, and at such points as would enable their removal to be effected to Frederick and thence to Baltimore and Fortress Monroe to their own lines [i.e. exchanged]. They were removed as rapidly as their recovery would permit.[44]

After the war, Dr. John H. Brinton recorded that as early as the Battle of Rich Mountain (fought in western Virginia in August 1861), field aid stations treated wounded prisoners the "same as our own men, on both sides." In an improvised Union hospital, "the captured enemy received the same

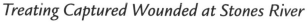

Treating Captured Wounded at Stones River

In his book, *The Surgeon and the Hospital in the Civil War,* Hart quotes a surgeon who was at Stones River:

> Stones River [Murfreesboro, Tennessee] was fought December 31, 1862 . . . By noon we had received at our division hospital two or three hundred of the wounded. Among them were a number of rebel soldiers who were lying side by side with our men, and receiving the same care . . . A line of perhaps two hundred rebel cavalry appeared in front of our hospital, . . . driving our men through and beyond our tents and capturing our hospital.
>
> I made my green surgeon's sash as conspicuous as possible. My servant brought my horse to me at the house which was our headquarters, and I was holding the bridle-rein. Four rebel cavalrymen rode up and one on foot carrying a saddle. This man, with a bitter oath, seized the rein and demanded my horse. "You can't have him. I am a surgeon and this is a hospital. We are taking care of your wounded. Lieutenant, go in and see for yourself." He went in and came back, saying, "Yes, it's true; go in, Tom, and see yourself; you'll have to give the doctor his horse."[46]

care as our own."[45] After the wounded men recovered, they were sent to prisons, where, Brinton noted, their medical care was not nearly as good.

The principle of treating captured wounded interchangeably with an army's own men extended beyond surgical care to the provision of extra food and "treats." Federal surgeon John Shaw Billings noted that after the Peninsula campaign of 1862 when wounded men poured into the Washington area, the older residents of Georgetown and Washington were mostly in sympathy with the Confederates and brought wounded Confederate POWs delicacies to eat and drink. Congressmen's families did the same for Union wounded. Billings established a policy that all gifts would go to those who needed them the most, whatever their side. The U.S. Sanitary Commission formally adopted the principle that in medical care, no distinction was to be made between Union and Confederate men, recognizing neither friend nor foe among the wounded.[47]

After Gettysburg, Lee's retreating army took as many of their wounded as they could, transporting them in a long and sorrowful wagon train. They left behind soldiers who were too severely wounded to survive the rigors of travel.[48] Sanitary Commission agents estimated that there were nearly

> 5,500 Confederates abandoned by their Army in its retreat, and were in a most deplorable condition of suffering and destitution. They were without Hospital supplies or even ordinary rations, and were saved from starvation only by the stores of the Government against which they were fighting."[49]

Immediately after the battle, a Commission inspector, Dr. Winslow, visited Confederate surgeons in a field hospital they had set up during the fighting. Since the Union Medical Department, overwhelmed with their own casualties, had not yet taken over this hospital, Winslow explained the nature of the Commission's work and offered to supply their needs from its stores. The Confederates were astonished and grateful:

> they eagerly availed themselves of his offers, and one of the strangest of the many strange and wonderful sights of which the Commission's depot at Gettysburg was the scene after the battle, was the mingling in that busy crowd of friend and foe, National uniform and Confederate uniform.[50]

Similar scenes occurred in Richmond, where prominent women formed an aid association to bring food to the hospitalized men. When one of the leading citizens, Mrs. Randolph, proposed that all benefits be shared equally among Union and Confederate wounded, certain "fierce old dames shrieked at the mere idea of putting their noble soldiers on a par with the Yankees." But Mrs. Randolph prevailed and "captured federal wounded were surprised and grateful at receiving the same care as their wounded enemies."[51] Richmond ladies also assisted the clergy in alleviating conditions at nearby prison camps, including Libby and Belle Island Prisons.

The terrible confusion after the Second Battle of Bull Run, at the end of August 1862, led to many instances of the two armies cooperating to care for the wounded. For example, when defeated General Pope evacuated his forces from nearby Centreville, he abandoned thousands of Union wounded. All the medical and hospital supplies fell into Confederate hands, and, initially, the Union wounded suffered terribly from the lack of food and drink, and from exposure first to heavy rain and then to hot sun. General Lee ordered his medical director to provide whatever sustenance he had to the Union wounded, but the food supplies were limited.

Observers concluded that, in general, Union authorities were kinder to sick and wounded prisoners than to those who were able-bodied. Captured Southern physicians wrote of the indifference and brutality of Northerners toward the Confederate prisoners but noted that the Union surgeons were compassionate. On the Union side, Gen. Benjamin Butler informed Secretary of War Stanton in February 1864 that he had "received less complaint of the treatment by rebels of Union prisoners in hospitals than elsewhere."[52]

CAPTURED PHYSICIANS

Throughout the war, both sides occasionally abandoned their wounded because they lacked ambulances or the time to collect them. They also left the wounded when they were too badly injured to be moved. Surgeons remained behind to continue caring for these men, thus subjecting themselves to capture. Many of those who stayed behind were volunteers, others drew lots to see who would remain, and some were ordered to do so.

Dr. Hunter Holmes McGuire suggested a policy for dealing with these captured physicians during Stonewall Jackson's famous Valley campaign in the spring of 1862. McGuire, a surgeon from Winchester, became medical director of Jackson's army, as well as his personal friend and physician. When Jackson's forces occupied Winchester at the end of May, seven or eight Federal surgeons at the Union hotel-turned-hospital volunteered to stay behind and allow themselves to be captured in order to continue caring for badly wounded men. McGuire asked Jackson for permission to free these physicians unconditionally, with the understanding that they would report to the Federal secretary of war in Washington and urge the similar release of all captured Confederate surgeons. Jackson decided that the surgeons were non-combatants and agreed.

A short time later, on June 10, 1862, during the Peninsula campaign, General McClellan proposed to General Lee that medical officers be "viewed as non-combatants" and not be detained as prisoners of war. Lee agreed on June 17. Two days later, McClellan sent Lee a copy of General Order No. 60, which stated: "The principle being recognized that medical officers shall not be held as prisoners of war, it is directed that all medical officers so held by the United States shall be immediately and unconditionally discharged." On June 26, Lee issued his General Order establishing that all Union medical officers held as prisoners would be released.

Lee's concern about wounded captives is recorded in his wartime letters. In one to Gen. D. H. Hill on July 4, 1862, he wrote: "I understand that many of the enemy's wounded of Monday's fight are still on the field, they must have suffered greatly and every effort should be made to remove all of them where they will be comfortable."[53] Eleven days later he wrote to his nephew, Gen. Fitzhugh Lee,

> I am sorry to hear of the sufferings of the wounded prisoners, and I wish I could relieve them. I proposed to General McClellan on Tuesday, before the battle of that day, to parole and send to him all his wounded if he would receive them. Since that arrangement has been made, and the sick and wounded are being conveyed to him.[54]

The arrangement had advantages for both sides. Since physicians did not need to avoid capture, they did not have to risk moving severely wounded men when aid stations or hospitals were being overrun. This spared the men additional suffering and reduced the likelihood of life-threatening complications. It also lessened the burden on the other side's surgeons, who were already overwhelmed with their own wounded. Once the capturing army could assume the care of the wounded prisoners, the physicians were released. (See Figure 15.3.)

In 1863, over a year after Americans recognized physicians as being non-combatants, European countries officially adopted a similar set of guidelines for the release of captured medical personnel. This occurred in Geneva at the first international conference on the treatment of prisoners of war. The meeting was prompted by experiences in prior European wars, the Battle of Solferino in particular.[55]

The freedom of action afforded some captured physicians is illustrated by the experience of a contract surgeon, Dr. John Swinburne, from a New York volunteer regiment. Swinburne was captured during the Seven Days' Battle in Virginia at the end of June 1862, shortly after the exchange of messages between Lee and McClellan. While Generals Lee and James Longstreet were conferring on horseback on Long Bridge Road, Swinburne, whose field hospital had been captured, boldly went up to them. He asked for supplies and help caring for his wounded and for the Confederate wounded who had been brought to his station. Lee directed an aide to get him the help he needed. (Five years later, during the Franco-Prussian War, Swinburne was put in charge of an American field hospital in Paris that was highly regarded by the French.)[56]

On a few occasions, captured surgeons were not released in a timely fashion. Some Confederate surgeons were temporarily held at Fort Delaware, on Pea Patch Island in the Delaware River It was one of the worst of the Federal prisons. The surgeons complained bitterly of the detention and of the torment from the mosquitoes in particular, which, they emphasized, did not regard *them* as non-combatants.[57,58]

Figure 15.3: "Flag of Truce from the Rebels, the Campaign in Maryland:" Cooperation between Northern and Southern surgeons in the care of wounded after the Battle of Antietam, September 1862. (*Harper's Weekly*, sketched by A. R. Waud.)

The Experience of a Captured Union Surgeon

Union Surgeon Daniel M. Holt was captured while caring for his wounded men after Chancellorsville in May 1863. He recorded the kindness and respect that Confederate officers afforded him, even sharing their food. In addition,

> General Lee came to see me. Four times did this great man call and feelingly inquire if the men were receiving all the care that could be bestowed, at the same time remarking that it was beyond his power to yield such succor as his heart prompted. Their army, he remarked, was not supplied as ours, with Sanitary and Christian Commission supplies, neither was the Medical Department as completely and thoroughly equipped—no chloroform for minor cases of surgery—no stimulants for moderate or severe prostration, and as a consequence no means of relieving the suffering of their men. All that he could do, he did do. He sent the medical director of their army to look in on us, and to supply help in amputations, which by this time had become imperative . . . I found just as sympathetic hearts here as anywhere. I must in justice say for an enemy, that I never was treated with greater consideration by intelligent men, than I was by these very rebs for the ten days that I remained among them; at the same time I might say that I never had so hard a time in my life.[59]

Surgeon Holt, who was very proud of his horse and saddle, was upset that the rebels did not return his horse when he was released. He sent a note through the lines to General Lee, and subsequently wrote his wife, "I have good news to tell you. My horse, saddle, and everything captured by the rebels was regained the day we left White Oak Church. They were returned by flag of truce within four days from the time I addressed General Lee on the subject." He then sent Lee another note thanking him.[60]

PHYSICIANS AND THE PRISONS

How much responsibility did physicians have for the terrible suffering and mortality in the prison camps? Among the many books and articles written on Civil War POWs, a few authors blame the surgeons for much of the suffering and many of the deaths. They attributed the poor sanitation, disease-producing odors ("miasmas"), and scanty diet to the prison physicians' lack of attention and cruelty toward prisoners.

It is true that the results of the medical care at Elmira reflect poorly on the prison's medical staff. Northerners and Southerners alike condemned the surgeon-in-chief at Elmira, E. L. Sanger, for mistreating and neglecting prisoners in retaliation for the atrocities at Andersonville. Confederates described Sanger as a "club-footed gentleman with an abnormal head and a snaky look in his eyes." A prisoner who had been a member of the 10th Virginia claimed that he had overheard Sanger say, "I have killed more rebs than any soldier at the front."[61]

On the other hand, the official records reveal a continuing dispute over conditions for the prisoners between Sanger and Colonel Tracy, the camp commandant. On two occasions, medical inspectors from the Surgeon General's Office tried to help Sanger, advising him to bypass Tracy and report directly to Washington. Sanger did this, documenting innumerable difficulties in caring for patients and in getting his requisitions filled. The other physicians at the post also signed his report.[62] Confederate physicians who had been line officers and were imprisoned at Elmira described conscientious Union physicians, specifically praising Anthony Stoker and F. D. Ritter by name.

At Andersonville, Chief Surgeon Isaiah H. White repeatedly notified his superiors, especially General Winder, of "the deplorable condition of the prisoners." He petitioned for medical and hospital supplies, additional medical officers, an adequate supply of cooking utensils, hospital tents, and straw for bedding, and he asked specifically for antiscorbutics.[63] An inspector's report to General Winder emphasized the fact that physicians at Andersonville were doing their best under adverse conditions.[64]

Official records also reveal numerous physicians' requests at other prisons for better sanitary conditions, better hospital facilities, and more supplies. While these documents, as well as statements such as those made at Captain Wirz's trial which seem to convey physicians' concern and efforts, might be regarded as self-serving attempts to divert blame, medical inspectors' reports sent to Washington or Richmond generally support them. For example, a report by inspector John H. Brinton found that the prisoners in Elmira's hospital received very good care, but that when they were discharged from the hospital, they returned to the prison camp's miserable conditions.[65]

There are also many letters and reports by former prisoners on both sides complimenting the physicians who cared for them. When H. M. Davidson of the 1st Ohio Light Artillery and a former prisoner at Andersonville testified to a post-war Congressional Committee investigating that prison's conditions, he thanked many physicians "for their kindnesses and attempts to help although lacking in medicines and facilities." He mentioned that the physicians had constant exposure to

> breathing the unwholesome air, and in constant contact with these horrible diseases; but they were patient, faithful men, and their sympathy with the victims often benefited them as much as the medicines they prescribed ... I gladly record the little acts of kindness performed by them, for they were verdant spots in this vast Sahara of misery. Drs. Watkins, Rowsey, Thornburn, Reeves, Williams, James, Thompson, Pilott and Sanders deserve, and will receive, the lasting gratitude of the prisoners who received medical treatment at their hands during that memorable summer at Andersonville.[66]

It is difficult to apportion the blame for the conditions and the deaths in the prisons. While there were some callous physicians, there does not seem to have been a pattern of neglect or a failure to properly use the limited resources. Indeed, they regularly tried to obtain better facilities and more supplies for the prisoners. While surgeons could do little to treat disease given the limited medical knowledge of the time, mortality undoubtedly would have been greatly reduced had they been able to provide the diet needed to prevent malnutrition.

REFERENCES

1. McElroy J, Meredith R, Wirz H: *This Was Andersonville: The True Story of Andersonville Military Prison as Told in the Personal Recollections of John McElroy, Sometime Private, Co. L, 16th Illinois Cavalry.* New York: McDowell Obolensky, 1957, p. 306.
2. *O.R.*, Series 1, vol. XVII/2, p. 419.
3. Futch OL: *History of Andersonville Prison.* Gainesville, FL: Univ. of Florida Press, 1968, p. 10.
4. Ibid., p. 38.
5. Ibid.
6. Ibid., pp. 20, 32-34, 37.
7. Moore JN: *Confederate Commissary General Lucius Bellinger Northrop and the Subsistence Bureau of the Southern Army.* Shippensburg, PA: White Mane Pub., 1996, p. 61.
8. Blakey AF: *General John H. Winder, C.S.A.* Gainesville: Univ. of Florida Press, 1990, p. 190.
9. McElroy, et al. *This Was Andersonville*, p. 306.
10. Futch, *History of Andersonville Prison*, p. 19.
11. Ibid., pp. 90-91.
12. Blakey, *General John H. Winder*, p. 191.
13. Moore, *Confederate Commissary General L.B. Northrop*, p. 3.
14. Blakey, *General John H. Winder*, p. 201.
15. Moore, *Confederate Commissary General L.B. Northrop*, p. 4.
16. Blakey, *General John H. Winder*, p. 5.
17. *O.R.*, Series II, vol. VIII, pp. 588-632.
18. *Medical and Surgical History*, Medical Section, vol. 3, pp. 33 et seq.

19. Ibid., p. 39.
20. Futch, *History of Andersonville Prison*, p. 106.
21. *Medical and Surgical History*, Medical Section, vol. 3, p. 42.
22. *South Hist Soc Papers*. 1876 March;1(3):183.
23. U.S. Army Medical Service: *Internal Medicine in World War II*. vol. III. (Anderson RS, ed.) Washington, D.C.: Office of the Surgeon General, Dept. of the Army, 1961, pp. 256, 271.
24. Futch, *History of Andersonville Prison*, pp. 108-9.
25. Ibid.
26. Hamilton FH, ed.: *Surgical Memoirs of the War of the Rebellion Collected and Published by the U.S. Sanitary Commission*. New York: Hurd and Houghton, 1871.
27. *O.R.*, Series II, vol. VIII, pp. 588-632.
28. *The Photographic History of the Civil War*. New York: Review of Reviews, 1970 (orig. pub. 1911), vol. 4B, p. 78.
29. Futch, *History of Andersonville Prison*, p. 120.
30. Chipman NP: *The Andersonville Prison Trial: The Trial of Capt. Henry Wirz*. Sacramento: The Author, 1911. Repub: Birmingham, AL: Notable Trials Library, 1990, p. 206.
31. Ibid., p. 205.
32. Ibid.
33. Ibid., p. 108.
34. Robertson JI: The scourge of Elmira. *Civil War Hist*. 1962;8(2):184-201.
35. *Medical and Surgical History*, Medical Section, vol. 3, pp. 63, 56.
36. Gragg R, ed.: *The Illustrated Confederate Reader*. New York: Harper & Row, 1989, pp. 144-46.
37. Gillett MC: *The United States Army Medical Department, 1818–1865*. Washington, D.C.: Center of Military History, U.S. Army, 1987, p. 267.
38. *O.R.*, Series II, vol. VI, p. 158.
39. Ibid., p. 218.
40. *O.R.*, Series II, vol. VIII, p. 231.
41. *Medical and Surgical History*, Medical Section, vol. 3, p. 61.
42. *O.R.*, Series II, vol. IV, p. 263.
43. *O.R.*, Series I, vol. XIX/1, p. 112.
44. Ibid., p. 111.
45. Brinton JH: *The Brinton Manuscripts*. NARA, RG94, Entry #628, A478.
46. Hart AG: *The Surgeon and the Hospital in the Civil War*. Gaithersburg, MD: Olde Soldier Books, 1987, (orig. pub. 1902), p. 45.
47. Greenbie MLB: *Lincoln's Daughters of Mercy*. New York: G.P. Putnam's Sons, 1944, p. 143.
48. Imboden JD: The Confederate retreat from Gettysburg. *Battles and Leaders of the Civil War*. vol. III. New York: Thomas Yoseloff, 1956.
49. Stillé CJ: *History of the United States Sanitary Commission: Being a General Report of Its Work during the War of the Rebellion*. New York: Hurd and Houghton, 1868, p. 386.
50. Ibid.
51. Bill AH: *The Beleaguered City: Richmond 1861–65*. New York: Alfred A. Knopf, 1946, pp. 78, 138.
52. Gillett, *U.S. Army Medical Department*, p. 267.
53. Lee RE: *The Wartime Papers of Robert E. Lee*. New York: Da Capo Press, 1987, pp. 207-8.
54. Ibid., pp. 231-32.
55. Cantlie N: *A History of the Army Medical Department*. vol. 2. Edinburgh: Churchill Livingston, 1973, p. 271.
56. Horne A: *The Fall of Paris. The Siege and the Commune 1870–71*. New York: Penguin, 1990.
57. Mitchell SW: On the Medical Department in the Civil War. Address to Physicians' Club of Chicago, February 25, 1913, *J Am Med Assoc*. 1914 May 19;62(19):1445-50.
58. Faust PL, ed.: *Historical Times Encyclopedia of the Civil War*. New York: Harper & Row, 1986.

59. Holt DM: *A Surgeon's Civil War: The Letters and Diary of Daniel M. Holt, M.D.* Kent, OH: Kent State Univ. Press, 1994, p. 96.
60. Ibid., pp. 114-15, 151.
61. Robertson, *Civil War Hist,* 1962.
62. *O.R.,* Series II, vol. VII, p. 1094.
63. *Medical and Surgical History,* Medical Section, vol. 3, pp. 33-71.
64. Ibid., p. 42.
65. *The Brinton Manuscripts,* NARA, RG94.
66. *Medical and Surgical History,* Medical Section, vol. 3, p. 42.

16

Women of the Civil War: Soldiers, Sisters, and Socialites

Alas! Nothing I had ever heard or read had given me the slightest idea of the horrors witnessed here. . . . Certainly none of the glories of the war are presented here. But I must not say that; for if uncomplaining endurance is glory, we had plenty of it.

— Kate Cumming, Volunteer Nurse, Confederate Army

IN THE MIDDLE OF THE NINETEENTH CENTURY, nursing was the most effective component in the treatment of serious illness. The Civil War played a major role in the evolution of the nursing profession in the United States. Before the Civil War, there were few trained nurses in civilian life and none in the army. Most civilian nursing was done by family members. On the frontier posts, nursing was performed either by soldiers' wives or by other soldiers, who were usually recuperating patients themselves.

According to one contemporary description, "nurses were convalescent soldiers, wan, thin, weak, and requiring nursing themselves, and although they were kind to their comrades, they were wholly worthless as nurses."[1] If a soldier-nurse learned his tasks and began to do them well, he was usually declared healthy and transferred back to active duty.

THE BEGINNING OF NURSING

When the war began, nursing in rudimentary civilian hospitals was little better than in military institutions. It was said of Bellevue, a leading New

York hospital, that "at night no one attended the patients except the rats that roamed the floors."[2] (See Figure 16.1.) During emergencies, such as epidemics, nursing was provided primarily by prisoners from the jail that was part of the institution at Bellevue.[3] Most patients were nursed at home; only those without adequate housing, such as the poor and the homeless, were admitted to a hospital.

The initial lack of nursing care became critical as epidemics spread among the recruits and the number of casualties from the early battles grew. Numerous letters published during the war's early months described the horrible suffering soldiers endured. One such communication bemoaned the inadequate care given sick soldiers of the 5th Wisconsin Infantry at their training camp near Washington:

> In the hospital the nurses are "convalescent soldiers," so nearly sick themselves that they ought to be in the wards, and from their very feebleness they are selfish and sometimes inhuman in their treatment of the patients. In the camp we stout hearty fellows take care of the sick,—rough in our management, I doubt not, but we do not fail for lack of strength or interest. If we could be sure of being half-way well cared for when we get sick or wounded, it would take immensely from the horrors of army life. . . .
>
> We need beds and bedding, hospital clothing and sick-diet, proper medicines, surgical instruments, and good nurses,—then a decent building or a good hospital tent for the accommodation of our sick. I suppose we shall have them when the government can get around to it, and in the meantime we try to be patient.[4]

Such letters inspired civilians, particularly women, to work to improve the medical and nursing care provided to soldiers. As Mary A. Livermore of the Northwestern Branch of the Sanitary Commission wrote, these letters stimulated

> a resolute determination in the hearts of the people, that neither inexperience nor dogged adherence to routine should cause such wholesale slaughter of their beloved citizen soldiers [as had occurred in the Crimea]. . . . Whether sick or well, they should receive such care as the soldiers of no nation had ever known before. No failure of their plans of relief abated their ardor, and no discouragement stayed the stream of their beneficence. Especially did women refuse to release their hold on the men of their households, even when the government had organized them into an army. They followed them with letters of inquiry, with tender anxiety and intelligent provision, which eventually put them en rapport with the government, and developed a wonderful system of sanitary prevention and relief. For the outcome of their patriotism and zeal, their loyalty and love, was the Sanitary Commission.[5]

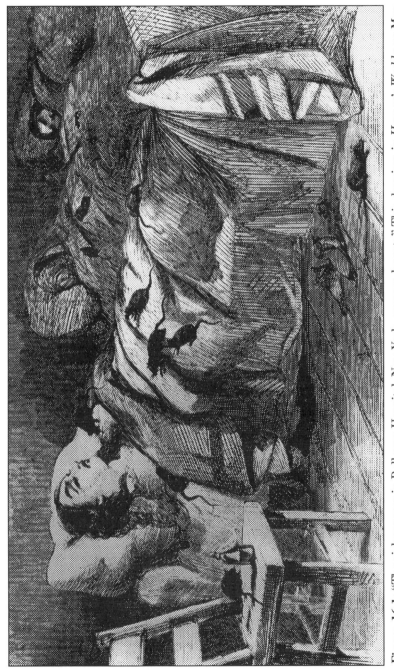

Figure 16.1: "The sick women in Bellevue Hospital, New York, overrun by rats." This drawing, in *Harper's Weekly* on May 5, 1860, illustrates conditions in pre–Civil War hospitals. (Courtesy of the Museum of the City of New York. © Museum of the City of New York. Reprinted with permission.)

During the Crimean War, Florence Nightingale's activities generated international publicity about the need for competent nursing and the contribution it could make to patient care. With her band of thirty-eight female nurses, she improved the scandalously filthy hospitals and the typically bad care of ill and injured soldiers, helping to lower the unbelievably high mortality rate. Nightingale's success was legendary on both sides of the Atlantic, and the nurses' training program she started in 1862 at St. Thomas Hospital in London quickly became famous. American women who served as nurses during the Civil War frequently were called "Nightingales."

DOROTHEA DIX

Several American women had gone to Britain, Turkey, and the Crimea to work with Nightingale. One was Dorothea Dix, who went to Turkey to meet Nightingale but missed seeing her. Dix had already received a great deal of attention for her pre-Civil War contributions to the care of the mentally ill, "paupers," and prison inmates.[6,7] In 1861, immediately after the fall of Fort Sumter on April 14, Dix attended the meeting organized by Dr. Elizabeth Blackwell that led to the formation of the Women's Central Association of Relief of New York City and, subsequently, the U.S. Sanitary Commission.

On April 19, Dix observed that the army was not prepared to care for even the small number of injured men from the 6th Massachusetts Militia Regiment, which had been attacked by a mob while moving between train stations in Baltimore. Losing no time, she approached the War Department in Washington and offered to provide 100 trained nurses to keep the hospitals in "hygienic condition." Initially ignored, she persisted and lobbied the secretary of war, President Lincoln's secretary, and others. Because of her excellent managerial skills, they made her superintendent of female nurses, with the authority to organize a woman's nursing corps.[8] Dix then wrote to Dr. Blackwell in New York asking her to recruit the nurses; she also agreed to have Blackwell arrange some training for them.[9] (See Figure 16.2.)

After receiving the request from Dix, Blackwell interviewed volunteers and chose 100 to receive three months of nursing training from Bellevue Hospital staff physicians. To decrease nurse mortality, she wisely required all those accepted to have had measles. Blackwell drew up a nurses' manual and trained a group herself at New York Infirmary.[10] The new nurses learned to fashion bandages from cornhusks (particularly useful at Antietam) and to improvise splints and crutches. After the training, according to trainee Georgeanna Woolsey, they felt "competent to handle any very small emergency."[11] These nurses went to work under Dix in Washington.

Figure 16.2: "The Nurses Destined for the Army Visiting the New York City Hospital." A physician from Bellevue Hospital is providing instruction on the wards. They are well dressed and appear to be society women. (Courtesy of the Museum of the City of New York. © Museum of the City of New York. Reprinted with permission.)

Dorothea Dix felt that only women from respectable (meaning wealthy and socially prominent) families were acceptable, provided they were not too attractive ("plain" was the characteristic she sought) and that they eschewed jewelry and other personal adornment. Their dresses had to be brown or black with no bows and, definitely, no hoops. Dix also had religious criteria: she accepted only Protestants. Despite a severe need for additional female nurses throughout the war, the rigid Dix denied women who did not meet her standards any opportunity to serve. Dix herself worked seven days a week, and she was highly regarded by most of the nurses she selected. Some, however, considered her dictatorial and called her "Dragon Dix."[12] She was described as having "a soft and musical voice . . . and very winning manners when she chose to use them,"[13] but one of her nurses described her as "arbitrary," and another as "a self-sealing can of horror tied up in red tape."[14]

Dix believed, as did Florence Nightingale, that trained nurses were responsible as much for discipline as for overseeing diets and dressing wounds. Nightingale felt that "patience and resignation" in a nurse "are but other words for carelessness or indifference—contemptible if in regard to herself, culpable if in regard to her sick."[15] Miss Dix strongly agreed. As a result, she was confrontational whenever she felt dissatisfied with a situation, and especially when the doctors did not properly accept her nurses or were otherwise, in her opinion, remiss. When anyone questioned her authority, Dix would haughtily respond, "I am Dorothea L. Dix, Superintendent of Nurses, in the employ of the United States Government!"[16]

Dix's attitude hampered the acceptance of her nurses and, combined with the restrictions she placed on their qualifications, aggravated the chronic shortage of nurses in the army despite an abundance of volunteers. The friction she created culminated in a directive issued by Surgeon General Hammond on July 14, 1862, which, although it repeated Dix's authorization to select and assign women nurses, put the "control and direction" of all nurses, women as well as men, under the "medical officer in charge." The order also specified one female nurse for every two male nurses.

General Order No. 357, issued on October 27, 1863 (after Hammond had been removed), again emphasized that female nurses were no longer exclusively under the control of Miss Dix nor independent of the Medical Department staff, but that they were controlled by the senior medical officers at the hospital in which they served. This meant that they could be assigned other duties or dismissed for incompetence or disobedience. The order also contained economy measures, specifying the use of no more than one nurse per thirty beds and reducing nurses' pay from $20.50 a month to $13 plus a $3 allowance for clothing. Dix personally was devastated by this development, and her influence continued to wane as the war progressed.

Given their pre-war social standing and contacts, Dix's nurses often brought considerable political influence to bear. When they felt the soldiers' welfare required it, they could vigorously pursue their objectives. A typical example was when Hannah Ropes, Louisa Mae Alcott's supervisor at Union Hospital, observed a corrupt hospital steward who served as the facility's administrator. After the hospital's surgeons failed to correct the situation, Ropes obtained support from Dorothea Dix and, eventually, contacted Secretary of War Stanton. She succeeded in getting the man removed from duty and arrested.[17]

Nurses were desperately needed throughout the war and there were repeated calls for women to serve, but Dix's policies limited the number she allowed to work. During the war, 3,214 women served in Dorothea Dix's corps of female army nurses, assigned mainly to large general hospitals in major cities. But they represented only a small percentage of the women who served as paid nurses, matrons, cooks, and laundresses in the Union army.

OTHER UNION WOMEN WHO SERVED

Many women simply appeared and went to work in army hospitals without Dix's blessing or knowledge, especially in the smaller hospitals located in camps and near battlefields. These volunteer nurses often helped to collect and care for wounded immediately after the fighting ceased, sometimes working under fire. The army paid at least 18,000 women for such services; roughly 2,000 more served as unpaid volunteers. Some women were actually enlisted by regiments and were called "battle nurses" and "daughters of the regiment."

Many women suffered terrible consequences for "doing their duty." An unrecorded number died of typhoid fever or other diseases acquired while caring for sick soldiers. One Union army nurse pricked her finger while pinning a bandage and subsequently died of "blood poisoning."[18] Louisa Mae Alcott, one of Dix's troop, acquired typhoid fever and then developed toxicity from the mercury with which she was treated, almost dying before her father took her home. Alcott later described her experiences as "Nurse Periwinkle" in *Hospital Sketches*.[19]

Clara Barton served as a nurse independent of Dorothea Dix. When the war began, the Massachusetts native was a clerk in the patent office in

Daughters of the Regiment

Kady Brownell, a sergeant's wife, served as the 3rd Michigan Infantry Regiment's color bearer. She had grown up in a British army camp and could ride and shoot better than most of the men. The regimental surgeon taught her to apply wound dressings on the battlefield. In action, she rode in front of the troops, wearing a costume of her own design that included the regimental colors, loose trousers, and a full tunic with a wide cartridge belt.

Emma Edmonds served in the unit commanded by Gen. Samuel P. Heintzelman, along with a chaplain's wife known only as Mrs. Kate B. (Many women who worked in the army used assumed names to keep their social standing.) The two women worked with the chaplain-husband and two doctors to provide nursing care. They tried to ensure hospital cleanliness and a proper diet for the sick, and even went fishing to provide variety in the men's diet. They insisted on sanitary privies and took turns digging them, saying, "Here's how the Northern shovelry will beat the Southern chivalry."[20]

Washington. Learning that 6th Massachusetts soldiers had been injured in Baltimore, she finally located them in the Capitol's rotunda. The men needed food and other supplies, as well as medical and nursing care. Barton began to dress their wounds and used her own money to provide them with food and other necessities. A Boston newspaperman who had come to see his hometown troops reported on her work, and the resulting publicity produced a flood of contributions of money and supplies.

With these funds, as well as the political help necessary to obtain battle-field passes (Senator Wilson from Massachusetts was a close friend), Barton was able to continue working on her own, and she purchased supplies, hired wagons and drivers, and moved with the army when fighting erupted. Barton cared for wounded soldiers after numerous battles throughout the war, including General Burnside's disastrous assault on Fredericksburg in December 1862, and on Morris Island after an unsuccessful Union attempt to capture Charleston.[21] She was so helpful after Antietam that she is depicted in paintings of the event.

Barton was careful to avoid the institutions in which Dorothea Dix's nurses worked. She preferred to maintain her independence, and never crossed swords with the army's nominal head of female nursing. After the war, she played a major role in establishing the American Red Cross and was its first president. (The International Red Cross had been founded in Switzerland during the American Civil War, primarily in response to the carnage and suffering in European wars of the 1850s.)

The epidemic diseases that overwhelmed the camps on both sides in late 1861 and early 1862 illuminated the deficiencies in military medical care. Public knowledge of these medical meltdowns brought out hundreds of women volunteers from all social strata. Despite the traditions that denied such opportunities to women, the female volunteers became so valuable that they earned official status. As Mary Elizabeth Massey stated, "The Civil War provided a springboard from which they leaped beyond the circumscribed 'woman's sphere' into that heretofore reserved for men."[22]

Some women were designated "matrons," in charge of wards and of the soldier-nurses. Others changed dressings, helped with surgical procedures, supervised other volunteer nurses, prepared food (and occasionally, especially on the Southern side, obtained the food), and provided other comforts. Some women had more responsibilities. Phoebe Pember, for example, a matron of a major unit at Chimborazo Hospital in Richmond, was an exceptional Confederate hospital administrator.

Most notable on the Union side was Mary Ann Bickerdyke. (See Biographical Box, p. 414.) Known as "Mother Bickerdyke" to the men, she was so effective that she received special protection and support from Generals Grant and Sherman. She followed Sherman's army until the end of the war. Early in the war, Mother Bickerdyke's efforts and effectiveness came to the attention of the Sanitary Commission's Northwestern Branch, and she was quickly given all the supplies and equipment she requested, worth enormous sums, without questioning or paperwork. They knew she was entirely reliable, and "God help any creature" who tried to use her supplies for any purpose other than caring for her "boys."[23] It took considerable effort to get her to accept a small salary to help with the expenses of caring for her two sons, whom she had left with friends in Chicago.

NUNS AS NURSES

According to several contemporary sources, doctors, including those who were Protestant, preferred Catholic nuns to other nurses. Early in the war, Medical Director Tripler stated:

> We can get female nurses through Miss Dix and from among the Sisters of Charity. It is a very damaging position for any one to take and avow, but in the honest discharge of my duties, though a Protestant myself, I do not

Mary Ann ("Mother") Bickerdyke (1817–1901)

A widow living in Galesburg, Illinois, before the war, Mrs. Bickerdyke eked out a living as a "botanic physician." At the start of the war, the citizens of the town raised $500 to purchase supplies to relieve the reported suffering of soldiers in the ill-equipped rudimentary hospitals in Cairo at the southern tip of Illinois. Mrs. Bickerdyke volunteered to take the supplies to the hospitals. When she saw the condition of the facilities, she decided to stay and clean them up. Moving from task to task "like a cyclone," she became known as the "Cyclone in Calico." After receiving training in nursing and hospital management from a physician friend, she developed her own thoroughly trained cadre of subordinates.

Mrs. Bickerdyke procured equipment and supplies through the Northwestern Branch of the Sanitary Commission with special help from Mary Livermore, and established diet kitchens and laundries for the soldiers. She organized a veritable army of freed or runaway slaves, known as "contrabands," to work in these facilities; there were so many that she was sometimes called "General Bickerdyke."[24]

Tales of her adventures abound. She was celebrated for getting incompetent or drunken doctors removed from the service—she had about twelve discharged and several others reprimanded. On one occasion, she arrived in a ward late in the morning and found that the men hadn't been fed yet because the surgeon had not arrived to order their meals. As the story goes, she is quoted as saying, "Haven't had their breakfasts! . . . These poor fellows must be fed immediately!" At that point, the surgeon arrived, looking as if he had just slept off a night's debauch. Mrs. Bickerdyke immediately accosted him, exclaiming, "You miserable, drunken, heartless scalawag! . . . Off with your shoulder straps and get out of this hospital . . . This is your fourth spree in a month," while tearing off his symbols of rank. The surgeon, realizing that he was in deep trouble, went to his corps commander to appeal. Major General Sherman listened to his tale and then asked who his accuser was. When told it was "Mother" Bickerdyke, Sherman said that he could not do anything about it because "she ranks me."[25]

Bickerdyke served with the Western army and was present during the Vicksburg and Atlanta campaigns and Sherman's March to the Sea and through the Carolinas. The affection she had for her "boys" was returned in kind. At the end of the war, they insisted that she accompany them during the army's "Grand Review" on May 23, 1865, where she rode in an ambulance wagon down Washington's "Chiefest Avenue."

hesitate to declare that in my opinion the latter are far preferable to the former, being better disciplined, more discreet and judicious, and more reliable. In the arrangement of the hospitals it might be judicious to assign one section to the Sisters of Charity and the other to the Protestant nurses.[26]

The doctors preferred the nuns because they were more agreeable, less confrontational, and much easier to work with. More importantly, they worked hard and did not write letters to Congressmen or the newspapers. The nuns accepted miserable accommodations without complaint—in at least one hospital, ten nuns crowded into one room to sleep, with little space between the beds—and they did not bring or request servants of their own. Senior Surgeon John H. Brinton, contrasted the two types of "women of the North" who acted as nurses:

> They [the socialites] besieged officers and persons in high authority, and these upon the general military principle of sending a disagreeable person as far away as possible, sent their fair petitioners to as far away positions as they could. . . . "They did not wish much," not they, "simply a room, a bed, a looking glass, someone to get their meals, do little things for them," . . . In answer to my request to the Catholic authorities of, I think, North or South Bend, Indiana, a number of sisters were sent down to act as nurses in the hospital. They were sent from a teaching and not from a nursing order, but in a short time adapted themselves admirably to their new duties . . . when I asked the Mother who accompanied them, what accommodations they required, the answer was, "One room, doctor," and there were in all, I think, fourteen or fifteen of them. . . . The sick patients gained by the change, but for a few days I was the most abused man in the department, for the newspapers gave me no mercy.[27]

A key member of the Northwestern Branch of the Sanitary Commission thought that physicians had more personal reasons for their religious preferences in nurses:

> I found everywhere, at this time, the greatest prejudice against Protestant women nurses. Medical directors, surgeons, and even wardmasters, openly declared they would not have them in the service, and that only the "Sisters" of the Catholic Church should receive appointments. I sought for the cause of this decision. "Your Protestant nurses are always finding some mare's-nest or other," said one of the surgeons, "that they can't let alone. They all write for the papers, and the story finds its way into print, and directly we are in hot water. Now, the 'Sisters' never see anything they ought not to see, nor hear anything they ought not to hear, and they never write for the papers—and the result is we get along very comfortably with them."[28]

In all military zones, nuns of various orders made themselves indispensable as hospital nurses. In many instances, the surgeons in charge specifically requested nursing help from nearby orders. At least twelve orders of nuns participated during the war, including Sisters of Charity (several branches), Sisters of Mercy, Sisters of St. Joseph, and Sisters of the Holy Cross. Nuns served as nurses on both sides and sometimes, as the fortunes of war changed on a battlefield, on both sides simultaneously.

The first nuns to enter the war as nurses were the Sisters of Charity of Emmitsburg, Maryland. The Confederates asked them for help in June 1861, before First Bull Run. After the battle, General Johnston ordered that the sick and wounded be sent to Richmond, and the nuns went with them. Later, Confederate Surgeon General Moore "begged that the Sisters would take charge of the Stuart Hospital" in Richmond, which they did.[29]

The Sisters of Charity at Emmitsburg were repeatedly asked to provide nurses. In June 1862, Federal authorities telegraphed the Order to ask sisters to work in nearby Frederick City. The following month, the Federal surgeon general asked that 100 sisters be sent to White House, Virginia, to help during the Peninsula campaign. General McClellan also requested help from the Order at Emmitsburg after Antietam. The sisters attended sick and wounded after Gettysburg in the Catholic and the Methodist churches in that town.

In Mound City, Illinois, at the start of the war, a military general hospital was created from a block of stores to serve the large army base established at Cairo on the Mississippi River. Although the hospital was originally meant to hold 1,000 beds, epidemic diseases soon forced 1,500 men to crowd into it. Nevertheless, it was reported to be a "superb hospital," thanks to the

> administrative talent of Dr. E. S. Franklin of Dubuque, Iowa, . . . [and the fact that] Sisters of the Holy Cross were employed as nurses, and by their skill, quietness, gentleness, and tenderness, were invaluable in the sick wards. Every patient gave hearty testimony to the kindness and skill of the "Sisters."[30]

Both Presidents Lincoln and Davis complimented the sisters for their nursing. Lincoln commended the nuns he saw in action, particularly at Stanton Hospital. On one occasion, Lincoln warned a general that he would incur the president's displeasure if he interfered with the work of the Sisters of Charity. In an address to the sisters after the war, Jefferson Davis said: "I can never forget your kindness to the sick and wounded in our darkest days, and I know not how to testify my gratitude and respect for every member of your noble order."[31]

WOMEN PHYSICIANS

It is unclear how many women were working as physicians in the United States before the Civil War. In the mid-1800s, medical students commonly learned from a preceptor without attending a formal medical school. At least one woman, Margaret Cannon Osborne, is known to have acquired her education in this manner and entered practice, and there may have been others like her. Also, many women learned medicine from their husbands or fathers in this fashion and then assisted in their practices. An unknown number of women attended medical school during this period dressed in male attire and went on to practice medicine pretending to be men.

While many male and female practitioners who graduated from unorthodox medical schools applied for admission to the Medical Corps of both armies, they were rejected. In desperation, a delegation of male homeopaths appealed directly to President Lincoln, but he would not support their application for army appointments.

Aside from Dr. Blackwell, at least two women who attended orthodox (allopathic) medical schools served as physicians during the war. Although some details of the career of Dr. Mary Edwards Walker (1832–1919) are vague, there is no doubt that she heroically served the Union cause. Born in Oswego, New York, she became a physician during the 1840s or 1850s, graduating from Syracuse Medical College at some point. She struggled in her attempts to practice medicine in Cincinnati, and, when the Civil War began, she was allowed to work in the Union army only as a nurse. In 1864, after three years as an army nurse, a regiment from Ohio hired her as a contract physician. As such, she was able to pass back and forth through the Union and Confederate lines. This allowed her to function as a spy, reporting her observations to Union officers. In October 1864, she received an army commission as an assistant surgeon and functioned in that official capacity until the war ended. Captured while treating a Confederate soldier on a battlefield, she spent four months in a Confederate prison.

While in the army, Dr. Walker wore the same military uniform as male physicians, but kept her hair long so that people would know that she was a woman. After the war, she continued to wear male attire and was active in women's rights movements. In 1897, she tried to establish a colony for women only, calling it "Adamless Eden." Her militancy caused most people, including her family, to shun her, and she died poor and alone in Oswego.

Her dangerous Civil War exploits led to her being awarded the Medal of Honor. However, after the criteria for awarding such medals were revised, the Board of Medals officially revoked the medal and asked her to return it. She

Dr. Elizabeth Blackwell (1821-1910)

Dr. Elizabeth Blackwell was the first woman known to have received a regular medical degree in the United States. She was born in Bristol, England, but at the age of nine moved with her family to the United States, living first in New York City and then in Cincinnati. She taught school in Henderson, Kentucky, but, in 1844, she decided to study medicine. After being refused admission to many medical schools, she was finally accepted at Geneva (New York) Medical College in 1847.[32] (The first medical school for women was established in 1850 in Philadelphia.)

When she received her M.D. degree in 1849, it provoked a great deal of press coverage in the United States and abroad; her biographers state that most people considered her "either mad or bad." Despite the negative attitude toward her in most of the press, the British humor magazine *Punch* commented on her graduation:

> Young ladies all, of every clime,
> Especially of Britain,
> Who wholly occupy your time,
> In novels or in knitting,
> Whose highest skill is but to play,
> Sing, dance, or French to clack well,
> Reflect on the example, pray,
> Of the excellent Miss Blackwell.[33]

After Blackwell graduated, she was unable to find a hospital in the United States that would admit her for further training. She went to Paris, where she met with the leading physicians of the era, including Dr. Pierre Louis. None of them would accept a woman for training, and Louis advised her to enroll for midwife training. Taking his advice, she trained at La Maternité in Paris in 1849.[34]

When Blackwell then received an appointment at St. Bartholomew's Hospital in London, she received congratulations from Florence Nightingale, and they began a lifelong friendship. Blackwell encouraged Nightingale to enter nursing, even though her family strongly opposed such a move.

Blackwell returned to New York in 1850 and set up a private dispensary. Joined by her sister and Dr. Marie Zakrzewska (who had both obtained medical degrees at the Western Reserve University Medical School in Cleveland)[35] and other women, she established the New York Infirmary for Women and Children on Bleeker Street in May 1857.

continued . . .

Dr. Elizabeth Blackwell, continued

In 1868, they started the New York Medical College for Women at New York Infirmary. Blackwell insisted that it be staffed by women and have a curriculum and standards more demanding than most other medical schools at the time.[36] It was financially supported by Quakers. (See Figure 16.3.)

In 1869, Blackwell returned to England to campaign for the acceptance of women into the medical profession. She became the first woman ever admitted to the Medical Register of the United Kingdom and a professor at London School of Medicine for Women, which had just been founded. She remained on the faculty until 1907, when an accident enfeebled her. She was buried in England after she died in 1910.[37]

---

reportedly said, "They can have it over my dead body." She died the next day, February 21, 1919. In 1977, the award was officially reinstated.[38]

Dr. Esther Hill Hawks (1833–1906) was another army physician. After marrying Dr. John Milton Hawks, Esther Hill Hawks studied his medical books and decided to go to medical school. Graduating from New England Medical College for Women in 1857, she practiced in various locales with her husband. He was an ardent abolitionist, and, after Hilton Head and the surrounding areas were occupied by Union forces, he obtained a job providing medical care and running a plantation set up for freed slaves along the coast of South Carolina. Esther joined him there and helped provide medical care to the blacks. She also worked as a contract physician in General Hospital Number 10, which was established for black soldiers in Beaufort, South Carolina. Hawks helped care for soldiers from the 54th Massachusetts Colored Infantry after its famous ill-fated attempt to take Morris Island under Col. Robert Shaw. After the war, she continued to work in the area, caring for former slaves and teaching school.[39]

ACCEPTANCE OF WOMEN AS NURSES AND SUPERVISORS

Most of what has been written about Civil War nursing has focused on the conflicts between Dorothea Dix's nurses and Civil War doctors. One article summarized the subject in its title: "The war within a war: Women nurses in the Union army."[40] Yet more than 80% of the women who worked as matrons and nurses in the Union armies served independently of Dix, and there is

Figure 16.3: The main anatomy laboratory in the New York Medical College for Women, started by Dr Elizabeth Blackwell. Mary Safford, who had served as a nurse with the Western army, graduated from this school. Drawing by Frank Leslie, April 16, 1870. (Grafton J: *New York in the Nineteenth Century*. New York: Dover Publications, 2nd ed., 1980, p. 185.)

little evidence of any such conflicts with those nurses. Even within the official Dix corps, most of the problems existed in just a few eastern cities. For example, a Mrs. Davis of New York reported that she nursed patients at all the hospitals in her area and "at all of these she was welcomed and her efforts most gratefully received."[41]

Some of the problems arose because Dix's volunteers were socially prominent women who were accustomed to luxuries and were often accompanied by servants. As a group, they were articulate, educated, and self-confident, and many chafed at traditional male dominance, especially that found in military institutions. The majority of nurses were also mothers who had directed the care of sick family members before the war and had received little worthwhile help from the doctors they allowed into their homes to consult. Moreover, most doctors were from a distinctly lower social class than were the nurses, thus some of Dix's nurses looked down on them.

Another conflict derived from both Blackwell's and Dix's original belief that women were better fitted than men to supervise nursing. They anticipated that their nurses would direct and train soldiers who would do the actual nursing, a role similar to that assumed by Nightingale's nurses in the Crimean War. The original calls for volunteers specifically described this role and added that the women "were not going to take any nonsense from the army."[42]

In their autobiographies, several of Dix's nurses emphasized that the doctors were "determined to make their life so unbearable that they should be forced in self-defense to leave . . . Hardly a surgeon of whom I can think, received or treated them with even common courtesy."[43] Mary Phinney, the Baroness von Olnhausen and also a protégé of Dorothea Dix, called the first two surgeons she encountered "the most brutal men I ever saw."[44]

After receiving complaints about their treatment from the nurses trained in New York, Louisa Lee Schuyler, executive secretary of the Women's Central Association of Relief of New York City, sent letters to numerous Ladies' Aid Societies to discourage further volunteers, stating:

> It is regretted that a more favorable account of the way in which the nurses have been received and treated in the hospitals cannot be given. They have not been placed as they expected and were fitted to be, in the position of head-nurses . . . [they have been] worn down with menial and purely mechanical duties, additional to the more responsible offices and duties of nursing. They have encountered a certain amount of suspicion, jealousy, and ill-treatment, which has rendered their situation very trying . . . The association does not feel authorized to send on more from the same class of life from which they have come—certainly not until their position and relations are essentially improved.[45]

"I Can See Now How Good Our Surgeons Were"

When Mary Phinney, the Baroness von Olnhausen, began her service at Mansion House Hospital in Alexandria, Dorothea Dix warned her that the doctors were opposed to female nurses and would make her life as unpleasant as they could. Dix was right, and Olnhausen's unfavorable comments about the doctors have been cited often. However, she also recorded that she developed an excellent relationship with the surgeon she at first called "brutal," that he complimented and valued her work, and that she was upset when he was promoted and transferred. She wrote that she respected many other surgeons she had met during her prolonged service in the Civil War.

After the war, Phinney missed the sense of fulfillment she had obtained working as a nurse, so, when the Franco-Prussian War broke out, she learned German and went to serve with her deceased husband's countrymen. Her diary entries indicate how she viewed her Civil War experience:

> I feel as if I were back again in our War; only here there seems no order at all; everybody flies about, distracted. The way they dress wounds is abominable; they are not even where we were in '62. . . . I have been to other hospitals to-day, and I can hardly contain myself to see the treatment of the wounds. It seems like actual murder. We never treated amputations so badly . . . I can see now how good our surgeons were. One good thing we have here is carbolic acid in all its forms; this alone will save many lives.[46]

After visiting an English field hospital at Épernay, she wrote,

> It is the forlornest place that can be thought of, so dirty, so disorganized in every way, not a decent hospital in the town. What can be expected when all the wounds are dressed with raw cotton, carbol oil, flannel bandages, and oil silk, besides a heap of nasty lint. Not a single amputation of the leg, so far, has lived; hardly one of the arm, and those are doing badly enough. Every wound, for a finale, is covered with a triangle of cotton; these triangles are a peculiar German institution and are used for everything. How I do long to have one wound in my own hands![47]

Similar letters were also sent to members of Congress and other government officials.

The much larger group of women who volunteered and worked independently of Dix were, as a group, less socially prominent, less articulate, and left fewer memoirs and autobiographies. While there was some initial tension between them and the doctors and regular army officers, these women had much less difficulty being accepted. They were considered to be of enormous value in the care of sick and wounded soldiers; both soldiers and doctors appreciated their contributions. This was demonstrated when some of the hospitals constructed during the war, such as Harewood Hospital in Washington, contained specially built brick buildings to serve as quarters for female nurses, while the patients were housed in wood facilities or in tents.

As the war progressed, the nurses proved their worth and gained acceptance. They not only improved the hospitals' sanitary conditions, but also brought "home" to the men.[48] They set up special diet kitchens—which some observers felt was their most valuable contribution, given that diet was considered a key element of medical therapy (a point emphasized by Florence Nightingale).[49] They also read to and wrote letters for the soldiers, listened to confessions and dying words, wrote to parents and wives after a man had died, helped the men learn to use crutches and cope with the loss of an arm or a leg, and entertained whole wards by singing and playing musical instruments.

Dix's nurses served primarily as supervisors and concerned themselves with the availability of supplies and drugs, obtaining special diets, and consoling men in pain or distress about disfigurement. They also helped to arrange furloughs, assisted visiting families in finding hospitalized loved ones (or their graves), and provided considerable religious nurturing. Convalescent soldiers continued to work with Dix's nurses, functioning as attendants who dressed wounds, changed linens, helped with surgical procedures, passed out medications, and distributed meals.

By the end of the war, nurses clearly were so indispensable that when the development of aseptic surgery necessitated the establishment of many new hospitals in the 1880s, the medical profession supported the establishment of civilian nursing schools for women. With this, the role of female nurses in hospitals became firmly established. The first nursing school in the United States was established at Bellevue Hospital in 1873, largely due to the efforts of Louisa Lee Schuyler (see Biographical Box, p. 424). Many of the women who played key roles in organizations such as the Sanitary Commission and Dorothea Dix's Nursing Corps subsequently became active in the women's suffrage movement, as well as the temperance movement.

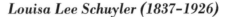

Louisa Lee Schuyler (1837–1926)

A member of New York society and great-granddaughter (on both sides) of Alexander Hamilton, Louisa Lee Schuyler became active in social causes very early in life. She worked as a volunteer for the Children's Aid Society for a year before the Civil War and then helped organize the Women's Central Association of Relief of New York City, which played a major role in founding the Sanitary Commission.

Throughout the war, she served as the organization's chief executive, recruiting nurses for Dr. Blackwell's training program and for Dorothea Dix's Corps.[50] She handled fund-raising efforts and disbursement, the procurement and shipping of Sanitary Commission supplies, and the establishment of soldiers' aid stations throughout the East. She was described as having the "mind of a lawyer and the will-power of a captain of industry."[51]

Exhausted by her Civil War work, Schuyler recuperated in Europe and Egypt after the war, then returned home and started the New York State Charities Aid Society. After visitors from that Society observed the appalling conditions at Bellevue Hospital, Schuyler personally appealed to them to establish a nurses' training school. This led, in 1873, to America's first formal school for female nurses, The New-York Training School for Nurses. Attached to Bellevue Hospital, it was sanctioned by the hospital's medical board.[52,53]

Schuyler continued to be active in social causes, including leading a campaign for state care of the insane and the establishment of the National Committee (later Society) for the Prevention of Blindness, until her death at age 89.

The role of women in American life changed completely after the Civil War, due to their achievements not only in nursing, but also in organizing and administering soldiers' relief societies. Individual women, Ladies' Aid Societies, and official branches of the Sanitary Commission, in which women played a prominent role, raised an enormous amount of money for the Commission's activities: The total from various states and eighteen foreign countries reached just over $2 million, with individual and group contributions as high as $100,000. Monetary contributions from states and territories ranged from $8 (North Carolina) and $10.50 (Nebraska Territory) to $1,233,978 (California).

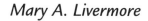

Mary A. Livermore

The career of Mary A. Livermore illustrates the influence of the war on the life of American women. A Chicagoan, Livermore was the only female journalist accredited to attend the Republican Convention in Chicago that nominated Abraham Lincoln. After the war began, she helped to organize and direct the Western Branch of the U.S. Sanitary Commission (also called the Northwestern Branch). She visited almost all the hospitals in the Western theater and organized and assisted in nursing.

She found and then supported Mary Ann "Mother" Bickerdyke throughout the war, providing her with the equivalent of an unlimited expense account. She also helped arrange for the railroads to transport supplies for the Sanitary Commission free of freight charges and for express companies to carry its packages at half price, and saw that telegraph companies "remitted their usual charges on its messages."[54]

Livermore organized the first "Sanitary Fair," which raised a huge amount of money for the Commission's programs. The success of this event resulted in similar fairs being held in many Northern cities. While Livermore was planning her fair, a builder refused to sign a contract to erect the necessary hall. Livermore said she would pay in advance with her own money, but the builder refused because the law stated that a wife's money belonged to her husband, no matter how she acquired it! Livermore obtained her husband's signature allowing the payment, but vowed that she would work to change the legal status of women. She became one of the leaders of the suffrage movement after the war.

Based on the composite commodity price index, the relative value of the 1860 dollar to the 2001 dollar is approximately 1:19.8.[55] The $1.2 million California contributed, for example, is equivalent to nearly $24 million in 2001. In view of the official hostility of the British government toward the Union cause, it is notable that the largest foreign contribution listed was $36,790 from the "London Branch [of the Commission]."[56]

SOUTHERN WOMEN WHO SERVED

Fewer Southern women are known to have served as full-time nurses. The barriers to working outside the home were greater, but many women, such as Phoebe Pember, broke through them and found ways to help. Like

Mary Safford

Mary Safford, who also worked as a volunteer nurse, was the first woman to attack the problems of hygiene in camps and hospitals in the West. Safford reorganized the first hospitals set up near Cairo, Illinois, bringing "order out of chaos, . . . and with her own means, assisted by her wealthy brother, had furnished necessities which could be obtained in no other way."[57]

Army officers and doctors at first opposed Safford's effort, "but she disarmed them by the sweetness of her manner and speech, and did what she pleased." When she entered one of her hospitals, the effect of her presence was described as "magical. . . . Every face brightened." She was well-educated and spoke several languages; as she moved from bed to bed, "now she addressed one in German—a blue eyed boy from Holland—and then she chattered in French to another, made superlatively happy by being addressed each in his own tongue."[58]

Safford is remembered for walking the battlefield looking for abandoned wounded after the Battle of Belmont in Northern Missouri (November 1861) using her own flag of truce. She was a tiny, frail woman, resembling "a girl of twelve summers, and utterly unaccustomed to hardship."[59] She worked closely with Mary Bickerdyke but the strain of caring for the wounded of Fort Donelson, where she became known as "the Angel of Cairo," caused her to collapse.

Her health broke again after caring for the wounded from the Battle of Shiloh, and her family took her to Europe to recuperate. Returning to the United States after the war, she entered New York Medical College for Women, which had been founded by Dr. Elizabeth Blackwell. After graduating in 1869, Dr. Safford studied surgery at Vienna's famous General Hospital and then worked in Breslau, Germany. She returned to Chicago to practice medicine, then joined the faculty of Boston University School of Medicine until ill health finally forced her to retire.[60]

Northern women, they cut up linens for bandages, scraped lint to make dressing material, and sewed clothing for the soldiers. Ella King Newsome trained as a nurse at Memphis City Hospital and cared for the sick and wounded in Gen. Albert Sidney Johnston's command in December 1861; she later functioned as a superintendent of hospitals in Bowling Green, Nashville, Chattanooga, and Atlanta.

Mrs. Arthur F. Hopkins, wife of the Chief Justice of the Alabama Supreme Court, served as a nurse in the field and was wounded twice during the Peninsula campaign in 1862.[61] The most famous of these Southern women was Sally Louisa Tompkins, who ran a hospital in Richmond (see Chapter 8, *Civil War Hospitals*).

After helping to establish hospitals in Nashville for wounded Confederate soldiers, Mrs. Felicia Grundy Porter set up a Women's Relief Society. Under her leadership, it evolved to cover all of Tennessee and, eventually, the entire Confederacy. Mrs. Porter's society raised a large amount of money for soldiers and hospitals, and played a role resembling that of the U.S. Sanitary Commission. After the war, she served as president of the Benevolent Society of Tennessee, which raised money to buy artificial limbs for disabled Confederate soldiers. In a tribute to her work, a large escort of former Confederate soldiers accompanied her body when she was buried near the Confederate Monument in Nashville's Mount Olivet Cemetery.[62]

As in the North, most books and articles concern themselves with the wealthy, socially prominent Southern women who served, especially those who kept diaries and had political or social contacts. Some of these women traveled great distances to be of use. Their jobs consisted of "running up and down stairs, attending to poultices, giving medicines and answering questions." For the most part, these women lived comfortably, accompanied by servants (slaves), and led active social lives while helping in hospital units devoted to care of men from their home state.[63]

Meanwhile, a host of unknown women served quietly in general, field, and wayside hospitals, and even near battlefields under fire. Although no government-recognized organization analogous to the Sanitary Commission arose in the Confederacy, individuals and small groups of women performed similar functions. There were innumerable ladies' aid associations, fundraising drives, and similar small-scale efforts.[64] Most of these were devoted to state-specific objectives, with the proportion of women involved probably similar to that in the North. Early in the war, when wounded men crowded into hotels, churches, railway depots, and schools, local Southern women provided nursing, bandages, blankets, coffee, and other nourishment. Many took the wounded into their own homes, caring for individuals or small groups of men until they could be transferred to military hospitals. In many cities along major travel routes, women established wayside homes where soldiers could receive food, shelter, and rest while on the way home or back to their units.[65]

Two hundred Sisters of Charity, Sisters of Mercy, and nuns from other orders served in various Confederate hospitals despite the greater prejudice against Catholics in the South. Many from the Sisters of Mercy had prior nursing training, and their dignity, devotion, and value "would have been a credit to a much larger group."[66] (See Figure 16.4.)

The invaluable contribution of Confederate women was acknowledged by J. J. Chisolm in the third edition of *A Manual of Military Surgery* (1864):

> The experience of the Confederate hospitals, in recognizing the vast amount of good which female nurses accomplish, and the incalculable services which they are capable of performing, when judiciously selected and properly organized, is a sufficient reason why they should be attached to every hospital, and especially in times of war, when their many and peculiar services can not be dispensed with.

NURSING CARE OF PRISONERS

Wounded soldiers who were captured received appropriate, but not particularly sympathetic, nursing care. Continued contact with the prisoners tended to soften attitudes, however, and many women provided sympathy, as well as medical care, equal to that given to their own soldiers. Yet there were nurses who remained correct but aloof. One Confederate nurse recorded that when "two wounded Yankees were brought in . . . I would rather not have them."[67] Later she noted,

> The Yankee prisoners seem very comfortable since their wounds were dressed, . . . the men [the soldier-nurses] are very kind to the two Yankees . . . I force myself to ask after their health once a day and see that they get food regularly. I have never inquired there [sic] names nor do I intend to.[68]

Women with conflicting loyalties provided another aspect to prisoners' care. For example, many Southern women had married into Northern families and settled in the New York area, but their hearts were still in Dixie. These Confederate sympathizers provided comforts for captured rebels, most notably for convalescent prisoners captured at Gettysburg who were sent to DeCamp General Hospital on Davids' Island in Long Island Sound. The women brought food, sweets, warm clothes, and playing cards to the soldiers, and even wrote letters home for them. This behavior resulted in protests from the Union soldiers in the hospital who, although in separate units, resented the attention and extra comforts provided to the captured rebels. Nonetheless, the special attention continued.

Figure 16.4: Women from the Christian Commission nursing wounded on a battlefield. (*HW*)

Similarly, sick Union soldiers imprisoned at Camp Ford in Tyler, Texas, received kind treatment from women sympathetic to the Northern cause. When the prisoners were sent to a hospital in Marshall, Texas, they

> found an openly avowed sentiment of loyalty. The ladies of the town came to the wards and nursed them, fed them with food from their own tables, and attended personally to their wants, as if they were kindred instead of strangers. . . . Had they been in a Chicago hospital they could not have received kinder or more generous treatment.[69]

Nursing in the more infamous prison camps, however, fell primarily to other prisoners and was, at best, minimal.

THE INVALID CORPS

To ease the chronic nursing shortage, the army established the Invalid Corps in April 1863. Soldiers whose injuries or illnesses kept them from combat but who could function in less demanding roles remained in the service. The men of the Second Battalion of the Corps were assigned duties such as guard, nursing attendant, cook, and clerk in the hospitals. In his Annual Report of October 1863, Acting Surgeon General Barnes described the success of the new organization:

> Companies of the Second Battalion, Invalid Corps, composed of meritorious officers and soldiers disabled for active service, have been assigned to many of the general hospitals as a part of their organization, under the direction of the surgeons in charge. The experience of a few months warrants the belief that this military organization will prove the most economical and advantageous mode of supplying a permanent corps of nurses and attendants to such hospitals, and make available for active service the able-bodied hitherto detailed for these duties.[70]

The Invalid Corps expanded as the war went on.[71] During the second half of the war, when careful pre-induction physical examinations were routinely done, men capable of only limited duty, such as those with severe near-sightedness, were inducted directly into the Corps.[72] The group was given a distinctive badge and uniforms that prominently displayed the letters "IC." Unfortunately, the initials also stood for "inspected and condemned," a designation the Quartermaster Department used for worthless items. To avoid this connotation, the unit was renamed the Veterans Reserve Corps in 1864, with a corresponding change in their insignia. Over 60,000 men served in this Corps during its three-year existence.

REFERENCES

1. Livermore MAR: *My Story of the War. A Woman's Narrative of Four Year's Personal Experience as a Nurse in the Union Army, and in Relief Work at Home, in Hospitals, Camps, and at the Front during the War of the Rebellion. With Anecdotes, Pathetic Incidents, and Thrilling Reminiscences Portraying the Lights and Shadows of Hospital Life and the Sanitary Service of the War.* Hartford, CT: A.D. Worthington, 1888, p. 203.
2. Nutting ME, Dock LL: *A History of Nursing: The Evolution of Nursing from the Earliest Times to the Foundation of the First English and American Training Schools for Nurses.* New York: Putnam, 1907.
3. Carlisle RJ, ed.: *An Account of Bellevue Hospital.* New York: Society of the Alumni of Bellevue Hospital, 1893 (repub. 1986), p. 35.
4. Livermore, *My Story of the War*, p. 127.
5. Ibid., pp. 128-29.
6. Wilson D.C.: *Stranger and Traveler: The Story of Dorothea Dix, American Reformer.* Boston: Little Brown, 1975.
7. Greenbie MLB: *Lincoln's Daughters of Mercy.* New York: G.P. Putnam's Sons, 1944, pp. 60-61.
8. Livermore, *My Story of the War*, p. 245.
9. Greenbie, *Lincoln's Daughters of Mercy*, p. 61.
10. Committee of Hospital Physicians of City of New York. *Manual of Directions Prepared for the Use of Army Nurses.* New York: Women's Central Association for Relief to the Army, 1861.
11. Dannett SGL: *Noble Women of the North.* New York: Thomas Yoseloff, 1959, pp. 62-63.
12. Ibid.; and Greenbie, *Lincoln's Daughters of Mercy*, pp. 60-61.
13. Livermore, *My Story of the War*, p. 247.
14. Maxwell WQ: *Lincoln's Fifth Wheel: The Political History of the U.S. Sanitary Commission.* New York: Longmans Green, 1956, p. 65.
15. Rosenberg CE: Florence Nightingale on contagion: the hospital as moral universe. In: Rosenberg CE, ed.: *Healing and History: Essays for Charles Rosen.* New York: Science History Publications, 1979.
16. Oates SB: *A Woman of Valor: Clara Barton and the Civil War.* New York: Macmillan, 1994, p. 23.
17. Brumgardt JR: *Civil War Nurse: The Diary and Letters of Hannah Ropes.* Knoxville: Univ. of Tennessee Press, 1993.
18. Dannett SGL: Lincoln's ladies in white. *NY State Med J.* 1961 June 1;61(11):1946.
19. Alcott LM: *Hospital Sketches.* (Jones, BZ, ed.) Cambridge, MA: Harvard Univ. Press, 1960.
20. Greenbie, *Lincoln's Daughters of Mercy*, p. 90.
21. Gillett, *The United States Army Medical Department, 1818–1865*, p. 215.
22. Massey ME: *Bonnet Brigades:American Women and the Civil War.* New York; G.P. Putnam, 1966, p. 367.
23. Oates, *A Woman of Valor*, p. 476.
24. Greenbie, *Lincoln's Daughters of Mercy*, p. 191.
25. Denney RE: *Civil War Medicine: Care and Comfort of the Wounded.* New York: Sterling, 1994, p. 298.
26. *O.R.*, Series I, vol. V, p. 85.
27. Brinton JH: *Personal Memoirs of John H. Brinton, Civil War Surgeon, 1861–1865.* Carbondale, IL: Southern Illinois Univ. Press, 1996, pp. 43-45.
28. Livermore, *My Story of the War*, p. 224.
29. Candido JH: Those are the Sisters . . . They are not afraid of anything: sisters and nuns who were nurses during the Civil War. *Blue and Gray Magazine.* 1993;11(1):30.
30. Livermore, *My Story of the War*, p. 218.
31. Barton G: *Angels of the Battlefield: A History of the Labors of the Catholic Sisterhoods during the Late Civil War.* Philadelphia: Catholic Arts Pub. Co., 1897, pp. 169, 174.

32. This school opened on February 10, 1835, and was later called Hobart College. In 1872, the medical school became the Medical Department of Syracuse University and, in 1948, it became a unit of the State University of New York.
33. Smith D: A persistent rebel. *Am Hist Illus.* 1981;15:28.
34. Warner JH: *Against the Spirit of the System: The French Impulse in Nineteenth-Century American Medicine.* Princeton, NJ: Princeton Univ. Press, 1998, pp. 105-6.
35. Bullough B, Bullough V: The origins of modern American nursing: the Civil War era. *Nurs Forum.* 1963;2(2):13-27.
36. Smith, *Am Hist Illus,* 1981.
37. Johnson A, Malone D, eds.: *Dictionary of American Biography.* vol. 3. New York: C. Scribner, 1930.
38. Faust PL, ed.: *Historical Times Encyclopedia of the Civil War.* New York: Harper & Row, 1986, p. 798.
39. Hawks EH: *A Woman Doctor's Civil War: Esther Hill Hawks' Diary.* Columbia: Univ. South Carolina Press, 1984.
40. Wood AD: The war within a war: women nurses in the Union army. *Civil War Hist.* 1972;18:197-212.
41. Brockett LP: *Women at War: A Record of Their Patriotic Contributions, Heroism, Toils, and Sacrifice during the Civil War.* Woodbury, NY: Longmeadow Press, 1993, p. 355.
42. Greenbie, *Lincoln's Daughters of Mercy,* p. 105.
43. Dannett, *NY State Med J,* 1961.
44. Wood, *Civil War Hist,* 1972.
45. Greenbie, *Lincoln's Daughters of Mercy,* p. 106.
46. Olnhausen MP: *Adventures of an Army Nurse in Two Wars.* Boston: Little Brown, 1903, pp. 231-32.
47. Ibid., p. 236.
48. Wood, *Civil War Hist,* 1972.
49. Culpepper MM, Adams PG: Nursing in the Civil War. *Am J Nurs.* 1988;88(7):981-84.
50. Johnson A, Malone D, *Dictionary of American Biography,* p. 323.
51. Ibid., p. 474.
52. Carlisle, *Account of Bellevue Hospital,* p. 79.
53. North FH: A new profession for women. *Century Ill Monthly Magazine.* 1882;25(1):38-47.
54. Livermore, *My Story of the War,* p. 130.
55. Woodrow Federal Reserve Bank of Minneapolis. Website www.minneapolisfed.org/economy/calc/hist1800.html. Accessed 14 March 2001.
56. Stillé CJ: *History of the United States Sanitary Commission: Being a General Report of Its Work during the War of the Rebellion.* New York: Hurd and Houghton, 1868, appendix.
57. Greenbie, *Lincoln's Daughters of Mercy,* p. 83.
58. Livermore, *My Story of the War,* p. 207.
59. Ibid., p. 206.
60. Faust, *Historical Times Encyclopedia of the Civil War,* p. 650.
61. Bill AH: *The Beleaguered City: Richmond 1861–65.* New York: Alfred A. Knopf, 1946, p. 184.
62. Roberts DJ. In: *The Photographic History of the Civil War.* New York: Review of Reviews, 1970 (orig. pub. 1911), Vol. 4B, p. 257.
63. Berlin JV: *A Confederate Nurse: The Diary of Ada W. Bacot, 1860–1853.* Columbia: Univ. South Carolina Press, 1994, p. 76.
64. Ibid., p. 14.
65. Wiley BI: *Confederate Women.* Westport, CT: Greenwood Press, 1975, p. 144.
66. Ibid., p. 145.
67. Berlin, *A Confederate Nurse,* pp. 14, 125-26.
68. Ibid., pp. 125-26.
69. Livermore, *My Story of the War,* p. 406.

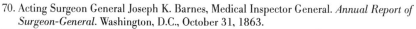
70. Acting Surgeon General Joseph K. Barnes, Medical Inspector General. *Annual Report of Surgeon-General.* Washington, D.C., October 31, 1863.
71. *Medical and Surgical History*, Medical Section, vol. 3, p. 958; and Gillett, *U.S. Army Medical Department*, p. 289.
72. Circular No. 100. *Provost Marshall General's Office.* Washington, D.C., November 9, 1863, *O.R.*, Series III, Vol. III, p. 1072.

Re-Evaluating Civil War Medical Care: Shattering the Myths

As far as my observation extends, the medical officers of the army, and the citizen surgeons who were employed during the emergency, discharged their arduous duties with fidelity and ability. I never saw men work harder and complain less of the difficulties that surrounded them.

– John M. Cuyler, Medical Inspector,
U.S. Army, July 27, 1863

It would be quite beyond my power to do justice to the skill and knowledge with which the Medical Corps has performed their task.

– Jefferson Davis

THE SUFFERING ENDURED BY CIVIL WAR SOLDIERS has never been equaled in American history. Of all able-bodied Union men, approximately one in ten died or became incapacitated during Civil War military service. Among Southerners, it was about one in four men (including male slaves).[1] How much did incompetent or uninformed doctors contribute to this appalling carnage?

A great deal, according to typical depictions of Civil War medicine—images of arms and legs piled outside operating facilities and wounded soldiers' letters and newspaper editorials blaming doctors for the suffering. Compounding this are the outrageous quotes Civil War histories often repeat, including Confederate Sen. William E. Simms's (Kentucky) statement that the medical officers "had slain more of our troops than all of Lincoln's minions" and a Richmond editor's description of the Medical Department staff as "unfeeling, shameful and brutal."[2]

Yet not all the press was critical. A *Cincinnati Lancet and Observer* editorial after the Battle of Gettysburg noted the general lack of appreciation for the medical staff's efforts:

> Our readers will not fail to have noticed that everybody connected with the army has been thanked, excepting the surgeons . . . The newspapers have been filled with eulogies of everyone except the Surgeons. The rule has been to censure them, to abuse and slander them.[3]

In October 1864, the *Springfield* (Illinois) *Republican* described wondrous new wound treatments that today we know as plastic surgery:

> The surgery of this Army is reaching an extraordinary high scale as weapons reach perfection. Men wounded in the head or neck are fed for weeks through silver or rubber tubes. Such is the progress of the medical department in these parts that half of a man's face demolished by a ball or piece of shell is replaced by a cork face.[4]

The evaluation of Civil War medicine and its practitioners, initially negative, gradually evolved into positive, even laudatory comments as the war progressed. Many retrospective analyses heaped even greater praise on these battlefield surgeons when their conduct and capabilities were compared to foreign medical corps in subsequent wars. The positive evaluations have been largely forgotten, while the negative have been perpetuated.

OFT-QUOTED NEGATIVE COMMENTS

Early in the war, newspapers and soldiers' letters cited the miserable medical care soldiers on both sides received. As early as June 1861, *The New York Times* correctly described the army's Medical Department as

> utterly unable to carry out or even support those great scientific sanitary measures required for permanently securing the health of an improvised army so vast as that which we now have in the field. . . . we raise a warning voice now while it is yet time, and before the appalling experience with our volunteers in Mexico is again repeated.[5]

A Confederate soldier's letter, written in June 1862 upon his recovery from typhoid fever after the Battle of Shiloh, is typical of the time: "[My] greatest enemies . . . were hunger and the doctors."[6]

A Doctor Defends His Actions to a Senator

One physician, Dr. Alexander H. Hoff, had to defend himself after U.S. Sen. James Harlan of Iowa accused him of "treating the men in an inhuman and brutal manner."

The complaint originated when Hoff, the surgeon-in-charge on the hospital ship *D.A. January*, asked two women (one was the senator's wife) to leave a wounded soldier's bedside. (The patient had requested that Dr. Hoff ask them to leave because he needed to urinate and was embarrassed to say so to the women.) The women were providing "consolations of the Christian religion" at the time and did not know the reason for the request. They were offended, and vigorously complained about Dr. Hoff to Senator Harlan.[7]

An inquiry was held and Dr. Hoff was criticized for expelling the women, but no punitive action was taken. Hoff continued to serve on the *D.A. January* for most of the war. The hospital ship made eighty-one trips on the Mississippi River and its tributaries, transporting 23,738 wounded and sick soldiers.[8]

Some soldiers' negative attitudes toward the medical staff were generated when soldiers, who the physicians believed were malingering, requested medical furloughs. When a soldier who was mistakenly believed to be malingering turned out to be very sick, the men retaliated with derogatory comments about military doctors. One surgeon wrote in his diary that the men hated him when he turned down requests for medical leave.[9]

Many comments, especially from nurses, described doctors' callous behavior and occasional drunkenness. Surgeons, among others, had access to the stores of medicinal alcohol which often mysteriously vanished. During 1862, editorials deplored the reports of drunkenness in the Army of the Potomac, not specifying any particular problem with alcoholism among army surgeons, but, rather, lamenting their general incompetence.[10] Contemporary observers noted that while alcoholism was common within the Army of the Potomac, drunkenness was less common among physicians than among other officers.[11]

Many society women who served as nurses wrote memoirs filled with complaints about the doctors, although they are often misrepresented. For example, the diary of Mary Phinney (the Baroness von Olnhausen) has been inaccurately described as "one long denunciation of doctors, hospitals, mistreatment of nurses, confusion, neglect of wounded, bad food, misuse and theft of supplies."[12] In fact, Mrs. Phinney made many positive comments about physicians after describing her initial offensive experience.

Civil War physicians did not stint on castigating their colleagues early in the war when there was much to criticize. In 1862, an editorial in the *American Medical Times*, a leading medical journal, stated that "the War of the Rebellion found the medical department of the army unequal to the exigencies," blaming the "pernicious system of promotions by seniority."[13]

A short time later, it published an editorial written by Dr. Frank Hastings Hamilton, a professor at Bellevue Medical College who had served as medical director of the 4th Corps at the Battle of Fair Oaks. Hamilton emphasized that the army was woefully short of experienced surgeons. He estimated that "not less than 3,000" wounded were treated after the battle, describing the incredible chaos, lack of supplies and ambulances, and resultant difficulties in transporting the wounded.[14]

In early September 1862, the *American Medical Times* criticized the performance of the surgeons who had volunteered during McClellan's Peninsula campaign. The editorial, entitled "Voluntary Surgical Aid," pointed out that many surgeons responded to the call but a high proportion of them were simply anxious to get surgical experience and would not do what was needed of them. These were the contract surgeons whose behavior led to the lasting condemnation of all such volunteers. Although many contemporary medical observers confirmed the editorial's comments, two weeks later a letter signed "Senex" attempted rebuttal, claiming that the voluntary surgeons "were willing to do anything and suffer any hardship for the relief of the wounded."[15]

FORGOTTEN FAVORABLE OBSERVATIONS

Civil War physicians and their medical teams had many supporters. Clara Barton praised the physicians with whom she had worked, stating that they did all that they could, adding, "no provision had been made for such wholesale slaughter."[16] Louisa Mae Alcott complimented the compassion and ministrations of most of the doctors she observed. Alcott reserved her severest criticisms for some chaplains, who, she said, "might turn away more soldiers

Congressional Condemnation

The *British Medical Journal* regularly reported on the American Civil War. A column entitled "The Week, March 14, 1863" described the Congressional debate over a bill to correct problems in administering a Medical Department burdened by pre-war regulations:

> The *American Medical Times* tells us that when measures were lately brought before Congress to improve the defective condition of the medical department of the army, the senators instead of fairly judging and advancing the measure played upon each other's sympathies by relating incidents of cruelty of medical men to sick soldiers, of their incompetency, and even of their knavery. Not a surgeon was spoken of in a complimentary manner. Of the large number who have been killed while caring for the wounded on the field of battle, there was not a word of praise. The narration of cases of amputation against the wish and judgment of the parties afforded more congenial topics for senatorial debate.[17]

from religion than all the combined forces of the devil." Fannie Beers, who served as a Confederate hospital matron, recorded that she

> never saw or heard of a more self-sacrificing set of men than the surgeons [under whom she served] . . . They were devoted to their patients, and as attentive as in private practice or as the immense number of sick allowed them to be.[18]

Late in 1864, Walt Whitman summed up his opinions about the surgeons that he had observed:

> I must bear my most emphatic testimony to the zeal, manliness, and professional spirit and capacity, generally prevailing among the surgeons . . . in the hospital and the army. I will not say much about the exceptions (but I have met some of these few, and very incompetent and airish they were). I never ceased to find the best young men, and the hardest and most disinterested workers among these surgeons . . . They are full of genius, too. I have seen many hundreds of them, and this is my testimony.[19]

Although soldiers' complaints are more frequently quoted, many expressed gratitude for the care they received from army doctors. Former patients cheered one regimental surgeon when he visited them on the wards of a Philadelphia hospital. On another occasion at a large convalescent hospital, the amputees who were able to walk formed ranks, marched in review past the doctors' quarters, and cheered loudly while "the astonished doctors thereupon returned the cheers with a tiger."[20] Showing amazing insight, a private in Maj. Gen. George E. Pickett's division recorded that

> [It is] usual to abuse doctors all over the world . . . [But surgeons performed their duties] with as much sympathy as familiarity with suffering is likely to leave . . . where death and sickness is disrobed of its natural appeals by reason of its daily occurrence and constant existence.[21]

After Gettysburg, the care of the wounded was prominent in everyone's minds. The *British Medical Journal* quoted an *American Medical Times* article praising the quality of American surgeons: "We may safely challenge the governments of the old world to improvise armies of such magnitude and supply them a medical corps from civil life which will present a more honourable record. Whatever may have been our deficiencies in the knowledge of military surgery heretofore, it is now certain that we shall soon, if we do not already, surpass all other nations in proficiency in this department."[22] Another article praising the Medical Department's performance after Gettysburg appeared in the *Chicago Medical Journal*:

> When suffering or calamity befalls . . . the first inquiry and most natural are as to its cause. "Someone has blundered," or worse, . . . [the medical officers] have been grossly misjudged and misrepresented. Exceptions there are, but we do not hesitate to say that the most hard-working, self-denying, earnest and conscientious officers in the army are its surgeons.[23]

On October 24, 1863, the *American Medical Times* ran an editorial, "The Efficiency of the Army Surgeon," decrying what they now saw as unwarranted attacks against military physicians:

> The medical staff of our volunteer army has been subjected to much scandal and harsh and unjust censure for alleged incompetency. It has, in truth, become popular to talk disparagingly of the army surgeon, and sweeping denunciations are made of the entire staff on account of the reprehensible conduct of individual members.[24]

The editorial described the stresses on army surgeons, their problems convincing officers of the need for sanitation, and the skills and experience necessary to perform surgery, and concluded:

> This kindly appreciation of the difficulties under which the medical staff of the volunteer army has labored, will be grateful to the individual

members [sic]. Heretofore they have received only censure, and that often of the most unjust and cruel kind. We do not doubt that impartial history will be . . . lenient in its judgment.[25]

Although written by fellow physicians, efficiency reports from hospitals are relevant and also contain many favorable comments on the surgeons' quality. One such report from Confederate Oliver Hospital in La Grange, Georgia, stated,

> Surgeon James Bratton . . . [shows a] fine administrative ability, has a thorough acquaintance with his profession. . . . Surgeon Samuel Annan is full of the milk of human kindness . . . he is very accomplished in his profession—shows an energy—activity & zeal for service that is surprising for his age (is nearly 70 years old).[26]

LATER EVALUATIONS

Once the war ended and emotions cooled, it was easier to see what a fine job Civil War physicians had done. Several senior physicians in the Confederate Medical Department recorded their evaluations of their colleagues. Dr. Hunter Holmes McGuire observed that "some of the best military surgeons in the world could be found in the Confederate army." Surgeon Samuel H. Stout, who was exemplary as director of hospitals for the Western Confederate army, wrote, "Never before in the history of wars was there such a corps of medical men as served the Confederate soldiers."[27]

Dr. William M. Caniff, professor of surgery at Victoria College in Toronto, praised the organizational efforts of Surgeon General Hammond and the research being conducted at the Army Medical Museum. He was particularly impressed by the postmortem study of the injuries caused by different projectiles and the attempt to determine the paths of bullets based on the entry site and a soldier's position.

American textbooks of military surgery published during the war impressed British physicians. In 1865, the *British Medical Journal* reviewed Dr. Frank Hastings Hamilton's *Treatise on Military Surgery*. They stated that the book was "of great merit" and "a most valuable addition to the medical literature." A chapter on hospital gangrene, written by Dr. Frank Hastings Hamilton Jr., received special praise and compliments for his description of Dr. Middleton Goldsmith's studies of the use of bromine.[28]

An International Congress of Medicine was held in Philadelphia in July 1876. Several physicians presented papers summarizing the state of

American medicine. Dr. Paul Eve, former dean at the Medical College of Georgia who was then professor of clinical and operative surgery at the University of Nashville, gave the "Address on Surgery." Describing the quality of the care given by Civil War surgeons, Dr. Eve noted that

> the commendation from foreign sources has been most gratifying to our national pride. The Medical Inspector of the French Army and Director of the School for the Medical Staff of the Army, Mons. Sédillot, wrote in 1866 that American surgery had proved itself equal to cope with the exigencies of a war of incomparable magnitude; surgeons everywhere, said he, were proud of the marvels accomplished in science and self-devotedness.[29]

Eve relayed comments from foreign physicians that "publications issued from the office of the Surgeon General were pronounced to be incomparably the most minute, comprehensive, and valuable ever issued." He added that both France and Prussia had adopted the "American ambulance" system (by which he meant the organization of field hospitals and an ambulance corps).

CIVIL WAR MEDICINE: A REASSESSMENT

Much modern criticism of Civil War medicine presumes that Civil War physicians should have acted on knowledge they did not yet possess. Examples of such knowledge include the rationale for and methods of antiseptic surgery and the role of microorganisms in disease. In addition, some forget that today's technology was not available during the war.

Those who offer such judgements should first ask themselves how they would fare—even with our modern knowledge. For example, how would I have performed on the field at Antietam, Gettysburg, or Spotsylvania without the intravenous fluids, blood products, antibiotics, and sterile equipment that are now a routine? Could I have operated using the available surgical instruments and inadequate lighting and without trained anesthesiologists and nurses, monitoring equipment, and x-rays or CT scans? Could I have coped with hundreds of wounded men, many of them lifelong friends from my hometown, moaning in pain and begging for my help? It is hard to imagine that modern physicians could have done much better than did their counterparts, especially in the last two years of the war.

Medical care evolved during the war as surgeons learned from experience, going through at least two phases. First was the unprepared phase, when the Union Medical Department's fossilized administration was unable to adapt to the demands of a huge, rapidly created army. Everyone expected a short, fairly bloodless war. Physicians of varying quality and experience were thrust into caring for an unanticipated enormous number of diseased and wounded soldiers. They were also hampered by archaic regulations designed for a tiny frontier army. The Confederate's new medical organization was comprised almost entirely of people with no military experience. They too faced similar problems with diseased and wounded troops.

The second phase occurred after many commanders implemented sanitation measures and most soldiers were veterans and immune to many of the worst diseases. By this time, illness due to contagious disease had become much less common, and both medical departments had created innovative systems to care for wounded soldiers near battlefields. As surgeons acquired experience, they exercised better judgment and devised and tested new surgical procedures to save and rehabilitate more wounded men. Controls were imposed to avoid excessive amputations. During this phase, they also implemented evacuation systems to more quickly move ill and injured soldiers to better-staffed and -equipped hospitals.

What would we do if we could be transported back in time to wear either Blue or Gray? What type of medical care would we expect our medical colleagues to provide given the knowledge of the time? Civil War surgeons did virtually everything we could expect. They constantly pressured military commanders to improve sanitation to minimize the spread of diseases. They studied European and American military surgery texts and organized medical societies to learn from each other's experiences and to debate the best methods of dealing with their unprecedented problems. They invented splints, other medical devices, and new surgical procedures.

Civil War physicians universally used the newly discovered forms of general anesthesia, studying their effects and evaluating different methods of administration, despite some doctors' belief that pain was a valuable stimulus to men in shock and forceful opposition from some clergy. Throughout the war, using data from the field, physicians compared results from various treatments and continuously challenged the status quo. In general, they accepted and promoted the training of women as nurses, utilizing their skills and knowledge regardless of considerations such as religion.

They developed a flexible emergency care system, with mobile field hospitals that could be erected near the battlefield, preferably in tents. They developed an efficient ambulance service, under the control of the Medical Corps, with trained personnel to transport wounded and specially designed transports, including hospital boats and railroad cars. Large hospitals were constructed in remote, safe areas, with permanent hospitals in big cities to provide prolonged care. New hospitals were devoted to emerging medical specialties, staffed by physicians who became pioneers in their fields. These physicians extracted the most information they could from their observations, learned from experience, published papers, and educated others.

As the war progressed, we would expect that the accumulated experience and improved organization would result in decreased rates of disease and improved rates of survival from wounds. As the large body of information available shows, *all these "expectations" actually did happen.*

A FINAL NOTE

In a 1913 speech, Dr. S. Weir Mitchell, a founder of neurology who became one of America's foremost physicians, spoke of his wartime experiences. He then expressed his regret that he was unable to give the audience

> a sense of the immensity of the task which as a profession we dealt with. We hear little or nothing of the unequaled capacity with which we met the call on energy and intelligence or of the extraordinary power of the trained American to deal with the unusual . . . I despair of making you realize through statistics the vastness of our task. Large figures only bewilder the imagination and do not fully assist it to realize how perfect was our achievement through those years of disaster and final triumph. . . . [I have] failed to tell you fitly this story of eminent achievement. We had served faithfully as great a cause as earth has known; we had built novel hospitals, organized an ambulance service as had never before been seen, contributed numberless essays on disease and wounds, and passed again into private life the unremembered, unrewarded servants of duty.[30]

In passing, Dr. Mitchell mentioned in his speech that nearly every village in the country had a statue commemorating Civil War soldiers and honoring famous generals, but none had a monument to a Civil War surgeon. Perhaps it is time to correct this deficiency.

REFERENCES

1. Sharpe WD: The wounds of war with particular reference to 1861–1865. *NY State J Med.* 1985;85(2):61-63.
2. Commager HS: *Blue and Gray.* vol. 2. Indianapolis, IN: Bobbs-Merrill, 1950, pp. 129-34.
3. Personal communication from Nancy Eckerman, Librarian, Univ. of Indiana. Quoting: *Cincinnati Lancet and Observer.* September 1863.
4. Medical News. *Br Med J.* 1864 Oct 8;2:173.
5. Editorial. *NY Times.* June 17, 1861, p. 4.
6. Haddaway CL: With loyalty and honor as a patriot: recollections of a Confederate soldier. *Alabama Hist Q.* 1971;33:240-63.
7. Brodman E, Carrick EB: American military medicine in the mid-nineteenth century: the experience of Alexander H. Hoff, M.D. *Bull Hist Med.* 1990;64(1):63-78.
8. *Medical and Surgical History,* Surgical Section, vol. 3, p. 977 et seq.
9. Shaffner L: A Civil War surgeon's diary. *N Carolina Med J.* 1966;27:409-15.
10. *Br Med J.* 1862;1:72 (quoting the *Am Med Times*).
11. Denney RE: *Civil War Medicine: Care and Comfort of the Wounded.* New York: Sterling, 1994.
12. Wood AD: The war within a war: nurses in the Union army. *Civil War Hist.* 1972;18:197-212.
13. Editorial. *Am Med Times.* 1862;5:93-94.
14. Editorial. *Am Med Times.* 1862;5:116-18.
15. *Am Med Times.* 1862;5:166.
16. Oates SB: *A Woman of Valor: Clara Barton and the Civil War.* New York: Macmillan, 1994, p. 237.
17. *Br Med J.* 1863;1:230.
18. Cunningham HH: *Doctors in Gray: The Confederate Medical Service.* Baton Rouge: Louisiana State Univ. Press, 1958, pp. 262-63.
19. Whitman W: *Walt Whitmans' Memoranda during the War (&) Death of Abraham Lincoln.* Bloomington: Indiana Univ. Press, 1962 (facsimile), pp. 9-10.
20. Adams GW: *Doctors in Blue: The Medical History of the Union Army in the Civil War.* Dayton, OH: Morningside Press, (reprint), 1985, p. 56.
21. Cunningham, *Doctors in Gray,* p. 263.
22. *Br Med J.* 1863;1:310.
23. Personal communication with Nancy Eckerman, Librarian, Univ. of Indiana. Quoting: Statement in Sanitary Reporter. *Chicago Med J.* 1863.
24. The efficiency of the army surgeon. (editorial) *Am Med Times.* 1863 Oct.;7:196.
25. Ibid.
26. Cunningham, *Doctors in Gray,* p. 262.
27. Ibid., p. 261.
28. *Br Med J.* 1865 April 1;1:318-21.
29. Eve PF: Address on Surgery. In: *Transactions of the International Medical Congress of Philadelphia. 1876.* (Ashhurst J, ed.) Philadelphia, PA: Printed for the Congress, 1877.
30. Mitchell SW: On the Medical Department in the Civil War. Address to Physicians' Club of Chicago on February 25, 1913, *J Am Med Assoc.* 1914;62(19):1445-50.

APPENDIX A

CIVIL WAR TIMELINE

The North and the South usually referred to battles by different names. Northerners named most battles after a nearby stream or other body of water (e.g., the creeks called Bull Run and Antietam). In the South, battles were named after the nearest town (e.g., Manassas and Sharpsburg). In the following timeline, both names are given, with the Confederate title in parentheses.

— 1861 —

April 13	Fort Sumter surrenders.
April 17	Virginia votes for secession; Lincoln calls for 90-day volunteers.
April 19	Lincoln blockades Southern ports; 6th Massachusetts Volunteers, en route to defend Washington, attacked by Confederate sympathizers in Baltimore.
April 29	Dr. Elizabeth Blackwell establishes Women's Central Association of Relief.
May 15	Dr. Clement A. Finley appointed Federal surgeon general.
June 9	U.S. Sanitary Commission approved by Secretary of War Simon Cameron.
June 10	Dorothea Dix appointed superintendent of female nurses.
July 11	Gen. George B. McClellan engages Gen. Robert E. Lee at Rich Mountain, Virginia (now West Virginia).
July 21	First Battle of Bull Run (First Manassas).
July 27	McClellan appointed commander of Union army, later renamed the Army of the Potomac.
July 30	Dr. Samuel P. Moore appointed Confederate surgeon general.
August 12	Dr. Charles Tripler appointed medical director of Army of the Potomac.
August 28	Union forces capture Fort Hatteras, North Carolina.
September 6	Federal gunboats capture Paducah, Kentucky.
September 11–16	Cheat Mountain campaign, western Virginia.
September 12–20	Siege of Lexington, Missouri.
October 21	Battle of Ball's Bluff, Virginia.
November 1	McClellan appointed general-in-chief, relieving Gen. Winfield Scott.
November 7	Battle of Port Royal Sound, South Carolina; occupation of Hilton Head Island and Beaufort, South Carolina.
November 7	Battle of Belmont, Missouri, Gen. Ulysses S. Grant's first engagement.

— 1862 —

February 6	Surrender of Fort Henry, Tennessee, to Grant.
February 8	Battle of Roanoke Island, North Carolina.
February 13–16	Siege and surrender of Fort Donelson, Tennessee, to Grant.
February 21	Battle of Valverde, New Mexico Territory.
February 25	Federal troops occupy Nashville, Tennessee.
March	McClellan lands Army of the Potomac on York Peninsula, Virginia.
March 6–8	Battle of Pea Ridge (Elkhorn Tavern), Arkansas.
March 9	Battle of CSS *Virginia* (formerly USS *Merrimac*) with USS *Monitor*.
March 14	Federal troops capture Newbern, North Carolina and New Madrid, Missouri.
March 23	Battle of Kernstown, Virginia.
March 26	Battles of Apache Canyon and Glorieta Pass, New Mexico Territory.
April 6	Siege of Yorktown begins.
April 6–7	Battle of Shiloh (Pittsburg Landing), Tennessee; Grant captures Island No. 10 in the Mississippi River in Tennessee.
April 25	Dr. William A. Hammond appointed Federal surgeon general; New Orleans surrenders.
May 3	Confederates evacuate Yorktown, Virginia.
May 5	Battle of Williamsburg, Virginia.
May 25	Battle of Winchester, Virginia; Gen. "Stonewall" Jackson releases captured Union surgeons as "non-combatants."
May 30	Confederate forces under Gen. Pierre Beauregard evacuate Corinth, Mississippi, because of disease; Union troops under Gen. Henry Halleck enter and develop same diseases.
May 31–June 1	Battle of Fair Oaks (Seven Pines), Virginia; Lee assumes command of Confederate army in Virginia.
June 6	Battle of Memphis, Tennessee.
June 9	Battle of Port Republic, Virginia.
June 25	Peninsula campaign: Seven Days' Battles begin.
June 26	Peninsula campaign: Battle of Mechanicsville, Virginia.
June 27	Peninsula campaign: Battle of Gaines's Mill (First Cold Harbor), Virginia.
June 29	Peninsula campaign: Battle of Savage Station, Virginia.
June 30	Peninsula campaign: Battle of White Oak Swamp (Frayer's Farm), Virginia.
July 1	Dr. Jonathan Letterman replaces Tripler as medical director of Army of the Potomac; Battle of Malvern Hill, Virginia.

August 9	Battle of Cedar Mountain, Virginia.
August 26	Battle of Second Bull Run (Second Manassas).
September 14	Battles of South Mountain and Crampton's Gap, Maryland.
September 17	Battle of Antietam (Sharpsburg), Maryland.
October 8	Battle of Perryville, Kentucky.
December 13	Battle of Fredericksburg, Virginia.
December 31	Battle of Stones River (Murfreesboro), Tennessee.

— 1863 —

January 2	Second day, Battle of Stones River (Murfreesboro), Tennessee.
January 11	Federals capture Fort Hindman, Arkansas.
January 22	Army of the Potomac's "Mud March" under Gen. Ambrose Burnside.
February 25	Federal Congress passes Conscription Act.
April 3	Bread riots in Richmond.
April 17	Col. Grierson's cavalry raid into Mississippi begins.
May 1–4	Battle of Chancellorsville, Virginia; "Stonewall" Jackson wounded.
May 3	Second Battle of Fredericksburg, Virginia, and Battle of Salem Church, Virginia.
May 10	Death of "Stonewall" Jackson.
May 12	Vicksburg campaign: Grant attacks Raymond, Mississippi.
May 14	Vicksburg campaign: Engagement at Jackson, Mississippi.
May 16	Vicksburg campaign: Battle of Champion's Hill, Mississippi.
May 17	Vicksburg campaign: Engagement at Big Black River, Mississippi.
May 18	Investment of Vicksburg, Mississippi; siege begins.
May 21	Siege of Port Hudson, Mississippi begins.
June 9	Cavalry battle at Brandy Station, Virginia.
June 14–15	Second Battle of Winchester, Virginia.
July 1–3	Battle of Gettysburg.
July 4	Surrender of Vicksburg, Mississippi.
July 8	Surrender of Port Hudson, Mississippi.
September 20	Battle of Chickamauga, Georgia.
October 27	Confederate siege of Chattanooga broken.
November 19	Lincoln's Gettysburg Address.
November 20	Lincoln develops smallpox.
November 23–25	Battles for Chattanooga, Tennessee, including Lookout Mountain and Missionary Ridge.

November 26	Mine Run campaign in Virginia begins.
November 29	Confederate attack on Fort Sanders at Knoxville, Tennessee.

— 1864 —

February 14	Federals capture Meridian, Mississippi.
February 20	Battle of Olustee, Florida.
February 24	Camp Sumter, the prison at Andersonville, Georgia, opens.
March 1	Kilpatrick/Dahlgren cavalry raid on Richmond fails.
March 9	Grant commissioned lieutenant general and commander of all U.S. armies.
March 11	Congress passes bill reorganizing medical department and establishing Ambulance Corps.
March 12	Beginning of Red River campaign in Louisiana.
May 4	Army of the Potomac's 1864 campaign starts.
May 5–6	Battle of the Wilderness, Virginia.
May 7	Atlanta campaign of Gen. W. T. Sherman against Gen. Joseph Johnston begins.
May 8–12	Battle of Spotsylvania Court House, Virginia.
May 12	Atlanta campaign: Confederates evacuate Dalton, Georgia.
May 14–15	Atlanta campaign: Battle of Resaca, Georgia.
May 15	Orders given to set up prison camp at Elmira, New York; Battle of New Market, Virginia.
May 16	Battle of Drewry's Bluff, Virginia.
May 18–19	Additional fighting at Spotsylvania Court House, Virginia.
May 23–26	Battle of North Anna River, Virginia.
May 31–June 3	Battle of Cold Harbor, Virginia.
June 14	Army of the Potomac crosses James River; Atlanta campaign: Battle of Pine Mountain, Georgia.
June 16–18	Siege of Petersburg, Virginia, begins.
June 23	Siege of Petersburg: Engagement at Weldon Railroad.
June 27	Atlanta campaign: Battle of Kennesaw Mountain, Georgia.
July 9	Gen. Jubal Early's raid on Washington; Battle of Monocacy, Maryland.
July 11	Early stopped at Fort Stevens in Washington suburbs.
July 14	Battle of Tupelo (Harrisburg), Mississippi.
July 17	Atlanta campaign: Hood replaces Johnston as commander of Confederate Army of Tennessee.
July 20	Atlanta campaign: Battle of Peachtree Creek, Georgia.
July 22	Atlanta campaign: Battle of Atlanta, Georgia.
July 28	Atlanta campaign: Battle of Ezra Church, Georgia.

July 30	Siege of Petersburg: Battle of the Crater (mine explosion).
August 5	Battle of Mobile Bay begins.
August 18	Change of Federal policy ends prisoner exchanges.
August 18	William A. Hammond convicted in court-martial and removed as Federal surgeon general.
August 18–19	Siege of Petersburg: Battle of Weldon Railroad, Virginia.
August 22	Dr. Joseph K. Barnes officially appointed Federal surgeon general.
August 25	Siege of Petersburg: Battle of Reams Station, Virginia.
August 31	Atlanta campaign: Battle of Jonesboro, Georgia.
September 1	Confederates evacuate Atlanta, Federal forces occupy city.
September 19	Third Battle of Winchester (Opequon Creek), Virginia.
September 23	Battle of Fisher's Hill, Virginia.
Sept. 29–Oct. 2	Battle of Peeble's Farm and Chaffin's Bluff (Fort Harrison), Virginia.
October 5	Engagement at Altoona, Georgia.
October 9	Engagement at Tom's Brook, Virginia.
October 19	Battle of Cedar Creek, Virginia; Confederate raid on St. Albans, Vermont.
October 23	Battle of Westport, Missouri.
October 27	Engagement at Burgess Mill (Boydton Plank Road), Virginia.
November 16	Sherman begins "March to the Sea."
November 21	Gen. John Bell Hood's Army of Tennessee begins march north to Tennessee.
November 30	Hood attacks Gen. George Henry Thomas in Battle of Franklin, Tennessee.
December 13	Sherman's forces capture Fort McAllister, near Savannah, Georgia.
December 15–16	Hood attacks Thomas in Battle of Nashville, Tennessee.
December 20	Sherman captures Savannah, Georgia.
December 24–25	Federal attacks on Fort Fisher, near Wilmington, North Carolina.

— 1865 —

January 13–15	Capture of Fort Fisher, North Carolina.
January 19	Sherman begins march north into Carolinas.
January 24	Prisoner exchanges resume.
February 5–7	Siege of Petersburg: Battle of Hatcher's Run, Virginia.
February 17	Sherman's forces capture and burn Columbia, South Carolina; Confederates forces evacuate Charleston.

April 2	Siege of Petersburg ends as Lee removes troops; Richmond evacuated.
April 3	Fire begins in Richmond around 3 A.M.; Federal troops enter later in day.
April 9	Lee surrenders Army of Northern Virginia to Grant at Appomattox Court House.
April 12	Surrender of Mobile, Alabama.
April 14	Lincoln shot in Ford's Theater and dies next morning.
April 26	Army of Tennessee surrenders to Sherman near Durham, North Carolina.
May 4	Gen. Richard Taylo's forces surrender at Citronelle, Alabama.
May 12	Engagement near Palmito Ranch, Brownsville, Texas.
May 23–24	Grand Review of Army of the Potomac and Sherman's army, Washington, D.C.
May 26	Confederate Army of Trans-Mississippi surrenders at New Orleans.

APPENDIX B

ORGANIZATION OF CIVIL WAR FIELD ARMIES

Unit	Approximate Size	Usual Commander
Company*	100 men	Captain
Regiment	1,000 men	Colonel
Brigade	4,000 men	Brigadier General
Division	12,000 men	Major General
Corps	2 to 4 divisions	Major General

*Some units consisting of 2 to 10 companies were designated as battalions.

During the Civil War, "regiments" nominally had about 1,000 men, but few actually reached that number. The average strength of regiments diminished progressively as the war continued, since most new recruits were organized into new regiments rather than being used as replacements in existing units.

Regiments were organized into "brigades," which nominally had four to six regiments (4,000 to 6,000 men), although again there was considerable variation.

"Divisions" were made up of three or four brigades, and thus twelve or more regiments (12,000 to 24,000 men). "Corps" were a late development. They first appeared in the Confederate army in November 1862 and were later adopted in the Union armies. They had two or more divisions.

APPENDIX C

U.S. WARTIME DEATHS

Deaths from Battle and Disease in American Wars

	Battle Related	Non-Battle Related	Total
Revolutionary War (1775–83)	no reliable estimates		~10,000
Mexican War (1846)	1,549	10,986	12,535
Spanish-American War (1898)	968	5,438	6,406
World War I (1917–18)	50,585	71,857	122,442
World War II (1941–45)	292,100	8,460	300,560
Korean War (1950–55)	33,629	20,617	54,246
Vietnam (1965–75)	46,226	10,326	56,552
Total of above wars			**562,741**
Civil War:			
Union	110,070	230,458	359,528
Confederate (estimated)			200,000
Total			**559,528**

Data for the Union army derived from Fox WF: *Regimental Losses in the American Civil War 1861–1865: A Treatise on the Extent and Nature of the Mortuary Losses in the Union Regiments, with Full and Exhaustive Statistics Compiled from the Official Records on File in the State Military Bureau and at Washington.* Albany, NY: Albany Publishing Co., 1889, p. 526.

Data for the Confederate army derived from Jones J: Observations upon the losses of the Confederate armies from battle, wounds and diseases during the American Civil War of 1861–65, with investigations upon the number and character of the diseases supervening from gun-shot wounds. *Richmond Louisville Med J.* 1870 June 9;6:635-57.

Data for the other wars derived from Blaisdell FW: The Civil War. *Bull Am Coll Surg.* 1998 April;83(4):32; and Dupuy RE, Dupuy TN: *Encyclopedia of Military History.* 2nd ed. New York: Harper and Row, 1986.

APPENDIX D

MAJOR GENERAL GEORGE B. MCCLELLAN'S ORDER ESTABLISHING AN AMBULANCE CORPS IN THE ARMY OF THE POTOMAC

(Official Records, Series I, Volume XI, Part I, pp. 217-19)

GENERAL ORDERS No. 147

HEADQUARTERS ARMY OF THE POTOMAC

Camp near Harrison's Landing, Virginia., August 2, 1862

The following regulations for the organization of the ambulance corps and the management of ambulance trains are published for the information and government of all concerned. Commanders of army corps will see that they are carried into effect without delay:

1. The ambulance corps will be organized on the basis of a captain to each army corps as the commandant of the ambulance corps, a first lieutenant for a division, second lieutenant for a brigade, and a sergeant for each regiment.

2. The allowance of ambulances and transport carts will be 1 transport cart, 1 four-horse and 2 two-horse ambulances for a regiment; 1 two-horse ambulance for each battery of artillery and 2 two-horse ambulances for the headquarters of each army corps. Each ambulance will be provided with two stretchers.

3. The privates of the ambulance corps will consist of two men and a driver to each ambulance and one driver to each transport cart.

4. The captain is the commander of all the ambulances and transport carts in the army corps, under the direction of the medical director. He will pay special attention to the condition of the ambulances, horses, harness, &c., requiring daily inspections to be made by the commanders of division ambulances, and reports thereof to be made to him by these officers. He will make a personal inspection once a week of all the ambulances, transport carts, horses, harness, &c., whether they have been used for any other purpose than the transportation of the sick and wounded and medical supplies; reports of which will be transmitted through the medical director of the army corps to the medical director of the army every Sunday morning. He will institute a drill in his corps instructing his men in the most easy and expeditious method of putting men in and taking them out of the ambulance, taking men from the ground and placing and carrying them on stretchers, observing that the front man steps off with the left foot and the rear man with the right, &c. He will be especially careful that the ambulance and transport carts are at all times in order, provided with attendants, drivers, horses, &c., and the kegs rinsed and filled daily with fresh water, that he may be able to move at any moment. Previous to and in time of action he will receive from the medical director of the army corps his orders for the distribution of the ambulances and the points to which he will carry the wounded, using the light two-horse ambulances for bringing men from the field and the four-horse ones for carrying those already attended to farther to the rear, if the medical director considers it necessary. He will give his personal attention to the removal of the sick and

wounded from the field and to and from the hospitals, going from point to point to ascertain what may be wanted, and to see that his subordinates (for whose conduct he will be responsible) attend to their duties in taking care of the wounded, treating them with gentleness and care, and removing them as quickly as possible to the places pointed out, and that the ambulances reach their destination. He will make a full and detailed report after every action and march of the operations of the ambulance corps.

5. The first lieutenant assigned to the ambulance corps of a division will have complete control under the commander of the whole corps and the medical director, of all the ambulances, transport carts, ambulance horses, &c., in the division. He will be the acting assistant quartermaster for the division ambulance corps, and will receipt and be responsible for the property belonging to it, and be held responsible for any deficiency in ambulances, transport carts, horses, harness, &c., pertaining to the ambulance corps of the division. He will have a traveling cavalry forge, a blacksmith, and a saddler, who will be under his orders, to enable him to keep his train in order. He will receive a daily inspection report of all the ambulances, horses, &c., under his charge from the officers in charge of brigade ambulance corps, will see that the subordinates attend strictly to their duties at all times, and will inspect the corps under his charge once a week; a report of which inspection he will transmit to the commander of the ambulance corps.

6. The second lieutenant in command of the ambulances of a brigade will be under the immediate orders of the commander of the ambulance corps for the division and have superintendence of the ambulance corps for the brigade.

7. The sergeant in charge of the ambulance corps for a regiment will conduct the drills, inspection, &c., under the orders of the commander of the brigade ambulance corps, and will be particular in enforcing rigidly all orders he may receive from his superior officers. The officers and non-commissioned officers of this corps will be mounted.

8. The detail for this corps will be made with care by commanders of army corps, and no officer or man will be selected for this duty except those known to be active and efficient, and no man will be relieved except by orders from these headquarters. Should any officer or man detailed for this duty be found not fitted for it, representations of the fact will be made by the medical director of the army corps to the medical director of this army.

9. Two medical officers from the reserve corps of surgeons of each division, and a hospital steward, who will be with the medicine wagon, will be detailed by the medical director of the army corps to accompany the ambulance train when on the march, the train of each division being kept together, and will see that the sick and wounded are properly attended to. A medicine wagon will accompany each train.

10. The officers connected with the corps must be with the trains on a march, observing that no one rides in the ambulances without the authority of the medical officers, except in urgent cases; but men must not be allowed to suffer, and the officers will, when the medical officers cannot be found, use a sound discretion in this matter and be especially careful that the men and drivers are in their proper places. The place for the ambulances is in front of all wagon trains.

11. When in camp, the ambulances, transport carts, and ambulance corps will be parked with the brigade, under the supervision of the commander of the corps

for the brigade. They will be used, on the requisition of the regimental medical officers, transmitted to the commander of the brigade ambulance corps, for transporting the sick to various points and procuring medical supplies, and for nothing else. The noncommissioned officer in charge will always accompany the ambulances or transport carts when on this or any other duty, and he will be held responsible that they are used for none other than their legitimate purposes. Should any officer infringe upon this order regarding the uses of ambulances, &c., he will be reported by the officer in charge to the commander of the train, all the particulars being given.

12. The officer in charge of a train will at once remove anything not legitimate, and if there be no room for it in the baggage wagons of the regiment will leave it on the road. Any attempt by a superior officer to prevent him from doing his duty in this or any other instance he will promptly report to the medical director of the army corps, who will lay the matter before the commander of that corps. The latter will at the earliest possible moment place the officer offending in arrest for trial for disobedience of orders.

13. Good serviceable horses will be used for the ambulances and transport carts, and will not be taken for any other purpose except by orders from these headquarters.

14. The uniform for this corps is: For privates, a green band 2 inches broad around the cap, a green half chevron 2 inches broad on each arm above the elbow, and to be armed with revolvers; non-commissioned officers to wear the same band around the cap as a private, chevrons 2 inches broad and green, with the point toward the shoulder, on each arm above the elbow.

15. No person will be allowed to carry from the field any wounded or sick except this corps.

16. The commanders of the ambulance corps on being detailed will report without delay to the medical director at these headquarters for instruction. All division, brigade, or regimental quartermasters having any ambulances, transport carts, ambulance horses, or harness, &c., in their possession will turn them in at once to the commander of the division ambulance corps.

By command of Major-General McClellan:

S. WILLIAMS
Assistant Adjutant-General

APPENDIX E

THE U.S. SANITARY COMMISSION

On April 15, 1861, one day after Fort Sumter surrendered, President Lincoln called out 75,000 state militia to assist in retaking the U.S. property seized by Confederate forces. The same afternoon, the women of Bridgeport, Connecticut, organized the first Ladies' Aid Society, which was soon emulated throughout the North.

That day also saw the conception of the U.S. Sanitary Commission, which would have a major impact on health care during the war. In New York City, Dr. Henry Whitney Bellows, pastor of All Souls Unitarian Church, and Dr. Elisha Harris, a prominent physician, met with Dr. Elizabeth Blackwell at the New York Infirmary for Women. Their conversation probably centered on the need for nurses and their desire to avoid the medical, or "sanitary," disasters of the recent Crimean War. Dr. Blackwell then arranged a meeting on April 30 of "92 most Respected Gentlewomen" at Peter Cooper Institute in New York to form the Women's Central Association for Relief of New York City. Indicating its importance, U.S. Vice-President Hannibal Hamlin opened the meeting. A board of managers was formed and Dr. Valentine Mott, professor of surgery at Bellevue Medical College, accepted the presidency. At age 76, Mott was perhaps the most prominent surgeon in the city at that time. Miss Louisa Lee Schuyler, age 24 and the great grand-daughter of Alexander Hamilton on both sides, became the Association's executive secretary.

One of the Association's original objectives was to train women to serve as army nurses. But the scope of activities was soon broadened as they received letters from aid societies around the country that painted an appalling picture of incompetence and inexperience in the army's Commissary, Quartermaster, and Medical Departments. Uniforms were poorly made and fell to pieces on the first wearing and there was extensive profiteering in food. Profiteering in horses was even worse—of 2,500 horses assembled for the army at Chicago, all but 27 were diseased, maimed, or dying. Because of this perceived need for civilian oversight to prevent a recurrence of the Crimean War's disasters, the Association became the nucleus of a national organization with much broader functions, the U.S. Sanitary Commission (USSC).

After being rebuffed by the army's medical purveyor in New York City, four Sanitary Commission representatives went to Washington: Bellows, Harris, Dr. W. H. Van Buren of New York's College of Physicians and Surgeons, and Dr. Jacob Larsen of the Lint and Bandage Association. On May 16, they met Dr. Robert C. Wood, the acting surgeon general. Wood, a career army physician, humored them but declined to allow any formal relationship between the Sanitary Commission and the army. They were "bowed in and out for 20 days" but, finally, on June 9, 1861, Secretary of War Cameron approved the U.S. Sanitary Commission and President Lincoln (who expressed doubts about the utility of the organization, and described it as a "fifth wheel to the coach") agreed to a formal role for the organization.

Dr. Clement Alexander Finley was soon appointed surgeon general. He allowed the Sanitary Commission to get involved with the volunteer troops but not with the 15,000 regular army troops. Finley assumed that volunteers would not make good soldiers and that the regular army, who remained in separate regiments, would do all the fighting. His assumptions were incorrect.

On June 9, Secretary Cameron appointed nine individuals to serve as the first USSC commissioners. The number of commissioners varied during the war as personnel changed. The commissioners selected Rev. Henry W. Bellows to be president, with Alexander Douglas Bache as his vice-president, roles they were to keep throughout the war. The president, executive secretary, board members, and members of various committees all served without remuneration. Other men who served as commissioners include: William H. Van Buren, M.D.; Wolcott Gibbs, M.D.; Robert C. Wood, M.D. (who was the acting surgeon general; Wood resigned from the Commission in December 1861); G. C. Collum, U.S. Army (resigned February 1864); Alexander E. Shiras, U.S. Army (resigned Dec 17, 1864); Samuel G. Howe, M.D.; Elisha Harris, M.D.; Cornelius R. Agnew, M.D.; George T. Strong, Esq.; John S. Newberry, M.D.; Frederick Law Olmstead (who became executive secretary); Rt. Rev. Thomas M. Clark; Horace Binney, Jr., Esq.; Hon. Mark Skinner; Rev. J. H. Heywood; J. Huntington Wolcott, Esq.; Charles J. Stillé, Esq.; and Ezra B. McCagg, Esq.

The Commission set up a central office in the Treasury Building in Washington, D.C. on October 16, 1861. This became known as the Eastern Department, with branches formed throughout the northeast. In late 1861, John S. Newberry, M.D., one of the original USSC commissioners, established the Western Department to handle operations "out west." Their main office was in Louisville, Kentucky, with branches in Chicago (The Chicago and Northwestern Branch), Cleveland (The Soldier's Aid Society of Northern Ohio), Columbus, and Cincinnati. (The Western Department should not be confused with the Western Sanitary Commission, an independent organization that declined to join the USSC. Its base was located in St. Louis.)

Surgeon General Finley came to believe that the USSC consisted of troublemakers and he refused to cooperate with them. His opinion was echoed by Dr. Charles Tripler, the initial Medical Director of the Army of the Potomac. This official disdain hampered the Commission's efforts. In April 1862, the Commission finally prevailed on Secretary of War Stanton to relieve the obviously incompetent Finley and replace him with their nominee, Dr. William Hammond. The relationship between the Commission and the Surgeon General's Office remained cooperative until 1864, after Dr. Joseph K. Barnes replaced Hammond. By then, however, the effectiveness of the Commission protected it from interference. Their functions changed little from 1862 to the end of the war.

Operation of the Sanitary Commission

The Sanitary Commission worked through two general committees: a Committee of Inquiry and a Committee of Advice. The Committee of Inquiry, which looked into medical matters, had three distinct subcommittees. One subcommittee considered preventive measures that had proved useful in prior wars, a second inspected camps and hospitals, and the third answered health-related questions sent to the Commission.

The Committee of Advice was also divided into three subcommittees. According to the official history of the Commission, "The General objective of this branch was to get opinions and conclusions of the Commission approved by the Medical Bureau, ordered by the War Department, and carried out by the officers and men." The Commission also formed a Board of Legislature Council, which met quarterly in Washington and gathered field reports from agents. When they were not in session, the Board's Standing Committee reviewed these reports, which were the basis for policy changes.

The executive secretary, the Commission's chief executive officer, lived in Washington. Frederick Law Olmstead had shown his executive skills as superintendent in charge of the design and construction of Central Park in New York City, begun in 1857. He remained executive secretary from June 1861 until his resignation in September 1863, when Dr. J. Foster Jenkins succeeded him. After ill health forced Jenkins to resign, he was succeeded by John S. Blatchford, formerly the superintendent of relief for the USSC in Boston. Associate secretaries, one each for the Eastern and the Western Departments, oversaw those regions and reported to the executive secretary.

The executive secretary's duties included ensuring that sufficient supplies were accumulated at points near the army to meet its needs and evaluating the methods used to retrieve the wounded and to transport them to general hospitals. The Commission seemed to have a special gift for predicting where battles would occur and usually dispatched supplies to the area well ahead of the army's own supply trains. When medical supplies and food were needed after a battle, especially after Gettysburg, the Commission's agents were there with the necessary items at the critical period just after the fighting.

To disseminate the information they gathered and to update healthcare policies, the Commission published reports, broadsides, circulars, posters, as well as monographs and pamphlets they asked physicians to write. They also hired photographers to record the appearance of Sanitary Commission wagons in the field.

One of the Sanitary Commission's most lasting contributions was the meticulous records they kept. They published a hospital directory with the names of over 600,000 men, including the black troops. The directory helped soldiers obtain pay and secure bounties, pensions, and back pay. An important part of their records was generated by their Statistical Bureau, headed by Mr. E. B. Elliot. Elliot went to Berlin to attend the International Statistical Congress in August 1863. Some of their data was generated by physicians who, under USSC auspices, examined Union soldiers and Confederate prisoners to compare age, birth place, strength, profession, etc. Many of their statistics are based on monthly "Gain and Loss" regimental reports that the Adjutant General's office provided. (They stopped providing them for the last four months of the war and, as a result, Commission statistics lack data on black troops.)

The Commission helped soldiers in a myriad of ways. One was to help them fill out forms and handle military bureaucracy, especially for the men whose condition didn't allow them to stand in long lines. The Commission established "Soldier's Homes" for traveling men, the first was built in Washington in 1861. They provided food and medical supplies for the troops when official supplies were deficient or delayed and helped to transport wounded or sick soldiers. The need for such supplies and transportation assistance decreased as the army became better organized and more efficient. The Commission then concentrated on the Soldier's Homes and other needs of soldiers while on leave or after discharge.

On February 10, 1863, they established a Free Pension Agency (the name was later changed to the Army and Navy Claim Agency) to forward pension claims of wounded soldiers. It had more than 100 sub-agencies and presented more than 60,000 claims for pensions on behalf of soldiers, widows, mothers, and orphans. The Agency functioned until 1868, although the Commission had otherwise gone out of existence.

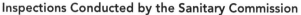
Inspections Conducted by the Sanitary Commission

The Commission, under direction from its Medical Committee, inspected army general hospitals from September 1862 until May 1863, when army inspectors officially approved by Congress took over the function. The Medical Committee included Drs. Van Buren, Agnew, and Wolcott Gibbs. Henry G. Clark, M.D. of Boston was inspector-in-chief, responsible for supervising camp and hospital inspections. Over 100 physicians were invited to become USSC inspectors and 60 accepted, enlisting for only one month of actual inspection, since they had to return to their private practices. The inspectors reported on the location of hospital buildings, the surgeons in charge, the number of medical officers and stewards, and the patients' diet and hygiene. They then forwarded their reports, in confidence, to the surgeon general. Inspections began in the Washington area, but soon included army hospitals from New England to the Gulf.

Initially, hospital inspection reports were filed on Form No. 19. It included 175 questions such as: name and location of the camp; date of inspection; nature of the soil, subsoil, and drainage of the camp; quality of tents and condition of tent's surroundings. They noted and reported on the type of blankets, clothing, and underclothing of the soldiers; camp facilities; type of food available; and quality of the water. They also studied the soldiers' morale, including the availability of liquor and the number of intoxicated soldiers, the availability of entertainment, and how often soldiers corresponded with their families. Information was also gathered about the quality of the surgeons and their medical backgrounds.

A revised, and somewhat more organized, version of Form No. 19 soon appeared. Questions were organized into twenty-one subject areas and the number increased to 180, with several expanded by adding subsections. A third inspection form, issued about March 1862, included a note hinting that the Commission was not completely satisfied with prior reports and some inspectors' diligence in gathering data. It noted that "inspectors will be careful to remember that the answers of the Returns are expected to present evidence of investigation."

Another new form (Form A) added 11 more questions, raising the total to 191. Many questions were expanded: The name of the commanding officer was recorded, along with information as to previous military experience, including whether he was educated at West Point. Under personal cleanliness the inspector now asked: "Does each man (as a rule) wash his head, neck, and feet once a day?" Subsequent revision of this form omitted this question but added a five-part examination of the facility's hygiene. The inspectors also inquired about courts-martial, indecent behavior, if there was a place for divine worship, and the frequency of use of profane language. Still further modifications of these report forms occurred as the Commission tried to keep improving its information and standards for evaluating the army's hospitals.

During the first six months, when Medical Director Tripler still relied on small regimental hospitals, USSC Executive Secretary Olmstead described the inspection results from over 200 of these tiny hospitals: 105 were considered good, 52 were tolerable, 26 were bad, 14 regiments had no hospital, and 4 did not report. Nursing was described as bad, with negligent attendants and no nurses employed for night duty. In December 1861, after receiving the army camps' inspection reports, Olmstead concluded that 5% of the camps were in admirable order, 4% were fairly clean and well-policed, 2% were negligent and slovenly, and 24% were "decidedly bad, filthy, dangerous." In many, tents were pitched too close together and rubbish was left to rot in the spaces between them.

The only saving grace was that, in general, army camps moved, on average, every twenty-one days, reducing the effects of poor sanitation. Key to proper sanitation was the privy or "sink," usually a pit surrounded by a rail with earth thrown over it each day. The inspectors found that 80% of the privies were in good condition, properly arranged, kept in good order, and free of offensive odor. The remaining 20% were described as a threat to good health. In 32% of the camps, officers did not enforce the order confining men to exclusive use of privies; soldiers used any convenient tree or bush. In 35% of camps, men were even allowed to urinate within camp limits at night.

The Commission also found that the supplies and medical equipment were generally poor and inadequate. Most men were issued one thin and shoddy blanket, while about 5% were issued none at all. Overcoats were considered adequate in about 82% of cases, 11% had none, and 3% had coats of poor material. The diet was described as limited and poor.

"Relief Agents"

All the efforts of the Sanitary Commission and related agencies were called "relief," whether they pertained to the health of the soldiers, sanitary matters, food, medical supplies, or programs for families and discharged soldiers. The "relief agents" who worked for the Commission usually received moderate compensation, although many refused pay and worked as volunteers. They tended sick soldiers, but often became sick too. The number of relief agents on the roster of the USSC at any one time varied from 150 to 700; it averaged about 300 and included women and blacks.

Fund Raising and Sanitary Fairs

The Sanitary Commission received no government money, instead they solicited contributions from insurance companies, held "Sanitary Fairs," and received some money from abroad. (England, Scotland, France, Germany, Belgium, Italy, Russia, Turkey, China, Japan, the Sandwich Islands, Costa Rica, Chile, Peru, Buenos Aires, Canada, and Newfoundland all sent contributions.) The California Branch, which was officially organized in August 1864 and superseded a Soldier's Relief Fund Committee, was the largest single contributor to the USSC, giving over $1 million. An English Branch, established March 3, 1864, in a London tavern, solicited funds from Americans living abroad.

Successor Organizations

The USSC was officially terminated in July 1865, but representatives continued to minister to veterans with their remaining funds. Although local aid societies often requested funds to aid widows and children, the USSC found it only had enough to assist veterans.

Jean-Henri Dunant, a Swiss who had helped to organize emergency aid services for soldiers wounded at the Battle of Solferino, Italy (June 1859), proposed in his 1862 book, *A Memory of Solferino*, that all countries form voluntary relief societies. In 1864, the first such societies were formed in Europe. The U.S. equivalent, the American Association for the Relief of Misery on the Battlefields, was formed in New York in 1865.

Rev. Dr. John W. Bellows was president of the American Association for the Relief of Misery on the Battlefield. Its nineteen-member board included many men who had served on the Sanitary Commission, such as Dr. Elisha Harris, Dr. J. Foster Jenkins, Frederick Law Olmstead, and Charles J. Stillé. The organization planned to observe the corresponding international organization and give advice based on American Civil War experiences. The organizers wanted the United States to formally adopt an international pact for this purpose but Congress declined, fearing American involvement in European wars (the Franco-Prussian war had begun).

From 1866 to 1870, the Association was a branch of the Geneva-based International Society of Relief for Wounded Soldiers. In 1870, the American Branch made an appeal for contributions to aid the sick and wounded soldiers of the Franco-Prussian War. Eventually, the Geneva-based organization evolved into the International Red Cross, whose early goal was to secure neutrality in time of war for hospitals, ambulances, surgeons, and all persons legitimately engaged in caring for sick and wounded soldiers. Although the United States was not officially a member of the international organization, in 1881, the American National Red Cross was founded, largely through the work of Clara Barton.

Sources

Documents of the U.S. Sanitary Commission, New York Public Library.

Dunant JH: *A Memory of Solferino (Un Souvenir de Solferino)*. Washington D.C.: American National Red Cross, 1939.

Greenbie MB: *Lincoln's Daughters of Mercy*. New York: G.P. Putnam's Sons, 1944.

Maxwell WQ: *Lincoln's Fifth Wheel: The Political History of the U.S. Sanitary Commission*. New York: Longmans, Green & Co., 1956.

Stillé CJ: *History of the United States Sanitary Commission: Being a General Report of its Work during the War of the Rebellion*. New York: Hurd and Houghton, 1868.

APPENDIX F

CIVIL WAR EXPENDITURES IN TERMS OF THE VALUE OF THE DOLLAR

The U.S. dollar is not worth as much as it used to be!

That makes it hard to grasp the significance of how much was really spent during the Civil War. For example, over the course of the war, the Union Army Medical Bureau spent about $45 million. A review of the dollar's change in value, based on the composite commodity price index, reveals the relationship between 2001 and 1860 dollars as a factor of approximately 19.8:1. That means their expenditure was about $891 million in today's dollars!

Confederate Medical Department expenditures are more difficult to evaluate due to the rampant inflation during the course of the war. Furthermore, commodity prices varied enormously in different regions of the Confederacy, making it impossible to generalize about the value of the Confederate dollar. In relation to Federal dollars, however, both sides spent a similar amount.

There are reports of Gettysburg farmers profiteering after that great battle. Field hospitals ran short of supplies, including food, because most of the supply wagons left with General Meade's Army of the Potomac to pursue General Lee. Some farmers reportedly insisted that soldiers pay 75 cents for a loaf of bread, while others apparently demanded a dollar apiece to use their farm wagon to carry soldiers from field hospitals to a railroad depot. In today's dollars, the bread cost soldiers nearly $15, and the painful wagon ride cost nearly $20.

APPENDIX G

EMBALMING DURING THE CIVIL WAR

By the time of the Civil War, embalming had developed in the United States to a point where wealthy political figures and, occasionally, common folk were routinely embalmed. When the war started, embalmers flocked to the battlefields seeking business. They advertised their services to such an extent that Gen. Benjamin Butler, on one occasion, considered them a disastrous influence on morale and banned them from his command. Over the course of the war, demand for embalming grew with the number of casualties. The technique of injecting the body with preservatives through a femoral artery was quite effective, and coffins containing embalmed remains were commonplace on trains and ships heading north. The usual charge for embalming and shipping a body home was about fifty dollars for an officer and twenty-five dollars for an enlisted man, although late in the war, eighty dollars and thirty dollars respectively were more common.[1]

Because Civil War soldiers wore no name tags, identification of the corpses was often very difficult, especially if enemy troops had stripped clothing and other personal effects from the body. As a result, about half of the graves in Civil War battlefields are marked "unknown." Soldiers who died in a hospital were much more likely to be identified and their bodies more likely to be embalmed and shipped home.

The most colorful figure in the history of modern embalming was "Dr." Thomas Holmes (1817–1900), who is considered the "Father of American Embalming." After attending the College of Physicians and Surgeons in New York City during 1844–45 (it is uncertain whether he graduated, and some histories claim that he was dismissed from New York University Medical College for "an unnatural attraction to dead bodies"),[2] Holmes practiced medicine in New York and Brooklyn. He became interested in preserving bodies and experimented with a variety of agents and techniques, which he perfected while serving as coroner in New York City. He made a considerable amount of money selling the embalming fluid he invented, calling it "Innominata."[3]

At the start of the war, Holmes went to Washington where his preserved bodies received a great deal of attention, particularly after he embalmed the body of Col. Elmer Ellsworth, who had been a friend and secretary to President Lincoln. Ellsworth had formed a regiment of "Fire Zoaves" from New York and received much press attention when the regiment, dressed in their exotic Turkish uniforms, provided protection for Lincoln during his trip to Washington for the inauguration.

On May 24, 1861, Ellsworth was shot and killed by an innkeeper in Alexandria while leading a contingent to tear down a Confederate flag that the man had raised over his building. (The innkeeper was immediately killed by the Union troops on the scene.) The colonel's death elicited national mourning—there had been few casualties before that time—and thousands of Northern babies born that year were given the first and middle names "Elmer Ellsworth." President Lincoln, on the advice of Secretary of State Seward, who was from New York, had the body embalmed by Dr. Holmes at the Washington Navy Yard and then carried to the East Room of the White House for public viewing. The "natural" appearance of Ellsworth's face greatly enhanced Holmes's reputation.

After the war, Holmes claimed to have embalmed "4,028 soldiers and officers," a number which has been questioned unless one includes all the work done by associates and people he trained. Among the many myths associated with Holmes is the often-repeated story that he embalmed President Lincoln's body, a claim Holmes himself never made.[4]

A physician named C.H. Cleveland published a "Physician's Pocket Memorandum" in 1869 that described the embalming techniques used during the war. According to the pamphlet,

> A strong solution of zinc chloride—1/2 ounce of the salt to a quart of alcohol and water may be employed directly into the artery to prevent decomposition. Creosote [carbolic acid] may be used as an anti-putrefactive, but its odor is objectionable . . . With a common pewter syringe, it may be thrown into the arterial system, the nozzle of the instrument being introduced into a slit made in the femoral artery.
>
> It is customary to transport bodies in metallic burial cases, or heavy wooden boxes lined with zinc plates.[5]

After the war, in part due to a public fear of premature burial, the practice of embalming became much more common. The first U.S. textbook devoted to embalming, *The Undertaker's Manual*, was published in 1878, and formal schools for embalmers appeared in the 1880s.[6]

References

1. Habenstein RW: *The History of American Funeral Directing*. 2nd ed. Milwaukee, WI: National Funeral Directors Assoc., 1981, p. 209.
2. Mayer RG: *Embalming: History, Theory, and Practice*. Norwalk, CT: Appleton & Lange, 1990, p. 41.
3. Ibid., p. 46.
4. Habenstein, *History of American Funeral Directing*, p. 210.
5. Dammann G: *A Pictorial Encyclopedia of Civil War Medical Instruments and Equipment*. Missoula, MT: Pictorial Histories, 1983.
6. Iserson KV: *Death to Dust: What Happens to Dead Bodies?* 2nd ed. Tucson, AZ: Galen Press, Ltd., 2001.

BIBLIOGRAPHY

Books

Many of the authors listed here have also written articles concerning various aspects of the Civil War. A listing of the most relevant journals, including a few specific articles, appears after the book list. Readers are encouraged to run searches for specific topics and/or authors.

Adams CF: *Charles Francis Adams 1835–1916: An Autobiography*. Boston: Houghton-Mifflin, 1916.

Adams GW: *Doctors in Blue: The Medical History of the Union Army in the Civil War*. Dayton, OH: Morningside, 1985.

Alcott LM: *Hospital Sketches*. (Jones BZ, ed.) Cambridge, MA: Harvard Univ. Press, 1960.

Baird ND: *David Wendel Yandell, Physician of Old Louisville*. Lexington: Univ. Press of Kentucky, 1978.

Barnes JK: *The Medical and Surgical History of the War of the Rebellion, (1861–1865)*. Washington, D.C.: GPO, 1870–88.

Barton J: *Angels of the Battlefield: A History of the Labors of the Catholic Sisterhoods during the Late Civil War*. Philadelphia: Catholic Arts, 1897.

Battles and Leaders of the Civil War. New York: Thomas Yoseloff, 1956. (Orig. pub. in *Century Magazine*, Nov. 1884 to Nov. 1887.)

Bauer KJ, ed.: *Soldiering: The Civil War Diary of Rice C. Bull*. New York: Berkley Books, 1977.

Beers HP: *The Confederacy: A Guide to Archives of the Government of the Confederate States of America*. Washington, D.C.: NARA, 1986.

Bellard A: *Gone for a Soldier: The Civil War Memoirs of Private Albert Bellard*. Boston: Little Brown, 1975.

Berlin JV: *A Confederate Nurse: The Diary of Ada W. Bacot, 1860–1853*. Columbia: Univ. of South Carolina Press, 1994.

Bishop J: *The Day Lincoln Was Shot*. New York: Harper, 1955.

Blackford SL: *Letters from Lee's Army*. New York: C. Scribner's Sons, 1947.

Blakey AF: *General John H. Winder C.S.A.* Gainesville: Univ. of Florida Press, 1990.

Boatner MM: *Civil War Dictionary*. New York: David McKay, 1959.

Bordley J III, Harvey AM: *Two Centuries of American Medicine, 1776–1976*. Philadelphia: W.B. Saunders, 1976.

Breeden JO: *Joseph Jones, M.D. Scientist of the Old South*. Lexington: Univ. Press of Kentucky, 1975.

Brieger GH: *Medical America in the Nineteenth Century*. Baltimore: Johns Hopkins Univ. Press, 1972.

Brockett LP: *Women at War: A Record of Their Patriotic Contributions, Heroism, Toils, and Sacrifice during the Civil War*. Philadelphia: Zeigler McCurdy, 1867. (Reprint: Longmeadow Press, 1993.)

Brooks SM: *Civil War Medicine*. Springfield, IL: C.C. Thomas, 1966.

Brumgardt JR: *Civil War Nurse: The Diary and Letters of Hannah Ropes*. Knoxville: Univ. of Tennessee Press, 1993.

Buck G: *Contributions to Reparative Surgery*. New York: Appleton, 1876.

Burbank J: Jerome: *To My Beloved Absent Companion. Letters of a Civil War Surgeon to His Wife at Home Caring for Their Family*. Cullman, AL: S. Morris, 1996.

Burnett CH, Keen WW, White JW, eds.: *An American Text-book of Surgery: for Practitioners and Students*. Philadelphia: W.B. Saunders, 1892, 1898.

Bynum WF: *Science and the Practice of Medicine in the Nineteenth Century*. Cambridge: Cambridge Univ. Press, 1994.

Cantlie N: *A History of the Army Medical Department*. Edinburgh: Churchill Livingston, 1973.

Carlisle RJ, ed.: *An Account of Bellevue Hospital*. New York: Society of the Alumni of Bellevue Hospital, 1893.

Chesnut MBM: *Mary Chesnut's Civil War*. (Woodward CV, ed.) New Haven: Yale Univ. Press, 1981.

Chipman NP: *The Andersonville Prison Trial: The Trial of Capt. Henry Wirz*. Sacramento: The Author, 1911. (Reprint: Notable Trials Library, 1990.)

Chisolm JJ: *A Manual of Military Surgery for Use of the Surgeons in the Confederate Army*. 3rd ed. Columbia, SC: Evans & Cogswell, 1864. (Reprint: Morningside Press, 1992.)

Commager HS: *The Blue and the Gray*. Indianapolis, IN: Bobbs-Merrill, 1950.

Coco GA: *A Vast Sea of Misery: A History and Guide to the Union and Confederate Field Hospitals at Gettysburg, July 1-November 20, 1863*. Gettysburg, PA: Thomas, 1988.

Confederate States of America, Surgeon General's Office: *General Directions for Collecting and Drying Medicinal Substances of the Vegetable Kingdom: List and Description of Indigenous Plants, etc., Their Medicinal Properties, Forms of Administration, and Doses*. Richmond, VA: Surgeon General's Office, 1862. (Reprint: Bohemian Brigade, 1996.)

Cumming K: *Kate: The Journal of a Confederate Nurse*. Baton Rouge: Louisiana State Univ. Press, 1959.

Cunningham HH: *Doctors in Gray: The Confederate Medical Service*. Baton Rouge: Louisiana State Univ. Press, 1958.

——: *Field Medical Services at the Battles of Manassas*. Athens: Univ. of Georgia Press, 1968.

Da Costa JM: *Medical Diagnosis*. Philadelphia: J.B. Lippincott, 1864.

Dammann G: *A Pictorial Encyclopedia of Civil War Medical Instruments and Equipment*. Missoula, MT: Pictorial Histories, 1983.

Dannett SGL: *Noble Women of the North*. New York: Thomas Yoseloff, 1959.

Davis B: *Gray Fox: Robert E. Lee and the Civil War*. New York: Holt, Rinehart & Winston, 1956.

Davis WC: *Fighting Men of the Civil War*. New York: W.H. Smith, 1989.

Denney RE: *Civil War Medicine: Care and Comfort of the Wounded*. New York: Sterling, 1994.

Devens RM: *The Pictorial Book of Anecdotes and Incidents of the War of the Rebellion, Civil, Military, Naval, and Domestic*. Hartford, PA: Hartford Pub. Co., 1867.

Duncan LC: *The Medical Department of the United States Army in the Civil War*. Gaithersburg, MD: Butternut Press, 1985.

Dunglison R: *Medical Lexicon: A Dictionary of Medical Science: Containing a Concise Explanation of the Various Subjects and Terms of Physiology, Pathology, Hygiene, Therapeutics, Pharmacology, Obstetrics, Medical Jurisprudence, &c. with the French and Other Synonymes, Notices of Climate, and of Celebrated Mineral Waters, Formulae for Various Officinal, Empirical, and Dietetic Preparations, etc.* 9th ed. London: Sampson Low, 1853.

Dyer FH: *A Compendium of the War of the Rebellion*. New York: Thomas Yoseloff, 1959.

Dyer JP: *The Gallant Hood*. Indianapolis: Bobbs-Merrill, 1950.

Esposito VJ: *The West Point Atlas of American Wars*. New York: F.A. Praeger, 1959.

Estes JW: *Dictionary of Protopharmacology. Therapeutic Practices, 1700–1850*. Canton, MA: Science History Pub., 1990.

Evans BA: *A Primer of Civil War Medicine: Non-Surgical Medical Practice during the Civil War Years*. Knoxville, TN: Bohemian Brigade, 1998.

Evans TW: *Memoirs of Dr. Thomas W. Evans, 1823–1897. The Second French Empire*. New York: D. Appleton, 1905.

Faust PL, ed.: *Historical Times Illustrated Encyclopedia of the Civil War*. New York: Harper & Row, 1986.

Flint A: *A Treatise on the Principles and Practice of Medicine*. Philadelphia: Henry C. Lea, 1873.

Foltz CS: *Surgeon of the Seas: The Adventurous Life of Surgeon General Jonathan M. Foltz in the Days of Wooden Ships*. Indianapolis, IN: Bobbs-Merrill, 1931.

Foote S: *The Civil War, A Narrative*. New York: Random House, 1958.

Formento F: *Notes and Observations on Army Surgery*. New Orleans: L.E. Marchand, 1863.

Fox WF: *Regimental Losses in the American Civil War 1861–1865: A Treatise on the Extent and Nature of the Mortuary Losses in the Union Regiments, with Full and Exhaustive Statistics Compiled from the Official Records on File in the State Military Bureau and at Washington.* Albany, NY: Albany Pub., Co., 1889. (Reprint: Morningside Press, 1974.)

Freemon FR: *Microbes and Minie Balls: An Annotated Bibliography of Civil War Medicine.* Rutherford, NJ: Fairleigh Dickinson Univ. Press, 1993.

Fulton WF: *The War Reminiscences of William Frierson Fulton II: 5th Alabama Battalion, Archer's Brigade, A.P. Hill's Light Division, A.N.V.* Gaithersburg, MD: Butternut Press, 1986.

Futch OL: *History of Andersonville Prison.* Gainesville: Univ. of Florida Press, 1968.

Garrison WB: *A Treasury of Civil War Tales.* New York: Ballantine, 1988.

Gates PW: *Agriculture and the Civil War.* New York: A.A. Knopf, 1965.

Gillett MC: *The United States Army Medical Department, 1818–1865.* Washington, D.C.: Center of Military History, U.S. Army, 1987.

Glicksberg CI, ed.: *Walt Whitman and the Civil War.* New York: A.S. Barnes, 1933 (reprint).

Goldsmith M: *A Report on Hospital Gangrene, Erysipelas, and Pyemia, as Observed in the Department of the Ohio and the Cumberland, with Cases Appended.* Louisville, KY: Bradley & Gilbert, 1863.

Gordon JB: *Reminiscences of the Civil War.* New York: Chas. Scribner's Sons, 1905.

Goss WL: *The Soldier's Story of His Captivity at Andersonville, Belle Isle and Other Rebel Prisons.* Boston: Lee & Shepard, 1867.

Gragg R, ed.: *The Illustrated Confederate Reader.* New York: Harper & Row, 1989.

Grant US: *Personal Memoirs of U.S. Grant.* New York: C.L. Webster, 1885–86.

Gray HMW: *The Early Treatment of War Wounds.* London: Oxford Univ. Press, 1919.

Greenbie MLB: *Lincoln's Daughters of Mercy.* New York: G.P. Putnam's Sons, 1944.

Gross SD: *A Manual of Military Surgery or Hints on the Emergencies of Field, Camp and Hospital Practice.* Philadelphia: Lippincott, 1861. (Reprint: Normal Publishing, 1988.)

——: *System of Surgery Pathological, Diagnostic, Therapeutic, and Operative.* Philadelphia: Blanchard & Lea, 1862.

Guthrie GJ: *Directions to Army Surgeons on the Field of Battle.* 2nd ed. Washington, D.C.: U.S. Sanitary Commission, Bulletin No. 14, 1862. (Reprint: Bohemian Brigade, 1996.)

Hamilton FH, ed.: *Surgical Memoirs of the War of the Rebellion, Collected and Published by the United States Sanitary Commission.* New York: Hurd & Houghton, 1871.

Hamilton FH: *A Practical Treatise on Fractures and Dislocations.* 3rd ed. Philadelphia: Henry C. Lea, 1866.

——: *A Treatise on Military Surgery and Hygiene.* New York: Balliere Bros., 1865.

Hancock C: *South after Gettysburg. Letters of Cornelia Hancock from the Army of the Potomac, 1863–1865.* Philadelphia: Univ. of Pennsylvania Press, 1937.

Hart AG: *The Surgeon and the Hospital in the Civil War.* Gaithersburg, MD: Olde Soldier Books, 1987. (Orig. pub. 1902).

Hawks EH: *A Woman Doctor's Civil War: Esther Hill Hawks' Diary.* Columbia: Univ. of South Carolina Press, 1984.

Hebert WH: *Fighting Joe Hooker.* Indianapolis, IN: Bobbs-Merrill, 1944.

Henderson S, ed.: *The Adventures of a Prisoner of War, 1863–64.* Austin: Univ. of Texas, 1964.

Henry RS: *The Armed Forces Institute of Pathology. Its First Century, 1862–1962.* Washington, D.C.: Office of the Surgeon General, Dept. of the Army, 1964.

Hill SJF: *Mrs. Hill's Journal: Civil War Reminiscences.* (Krug MM, ed.) Chicago: Lakeside, 1980.

Holmes OW: *Medical Essays.* Boston: Houghton Mifflin, 1909.

Holt DM: *A Surgeon's Civil War: The Letters and Diary of Daniel M. Holt, M.D.* Kent, OH: Kent State Univ. Press, 1994.

Hoyt EP: *The Improper Bostonian: Dr. Oliver Wendell Holmes.* New York: Morrow, 1979.

Humphreys CA: *Field, Camp, Hospital and Prison in the Civil War, 1863–1865.* Boston: Geo. H. Ellis, 1918.

Iserson KV: *Death to Dust: What Happens to Dead Bodies?* 2nd ed. Tucson, AZ: Galen Press, Ltd., 2001.

James FA: *Civil War Diary: Sumter to Andersonville.* (Hammer JJ, ed.) Rutherford, NJ: Farleigh Dickinson Univ. Press, 1973.

Johnson CB: *Muskets and Medicine, or Army Life in the Sixties.* Philadelphia: F.A. Davis, 1917.

Jordan EL Jr.: *Charlottesville and the University of Virginia in the Civil War.* Lynchburg, VA: H.E. Howard, 1988.

Josyph P, ed.: *The Wounded River. The Civil War Letters of John Vance Lauderdale, M.D.* East Lansing: Michigan State Univ. Press, 1963.

Kernek CB: *Field Surgeon at Gettysburg. A Memorial Account of the Medical Unit of the 32nd Massachusetts Regiment.* Indianapolis: Guild Press of Indiana, 1993.

Kimball MB: *A Soldier-Doctor of Our Army: James P. Kimball, Late Colonel and Assistant Surgeon General, U.S. Army.* Boston: Houghton Mifflin, 1917.

Kimball WJ, ed.: *Richmond in Time of War.* Boston: Houghton Mifflin, 1960.

Kirkland F: *Pictorial Book of Anecdotes and Incidents of the War of the Rebellion.* Hartford, CT: Hartford Pub. Co., 1866.

Kuz JE, Bengston BP: *Orthopaedic Injuries of the Civil War: An Atlas of Orthopaedic Injuries and Treatments during the Civil War.* Kennesaw, GA: Kennesaw Mountain Press, 1996.

Lattimer JK: *Kennedy and Lincoln: Medical and Ballistic Comparisons of Their Assassinations.* New York: Harcourt Brace & Janovitch, 1980.

Lee RE: *Recollections and Letters of General Robert E. Lee.* Garden City, NY: Garden City, 1926.

——: *The Wartime Papers of Robert E. Lee.* (Dowdey C, Manarin LH, eds.) New York: Da Capo Press, 1987. (Orig. pub.: Little Brown, 1961.)

Leech M: *Reveille in Washington 1860–65.* New York: Harper & Bros., 1941.

Letterman J: *Medical Recollections of the Army of the Potomac / Memoir of Jonathan Letterman, M.D.* Knoxville, TN: Bohemian Brigade, 1994.

Lind J: *A Treatise on the Scurvy.* London: S. Crowder, 1772. (Reprint: Classics of Medicine Library, 1980.)

Livermore MAR: *My Story of the War. A Woman's Narrative of Four Year's Personal Experience as a Nurse in the Union Army, and in Relief Work at Home, in Hospitals, Camps, and at the Front during the War of the Rebellion. With Anecdotes, Pathetic Incidents, and Thrilling Reminiscences Portraying the Lights and Shadows of Hospital Life and the Sanitary Service of the War.* Hartford, CT: A.D. Worthington, 1888.

Locke EW: *Three Years in Camp and Hospital.* Boston: G.D. Russell, 1870.

Louis PCA: *Researches on the effects of blood-letting in some inflammatory diseases and on the influence of tartarized antimony and vesication in pneumonitis / Researches on phthisis.* Birmingham, AL: Classics of Medicine Library, 1986. (Orig. pub. 1844.)

Lowry TP: *The Story the Soldiers Wouldn't Tell: Sex in the Civil War.* Mechanicsburg, PA: Stackpole Books, 1994.

Macfarlane C: *Reminiscences of an Army Surgeon.* Oswego, NY: Lake City Print Shop, 1921.

Maher MD: *To Bind up the Wounds: Catholic Sister Nurses in the U.S. Civil War.* New York: Greenwood Press, 1989.

Mapp AJ: *Frock Coats and Epaulets.* New York: Thomas Yoseloff, 1963.

Marshall HE: *Dorothea Dix: Forgotten Samaritan.* Chapel Hill: Univ. North Carolina Press, 1937.

Massey ME: *Ersatz in the Confederacy: Shortages and Substitutes on the Southern Home Front.* Columbia: Univ. of South Carolina Press, 1952.

Massey ME, Berlin JV: *Women and the Civil War.* Lincoln: Univ. of Nebraska Press, 1994. (Orig. pub. as *Bonnet Brigades,* 1966.)

Maxwell WQ: *Lincoln's Fifth Wheel: The Political History of the United States Sanitary Commission.* New York: Longmans Green, 1956.

Mayer RG: *Embalming: History, Theory, and Practice.* Norwalk, CT: Appleton & Lange, 1990.

McElroy J: *This Was Andersonville: The True Story of Andersonville Military Prison as Told in the Personal Recollections of John McElroy, Sometime Private, Co. L, 16th Illinois Cavalry.* New York: McDowell Obolensky, 1957.

McPherson JM: *Battle Cry of Freedom: The Civil War Era.* Oxford: Oxford Univ. Press, 1988.

——: *Drawn with the Sword: Reflections on the American Civil War.* New York: Oxford Univ. Press, 1996.

——: *For Cause and Comrades: Why Men Fought in the Civil War.* New York: Oxford Univ. Press, 1997.

Mescher V: *"Making Do" or, Substitutions of Scarce Items during the Civil War.* Burke, VA: Nature's Finest, 1993.

Mitchel FA: *Ormsby Macknight Mitchel: Astronomer and General.* Boston: Houghton Mifflin, 1887.

Mitchell PB: *Confederate Camp Cooking.* Rev. ed. Chatham, VA: P.B. Mitchell, 1991.

——: *Yanks, Rebels, Rats, & Rations: Scratching for Food in Civil War Prison Camps.* Chatham, VA: P.B. Mitchell, 1993.

Mitchell SW, Morehouse GR, Keen WW: *Gunshot Wounds and Other Injuries of Nerves.* Philadelphia: Lippincott, 1864. (Reprint: Norman Publishing, 1989.)

Moore F: *Women of the War: Their Heroism and Self-Sacrifice.* Hartford, S.S. Scranton, 1866.

Moore JN: *Confederate Commissary General Lucius Bellinger Northrop and the Subsistence Bureau of the Southern Army.* Shippensburg, PA: White Mane Pub., 1996.

Munden KW, Beers HP: *The Union, A Guide to Federal Archives Relating to the Civil War.* Washington, D.C.: NARA, 1980.

Musicant I: *Divided Waters: The Naval History of the Civil War.* New York: Harper-Collins, 1995.

New York Academy of Medicine: *Military Hygiene and Therapeutics. Report of Committee on Military Surgery to the Surgical Section, July 3, 1861.* New York: S.S.&W. Wood, 1861. (Reprint: Bohemian Brigade, 1994.)

Nolan AT: *The Iron Brigade: A Military History.* New York: Macmillan, 1961.

Nutting MA, Dock LL: *A History of Nursing: The Evolution of Nursing from the Earliest Times to the Foundation of the First English and American Training Schools for Nurses.* New York: Putnam, 1907.

Oates SB: *A Woman of Valor: Clara Barton and the Civil War.* New York: Macmillan, 1994.

Olnhausen MP: *Adventures of an Army Nurse in Two Wars.* Boston: Little Brown, 1903.

Osler W: *The Principles and Practice of Medicine.* New York: Appleton Century Crofts, 1892.

Parish PJ: *The American Civil War.* New York: Holmes & Meier, 1975.

Parks JH: *Joseph E. Brown of Georgia.* Baton Rouge: Louisiana State Univ. Press, 1977.

Patterson GA: *Debris of Battle: The Wounded of Gettysburg.* Mechanicsburg, PA: Stackpole, 1997.

Pember P: *A Southern Woman's Story: Life in Confederate Richmond.* New York: G.W. Carleton, 1879. (Reprint: Mockingbird Books, 1987.)

Pinchon E: *Dan Sickles: Hero of Gettysburg and "Yankee King of Spain."* Garden City, NY: Doubleday Doran, 1945.

Pollard EA: *Southern History of the War.* New York: Fairfax Press, 1990. (Orig. pub.: West & Johnson, 1862.)

Porcher FP: *Resources of the Southern Fields and Forests, Medical, Economical, and Agricultural. Being Also a Medical Botany of the Confederate States; with Practical Information on the Useful Properties of the Trees, Plants and Shrubs.* Charleston, SC: Steampower Press, 1863.

Power JT: *Lee's Miserables: Life in the Army of Northern Virginia from the Wilderness to Appomattox.* Chapel Hill: Univ. of North Carolina Press, 1998.

Pullen JJ: *The Twentieth Maine: A Volunteer Regiment in the Civil War.* Philadelphia: J.B. Lippincott, 1957.

Ranger TO, Slack P, eds.: *Epidemics and Ideas: Essays on the Historical Perception of Pestilence.* Cambridge: Cambridge Univ. Press, 1992.

Robertson JI: *Soldiers Blue and Gray.* Columbia: Univ. of South Carolina Press, 1988.

Rosenberg CE: *The Cholera Years: The United States in 1832, 1849 and 1866.* Chicago: Univ. of Chicago Press, 1962.

—— ed.: *Healing and History: Essays for Charles Rosen.* New York: Science History, 1979.

Rothstein WG: *American Physicians in the Nineteenth Century: From Sects to Science.* Baltimore: Johns Hopkins Univ. Press, 1972.

Schildt JW: *Antietam Hospitals.* Chewsville, MD: Antietam Pub., 1987.

——: *Hunter Holmes McGuire: Doctor in Gray.* Chewsville, MD: J.W. Schildt, 1986.

Schroeder-Lein GR: *Confederate Hospitals on the Move: Samuel H. Stout and the Army of Tennessee.* Columbia: Univ. of South Carolina Press, 1994.

Sherman WT: *Memoirs of General William T. Sherman.* New York: D. Appleton, 1875.

Shryock RH: *Medicine and Society in America, 1660–1860.* Ithica: Cornell Univ. Press, 1960.

Simpson RW: *Far, Far from Home: The Wartime Letters of Dick and Tally Simpson, Third South Carolina Volunteers.* New York: Oxford Univ. Press, 1994.

Small AR: *The Road to Richmond: The Civil War Memoirs of Major Abner R. Small of the Sixteenth Maine Volunteers: Together with the Diary That He Kept When He Was a Prisoner of War.* New York: Fordham Univ. Press, 2000. (Orig. pub.: Univ. of California Press, 1939.)

Smith GW: *Medicines for the Union Army: the United States Army Laboratories during the Civil War.* Madison, WI: American Institute for the History of Pharmacy, 1962.

Spink WW: *Infectious Diseases: Prevention and Treatment in the Nineteenth and Twentieth Centuries.* Minneapolis: Univ. of Minnesota Press, 1978.

Steiner PE: *Disease in the Civil War: Natural Biological Warfare in 1861–65.* Springfield, IL: C.C. Thomas, 1968.

Stevens GT: *Three Years in the Sixth Corps. A Concise Narrative of Events in the Army of the Potomac from 1861 to the Close of the Rebellion, April 1865.* Albany: S.R. Gray, 1866.

Stewart WH: *A Pair of Blankets: War-time History in Letters to the Young People of the South.* Wilmington, NC: Broadfoot, 1990. (Orig. pub.: Broadway Pub., 1911.)

Stillé CJ: *History of the United States Sanitary Commission: Being the General Report of its Work during the War of the Rebellion.* New York: Hurd & Houghton, 1868.

Straubing HE: *In Hospital and Camp: The Civil War through the Eyes of Its Doctors and Nurses.* Harrisburg, PA: Stackpole Books, 1993.

Strode GK, ed.: *Yellow Fever.* New York: McGraw-Hill, 1951.

Tanner RG: *Stonewall in the Valley: Thomas J. "Stonewall" Jackson's Shenandoah Valley Campaign, Spring 1862.* Garden City, NY: Doubleday, 1976.

The Photographic History of the Civil War. 10 vols. in 5. Secaucus, NJ: Blue & Grey Press, 1987 (orig. pub.: Review of Reviews, 1911).

Townsend GA: *Rustics in Rebellion: A Yankee Reporter on the Road to Richmond, 1861–1865.* Chapel Hill: Univ. of North Carolina Press, 1950.

U.S. Navy Dept., Rush R, Woods RH, eds.: *Official Records of the Union and Confederate Navies in the War of the Rebellion.* Washington, D.C.: GPO, 1894.

U.S. Sanitary Commission, Flint A, ed.: *Contributions Relating to the Causation and Prevention of Disease, and to Camp Diseases, together with a Report on the Diseases, etc. among the Prisoners at Andersonville, GA.* New York: Hurd & Houghton, 1867.

U.S. Sanitary Commission Documents. 2 vols. New York: Hurd & Houghton, 1866.

U.S. Surgeon General's Office: *Report on the Origin and Spread of Typhoid Fever in U.S. Military Camps during the Spanish War of 1898.* 2 vols. Washington, D.C.: GPO, 1904.

U.S. War Dept.: *Revised Regulations for the Army of the United States, 1861 with a Full Index.* Philadelphia: Lippincott, 1861. (Reprint: Bohemian Brigade, 1989.)

U.S. War Dept.: *The War of the Rebellion: A Compilation of the Official Records of the Union and Confederate Armies.* 127 vols. in 69. Washington, D.C.: GPO, 1880–1901. (Reprint: National Historical Society, 1972.)

Waitt RW: *Confederate Military Hospitals in Richmond.* Richmond, VA: Richmond Civil War Centennial Commission, Official Pub. No. 22, 1964.

Wangensteen OH, Wagensteen SD: *The Rise of Surgery: from Empiric Craft to Scientific Discipline.* Minneapolis: Univ. of Minneapolis Press, 1978.

Warren L: *Joseph Leidy: The Last Man Who Knew Everything.* New Haven, CT: Yale Univ. Press, 1998.

Watkins SR: *1861 vs. 1882: "Co. Aytch" Maury Grays, First Tennessee Regiment; or, A Side Show of the Big Show.* Nashville: Cumberland Presbyterian Pub. House, 1882.

Webb G: *A Treasury of Civil War Tales.* New York: Ballantine, 1988.

Welch SG: *A Confederate Surgeon's Letters to His Wife.* New York: Neale Pub., 1911.

Welsh JD: *Medical Histories of Confederate Generals.* Kent, OH: Kent State Univ. Press, 1995.

Whitman W: *The Wound Dresser: A Series of Letters Written from the Hospitals in Washington during the War of the Rebellion.* Boston: Small, Maynard, 1898. (Reprint: Folcroft Library Editions, 1975.)

——: *Walt Whitman's Memoranda during the War (&) Death of Abraham Lincoln.* Bloomington: Indiana Univ. Press, 1962 (orig. pub. 1864).

Wilbur CK: *Antique Medical Instruments: Price Guide Included.* West Chester, PA: Schiffer, 1987.

——: *Civil War Medicine, 1861–1865.* Philadelphia: Chelsea House, 1995.

Wiley BI: *Confederate Women.* Westport, CT: Greenwood, 1975.

——: *Life of Billy Yank: The Common Soldier of the Union.* Baton Rouge: Louisiana State Univ. Press, 1952.

——: *Life of Johnny Reb: The Common Soldier of the Confederacy.* Indianapolis, IN: Bobbs-Merrill, 1943.

——: *Rank and File: Civil War Essays in Honor of Bell Irvin Wiley.* (Robertson JI, McMurry RM, eds.) San Rafael, CA: Presidio Press, 1976.

Wilkinson W: *Mother, May You Never See the Sights I Have Seen: The Fifty-seventh Massachusetts Veteran Volunteers in the Army of the Potomac, 1864–1865.* New York: Harper & Row, 1990.

Wilson DC: *Stranger and Traveler: The Story of Dorothea Dix, American Reformer.* Boston: Little Brown, 1975.

Wilson JS: *The Southern Soldier's Health Guide.* 2nd ed. Richmond, VA: West & Johnson, 1863.

Wittenmeyer A: *A Collection of Recipes for the Use of Special Diet Kitchens in Military Hospitals.* Mattituck, NY: J.M. Carrol, 1983 (orig. pub. 1864).

Woman's Central Association of Relief: *A Manual of Directions, Prepared for the Use of Nurses in the Army Hospitals, by a Committee of Physicians of the City of New York.* New York: Baker & Godwin, 1861. (Reprint: John M. Bracken & New Market Battlefield Military Museum, 1994.)

Woodward JJ: *Hospital Steward's Manual.* Philadelphia: J.B. Lippincott, 1862.

——: *Outlines of the Chief Camp Diseases of the United States Armies: As Observed during the Present War. A Practical Contribution to Military Medicine.* Philadelphia: J.B. Lippincott, 1863. (Reprint: Norman Pub., 1992.)

Wormeley KP: *The Other Side of the War, with the Army of the Potomac: Letters from the Headquarters of the United States Sanitary Commission during the Peninsular Campaign in Virginia in 1862.* Boston: Ticknor, 1888.

Journals, Associations, and Articles

Adams GW: Confederate medicine. *J South Hist.* 1940;6:151-66.

American Journal of Dental Science, 1867.

American Journal of Medical Science, 1860–71.

American Medical Times, 1861–65.

America's Civil War.

Anderson DL, Anderson GT: Nostalgia and malingering in the military during the Civil War. *Persp Biol & Med.* 1984;28(1):156-66.

Association for the History of Medicine.

Blaisdell FW: Medical advances during the Civil War. *Arch Surg.* 1988;123(9):1045-50.

——: The Civil War. *Bull Am Coll Surg.* 1998;83(4):32-42.

Blue and Gray Magazine.

Bollet AJ: Pierre Louis. The numerical method and the foundation of quantitative medicine. *Am J Med Sci.* 1973;266(2):92-101.

———: Scurvy and chronic diarrhea in Civil War troops. Were they both nutritional deficiency syndromes? *J Hist Med Allied Sci.* 1992;47(1):49-67.

———: The return of a major Civil War disease. *Inf Dis Clin Pract.* 1997;21:4.

Boston Medical & Surgical Journal, 1861–66.

Breeden JO: A medical history of the later stages of the Atlanta campaign. *J South Hist.* 1969;35:31-59.

———: The "forgotten man" of the Civil War: The southern experience. *Bull NY Acad Med.* 1979;55(7):652-69.

British Medical Journal, 1861–72.

Buist JR: Some items of my medical and surgical experience in the Confederate Army. *South Pract.* 1903;25:574-81.

Bulletin History of Medicine.

Bullough B, Bullough V: The origins of modern American nursing. The Civil War era. *Nurs Forum.* 1963;2(2):12-27.Butler BF: Some experiences with yellow fever and its prevention. *N Am Rev.* 1888;147(384):525-41.

Churchman JW: The use of quinine during the Civil War. *Johns Hopkins Hosp Bull.* 1906;17:175-81.

Civil War History.

Civil War Times Illustrated.

Confederate States Medical & Surgical Journal, 1864–65.

Confederate Veteran.

Culpepper MM, Adams PG: Nursing in the Civil War. *Am J Nurs.* 1988;88(7):981-84.

Da Costa JM: On irritable heart. *Am J Med Sci.* 1871;61:17-52.

Davenport H: Such is military: Dr. George Martin Trowbridge's letters from Sherman's army 1863–1865. *Bull NY Acad Med.* 1987;63(9):844-82.

Duffy J: Yellow fever in the continental United States during the nineteenth century. *Bull NY Acad Med.* 1968;44(6):687-701.

Earle CW: The opium habit: a statistical and clinical lecture. *Chicago Med Rev.* 1880;2:442-46.

Elliott WStG: Gunshot wounds of the mouth. *N.Y. Med J.* 1879;29:280-81.

Figg L, Farrell-Beck J: Amputation in the Civil War. physical and social dimensions. *J Hist Med Allied Sci.* 1993;48(4):454-75.

Franchetti MA: Trauma surgery during the Civil War. *South Med J.* 1993;86(5):553-56.

Freemon FR: The Siege of Vicksburg, 1863: how medicine affected the outcome. *Bull NY Acad of Med.* 1991;67(5):429-38.

Gillett MC: Joseph Woodward. *Med Heritage.* 1985;1:25.

Glenner RA, Willey P: Dental filling materials in the Confederacy. *J Hist Dentistry.* 1998;46:71.

Greisman HC: Wound management and medical organization in the Civil War. *Surg Clin NA.* 1984;64(4):625-38.

Haddaway CL: With loyalty and honor as a patriot: recollections of a Confederate soldier. *Alabama Hist Quart.* 1971;33:240-63.

Hambrecht FT, Rhode M, Hawk A: Dr. Chisolm's inhaler: a rare Confederate medical invention. *J South Carolina Med Assoc.* 1991;87(5):277-80.

Harvey AM: John Shaw Billings: forgotten hero of American medicine. *Persp Biol & Med.* 1977;21(1):35-57.

Hodgkin WL: Edward Maynard, a progenitor of the United States Army and Navy Dental Corps. *J Am Dental Assoc.* 1941;28(12):1968-78.

Hood RM: Medicine in the Civil War. *Texas Med.* 1967;63(3):53-55.

Hyson JM, Foley GPH: James Baxter Bean. The first military maxillofacial hospital. *Maryland State Dental Assoc J.* 1997;40:77.

——: Thomas Brian Gunning and his splint for jaw fractures. *Maryland State Dental Assoc J.* 1997;40:35.

Jacobs EC: A prelude to the bugle call "taps": born in an army field hospital on a Civil War battlefield. *Mil Med.* 1978;143(7):486-87.

Jones J: Medical history of the Confederate States Army and Navy. *South Hist Soc Papers.* 1892;20:109-66.

——: The treatment of prisoners during the War between the States. *South Hist Soc Papers.* 1876;1:177

Journal of Civil War Medicine.

Journal of Confederate History.

Journal of the American Medical Association.

Journal of the History of Medicine & the Allied Sciences.

Journal of the Society of Civil War Surgeons.

Keen WW: Military surgery in 1861 and in 1918. *Ann Am Acad Pol Soc Sci.* 1918;80:11-22.

Key JD: The U.S. Army Medical Department and Civil War medicine. *Mil Med.* 1968;133(3):181-92.

Lancet, 1860–70.

Lattimer JK: Autopsy on President Lincoln. Retrieval of a lost report. *JAMA.* 1965;193:99-106.

Lattimer JK, Laidlaw A: Good Samaritan surgeon wrongly accused of contributing to President Lincoln's death. An experimental study of the President's fatal wound. *J Am Coll Surg.* 1996;182(5):431-48.

Medical History.

Medical & Surgical Reporter, 1861–1870.

Military Medicine.

Military Surgeon.

Mitchell SW: On the Medical Department in the Civil War. Address to Physicians' Club of Chicago on February 25, 1913, *J Am Med Assoc.* 1914;62(19):1445-50.

Nashville Medical & Surgical Journal, 1866–71.

New York Times, 1860–70.

Oliver TE: The use and abuse of opium. *Rep Mass Board Health, Boston.* 1872;3:102-77.

Philadelphia Medical Times, 1870–87.

Quinones MA: Drug abuse during the Civil War (1861–1865). *Int J Addict.* 1975;10(6):1007-20.

Richmond Louisville Medical Journal, 1864–1870.

Riley HD, Jr.: Confederate medical manuals of the Civil War. *J Med Assoc Georgia.* 1988;77(2):104-8.

——: Joseph Jones, an early clinical investigator. *South Med J.* 1987;80(5):623-29.

Rosen G: Nostalgia: a 'forgotten' psychological disorder. *Psych Med.* 1975;5(4):340-54.

Ryons FB: The United States Army Medical Department, 1861 to 1865. *Mil Surgeon.* 1936;79:341-56.

Sanitary Commission Bulletin, 1863–67.

Sartin JS: Infectious diseases during the Civil War. the triumph of the "Third Army." *Clin Infect Dis.* 1993;16(4):580-84.

Sharpe WD. The wounds of war, with particular reference to 1861–1865. *NY State J Med.* 1985;85(2):61-63.

Shryock RH: A medical perspective on the Civil War. *American Quarterly.* 1962;14:161-73.

Smith DC: The rise and fall of typhomalarial fever, I. Origins. *J Hist Med Allied Sci.* 1982;37(2):182-220; II. Decline and fall. *J Hist Med Allied Sci.* 1982;37(3):287-321.

Society of Civil War Surgeons.

Stark RB: The history of plastic surgery in wartime. *Clin Plast Surg.* 1975;2(4):509-16.

Tebo HG: Oral surgery in the Confederate army. *Bull Hist Dentistry.* 1976;24(1):28-35.

Transactions of the Maine Medical Association, 1866–68.

Weir RF: Remarks on the gunshot wounds of the Civil War. *NY State J Med.* 1904;4:141-43.

INDEX

pus, 39, 200, 211
  "laudable", 200
pyemia, 148, 197, 200, 202, 207
Quartermaster Department (Confederate),
  106, 223
Quartermaster Department (Union), 12, 242,
  243
quinine, 236-38, 246, 247, 308
  substitutes for, 248
Quintard, Dr. Charles, 124

— R —

railroads
  as ambulances, 109-12
  Confederate, 341, 342
Rappahannock River, 134
rats, 212, 381, 406, 407
record keeping, 23-25, 47, 217
  Confederate, 217
  limitations, 260
recruits
  arthritis in, 264
  children as, 266-68
  Confederate, 263, 265, 269, 272, 275
  diseases of, 17, 257, 258, 269, 291
  epidemics and, 269
  epilepsy in, 265
  fatality rates, 259
  health of, 265, 266
  heart disease in, 264, 265
  hernias in, 265
  lack of immunity, 271
  measles in, 270
  meningitis in, 278
  mumps in, 270
  pneumonia in, 271
  rejection of, 263-64
  rejection rates, European, 263
  rejection rates, Great Britain, 265
  rejection rates, Union, 265
  respiratory tract infections in, 271
  rickets in, 264
  sanitation and, 259
  screening of, 17, 181, 258, 260-66, 430
    criteria, 263, 264
  skin diseases in, 265
  sunstroke in, 279
  typhoid fever in, 272-77
  Union, 265
  vaccination of, 291, 293
  women, 267
regimental camps, 261
  disease in, 269
  sanitation and, 261
"remittent fever", 276
  fatality rates, 330
  incidence of, 328

resection, 144, 154, 163
  fatality rates, 154
  instruments used, 147
  number of cases, 148
  vs amputation, 148, 156, 158
respiratory tract infection, 271
rheumatic fever (acute)
  heart disease, 308
rheumatism (acute), 240, 264, 307-9
  incidence of, 270, 310, 328
  treatment of, 308
rheumatism (chronic), 182, 309-12, 328
  incidence of, 310
rickets, 264
Roberts, Dr. Deering, 157
Robertson Hospital, 225
Ropes, Hannah, 274, 411
Rosecrans, Maj. Gen. William S., 20
Russell, William Howard, 9

— S —

Sabine
  scurvy and, 354
Safford, Mary, 420, 426
Sanger, Dr. E. L, 401
Sanitary Commission, British, 9
Sanitary Commission, U.S., 9-13, 458-63
  ambulance corps and, 43
  Bickerdyke and, 413, 414
  clinical investigations and, 44
  closes, 462
  depots, 360
  formation of, 10-12, 424
  Fredericksburg and, 132, 133
  Gettysburg and, 127, 243
  Hammond and, 19, 20
  hospital boats and, 112, 113, 118, 119
  hospital inspections and, 30, 225, 227, 229,
    461, 462
  neutrality of wounded, 395
  Nursing Corps and, 19, 415
  Peninsula campaign and, 118, 120
  pre-war surgeons and, 28
  publications, 189, 207, 259, 275, 372
  record keeping and, 460
  sanitation recommendations, 55
  scurvy and, 346, 348, 361
  volunteer troops and, 14, 262
  Western, 359, 425
  women and, 424
sanitary fairs, 425, 462
  vegetables and, 359, 361
Sanitary movement (U.S.), 55
sanitation, 51-55
  Crimean War and, 9, 54
  diarrhea and, 283
  dysentery and, 283

— T —

— U-V —

ABOUT THE AUTHOR

Dr. Alfred Jay Bollet has been a lifelong student of all aspects of the Civil War, and has studied the medical history of the war intensively for over a dozen years. Born in New York City and a graduate of New York University, he spent his professional career in academic medicine, serving as professor of internal medicine at the University of Virginia, the Medical College of Georgia, and the State University of New York at Brooklyn. (He was chairman of the Department of Medicine at the latter two institutions.) Recently, he has been a clinical professor of medicine at Yale.

Dr. Bollet has published numerous papers and presented lectures on various aspects of Civil War medicine at many medical schools, Civil War roundtables, and the Smithsonian Institution. He serves on the Honorary Board of Advisors for the Museum of Civil War Medicine in Frederick, Maryland. He is also a member of the Board of Directors of the Society of Civil War Surgeons.

ABOUT THE PUBLISHER

The name, Galen Press, was inspired by *Galen of Pergamum* (A.D. 130-201), the Greek physician whose writings guided medicine for more than a millennium after his death. As the father of modern anatomy and physiology, Galen wrote more than 100 treatises while attempting to change medicine from an art form into a science. As a practicing physician, Galen first ministered to gladiators and then to Roman Emperor Marcus Aurelius. Far more than Hippocrates, Galen's work influenced Western physicians and was the "truth" until the late Middle Ages, when physicians and scientists challenged his teachings. Galen Press, publishing non-clinical, health-related books, will follow Galen's advice that "the chief merit of language is clearness . . . nothing detracts so much from this as unfamiliar terms."

Pocket Protocols

for Notifying Survivors about Sudden, Unexpected Deaths

Pocket-sized booklet containing the protocols from *Grave Words*

ISBN: 1-883620-05-8 $ 6.95 (Bulk discounts available)

Slides for Grave Words

- Slide Sets of the Protocols & other tables from Grave Words
- Build your own Death Notification and Death & Dying Course using the specialized slide sets

Slide Set	Number of Slides
A. Main Protocol for Death Notification	65
B. General Set: Sudden Death/Nurse Interactions/ Grief/Communication/Survivors' Questions	50
C. Chaplains/Religions	42
D. Emergency Medicine/Trauma	35
E. Phrases: Helping and Hurtful	23
F. Telephone Notification Protocol	20
G. Students' Deaths	17
H. Emergency Medical Services	16
I. Telling Friends	16
J. Children: Telling & Grieving	13
K. Obstetrics	14
L. Disaster Survivors' Protocol	10
M. Organ Donation	10

Prices:

Item 1: Complete set of 330 slides:	$ 395.00
Item 2: Main Protocol + Any three other sets:	$ 345.00
Item 3: Main Protocol + Any two other sets:	$ 295.00
Item 4: Main Protocol + Any one other set:	$ 250.00
Item 5: Individual set:	$3.00/slide

Items 1-4: Includes one copy each of **Grave Words & Pocket Protocols**.
Add shipping of $12 for each item.

To order, and for more information, please contact Galen Press, LTD., at:

P.O. Box 64400   Tucson, AZ 85728-4400 USA
Internet: www.galenpress.com
Tel: (520) 577-8363   Fax: (520) 529-6459

Previews: We keep our prices low by not offering previews. See our 30-Day Guarantee.

Thirty Day Money Back Guarantee: You may return your purchase *within thirty days* for a refund of the purchase price. (Shipping costs not refundable.)

Note: Prices subject to change.

Order Form

Yes! . . . Please send me:

_____ copies of **Civil War Medicine: Challenges and Triumphs,**
     hardcover @ $44.95 each $ _____

_____ copies of **Death to Dust: What Happens to**
     Dead Bodies? @ $48.95 each $ _____

_____ copies of **Getting Into A Residency: A Guide For**
     Medical Students, 5th ed. @ $36.95 each $ _____

_____ copies of **The Companion Disk** @ $12.00 $ _____

_____ copies of **Grave Words: Notifying Survivors about**
     Sudden, Unexpected Deaths @ $38.95 each $ _____

_____ copies of **Pocket Protocols** @ $6.95 each $ _____

_____ copies of **After-Death Planning Guide** @ $3.00 each $ _____

_____ copies of **Ethics In Emergency Medicine, 2nd ed.**
     @ $39.95 each $ _____

_____ copies of **Résumés and Personal Statements for Health**
     Professionals, 2nd ed. @ $18.95 each $ _____

_____ copies of **Death Investigation: The Basics** @ $24.95 each $ _____

_____ copies of **Get Into Medical School! A Guide for the**
     Perplexed @ $34.95 each $ _____

_____ copies of **The International Medical Graduates' Guide**
     to U.S. Medicine @ $31.95 each $ _____

_____ copies of **House Calls, Rounds, and Healings:**
     A Poetry Casebook @ $12.95 each $ _____

_____ copies of **The Cost-Effective Use of Leeches and Other**
     Musings of a Medical School Survivor @ $14.95 each $ _____

AZ Residents – Add 7% sales tax $ _____

Shipping: $3.50 for 1st Book, $1.00 / each additional $ _____

Priority Mail: **ADD** $3.00 for 1st Book, $2.00 / each additional $ _____

TOTAL ENCLOSED (U.S. Funds Only) $ _____

❑ Check   ❑ VISA   ❑ MasterCard

SHIP TO: Name _____

  Address _____

            _____

  City/State/Zip _____

  Phone **(required)** _____

CREDIT CARD Number: _____

Expiration date: _____   Signature: _____

Send completed form and payment to:

Galen Press, Ltd.   Tel (520) 577-8363
PO Box 64400-D2   Fax (520) 529-6459
Tucson, AZ 85728-4400 USA   Orders: 1-800-442-5369 (US/Canada)

Visit our Home Page at www.galenpress.com

Also available through your local bookstore.

Prices Subject to Change

Pocket Protocols
for Notifying Survivors about Sudden, Unexpected Deaths

Pocket-sized booklet containing the protocols from *Grave Words*

ISBN: 1-883620-05-8 $ 6.95 (Bulk discounts available)

Slides for Grave Words

- Slide Sets of the Protocols & other tables from Grave Words
- Build your own Death Notification and Death & Dying Course using the specialized slide sets

Slide Set	Number of Slides
A. Main Protocol for Death Notification	65
B. General Set: Sudden Death/Nurse Interactions/ Grief/Communication/Survivors' Questions	50
C. Chaplains/Religions	42
D. Emergency Medicine/Trauma	35
E. Phrases: Helping and Hurtful	23
F. Telephone Notification Protocol	20
G. Students' Deaths	17
H. Emergency Medical Services	16
I. Telling Friends	16
J. Children: Telling & Grieving	13
K. Obstetrics	14
L. Disaster Survivors' Protocol	10
M. Organ Donation	10

Prices: **Item 1:** Complete set of 330 slides: $ 395.00
Item 2: Main Protocol + Any three other sets: $ 345.00
Item 3: Main Protocol + Any two other sets: $ 295.00
Item 4: Main Protocol + Any one other set: $ 250.00
Item 5: Individual set: $3.00/slide

Items 1-4: Includes one copy each of ***Grave Words & Pocket Protocols***.
Add shipping of $12 for each item.

To order, and for more information, please contact Galen Press, LTD., at:

P.O. Box 64400   Tucson, AZ 85728-4400 USA
Internet: www.galenpress.com
Tel: (520) 577-8363   Fax: (520) 529-6459

Previews: We keep our prices low by not offering previews. See our 30-Day Guarantee.

Thirty Day Money Back Guarantee: You may return your purchase *within thirty days* for a refund of the purchase price. (Shipping costs not refundable.)

Note: Prices subject to change.

Order Form

Yes! . . . Please send me:

_____ copies of **Civil War Medicine: Challenges and Triumphs,**
     hardcover @ $44.95 each $ _____

_____ copies of **Death to Dust: What Happens to**
     Dead Bodies? @ $48.95 each $ _____

_____ copies of **Getting Into A Residency: A Guide For**
     Medical Students, 5th ed. @ $36.95 each $ _____

_____ copies of **The Companion Disk** @ $12.00 $ _____

_____ copies of **Grave Words: Notifying Survivors about**
     Sudden, Unexpected Deaths @ $38.95 each $ _____

_____ copies of **Pocket Protocols** @ $6.95 each $ _____

_____ copies of **After-Death Planning Guide** @ $3.00 each $ _____

_____ copies of **Ethics In Emergency Medicine, 2nd ed.**
     @ $39.95 each $ _____

_____ copies of **Résumés and Personal Statements for Health**
     Professionals, 2nd ed. @ $18.95 each $ _____

_____ copies of **Death Investigation: The Basics** @ $24.95 each $ _____

_____ copies of **Get Into Medical School! A Guide for the**
     Perplexed @ $34.95 each $ _____

_____ copies of **The International Medical Graduates' Guide**
     to U.S. Medicine @ $31.95 each $ _____

_____ copies of **House Calls, Rounds, and Healings:**
     A Poetry Casebook @ $12.95 each $ _____

_____ copies of **The Cost-Effective Use of Leeches and Other**
     Musings of a Medical School Survivor @ $14.95 each $ _____

AZ Residents – Add 7% sales tax $ _____

Shipping: $3.50 for 1st Book, $1.00 / each additional $ _____

Priority Mail: **ADD** $3.00 for 1st Book, $2.00 / each additional $ _____

TOTAL ENCLOSED (U.S. Funds Only) $ _____

❑ Check   ❑ VISA   ❑ MasterCard

SHIP TO: Name _____

  Address _____

  _____

  City/State/Zip _____

  Phone **(required)** _____

CREDIT CARD Number: _____

Expiration date: _____   Signature: _____

Send completed form and payment to:

Galen Press, Ltd.   Tel (520) 577-8363
PO Box 64400-D2   Fax (520) 529-6459
Tucson, AZ 85728-4400 USA   Orders: 1-800-442-5369 (US/Canada)

Visit our Home Page at www.galenpress.com

Also available through your local bookstore.

Prices Subject to Change

—